Why You Don't Need Shoes

1st edition
(Full Version, unabridged)

This book is based on real events and experiences.

By

Xian Alana LomiKoling

For:

The Guys

May we have many more years of
ridiculous amounts of fun.
Love you dudes!

And Deng

Please Read: Sharing and reproduction of this Book:

Share, share, share! Share it with your family, friends, neighbours, colleagues, and with strangers, in fact I hope that you want to go and shout about 'Why You Don't Need Shoes' from the rooftops of the world! Let the Tribe grow! The more we share, the more we can begin to Shift and play together!

For private or educational purposes (if not commercial) you can copy selections from this document freely and pass it on as much as you like. For my own interest I would appreciate a quick note to me via my website to inform me of what you're doing. I am also approachable for assistance, lectures, courses etc, if you're sincere about your project.

For commercial use I request that you contact me to get written permission beforehand.

For further information about permission to reproduce selections from this book contact me on my website www.whyyoudontneedshoes.com.

This book contains information, which when used out of context, might not make sense or could be misrepresented. Please be aware of that fact and do not bend my words into something they're not. Please do not change the words/text when quoting passages.

Also note that a lot of work went into putting this book together, as you will begin to appreciate when you begin your journey through these pages. I can't tell you how many countless hours I spent creating and loving this little piece of magic so that you might benefit from it. That means that this information has value. It is the sales of this valuable information that makes the continued distribution of 'Why You Don't Need Shoes', and further works possible. So, if you use the information contained in this book and you feel that you would like to make a contribution, please refer to my website, where you can make an appropriate donation or purchase further paperback or electronic copies.

Thank you so much for respecting and appreciating my bread and butter, and many people's future joy...

With love
Xian Alana LomiKoling

PLEASE NOTE:

To retain autonomy as an author I self-copy-edited this document. Please look past any last oversights and get stuck in with the fantabulous content instead....

Keep checking www.whyyoudontneedshoes.com for further publications, lectures and courses by Xian.

Dear Reader,

At this moment in time, everything I am, everything I stand for,
everything I believe in is in this book.
'Why You Don't Need Shoes'
comes from deep within my Soul and Heart.

My life is a constant striving to increase my Consciousness, to
make my life as Easy and Joyful as possible, to be Happy, Radiant,
Relaxed and Peaceful in all situations, and for my Communications
and Relations to be Loving, Open, Truthful, Respectful
and full of Integrity
- and of course, to have lots of fun!

*There is a reason that this book found you -
and boy, would I like to see your face
when you find out...*

*- Xian   :0)
July 2007*

"WHY YOU DON'T NEED SHOES"

Yeah man,
The Universe! Serendipity! Co-incidences! Intuition!
Being Now, Aware and Conscious!
Always!
Do you want to know how to really play with
These Cosmic Toys
And not just talk about it?
Well, this is how to!

Know your Intuition from your Thoughts,
Every time!
Know Co-incidences from Random Happenings.
Follow Signs without Doubt!

Make friends with that little Thinking-Creature in Your Brain.
Understand Yourself: How you Behave, Think, Feel,
React and Interact.
Understand your Mind - Love it, Hate it, Blow it.
Rid yourself of Worry, Doubt and Fear.
Become super-Chilled while laughing!
Find out who you are, who others are, and why.
Find your Destiny.

Understand Love, feel Love, spread Love.
Go out, go Mad and Party with the Universe.

GET IT. GET LIFE. LIVE LIFE.
NOW.

Do all the Big Stuff everybody is talking about...
And all the even Bigger Stuff nobody is talking about yet!
Blow your Horizons and have ridiculous amounts of Fun.

Throw away your Mind, your Thoughts, your Conditionings,
Your Past, your Beliefs, your Ideals, your World.
Throw away your Shoes and everything they represent
And be prepared to be blown away -
Because Nowness Rocks!

This is no joke, this is as real as the shoes on your feet!
Right NOW!

PART 1

1   The Universe Looks After Me

Gone

She was gone. For good this time. He still couldn't believe it. It had all happened so fast. He breathed rapidly, sitting on the sofa, his mind racing. Strange how Thoughts took on a life of their own. The past took over all by itself. That time on their road trip, how she sat in the car with her feet up on the dashboard, laughing, throwing her head back. That time by the river, when she swam naked. How they had laughed, how they had loved. It was over. It had all been so sudden. She came home one night and told him that she was moving out. It had hit him like a sledgehammer.

Lee willed himself to breathe more deeply, more powerfully. He felt the air penetrate his Body, his flesh, his bones, his core. He raised his head and looked out of the window. He saw the trees, the wind playing with the leaves. Strength. He could feel it flooding back into his Body and into his Mind.

Strong. Powerful. Alive. Now. That had been his Mantra for years now. He had made himself to be like that. He had a strong personality, he had power and integrity, he loved life and lived it to the full. He was determined to keep his clarity throughout this mess.

Lee had played the scenario back in his mind a million times. His girlfriend (well, ex-girlfriend) Kate had met her ex-boyfriend while she'd been away on business and decided to give it another try. She had left Lee over night. Was it meant to be? Could he have foreseen that this was going to happen? Intuition, Thoughts. What was the difference? Had there been any Signs? Had he *missed* them? Had he *ignored* them? Had it been Co-incidence? Had it happened for a reason? Was he better off now? Were both of them better off? Was there anything *positive* he could find in all of this? *Anything* at all? Lee buried his head in his hands, closed his eyes and breathed deeply, trying to stay present.

He remained like that, for what seemed like ages, when something unusual happened in his brain; new synapses fired and made connections, chemicals whizzed between transmitters and receptors, latent neurons were stimulated, his Subconscious was being activated. All Lee was aware of though, was an unusual Thought. The word "Co-incidences" leapt at him from the depths of his Mind, waving a big red flag, briskly, forcefully. At first Lee didn't hear it, but the longer it went on, the more his Consciousness began to listen.

'Hang on,' he sat up straight. 'Co-incidences?' he listened more closely this time. His forehead creased with concentration.

"Co-incidence. Two incidences happening at the same time," his Rational Mind offered. Well, it had certainly been that. Kate had met the other guy on the one day Lee had been out of town and had been unable to take her phone calls. The first time in ages.

'Splendid Co-incidence,' he growled to himself.

Then, "Everything-Happens-for-a-Reason and Trust-your-Intuition", mingled in with the word "Co-incidences" in his Mind, and together, they repeated themselves in his brain again and again, slowly and determinedly, like a Mantra.

"Trust your Intuition?" How would that have helped? And "Everything happens for a reason?" Had the this break-up happened for a reason? If it had, Lee's Mind took the idea further all by itself, that would mean that Co-incidences are not just a *random* meeting of events, but two incidences meeting, with a *Significant* result. The Significant result being: him being single.

"Great. Very Significant. Thanks. That's useful. So what? Now what?' Lee said out loud to no-one in particular.

As Lee sat there, with his head buried in his hands again, little did he know, that he had just put out his very first request to… well, let's just say that he put it out there... and strangely it was listened to…

"Co-incidences are of a Different Dimension," the answer came. But Lee was already too busy thinking of Kate again to listen.

It's Just Too Obvious

In semi sleep, Lee's arm felt the empty space next to him. Kate? Entangled pictures and feelings had dominated his dreams. He'd slept badly. His Body was waking up slowly, his Consciousness rising above the clouds of the irrationality his dreams had submerged him in. Sleepily he began to feel the sunrays that had played with his eyelids for the past half an hour. He felt heavy and drowsy. He opened one eye tentatively to catch a glance of the alarm clock, and a flash of panic shot through his bones. With a start he sat up in bed, banging his head.

"Ouch!" - instantly awake! 'Why is that stupid shelf there again? Oh yeah, Kate had liked it there,' he remembered hazily. He really did have to take it down, it was too dangerous in the early morning hours.

'Great start to a Friday morning,' he moaned, feeling the bump growing on his head. 'Sorry boss, my alarm clock didn't go off - what a great school-boy excuse. Right up there with: The dog ate my homework,' Lee smiled for the first time this morning.

Luckily oversleeping didn't really matter, he'd always loved his job for that. It was full-on, stressful, and he had heaps of lots of responsibility, selling Stocks and Shares had never been his dream job, but as long as he made his quota and brought in the expected amount of business, nobody cared where he was, what he did, when he took days off or when he turned up at the office. Freedom within the Rat-Race, he'd always thought. Lee relaxed and slumped back into a more comfortable position, carefully avoiding the treacherous shelf. He didn't have any important meetings scheduled for the day and Fridays in his patch were usually pretty mellow anyway. Ernie could do two important calls for him and Lee could hold the fort down for Ernie next week, when he needed to pick up his children from school. Easy. Lee rubbed the sleep out of his eyes and looked out the window. Blue sky and sunshine helped to finalize the decision. He called the office to take a day off, then called Ernie to discuss the backup-plan. Once everything was arranged, he put the phone down and softly snuggled back against the pillow. Pure luxury. Now he had all the time in the world. Mmmhhh. He turned over and stretched comfortably in the warmth of his sheets and drifted back to sleep far too quickly to hear the faint little voice in the back of his head, that was followed by a little giggle, "You have no idea what we've got in store for YOU today!"

Lee had only slept for a few minutes, when he noticed something bouncing up and down in his sleepy Mind and wouldn't leave him alone: "Hey, sunshine is a rarity. It should be enjoyed, don't you think? Go to the park. The park really sounds like a great idea. Yep, definitely the park!"

Lee sat up, shook his head to disperse the cobwebs. Maybe he could go to the park, play some football, go for a run, a movie, clear his head. Feeling slightly more energized, he jumped out of bed and ambled to the bathroom. He brushed his teeth with determination, trying not to let the distinct lack of female toiletries distract him. He indulged in a nice long and leisurely shower, went back to the bedroom, put on a pair of old jeans and his favourite dark green Che Guevara T-shirt. Perfect for the rebellious surprise day-off. He went downstairs and treated himself to a special I-have-all-the-time-in the-world breakfast. The works. Good and proper. Freshly squeezed orange juice, toast, two eggs, branflakes (with raisins of course), and coffee. In a nutshell, pure bliss compared to his usual routine: Alarm clock, shower, suicidal shave, dress and leave. During the week, speed was of the essence. Today was different. Today was a holiday!

Lee carried his feast into the living room, laid back on the sofa, read the rest of yesterday's paper, sipped his coffee and devoured his breakfast. After he polished off the last crumb on his plate, he wandered down the shared hallway, to pick up his mail. As he turned to go back inside, he was just in time to see the door to his apartment slam shut, a split second before he heard it crash into the frame.

'Great!' he thumped the frame with his fist and leaned his head against the hard wooden frame. 'Fabulous! First the alarm clock and now this!' he groaned.

"Random event or Significant Co-incidence?" Lee's brain brushed the Thought aside before he even noticed it. Little did he know, that of all the Co-incidences in his life, this was to be one of the most Significant. His life was about to change, but all Lee thought about, was that he had locked himself out.

Lee had a mind to kick the door, when a sudden vision of a comedy sketch flickered across his Mind, the one where the Ben Elton stood butt-naked, barefoot in front of his flat, looking stupefied at a similarly closed apartment door. It had been hilarious. Well, it always was when it happened to somebody else.

He looked down on himself and grinned thankfully, 'Thank God that I had the sense to get dressed first. Well, but for big foot here,' he wriggled his bare toes. 'No point getting upset,' he thought. 'That's not going to open the door either.'

Reassured about his decency, though barefooted-ness, he contemplated what to do next. Ted, his neighbour, who kept the spare keys, because he was always, *always* home, wasn't. Sod's law. Ted had started a new job yesterday.

'Typical,' Lee grumbled. He leaned his back against the apartment door and slowly slid down it till he sat on the maroon carpeted floor, his legs stretched out in front of him. He rummaged through his trouser pockets hoping to find some cash that might have escaped the washing machine spin-cycle, but didn't have any luck. It suddenly hit him - how life and options changed when one didn't have any money in one's pocket. He couldn't take a bus to see Ted or even call him for help, and everybody else he knew would be at work at this time, miles and miles away. Lee wracked his brain. The best option - and the closest at that - was to walk to Ted's new office five miles out of town, borrow some money and somehow arrange to get his keys.

'Walk. Five miles. On foot. Barefoot. Phew, back to basics,' Lee sighed. 'But hey, the Aborigine do that all the time, right?' he tried to cheer himself up. 'And they do that through a jungle full of thorns and tigers, not nicely paved streets. It'll be cool. I'll be fine,' he tried to reassure himself while silently hoping that nobody would turn him in for being weird. 'Thank God it's not the middle of winter,' he rolled his eyes, got up and left the house. 'Hi Ho, Hi Ho, off to work we don't go,' his lips hummed quietly.

As he walked along the tree-lined road, minding his own business, he caught himself still whistling happily. Strange really, considering that he still felt gloomy that his day had taken such an unexpected turn. Things weren't exactly going right for him at the moment, he thought, but somehow he didn't seem to mind today. A good walk in the sunshine had never harmed anyone, he grinned a little more cheerful.

"Co-incidence. Everything-Happens-for-a-Reason. Trust your Intuition," his Subconscious received, his Conscious ignored.

Even though his Conscious Mind had still not noticed that his brain wasn't working the way it usually did, somehow his Body seemed to know. Without him being really aware of it, his feet took a slightly different route, just because it was nicer, because the grass on the other side of the road seemed just the tiniest bit softer, the pavement cleaner. They took the route towards the park, rather than to Ted's office.

'Funny, didn't something in my Mind tell me to go to the park this morning?' Lee hardly noticed the Thought, he was too distracted by his new mode of transport. Walking barefoot was an interesting experience. He had to walk much slower and softer, paying more attention to the road in front of him, making sure not to step on or into anything. It was strangely soothing. It made him feel present. Aware. Concentrating on his feet helped him keep his Mind off Kate. It felt good. He breathed. Strong. Powerful. Alive. Now.

He was peacefully wandering along, when a strong feeling of Significance permeated his Being. A feeling of complete and utter certainty.

"Watch out buddy, here it comes!" This time the words in his Mind were much more audible. As if moved by an invisible hand, his head turned, his awareness sharp and clear.

And there she was. Barely twenty feet away from him. Even though he'd only caught a glimpse of the woman's profile, his Mind knew that he'd never seen her before. His gut on the other hand seemed to think differently. His gut felt an odd confidence that he *did* know her, that he knew her with all his heart, with all his Being. While he was still contemplating that he really needed to talk to this woman, his feet had already begun to walk. They moved towards her on their own accord, steadily taking him along with them.

He studied her. The way she held herself, the way she walked softly, the beautiful, gentle, smile on her face made it impossible for him to look away.

'She's radiant,' he thought, surprising himself.

The woman turned slightly. He could see her face fully now. For a split second he saw straight into her eyes. The words "Compassion", "Love" and "WOW" sprang into his Mind from out of nowhere. Her eyes were sparkling with a life of their own. They were emanating a wondrous warmth, which filled him with comfort and serenity. He saw balance, contentedness and happiness. He saw eyes that belonged to a person who had found Peace - inside and out, while retaining a little twinkle and sparkle that was like nothing he had ever seen.

'Ha, listen to yourself,' Lee smiled to himself. 'I didn't even know my mathematical little Mind could come up with fluffy words like that.' A random string of Thoughts flew past his Mind, each only lasting a split second, 'Was this the reason? Was I supposed to lock myself out, so that I could bump into this young woman? Was I supposed to separate from Kate, just in time for something interesting to happen now?' Lee caught his Thoughts and laughed out loud, throwing back his head, then shaking it, tears of laughter flooding his eyes. 'Hilarious what the Mind comes up with, but hey, at least it made me laugh. A bit of wishful thinking never hurt anyone,' he added sheepishly.

To his surprise, he heard the little voice in the back of his Mind again, "Maybe not quite so wishful as you think, young man". He shrugged the voice off, but as soon as he looked back at the young woman, the voice inside his head chose to scream at him this time, "Hel-loooo! Are you deaf or what? Go and talk to her!"

Lee jolted with a start. This time he'd actually caught the goings-on in his brain loud and clear. Boy, this was different. He seemed to actually *know* that this meeting was Significant. There was not a flicker of doubt in his Mind. It was pure certainty.

'Is this what a *real* Intuition feels like?' he wondered. 'Is this more than a Co-incidence? Whatever! I have to go and talk to her,' his feet moved abruptly, and then stopped as abruptly again. How did one go up to a stranger to say, "Excuse me, I have this odd feeling that I need to talk to you. So, I guess, here I am, what shall we talk about?"

"Great chat up line," the familiar little devil, perched on his right shoulder whispered into his ear, "She'll laugh at you and then run away!"

But for a change the tiny hoofed creature didn't have any impact on the Strength and Certainty he was experiencing. As he brushed the devil aside without giving it another Thought, Lee's gut knew that he would finally get the answers he'd been looking for, whereas his Mind, strangely confused, tried to remember what the question had been in the first place.

'Hi,' he heard someone say. She stood right in front of him, looking up, smiling. Their eyes connected for a moment.

'Hi,' he said, as his eyes briefly scanned the young woman's Body. She had long, dark red-brown curly hair, blue-green eyes, a slim, yet curvy figure. She was about a head shorter than him. She wore a long, bright-green flowing skirt, a tight army-green coloured top with spaghetti-straps and a wide leather belt with a little bell on it. His eyes unwittingly stopped at her feet. As he was looking at his own bare feet opposite to hers, a broad grin lit up his face.

Her feet were shoe-less, strong, healthy and a little bit grubby. And what was that? It looked like a marker-pen scribbling. Was he dreaming? He closed his eyes, squeezed them for a second and opened them again. No, he was wide-awake. The girl had 'BE NOW' written on her left foot.

The Universe Looks After Me

Tara followed Lee's surprised glance downward, 'Ah, a soul mate. Now I understand why I had to talk to you', she said cheerfully. 'You know about it too?'

Lee was pleasantly dumbstruck. His Mind grinned to himself, 'A soul mate? *She* thought *she* had to talk to *me*?'

'Know about what?' he asked.

'Trust,' she said.

'Trust in what?'

'Trust in being looked after,' the girl said without hesitation and briefly raised her eyes towards the blue sky, before looking at him again.

Lee's reality-check only took a split second. 'Typical!' he mused to himself. He didn't exactly look his best today, but then again, on second Thought, he *was* sporting an unkempt attractiveness, an acceptable gruffness. His Hazelnut brown hair was ruffled, his beard stubbled, and he wore his old but favourite clothes. So that was all cool, and what was even better, was that he had this equally barefooted, and totally lovely young woman, which he'd happened to have some kind of premonition about, come up to him and talk to him. But now, why was she was talking about Trusting in something 'up there'!

"I mean, seriously!" his Rational Brain scolded him. "And anyway, what does barefooted-ness have to do with Trust?"

While his Brain was busy trying to dismiss the significance of the situation, his jaw started to move of it's own accord, 'I knew that I had to talk to you too.'

'Great,' the young woman said, holding out her hand in a friendly gesture, 'Tara.'

Lee shook it firmly, 'Lee.'

There was a small pause. Both of them looked at each other.

Her gaze was comforting and familiar, Lee noticed. 'So, you always walk around barefoot?' he asked casually.

'Of course,' Tara said matter-of-factly.

Lee was intrigued, she didn't seem to find it at all strange that she was the only other person in this town, maybe even in this country, that was walking barefoot, something which most people would regard as odd, or at least surprising. The way she had said, 'Of course,' made it seem that it was just what she did, regardless of what anybody thought.

'How can you do that without killing yourself?' he asked, 'I mean, I nearly cut my foot off about a million times,' Lee laughed, pointing back at the road behind him.

Tara grinned and said simply, 'To walk around barefoot, you have to trust that you're being looked after.'

'So you said. But looked after by what?'

'The Universe,' Tara replied.

'You must be kidding me!' Lee blurted out, as his Mind screamed inside his head, "Great, another fruit-loop, an alien fanatic, a guru-hopper, a Universe freak, getting messages from outer space, run while you can!"

Well, that was his *Mind*. Deep down he knew though that that Tara wasn't any of these things, and to his relief, instead of being offended at his outburst, Tara responded with a big, hearty and utterly beautiful laugh.

This Stuff Works or Now What? - Co-incidences and Intuitions

'No, I'm not kidding,' she said cheerfully.

'But you seem so normal,' Lee heard himself say with a roughish grin.

'I am,' Tara laughed again.

'Well, believing to be looked after by the Universe is rather borderline to normal, don't you think?' Lee said carefully.

Tara laughed again, 'Agreed.'

'Thank God, at least we're on the same page,' Lee said charmed. 'So, what's this Trusting in the Universe business about then?'

'Oh, that'll take some time to explain,' Tara said.

Lee's Rational Brain switched itself on again and urged him in the secure silent grounds of his brain, "Here we go, what did I say! It's the Guru out to convert! You can still get out of here!'

"Stay and keep talking to this girl!" his Intuition countered energetically.

For a split second Lee was caught in the middle. His Mind and his Intuition were holding a shouting match in his brain, both telling him contradictory things. It happened all the time. He never quite knew which one was which, it was sometimes confusing. Stay - go - stay - run. Then from out of nowhere, *that* feeling returned. Strong and unmistakable. "Your Intuition says stay!" The feeling was clear. He could sense the vibration of the words throughout his entire Body and he *knew* that was what he had to trust. Lee straightened his back and shoulders and boldly brushed his Mind aside. He had nothing to loose, he told himself. He could always still run if it got too weird. *And* she had BE NOW written on one of her feet! That was certainly worth asking about. Being Now, being Present had been his focus for a while now. His Mind was made up.

'Try me, I'm all ears,' he said finally.

'Do you believe in Significant Co-incidences?' Tara asked without batting an eyelid.

"There it is! Did you hear that? Co-incidences!" his Intuition triumphed. Lee stared for a moment with stunned surprise. The word echoed in his Brain. The same word that had been hopping around his Consciousness for days now. Co-incidences. He nodded slowly.

Tara smiled. 'Oh great. You do. What do you know about them?'

Lee's Mind mulled over the question. Besides all the Thoughts he'd had over the last couple of days with regards to Kate, if her meeting her Ex had been a Co-incidence, what else did he know? He thought for a moment. He remembered standing in a bar with his friends, about a year ago, overhearing a conversation at a table next to him.

'Co-incidences are more than just random occurrences. Co-incidences are two incidences coinciding, with a Significant outcome,' the young man with the checked coat had said. Lee's ears had pricked up as his brain had absorbed the words. 'Following your Intuition, your hunches, your gut feelings, and the Signs can lead you to people and situations, which can turn out to be of great Significance to you. Something you might call a Significant Co-incidence.' Check. 'People, follow your Intuition, follow the Signs!' the man had said with emphasis, but without preachy-ness.

Back then, Lee had felt as if something in him had been switched on. Intuition. Co-incidences. They were words, which had seemed so familiar, so part of him. Without really thinking about it, he'd taken the man's words to heart and had started to watch out for Co-incidences and

Signs, had tried to listen to his Intuition. In fact, he had met Kate, due to a pretty weird Co-incidence, and of course getting his motorcycle fixed so cheaply had also been pretty amazing... However, often nothing of Significance had happened, no matter how hard he tried to see the Signs. He didn't have a clue how to distinguish Intuitions from wishful thinking, how to tell random events that happened without a deeper meaning, from the *real* Signs, if there even was such a thing. What in the vastness of everyday life was he supposed to follow and what was he supposed to ignore? Sure, he *had* been led to some surprisingly odd, bizarre and wonderful situations, but in the end it had usually still always felt more like an accident, rather than something he was consciously taking part in.

What was more, in retrospect he realised, that in his ignorance, he had begun to *seek out* Co-incidences. He had moved straight from everything being *insignificant*, to everything being *Significant* instead. Suddenly *every* person was a messenger, *every* event was a possible Sign that could lead him to something big - or so he thought. Of course that didn't leave him any better off than before either. A few exhilarating experimental months were followed by indecisiveness, uncertainty and doubt. The more Lee got involved, the more he noticed that the entire affair was pretty unpredictable and rather confusing. The gist of it was: he really didn't know what he was doing.

His best friend Jason had stopped the whole Co-incidence and Intuition thing long ago. He said it was fun and he had become more aware of the world around him, which was nice, but he couldn't get any dependable and repeatable results either. That was Jason. Lee on the other hand couldn't shake off the feeling that there had to be more to it than just entertainment value and that there had to be a way to figure out how it all worked. In a last attempt to understand, he'd made a point to sort his general disappointment and exhilaration into simple statements and questions. He knew that he *did* have some strange and surprising successes. He just wasn't able to *recreate* them *deliberately*. Being a man of statistics, he knew that what happened once, can happen again, with time, of course. The question was just *how* he could play an active role in that recreation? It had to be possible to work *with* the Co-incidences, instead of just being at their mercy. Shouldn't he be able to *actively find* Significant events by following his Intuition? Was that really possible? Somewhere deep inside of him, he knew that it was. The question was just: How? And he was damned if he knew. So far nobody had been able to answer his questions, and slowly, over time, even Lee had lost interest and stopped playing with Co-incidences and Intuitions altogether. Strangely though, with him and Kate breaking up, the subject had crept back into his life.

While Lee was lost in Thought, Tara waited patiently for his answer. She knew how huge the subject was and how difficult it was to put into words. She watched him think contentedly, noticing how familiar he looked. Hadn't she seen his face before? Those eyes? "I'll remember those eyes anywhere...", she felt the words bounce on the fringes of her Consciousness, but before she could hold on to them, Lee had begun to answer her question.

Lee had finally come to the conclusion, that his whole experience with Intuitions and Co-incidences was too vast to do justice. He therefore decided to pick the main points out of his brain, and swiftly summarize them in the hope that it was somehow going to make sense. 'Ok, here it goes. Co-incidences are more than just random occurrences, they are *Significant* events. When you follow your Intuition and Signs, they will lead you to Co-incidences, Significant situations and events which you are supposed to be part of, or to people that you're supposed to meet.' As Tara's smile broadened, Lee continued, 'But man, so much stuff happens, how is one supposed to tell the Significant Signs or Co-incidences from some regular, random event? And anyway, so much stuff goes on in my head, how am I supposed to know what's my Mind and what's my Intuition? I know that I *should* be able to do it, but I just don't know *how*,' Lee shrugged his shoulders gruffly, giving away his frustration with the subject.

As if continuing with his breath, Tara picked up where Lee had left off, 'And even if you are one of the lucky ones who has figured out how to follow the right Signs, you'd still wonder, 'So what?' and then, 'Now what?' What's the *next* step?' Lee nodded and Tara carried on, 'Have you ever thought about how great it would be, if you were able to *actively* work *with* the Co-incidences, Signs and Intuitions, and not just be at their mercy?'

'Ok, now it's getting spooky!' Lee said in disbelief. 'You just perfectly summarised my exact previous Thoughts on Co-incidences. You even used some of the same words I did.'

'Na, not spooky, just meant-to-be,' Tara said simply, with a playful twinkle in her eyes.

"Well, just a little spooky then," Lee's Mind thought stubbornly.

"Be a bit more open, will you?" his Intuition told him.

Lee shook his head to clear his Brain. He felt a sudden urge to hug Tara. Right on queue, she stepped forward and gave him a huge bear hug, let go and grinned at him.

'She can even read my Mind. Madness,' Lee thought with a smile on his face. Today was definitely high up on the cool-barometer. Weird or not, his Intuition finally won.

'Do you fancy sitting down somewhere?' he asked her. 'I'd love to talk to you more about this stuff.'

'Sure,' Tara said, plonking herself down right where they had stood.

Lee looked down, looked around, grinned and sat down next to her on the edge of the pavement, his bare feet on the tarmac of the road next to hers. He leaned against the lamppost next to him and closed his eyes for a second. He couldn't believe that this was actually happening. Meeting a complete stranger, talking about far-out stuff within seconds and not thinking anything of it. Sitting on the pavement, people bustling by, cars passing, a dog sniffing his trouser leg. He was beginning to wonder if his alarm clock hadn't gone off yet after all and if he was actually still sleeping. But when he opened his eyes, the lamppost in his back and the girl called Tara next to him, were still as real as everything else around him. Lee's grin widened. What a great day this had turned out to be.

'Three cheers to the door-closing-Gods,' Lee thought happily, remembering bemusedly how upset he'd been earlier.

'So, tell me more then,' he finally said.

'Sure, but stop me when you get bored, I can talk about this stuff forever.'

'Deal,' he said appreciating the offer, 'go on then.'

'Mmh, where to start,' Tara thought with her index finger on her lips, looking into the distance. 'Oh yeah. From my experience, most people only notice Intuitions, Signs and Significant Co-incidences in *retrospect*. Sure, hindsight is a glorious thing, and you can learn a lot from it, but **the point is to *actively* work *with* Intuitions, Signs and Co-incidences. To notice them *as* and *when* they arise, *while* they're happening, rather than just noticing and analyzing them afterwards. The point is to be able to tell your Intuition apart from your Thoughts *every* single time, and then of course to have the guts and willingness to act on them, even if your Rational Mind comes up with the most fabulous reasons why not to do so.**' Tara saw a look of recognition on Lee's face and continued, 'That's where most of us have stumbled. Most of us have managed to follow the occasional Intuition, but when it comes down to it? We haven't got a clue. We have no idea what's behind the 'myth' of Intuition, how or why it works, or if it's maybe just an 'old-wives' tale after all. People say, follow your gut-feeling, follow your Intuition, but nobody ever tells you how to do that! Or how all of this ties in with Co-incidences, for that matter.'

'I agree wholeheartedly,' Lee nodded. 'More?' he prompted smiling boldly.

Tara grinned back. 'My pleasure.'

The Big Something

'So, if we know how to follow Signs and our Intuition, then they will lead us to Significant Co-incidences. You've already said that, right?' Tara begun. 'Now, if we look at the nature of Co-incidences, essentially, they all entail us meeting other people just-in-time, seeing a Sign or getting the right information about something just-in-time? Now, have you ever thought that these Co-incidences require some sort of connection between people and events? Maybe even that Co-incidences, the so called lucky events in our life, are co-ordinated in a certain way?'

Lee thought for a second and then replied, 'Mmh, yeah, I guess so. Otherwise, how could we explain a Significant Co-incidence happening to a *group* of people, who all followed the same Intuition to lead them there?' Unfortunately Lee had only heard of such things happening, he had not experienced them himself.

'Exactly. Lets assume that there is something out there that makes things happen, ok? Whether we can prove it or not doesn't matter for now. Can you do that?'

'No problem. I mean, most of us hope that there's Something out there or at least think that there *could* be something. And sure, we can't prove it, but I mean we can't *disprove* it either, can we? The question is just *what* it *would* be if there *was* something, and how we could describe it,' Lee was surprised to discover his very own Universe-Freak within himself.

Tara was about to speak, but then hesitated for a split second. She contemplated if she really wanted to talk to this random guy about her innermost beliefs, how she saw the world and the Universe, how she had discovered a totally bizarre and wonderful way to play with it. She could see genuine interest in Lee's face, and then of course her Intuition told her to keep talking to him, in fact, it urged her to continue. She smiled to herself, she had trained herself well. She could *always* tell her Intuition from her Mind. She *knew* what she had to do, no matter how many obstacles and doubts her Rational Mind tried to throw at her. And on top of everything, there was this feeling of connectedness between them. Lee had already commented on it and she could feel it too - and it was stronger than she usually felt it. He looked at her openly and for a second she lost track of her Thoughts. Tara looked at him more closely, his strong jaw, his long lashes, his hands. She laughed to herself, as her Intuition tugged at her, telling her to get on with it. That little voice, so clear, so obvious, standing out a mile in her own Thoughts, a voice which she had come to love so much. As usual her distracting Mind interrupted, "But it's nice to daydream. Why would I possibly want to worry about Co-incidences and such things, when I could just stare at his hands...?" she laughed to herself. She knew her Mind just as well as her Intuition, always trying to throw in the 'But-s,' the 'Maybe-s,' doubts and distractions into the clarity of her Intuitive messages. No matter how much her Mind tried to confuse her though, she always knew which voice to trust, which one to listen to. Tara smiled at her Thoughts, giggling at how ceaselessly her Mind tried to change her resolution to *'follow and act on every single Intuition'* she had. Confidently she brushed her Mind aside and followed her Intuition once again. Her mouth opened to speak as if of it's own accord.

'This is truly big stuff to get your head around,' Tara said auspiciously.

'Uoh, a big introduction...?' Lee marvelled, with a slight note of sarcasm in his voice, despite feeling more and more intrigued.

'Well, honours, where honours are due,' Tara said sincerely. 'I mean literally Big Stuff, as big as Infinity!'

'That *is* big,' Lee grinned and prodded expectantly, 'Go on then, tell me.'

Tara had a theatrical look on her face when she said, 'Ok, but try not to judge or rationalise anything I am about to say, ok? Just take it as... as a new theory.'

'Sure, no problem. Man, I'm on the edge of my seat here...' Lee said, exaggeratedly tapping his fingers on one of his knees.

'Ok, download activated,' Tara began with a dramatic gesture, switching an imaginary switch at the side of Lee's head, just behind his left ear. Lee laughed, he liked her playfulness. 'Get this,' Tara announced. 'All Beings, all Spirits, all Entities, all Souls on Earth, in different Dimensions or Universes or wherever, are part of this *one* big *Thing*. This one Thing is the *totality* of *Everything*. Literally Everything. Everything we can and cannot see or perceive. I mean *Everything*, everywhere. It's the Something we talked about earlier, the *link* between every single thing. People call it Infinity, God, the Universe and many other names,' Tara paused.

'Ok,' Lee said and motioned for her to continue, he enjoyed listening to her talk.

'Well, people often find it difficult to understand an abstract concept such as Infinity. It's too big to grasp, too far removed from our everyday lives. When I initially had the same problem, I tried to explain it to myself in a way, which made it easier to get my head around it.'

'I'm all ears,' Lee looked at her expectantly.

'Imagine the Something to be like a human Body,' Tara paused, trying to quiet her Mind to let her Intuition flow more freely. 'Let me explain first how I understand how a Body work and then I'll explain how this relates to the Big Something, how's that?' Lee nodded and Tara continued, 'It's simple really, a Body is made up of bones, muscle, all sorts of organs, gooey stuff and whatever else. Our entire Body is made up of cells and each cell contains DNA. DNA is like the Software on a computer, telling it what to do. Now, here it comes.

Biology and Chemistry tell us that every single cell, no matter out of which part of the Body we take it, contains exactly the *same* DNA, however, all cells *use* that DNA differently. Some make bone tissue, others make kidney or intestinal tissue, some make muscles. Each cell does it's own thing, unaware of the bigger picture - so the scientists say. Even though individual cells do not to *perceive* the entire Body, they nonetheless all work together to make *one* thing, a fully living entity, a creature made out of many, many smaller living creatures, the Body. So, Conscious of it or not, all cells are inherently linked, and they all work together to 'make' a Human Being.'

Lee mulled this over and then said, 'Basically you're saying that each part of the Big Something, is like a cell in the Body. Some of its parts make planets and Milky Ways, others make up our Earth, some make rocks, water or trees, some make animals, some make Humans. **We all appear to be separate from one another, we all appear to be doing our own thing, just like the different cells in a Body, but when we get down to it, we're all made up of exactly the same fundamental building blocks, and the totality of all of us makes up one big thing - the Something, the Universe. Thus we're all connected. Everything is connected**,' Lee paused thoughtfully.

'That's right,' Tara nodded, '**but us Humans are so far removed from knowing, understanding, or even believing this, that we see everything as separate and different from ourselves**. We don't realise or acknowledge that we are all part of the same thing, that we're all working towards a common goal: to make up one big equilibrium, perfect balance within ourselves, with others and within our environment, and thus perfect balance of the whole thing. In the human Body, equilibrium is worked towards automatically. If something attacks the Body, a virus for example, the Body's entire immune system pulls together, cells, Body temperature, lymphatic system, blood, the brain, everything works *together* to cure *the greater whole*. It's a natural reaction. It's just what it does, it doesn't need a reason or incentive. All its parts work together, because that instruction is part of every cell's information. In Nature, all animals and plants work on equilibrium or balance, automatically. **Even though some animals or plants feed on others, everything in nature only ever takes what it *needs*. This way everything remains in balance.** Nature balances itself by design, just like a healthy Body. *The Something, Oneness* is the Realisation of the perfect plan - it has perfect balance. But only if all entities within it play the game!'

'And humans don't play by the rules,' Lee butted in.

'Right,' Tara agreed. 'We've made up our own rules. Humans are like a Cancer in the human Body. We grow and take over everything, regardless. Humans are the only creatures that take more than required for survival. Humans don't act on *need*, they act on *greed*.'

'Scary really,' Lee mumbled gloomily.

Free Will?

'**I** know. Funnily enough, the one thing that we believe sets us above animals, is exactly the one thing that makes us destroy the natural balance and harmony of the Universe,' Tara said.

'And that one thing is?' Lee asked, curious to hear Tara's take on things.

'Free Will,' Tara said without a second Thought. 'Only because of that, can we choose what to do and how much to take.'

'Phew, that's so true. And boy, do we take advantage of that ability.'

Lee sighed and moved his legs a little to relief some pins and needles. He looked at her thoughtfully. '**Instead of being a useful part of the eco-system, we've become selfish and greedy**. Ha,' he suddenly grinned, '**us humans are part of an Ego-system, rather than an Eco-system**,' he winked at Tara who smiled at the play with words. 'We always want more. More for ourselves, and certainly more than others. We want to horde and save and we want power over other people. It's all want, want, want and me, me, me. We're never happy with what we've got.'

Lee's words were not empty of feeling, he spoke from experience. Right now he had money, but no time to spend it. He had the car, the computer, the phone, the nice apartment, the nice - oh no - he didn't have the nice girlfriend anymore. Well, anyway, he had stuff, but he still didn't feel content. Not really. His mates always chuckled when he talked about the meaning of life and that there must be more to it, but he didn't care. He was still looking.

'Sad but true,' Tara interrupted his Thoughts. 'By focussing on gaining possessions, and thus forgetting to support the common goal, we've separated ourselves from our environment and from other people more and more. The vicious cycle that follows, is one we all know. Once we've got material stuff, we get bored of it and want more stuff and on it goes. We become greedy, take more than we need and fall out of balance. It's an old hat, it's been talked about millions of times before.'

'So, the Free Will that we believe gives us Freedom and sets us above all living creatures, in fact disconnects and separates us from the whole,' Lee summarized.

'Right. Now, why is that not a good thing?' Tara asked rhetorically and then answered her own question, '**Because it's only when we're connected *with* the Something, that we're connected to Everything, and *that's* the dimension where we trust and follow our Intuition and where we're in balance with the flow of the Universe, and that's the true dimension of Co-incidences.**'

'But for that we have to give up our Free Will?'

'**Well, can you give something up if it's not real in the first place?**' Tara asked boldly.

'What do you mean 'not real'?' Lee asked slightly taken aback.

'Well, Free Will is not quite as free as you might think it is,' Tara said simply, her eyes becoming more focussed. 'It's quite ironic that, even though we think that we are *free* to do what *we* want, that we are *free* to choose and think what we want, that actually, we're *not*.'

'We're not?' Lee asked surprised.

'**No, because our so called *Free Will* is in fact, *Dependant Will*.** It would be *Free* if we'd *always do whatever we want*, regardless. You might say that's what humans do, but if you really look at it: we *think* about all the options before we do anything, right? We think about the pros and cons, what other people might think of us, we weigh up any considered actions and their possible outcomes, we compare to past experiences, situations and to other people's experiences. Our physical environment, lifestyle, daily pattern of activity, our past, our desired future, our upbringing etc, they all influence everything we do, think and feel. We are influenced by regulations, behavioural structures, reactionary patterns, trends, fears and standards that our society imposes on us, even sexual stereotypes. **Pretty much everything that comes in contact with our senses, consciously or unconsciously, has an affect on us and thus influences our decisions. So, whose free?**' Tara shrugged her shoulders nonchalantly.

'Phew,' Lee mulled over Tara's words, 'that's an interesting way of looking at it. **So, instead of being led by the Universe, our Intuition and the perfect Flow, we rely on our so called Free Will, which has actually been socially conditioned since the day we were born.**'

'Right, and sure, society is important, but it's not always in sync with the Universe. We follow the trends, rather than the Universal Balance. **We follow what we *think* is right, what we're *told* is right, rather than what actually *is* right**,' she looked at him a little sad. 'We constantly judge and measure ourselves against everything and everybody. We constantly feel as if we are not in line with the so-called 'desired norm.' We always feel that we are not good enough, not strong enough, successful or handsome enough or whatever.'

'Even when we most certainly are,' Lee grinned.

'Oh, absolutely,' Tara laughed and threw one of her long curls over her shoulder. 'But by always feeling that we *should* be better or different or more successful, we lose our freedom to simply *Be* ourselves. **By judging ourselves and by creating such powerful personal competition, we lose our Care-freeness to Stress, our simple Happiness to Status and the Need for Material things, and our Confidence to Self-judgement and Expectations.** We are never good enough for ourselves. **We are fighting ourselves as much as we are fighting others and our environment. How can we be in balance with others if we are not in balance with ourselves?**' Tara hung her head, then looked up at him.

'I know,' Lee said with a caring tone to his voice, 'in human society there is no balance. We fight each other, and boy you're right, we even fight ourselves. Phew, that's as if the cells in our Body would fight each other. Man, and when they're bored of doing that, they fight themselves! That's madness,' Lee shook his head in horror. 'That would be the worst disease ever. Our Body would fight itself. There'd be chaos. It would break apart. Can you imagine?' Lee contorted his face to a gruesome grimace, crocked his arms and legs, hung his head aside and made some un-intelligible grunting noises. They both burst out laughing. It was crude, but it made a point.

'Believe it or not, but that madness is the everyday life in the Brain of the average human being!' Tara said sadly.

They fell silent. Lee glanced down the road, the lanes becoming denser with lunchtime traffic. When Lee turned his head back, he saw Tara braiding her hair, slowly and consciously into two long braids.

'It's so like her to wear braids,' Lee thought gently. It fit her playfulness, he thought. He was still looking at her when she lifted her head - one braid at the front, one on her back - smiled at him and said,

'Actually, there's an easy way out of all of this,' a tiny twinkle lit up her eyes.

'Oh?' Lee grinned. 'Now that's what we like to hear. Hit me with it.'

'Well, all we need to do is understand that *everything is already perfect, just the way it is, and thus re-enter universal balance,*' Tara said without hesitation.

'Yeah right. Fat chance!' Lee said shrewdly. 'Knowing human kind as it is, we'll never understand that. And actually, I'm not sure if I agree with that either. I think I need some more details here.'

'No problem,' Tara said easily. 'Every cell in a human Body is perfect, just as it is, it doesn't need to be improved to do its job. It's the same with us humans. We're already perfect. Our True Being is perfect, our Soul is perfect. Every single human is perfect. We are all pearls, perfect the way we are.'

'Even though I might get that, I think that a lot of people would have a hard time agreeing with that,' Lee said, still not a hundred percent convinced.

'True, and there's a reason for that. It's because we search for happiness and entertainment, knowledge and advice, approval and love *outside* of our Selves. We listen to society and marketing about who and how we should be. **We have created a culture of dependence on other things, other people and others' opinions**.'

'Woha, Hippy alert,' Lee yelped mockingly. 'Are you saying that we should live like hermits instead? Off in a cave somewhere? Away from all the external fun stuff? Forgetting how to live real life? I don't think I'm up for that, and to be honest, no one else I know would be either.'

'Oh, I completely agree, but I'm not saying that you can't enjoy what the world has to offer. I'm saying that **by understanding that you don't have to be *dependent* on positive *external* influence for your happiness, you'd be able to actually enjoy life *more* - because you can then be happy *whatever* happens!** That's the trick!'

'Ah, right, now we're talking,' Lee listened up more closely.

'**All we need to do is flick the switch in our brain** that tells us: "Actually, I'm cool. I'm fine just the way I am. I don't need anything else around me to make me complete or better or stronger or whatever". That switch is inside of everyone! Regardless of who or what you are. **You just have to know where it is and then have the guts to switch it on**!' Tara continued casually, as if she hadn't just dangled the secret to happiness in front of Lee's face. '**If you are balanced inside, solid as a rock, then no outside influence can push you over**. If everything around you is positive, then that's great, but if it isn't, than that's ok too. You're still strong and happy inside,' Tara said with emphasis.

'Ok, I'm with you now. That makes sense,' Lee said and internally recited his old mantra: 'Strong, Powerful, Alive.' Silently he added: 'Happy.'

'Now, got any tips on how to do that? How do I flick that Switch?' Lee asked, quietly wondering if he could use the answer to help him get over Kate faster.

'Sure,' Tara said readily.

The Little Something

'Remember we said that the Big Something is perfect balance?' Tara begun. 'Well, even if we've forgotten, we're still part of that perfect balance, it's still within each of us. You see, our Soul is the strong, happy, fulfilled and thus balanced part within us, the part within us that is still in perfect sync with its surroundings. We just forgot how to tap into it! So, all we need to do is remember how to reconnect with the Big Something.'

'And?' Lee asked impatiently.

'And we do that via our Souls and our Intuition.' Before Lee could even ask the question, Tara already begun to answered it, 'Let me define what I mean by Soul.'

'That'll be great, please define ahead,' Lee ruffled his hair and looked at Tara attentively.

'Imagine the Big Something to be *one* big Soul, right? A Soul with lots of little parts allocated to individual Human Beings on earth, which ultimately remain connected to it. I call these little *connected* parts individual Souls, for the lack of better words.'

'Cool. So basically, the Big Something is a collection of 'individual' Souls,' Lee clarified.

'Yeah, kind of.'

'Is that what people call Collective Consciousness?' Lee wondered.

'Well, The Souls are our Cosmic Consciousness and *all* knowledge in the Universe is available to every single one of our Souls. So yeah, you could call it that.'

'I certainly prefer that to the collective *Un*-consciousness, which most of us seem to be tapping into at the moment. Present company excluded of course,' Lee winked at Tara.

'Of course,' Tara said, matching the mischievous tone in Lee's voice.

Lee leaned forward, touched Tara's shoulder and gave it a light squeeze. It was a gentle touch, non-assuming, friendly. 'I tell you, I'd never have thought this morning, that I'd talk about Collective Consciousness to a complete stranger on the street,' he smiled.

'Yeah, same here,' Tara smiled back at him. 'And you know, it gets even better than that.'

'Oh yeah?' Lee raised his left eyebrow.

Tara laughed. 'Well, **the Big Something is perfect balance, right? As it *is* Everything, it *is* the bigger picture. It's fully aware of what has to happen on earth for the perfect cosmic plan to be achieved, and of course where each human has its place in all of this**, right?'

'Right,' Lee waved for her to go on.

'**And as all Souls are part of that Something, each Soul knows also what each human being has to do to reach perfect balance and happiness.**'

'So, even though *we* have forgotten the 'big' picture, our Souls are still fully aware of it,' Lee picked up Tara's train of Thought.

'And just like the immune system of our Body, **our Souls would do Their job quite easily, if we would just stop interfering**,' Tara started to speak more animatedly, 'Believe it or not, our Souls *want* us to gain that balance within ourselves. And what's best, They will do as much as They possibly can to help us with that.'

'Like how? Like what?' Lee asked.

Tara leant her Body to one side and pulled one leg up into a half cross legged position. She straightened her back and looked at Lee, '**Our Souls are *already* trying to guide us, to talk to us, like all the time, right this minute! It's just that we are not listening**,' Tara tapped her finger onto the side of her head to emphasise the point. 'They constantly tell us what we need to do to make our lives more balanced, easier and more joyful. In fact, *whatever* we want, it's all up there, whenever we want it,' Tara pointed upwards. 'They are always there for us to tap into their knowledge, wisdom and direction for our lives. They hold the strings *and* They're pulling them into the right direction incessantly, but we're so unaware and stubborn with our Free Will, that we constantly pull the other way.'

'In our separated little State of Mind...,' Lee added with a sing-songy voice.

'Yeah. It's a shame really.'

'That's a bit of an understatement.'

'The understatement of the century!' Tara nodded heartily. 'Man, we can get so much help and guidance, tips and tricks on how to become happier and more balanced human beings from Them. It is always there for us, it always has been in fact, it's just that we've forgotten,' Tara paused. 'But **once we get back in tune with Them, we are back in the space of natural perfection, a space where everything just works out. Contentment, happiness and peace are the natural outcome**. All we need to do is remember and re-learn how to listen to The Little Guys again.'

'Hang on, Little Guys?' Lee interrupted with a broad grin on his face. 'Who are They?'

The Little Guys?

"Everybody can have their own personal connection with the Mystery."
-Lee Robbins in One Giant Leap

Tara grinned, 'Oh, sorry, haven't I mentioned Them yet? Let me explain. You know, this Big Something we were talking about? It's not a new concept. People have talked about it for decades. Do you remember when I said earlier that I trust in the Universe?' Lee nodded. 'That's only one of many names to call it. People call the Big Something all sorts of things. You called it Collective Consciousness earlier, others call it Souls, Pixies, Fairies, Angels, Spirits, God, It, Higher Consciousness, The Higher Self, Beings of Light, the Universe, the Cosmos. You can call it whatever you want to, in the end it's all the same thing. So, I just call it whatever *I* want to, and that just happens to be 'My Little Guys'.'

Lee looked at her in disbelief, this was just too funny, 'Tara, you are calling the Big Thing, The Big Something, It, the Universe, the Oneness, the perfect balance the whole world is after, you're calling *that* 'Your Little Guys?'' Lee shook his head and burst out laughing.

Tara laughed with him, 'I do. I find it useful to give any vast and complicated concept a familiar name. For example, if you want to talk about your foot, isn't it easier to call it a foot, rather than having to describe what it looks like and where it is situated on your Body?' Lee nodded slowly. 'Therefore, to be more comfortable with a concept as complex as One-ness or the Big Something, I feel more at ease if I address It with a name that works for me. And for simplicity I choose an easy name to work with on a day-to-day basis. Something small and familiar enough to grasp.'

'Yeah, that makes perfect sense, but,' Lee laughed heartily, 'where on earth did 'Little Guys' come from?'

'Oh, that's a funny one,' Tara rolled her eyes with amusement. 'When I started to play with The Guys, I knew I needed to find a way to address them, but somehow all the traditional names didn't work for me. You see, **my own personal experience with the Big Something didn't really fit into any conventional descriptions of It. Rather than ominous, full of reverence and awe, my experience was personal, fun and playful. The Universe just felt like a really close friend,**' Tara smiled at the memory. 'So, there I was, going through the naming dilemma, wanting a label a little more personal than 'It'.'

'Ha, that might be a bit counterproductive, as 'It' is the monster out of that Stephen King Novel!' Lee grinned.

'Well exactly,' Tara smiled, imagining The lovely Guys to be named after a monster in a horror story. 'So 'It' was out. The name 'Souls' didn't seem appropriate either, because the Souls are only part of the Big Something, so that didn't work either. Just 'Something' sounded a bit silly too. The 'Universe' or 'Oneness' were such big words, that I found them difficult to identify with. And anyway, they've been used in so many different contexts before, that it would be difficult to distance myself from any previous definitions.'

'Yeah, and besides, every silly Hippy out there has pretty much sucked any Significant meaning out of them,' Lee added.

'Right, so I wanted a term which I could feel comfortable with, which showed familiarity, a feeling of ease, something a bit more user-friendly, you know? A name which worked for me personally. And well, one day I talked to 'It', and then just said jokingly, 'Go on Guys, you know you want to, pretty please, with sugar on top!' - For some reason that stuck. From then on, they were just My Guys.'

'Tara, that's truly brilliant. I love it. May I present, the Universe, the Big Something as - The Little Guys,' he announced, bowing deeply, opening an imaginary curtain.

'For me it works fabulously,' Tara bowed to match Lee's performance. 'As I said, I treat the Universe as my Buddy, rather than this big mystical thing out there. It's my best mate.'

'Soul-mate,' Lee threw in with a twinkle in his eye.

'Yeah, nice one, literally. **The Little Guys are my Soul - Mates. In fact, they _are my_ Soul. They are a part of myself and of everybody else.**

Let me just stress that I don't call them My Little Guys to be disrespectful or anything, or because I think that They are little or separate or whatever, I simply call them that because it works for me. **When I address My Little Guys, I'm fully aware that I'm addressing the Collective Consciousness, all Souls, the big Thing, the Something, Oneness.**'

'The Little Guys. I really like that. It's charming, it's cute, even endearing,' Lee smiled softly.

'Yeah, it is I guess. I never really thought about it. But it's true, and **that's exactly the way They are. Charming, endearing and cute. If you let Them be.**'

Lee suddenly stood up, 'Excellent, now I'll get my Alien stories after all.'

Tara looked up in overplayed shock and horror, 'The Guys are not Aliens!'

'Just teasing!' Lee smiled broadly.

Tara winked light-heartedly at him, she liked his boyish charm. His tousled hair seemed to add to the effect. This was turning out to be exciting, Tara smiled to herself. Lee was on the same wave-length, genuinely interested, and he actually seemed to get what she was talking about.

"And he is very cute," her Mind threw in as an after-thought. She laughed.

"Pretty *and* clever *and* funny," Lee's Thoughts laid it bare, "not bad. Not bad at all." Kate suddenly seemed a million miles away. Reality check - boy, girl, met just two seconds ago, sitting on the pavement, in the middle of the days hustle and bustle, lost in deep cosmic conversations. Bizarre if you'd really think about it. But hey, who cared? Life was great, and fabulously, ridiculously surprising, that's all that mattered. He smiled.

A fleeting Thought whisped past Lee's Mind, together with an odd sensation that he was somehow *remembering* rather than thinking during his conversations with Tara. Information, pictures, sentences and words were accessible to him, which he hadn't really been aware of before. Was he tapping into the Collective Consciousness? Right this moment? But hang on, he didn't know how to do that or did he? The intensity of the sensation surprised him. Maybe he was finally getting an insight into some of the Universe's *real* mysteries, he marvelled to himself, hungry for more.

When he looked at Tara again, she too appeared to be deep in Thought. Very carefully, he pulled his ears into points, ala Mr. Spock, stuck his head right in front of Tara's face, and said in a soft robot-like voice,

'Earth to Tara, Earth to Tara, help needed on the earthly plane. Please return to the mother-ship.'

Tara opened her eyes and met his. They smiled as they recognised a special kind of carefree-ness in each other, a manner, which showed a wonderful ease with these 'Big' things. **People often took Cosmic Stuff far too seriously, when really, it could be so much fun**. They grinned at each other cheerfully.

Tara liked the fact that Lee had his own Mind, but still always remained open to new ideas and points of view. He didn't simply reject things he was unsure of, but tried to clarify them until he understood her correctly. It was good to have to explain and expand on her ideas, it forced her to put her theories into clear words for other people to understand. It was so good to be able to share her Thoughts with somebody who didn't want to put her into a big white jacket with long sleeves - elegantly knotted at the back.

For a lot of people, her ideas were too far-out, but for Tara, it was her life. She trusted it with all her heart. She had experienced and lived every single word of what she had talked about. Her heart ached with gratitude to The Little Guys for guiding her to Lee today and to everyone They'd sent along so far to help expand her perspectives and share her Thoughts with. It was perfect. As always.

'Thank you, Guys,' she whispered, 'Thank you, as always, for looking after me.'

Lee smiled, 'That's the way you talk to Them then, is it?'

Tara looked up in surprise, she hadn't realised that she'd spoken out loud. She smiled as the Warrior Princess emerged in her heart. She always felt like that when she talked about The Guys. It somehow felt as if she was fighting a battle for Them, **a battle to fight for people wanting to be happy, wanting to take an active part in directing their lives. A battle against people's strange habits to blame the world for their unhappiness. A battle for people wanting to rediscover themselves and the beauty around them. A battle for people to make use of the Cosmic Tools and all the wonderful Universal Toys out there, to help them make their lives easier, happier and more fulfilling.**

When she thought about it though, it didn't really feel like a battle. It felt more like a pillow fight, gently whacking people with new ideas, planting seeds. And actually, she wasn't really a Warrior Princess either, but just a little girl with a whole truck load full of dreams and hopes. She had found so much genuine joy, so much help, guidance and direction for her life, surely it could not be wrong to want to try and share this with others? Even if she just helped *one* person in her life to become as happy as she was, trusting in the Universe and chucking out their shoes... how great would that be?

Tara was still looking into the distance when Lee's attention returned back to her after its own little excursion. Ever so gently, he pulled her sleeve whispering, 'Joohoo... anybody home?' Tara looked at Lee, slowly coming back from very far away. She shook her head vigorously, her braids flying around her head. She squeezed her eyes shut, opened them, and looked at him brightly.

'Let's take your questions one by one, ok? Curtains up and here we go,' she said as she re-opened Lee's imaginary curtain with her hands and obligingly bowed deeply forward again. 'Let's start with the Why. *Why* we want to talk to The Guys.'

Why Do We Want To Talk To The Guys again?

'**O**h, actually, just quickly, to avoid any confusion,' Tara thought to briefly clarify something, 'instead of saying that I 'get back in contact' with the Universe or the Souls, I'll just say that I 'talk to The Guys', or 'Them', ok? Otherwise it always sounds so, so… I don't know…' Tara said.

'Far out?' Lee volunteered cheekily.

'Yeah. Far out,' Tara said, grateful for Lee's input

'Right, like talking to The Guys doesn't sound far out?' Lee sniggered. 'Don't worry, I'm just teasing,' he patted Tara's shoulder reassuringly, 'please go on.'

Tara laughed, recognising her own initial reactions in Lee's words, 'Well, imagine the Universe to be like a big playground, like a theatre. In the ideal case, if everybody was connected, the show would play itself along the perfect script - the perfect script for Universal Balance.

Now, us humans are puppets who've cut our strings. We're running wildly around the stage, arms flailing, and with complete and utter disregard for anybody else, let alone the script. We have what we call Free Will, but we lost the joy, the guidance, the ease, and the effortlessness of going with the flow of the universal script. Life often is a struggle as we're trying to *improvise*. Trying to figure out what our part in all of this might be, *who* we're supposed to play, *what* we're supposed to do, *who with*, and *how* we're supposed to fit in with all the other nutty happenings on stage. Sure, sometimes it's fun, but often it's utterly confusing and pretty hard work.'

'And The Guys help with that how?' Lee asked.

'Well, **The Guys know the script! They see the whole stage, the whole picture. They know where people are, and where they're supposed to be, as well as what they're supposed to do to be in sync with the show. They know how all Beings could be Happy**.'

'So, The Guys are the puppet masters?' Lee clarified.

'Not really. **It's not like They pull the strings and we have to follow. Actually, they are more like the prompter in the little box in front of the stage, helping you out when you forget the words. They're the directors, instructing the actors what to do, when we get lost. They guide us along the perfect script**.'

'Mmh, but **how do we know that Their plan is so perfect**?' Lee asked slightly doubtful.

Tara shrugged her shoulders, 'The *real* answer is that They *are* You, and They therefore want what's best for you. Anything They do to You, They do to Themselves.' Looking at Lee's face and anticipating a 'but', she added, 'The *practical* answer is that, unfortunately, until you've tried talking to Them and till you've experienced the amazing effect it can have on your life, you'll just have to take my word for it.'

'Sounds like a Chicken and Egg scenario to me. No involvement, no proof - no proof, no incentive to get involved and seek proof,' Lee shrugged is shoulders. 'But lucky for me, I think this stuff sounds so fascinating, I have plenty incentive to give it a try, evidence or not!' Lee said happily.

Tara patted Lee's shoulder approvingly and whispered, 'Good Boy.'

'We aim to please,' Lee spread his arms to the side and gave a regal nod.

'Pleased!' Tara hugged Lee quickly, then light-heartedly prodded his chest with her finger to emphasise the point she was about to make, **'You'll get the proof your Rational Mind needs soon enough, in fact as soon as you begin to play with it and practice it. But be prepared - once you jump, you will realise that everything we've talked about so far is just the tip of a huge iceberg. It's just the beginning of a whole new way of thinking, a new way of living. I can't even begin to explain how fabulous life becomes once you learned to talk to The Guys.'**

Lee's eyes widened so comically, that Tara couldn't help herself but ask, 'What?'

'Wow, I'm just imagining what it would be like to have a direct connection to The Guys, you know, to the very Source that knows the script, The Guys that can see all the perfect Co-incidences lined up for us? I mean, how much better can you get?' Tara grinned knowingly. 'So *how* do we talk to Them?' Lee wanted to know more.

2   The Guys, Co-incidences and Signs

'Actually, **it's much easier at the beginning to learn to** *Listen* **to The Guys than talking to Them,**' Tara said.

'Why's that?' Lee perked up.

'First, there's no point talking to Them, if you can't *Listen* **to the answer, and second, The Little Guys are** *already* **talking to us.'**

'What?' Lee was surprised.

'They are already talking to us. Right now. All the time. **They are constantly trying to get through to us to help and guide us in whatever we do. Therefore, just being able to Listen can do us a world of good.'**

'Ok, makes sense,' Lee adjusted the lamppost in his back, 'let's start with Listening.'

'Alright then. Luckily for us, the Guys are incredibly clever, you know?' Tara began affectionately. 'In an attempt to help us to Listen to Their subtle messages, They have come up with something to help us along the way, something hands-on, something we can touch, feel and notice in the physical world.'

'Signs and Co-incidences,' Lee blurted out, surprised by the sudden realisation that had jumped at him from out of nowhere.

'Exactly!' Tara said, her enthusiasm written all over her face. **'The Guys use Signs and Co-incidences to give us messages in the form of physical events.** They are the hints, the stepping-stones, the Signposts to navigate the river of life, they are physical Signs for you to follow. Once you can see those Signs and once you know which Co-incidences are Significant, then you can follow The Little Guy's guidance,' she looked at Lee. 'You know the Signs I'm talking about, don't you?'

'Yes,' Lee said confidently. 'In my experience a Sign would be something I notice, physically or intuitively, which seems to be related to something I need.'

As Lee observed the words come out of his mouth, he noticed vaguely that he didn't seem to 'think' them, but that they were coming straight from his gut, somehow bypassing his brain - "Bizarre," he briefly thought to himself before he continued,

'**Signs are all the little steps that help us do something, go somewhere or see somebody, right? If we follow them properly, they lead us to something - usually a lucky Co-incidence - which is perfect for that moment in time. It's the fabulous 'Wow-that's-so-cool-what-a-great-Co-incidence moment**," Lee remembered numerous incidences just like that.

'Yep and **it's those moments that make following the Signs so exciting and so much fun!**' Tara's eyes sparkled. '**But of course, most of us are novices at this Co-incidence stuff and sometimes we get the hint, whereas sometimes we don't.** Sometimes we see the Signs, sometimes we don't,' she shrugged her shoulders. 'Which, at the beginning, makes Co-incidences a rather complicated matter, right? If we don't know how to observe the Signs properly, then it's all a bit hit and miss.'

'That's exactly my problem!' Lee said, remembering his failed attempts to detect a pattern.

Tara nodded, 'Actually, that's most people's problem at the moment.'

'So what do we do about it?' Lee asked persistently.

Significant or Not - The Guys, Co-incidences and Intuition

Tara didn't disappoint, 'Well, **for a start, you need to learn to differentiate** *Significant* **Signs and Co-incidences from** *insignificant* **ones.**'

'Oh, yes please!' Lee said excitedly, seeing the answer to his questions right in front of him, inching ever closer.

'**You do that by Listening to your Intuition,**' Tara said simply.

'Which doesn't help, if my Intuition isn't up to scratch, if I can't tell if I'm having an Intuition or if my Mind is making things up.'

'Exactly! That's why **you need to learn how to distinguish** *random Thoughts* **and** *wishful* **thinking from the** *real* **hunches, the real** *Intuitions,* **the** *real messages from The Guys,* **that we are supposed to follow.**'

'Sounds great. And how do I do that?'

'Well, first of all, you have to get your head around the fact that this stuff is real,' Tara's voice trailed off. She pulled her legs up on the pavement and clasped her arms around them.

'What do you mean - real?' Lee asked.

'Well, some of this stuff gets pretty far-out, you know, and by nature us humans usually require pretty solid proof to change our habits. **Now, this stuff gives you proof which your Rational Mind can't explain, and some people find that tough to deal with. By reconnecting with The Guys, instead of trusting only what our Rational Mind can explain, we begin to dive into following Intuitions and hunches instead. Some of the things that begin to happen to you will feel like entering a different dimension, a place of experience that you're simply not used to yet.**'

'I can understand how that might take my Rational Mind a little while to get used to,' Lee nodded slowly.

'Well, to help your Rational Mind a bit, I could tell you how I came to find out about all of this, then you could follow my train of Thought and see that each individual progression is common sense, even if the totality of it sounds a bit far-out. How's that?'

'Sounds great. My Rational Mind says that that makes sense,' Lee grinned.

'Excellent,' Tara smiled, she liked Lee's quick wit. 'Oh, just one more thing to keep in Mind, I didn't have a teacher. I figured all this stuff out by myself and pretty much made things up as I went along. So, none of it should be set in stone and you are free to modify whatever you like, just as your little heart desires. Depending on how it resonates with you, you might even move much faster than I did.'

'Works for me,' Lee laughed at Tara's careful introduction, but nevertheless appreciated her sincerity. He wanted to know everything and couldn't wait for her to continue. This was miles better than going to work. And it was even better than hanging with Kate. He'd always missed not being able to talk to her about stuff like this.

Tara's voice brought him back to the moment, 'How about me giving you a quick summary of the main areas that'll help you get started with The Guys? Some of the things I had to work on to help me get confidence in myself and my Intuitions?' Tara asked.

Lee nodded in agreement while he was absentmindedly thinking of the moment he put his notebook into his trouser pocket this morning. It had literally jumped at him from the desk, begging him to take it along -eh, to pick up the mail? Why? He had thought it strange then, but hey, who could have argued with such a persuasive paper pad?

'Mmh, that must have been an Intuition,' Lee wondered briefly, but whatever, right now, the most important thing was that the book was in his pocket, just waiting for this moment. Lee sighed with relief. It always helped him think and understand when he wrote things down. He took the little green book out of his pocked and waved it in front of Tara's nose.

'Do you Mind if I make a note of some of this stuff? Otherwise I might actually doubt tomorrow morning that our conversation was real.'

'Of course, I feel flattered,' Tara gently took the notebook off him, lovingly opened it, straightened out a fresh page and held it back towards him.

Lee placed it on his lap and tapped his pencil in readiness, 'Go on then,' he said encouragingly.

Together they brooded over the page until the list read:

Significant or not?
• Understand how Co-incidences work
• Develop Mindfulness - the Here and Now
• Ask for stuff
• Follow hunches that seem related. Notice related Co-incidences
• Analyse past Co-incidences and learn about your Intuition
• Listen to The Guys
• Talk to The Guys

Lee sat up straight and rubbed his back where the lamppost had pushed in and looked over the list.

'There's so much to say about each point,' Tara started, 'I think I'll run you through them all fairly quickly to give you a general idea, and, if you're not bored by then, we can go into more detail, how's that?'

'Fabulous,' Lee said. It'll be good to get an overview first, he could always ask more questions later.

How Do Co-incidences Work? - Time, Space and Consciousness

'**O**k, the first one is a bit complicated,' Tara announced.

Lee wriggled his right index finger at Tara, 'Yeah right, unlike all the other insignificant, almost stupidly simple facts we have discussed so far,' he said and then added in the voice of the French skunk from Bugs Bunny, 'I luuuurve complicated matters cheriiiie, give it to me, give it to me... kiss, kiss, kiss,' he pounced around Tara and the lamppost, holding his hands at an angle in front of his chest like paws, trying not to get run over by the passing cars. Tara laughed out loud. His facial expressions were just too funny, his lips all pursed up, making little kissing noises.

'Your teachers must have hated you. Constant interruptions. This is a serious test on my old memory facility,' Tara teased.

'Teachers pet actually, teachers pet,' Lee said with a charmingly innocent look on his face.

'Yeah right,' Tara chuckled. In response Lee held up his paws again, stuck his tongue out like a little dog and cocked his head to one side. He sat back down again, this time cross-legged himself, feeling pride rise within him. He'd only really managed to sit like that a couple of months ago, after months and months of agony and stretching exercises - his knees had always been far to stiff.

Tara pulled herself together and said, 'Ok, **Co-incidences, in essence, are a meeting of Time, Space and Consciousness** or TSC for short,' she slammed down the facts. '**Imagine three layers of mesh, like a net. One layer is Space, one is Time, the final one is Consciousness. Whenever the three layers connect, an event occurs**, right?'

Lee gave Tara one of his what-on-earth-?- looks.

Tara shrugged her shoulders and returned a cheeky I-told-you-it's-complicated look, and went on, 'Time, Space and Consciousness happen all the time. Time always happens all over, Space exists everywhere, your Consciousness happens always too. When Space - a physical location for example, Time and our Consciousness fall together, our Consciousness experiences and perceives an event here and now. That's the _first scenario_.'

'That means that we're consciously aware of an event happening where we are, at a particular moment in time, right?' Lee clarified.

'Exactly. The _second scenario_ is where something happens in _our_ Time and Space, but our Consciousness does _not_ become aware of it. If we do not notice it, then TSC did not meet. An example would be you sitting in a pub, talking to somebody with music in the background. The music is kind of there, in your Time and Space, but because you're talking, you don't really consciously notice it, so TSC does not meet.'

'Until your favourite tune comes on and you suddenly click your Consciousness onto it. That's when we start to actively listen to it and as a result TSC meet and the situation turns into the first scenario,' Lee concluded.

'Wow, you're getting it quickly! Yes, that's exactly it.'

'Honours where honours are due,' Lee patted himself on the shoulder.

'In the _third scenario_,' Tara held three fingers in the air, 'Time and Space fall together and create an event, but it doesn't happen in our immediate physical Space or Time, so our Consciousness _cannot_ perceive it.'

'Check,' Lee saluted, 'that's an event happening somewhere else.'

'Yep. Sometimes an event of this third scenario can affect us indirectly though.'

'Can you give me an example?'

'Sure. An event which we are unaware of, kicks off a _chain reaction_ of other events, which in turn can become Significant for us. For example, we are looking for a job, somebody else becomes sick, so we get the job. As the other person's sickness, didn't happen in our Space, we did not know about it. But even though it is unknown to us, it still triggered a chain of events, which developed into a Significant Co-incidence for us: A vacancy has popped up, which we can fill.'

'Does that mean that all people live in different TSC and that they only connect from time to time?'

'Yes and no. Actually, it's a matter of _perception_,' Lee raised his eyebrows in a slightly confused look. Tara noticed Lee's facial expressions and went on explaining, 'What I mean, is that due to our physical nature, the simple fact that we have a physical Body, means that people are always in different locations. _Our Space_ is never quite the same as anybody else's, even when we are in the same room, even if we stand right next to one another. Therefore, as we view and feel the room's contents from slightly different angles, our _perception_ of the _Space_ will always be slightly different too.

Our _perception_ of _Time_ is quite different also. You have probably noticed how Time creeps along slowly if you're bored and seems to speed up if you're having fun?' she looked at Lee who nodded. 'So,' she continued, **'our _perception_ of time and how long we perceive every minute to be, is being influenced by how we feel**.'

'And that perception can differ between people, right?' Lee offered thoughtfully. 'One person is bored, while the other is having fun. One's perception of time is slow, the other's is fast.'

'Precisely. Our *perception* through our *Consciousness* varies too. We all think our own Thoughts, and we see ourselves as separate people.'

'And on top of that, due to the nature of our daily activities, we are all involved in different *chain reactions*,' Lee deducted.

'Exactly. Normally people are not consciously aware of the TSC layers and they don't know how to actively work with them. But you can learn how to do that,' Tara said simply.

'That sounds amazing, *actively* working with Space and Time. I feel like Stephen Hawkins. That's like proper science fiction stuff,' Lee felt excited like a little kid.

'Yeah, it's pretty cool, but actually, it's also pretty logical and down to earth once you know what you're doing. And of course what's best, it helps you to understand how Co-incidences work,' Tara paused for effect. **'Analysing the three layers, can help us see the entire path a Co-incidence took until we noticed it. Analysing the layers can show us how seemingly unrelated events in Time and Space suddenly come in contact with our Consciousness. We can understand how the three layers affect our lives and we can begin to see the role other people play in all of that.'**

'And we can see how some of the TSC connections 'created' a Co-incidence?'

'Yes. **With a bit of practice, we can understand the entirety of cause and effect with relevance to TSC and thus Co-incidences.'**

'Cool.'

'Now there's an understatement if I ever heard one. The Universe on a plate and you say, 'cool!'" Tara chided playfully.

'Eh, *very* cool?' Lee shrugged his shoulders casually and looked at her all innocently.

'That'll do,' Tara grinned broadly. 'Actually, there's something else that's important to understand with regards to the first scenario.'

'The one, where Time, Space and Consciousness meet and we consciously become aware of an event?'

'Right. **Now in that scenario, there can be *two* possible outcomes, depending on whether we *choose* to classify the event, which could be a possible Sign for example, as *Significant* or not. Now here comes the crux, *that* precise moment of choice, *that*** moment where an event hits the button and we're about to react to it, *that's* **the split second we have to learn to notice.'**

'And that's the difficult bit?' Lee asked.

'Well, yes. Old chap Sir Winston Churchill put it nicely when he said, "Men stumble over the truth from time to time, but most pick themselves up and hurry off as if nothing happened." You see, **most of the day we walk around in such a haze that we don't notice *anything* around us properly. We walk around our little lives with our eyes wide shut and our head deeply in the clouds, blissfully unaware.'**

'Or not so blissful for that matter,' Lee added cynically.

'Precisely. We're so far away, we wouldn't see anything Co-incidence- or Sign-like if it would hit us straight in the face.'

'We can't see the forest for the trees,' Lee said and laughed, 'I have such a funny story about stuff like that. As a dare, a friend of mine and twenty of his friends, ran across a street in his hometown, butt naked. You know what? Most people didn't even look up from their papers, people on the bus looked straight through them.'

'Are you serious? That's hilarious,' Tara's eyes widened at the Thought.

'I know. Scary too though. It shows how people are so preoccupied all the time. I mean, we're talking *serious* clouds here.'

'That's how most people walk around all day. Now, imagine,' Tara said with emphasis, '**if somebody doesn't notice twenty stark naked people running by, how on earth are they supposed to pick up The Guys' subtle hints**?' Tara threw her hands in the air in a gesture of desperation. 'I sometimes feel quite sorry for Them, you know? **They give us Signs and pointers all day long, fabulously good stuff happens around us constantly, but in the end the question is just if we are aware enough to notice them or not**. Mostly we're not.'

'Therefore, **the most important contribution to success in increasing the Co-incidence hit-rate, is to break out of the cloud and get some Awareness**, I assume,' Lee said.

'Yeah. **Awareness of what's going on around us**, seeing the individual trees in the wood. **We need to Shift our attention to our environment and become fully conscious of it. To do that, we need to make an active decision to Shift our Consciousness from *not looking* to *looking*.'**

'Sounds logical. Clouds, watch out, you're up for the chop! So, have you got any tips on how to do that?'

'Sure,' Tara said confidently.

'Of course you do,' Lee mumbled happily.

The Here and Now - 5 Senses

'**To Shift from** *not looking* **to** *looking,*' Tara said, '**we need to learn how to be in the Here and Now, in what I call Nowness**. I'll talk about the true Significance of being in Nowness a bit later, but for the moment, suffice to say that **the Here and Now is the space where** *everything* **happens, the space where we're one hundred percent aware of what's going on around and within us**.'

'Great, get me into that space, baby!' Lee prodded Tara's arm.

'You'll have to get yourself there, baby,' Tara prodded Lee back with a grin.

'Ok then, if I can't hitch a ride, what about some directions?' Lee pretended to be humbled.

'Nothing easier than that. **To get into that space, we have to become familiar with** *how* **we** *perceive* **the world around us and the things happening within it, which includes Signs from The Guys**.'

Lee lifted his hand to stop her, 'Hang on, let me think about this one. Any contact with the outside world has to go through our five senses to be processed, right? So I'd say **we become aware of the world by using our five senses**.'

'Yep. Well deduced. Extra points.'

'Cheers. So it's about our five senses. Mmh, what about the sixth sense?' Lee asked half serious, half joking.

'We can talk about that one in a bit, if you remind me,' Tara said casually.

'Are you serious?' Lee's jaw dropped.

'Sure,' Tara smiled at Lee's reaction.

'Daaa, of course. Phew, the sixth sense, I can't wait!' he rolled his eyes.

'Well, actually, the first five senses are pretty cool too, if we would use them properly that is, so let's focus on them for now.'

'Oh, spoil sport,' Lee pushed his lower lip forward, pretending to sulk. 'But hey, because it's you, I'm happy to listen to the first five first.'

'Only if you want to,' Tara tilted her head enticingly.

'Are you kidding me?' Lee pulled up his eyebrows. 'I'm hanging onto every word you're saying and you're asking me if I'm interested?'

'Well, as long as you tell me if you do get bore.'

'Cross my heart, hope to die,' Lee said, crossing his heart with his fingers in a dramatic gesture, the twinkle never leaving the corner of his eyes.

Tara laughed, 'Ok, our five senses, let's have'm. **We see, hear, taste, touch, and smell everything around us, all day long. But** most of the time, we're not consciously aware of any of it because we're not putting our attention onto our senses.'

'Like the music in the background in the pub?'

'Exactly. In that example, at the moment, where our senses perceive the music, the moment, where we become consciously aware of the tune, then TSC meet. **This space, where TSC meet, is what I call the Present, the *Now* or *Nowness*. The Signs The Guys give us, all happen in Nowness,**' Tara looked at Lee to make sure he was following her train of thought. Lee motioned for her to continue. '**So to become aware of the Signs, we have to constantly remind ourselves to just STOP our preoccupation and watch out instead. To *stop* and *look* at what's going on in *each* and *every* moment in time - *Now*, to become Mindful about what's going on inside and outside of us. Just by being in the Now, in the Present, by being Mindful about what you're doing right Now, by *consciously observing* your environment, you can determine a Significant event,**' Tara finished.

'**Simply because I actually notice it, which might enable me to make a Significant connection to something I need,**' Lee slotted all the pieces into place.

'That's it. **Like this you're taking your head out of the clouds,**' Tara parted some imaginary clouds with her hands.

'That's interesting,' Lee rubbed his chin thoughtfully. 'I'm beginning to get the hang of this. **Nowness and Co-incidences walk hand in hand, right? Looking for Co-incidences can help us to be in the Now, and being in the Now, can help us to notice things around us that lead us to Co-incidences.**'

'Full marks.' Tara was delighted that she had managed to explain her ideas in a way that Lee understood them so easily. It was so much fun to share.

'Now, how do we make sure that with our newly developed awareness of all events around us, we don't fall into the trap where we suddenly think that all events are significant? Which is exactly what I did before,' Lee asked.

Ask for Stuff

'Ah yes, good question. **First, we need to find a way to make the Co-incidence thing less random,**' Tara suggested

'That'll certainly be useful.'

'It'll make it easier to spot a Co-incidence, if we'd have some kind of idea as to what to watch out for, wouldn't it?' Tara asked.

'Of course.'

'Good. Let me give you an example. You're reading the paper and you see an interesting job advert, but you're not looking for a job. So, even though you might be *aware* of the advert, you don't make a *conscious* connection to a *need.'*

'So, it's classified as insignificant.'

'Exactly. But if on the other hand, you *are* looking for a job, then Time, Space and Consciousness meet in a Significant event, because your focus and your Awareness are looking for anything related to a job. Thus the ad is a Sign, a stepping-stone towards something you want.'

'The gist is that because our interest and thus our Awareness has changed, an otherwise insignificant event, becomes Significant,' Lee summarized.

'More brownie points coming up,' Tara counted a few points off on her fingers. 'Now, **there's a trick to ensure that you notice absolutely everything around you that could be relevant to what you need.**'

'All ears,' Lee chirped.

'**All you need to do is ask for it**,' Tara said.

'What do you mean?' Lee was confused.

'Well, ask the Little Guys for things.'

Lee was baffled, 'Wow, we can *ask* Them for stuff?'

'Sure,' Tara said casually.

'Well, I'll be damned, *proper* talking to the Cosmos.' Lee gave Tara a quizzical look, 'Are you serious? Isn't that a bit far fetched?' Lee's rational thinking had switched itself on again and, for a second, overrode his gut feeling that everything sounded strangely familiar and spot on.

Tara laughed, 'Actually, if you put it like that, it does sound a bit far out, but if you'd change the terminology just ever so slightly and called the Cosmos something different,' she hesitated for a split second, then carefully said, 'God for example, then asking the cosmos for stuff suddenly becomes something accepted by millions.' She quickly added, 'I don't want to offend anyone by saying that. I'm just trying to make a point.'

'Ok, fair point,' Lee nodded.

Tara continued, 'There are millions of people out there talking to God, and nobody thinks anything of it. Well, lets put it this way, some people believe in it and others don't, but hardly anybody thinks it's far-out. Some people ask God by default, because that's what they've been taught to do, whereas others say: "Well, if it makes them happy, everybody needs to believe in something". Talking to God is usually accepted as something people do. Have you never prayed? Maybe when you were little?' Tara asked.

Lee thought for a moment, 'I guess so, but usually just as a last chance resort or last hope. But even then, I never really expected God to listen. I guess, it's just what one does when one really needs help in a moment of despair.'

'And that's exactly how we *limit* ourselves!' Tara pointed out heartily. 'We always just talk to God when it's our last resort, and when we do, we don't really trust that it's going to do any good. That's the way most people work, anyway. But in all seriousness, have you ever observed that when your requests were reasonable, they were actually fulfilled?'

Lee hesitated, 'Possibly. I think. I don't know.'

'Well, once you start to play with The Guys, you'll be able to give a bit more assertive of an answer, like: YEEESS!!!' Tara threw her arms excitedly into the air. 'You'll realise quickly, that **if you know *how* to ask, *what* to ask for and *how* to look for the Signs, that you get what you need more often than not**. But if you don't know how to play the game? Tough shit. Darkness prevails.'

Lee looked at Tara for a few seconds. He hoped that she wasn't trying to make him believe in God or Miracles or something like that. It was not that he didn't trust her, but if he thought about it, he hadn't really known her for very long either. 'Tara, that sounds scarily close to rabbit-in-the-hat-stuff to me. You are not trying to give me a lesson in magic here, are you?' he asked carefully.

To Lee's relief, Tara laughed, 'Lee, the eternal rationalist. **This has nothing to do with magic, I promise. Magic is make-believe, it's not real, not hands-on, it's an illusion. This stuff *is* real. You don't have to take my word for it, you can try it and see for yourself!**'

Lee picked up Tara's enthusiasm again. No matter how out of the ordinary this conversation was, Tara certainly seemed have found something that made her unusually light hearted and carefree, and it was infectious. No harm in trying, Lee assured himself.

Tara spoke gently into the silence, 'If you want to, I'll explain a bit later exactly how to ask the questions, but for now, to put your Mind at rest, let me give you some more rational explanations as to *why* asking for things actually works.'

'Brownie points for rational stuff, rational stuff's always welcome, thank you very much. Thank you,' Lee said appreciatively.

Follow Hunches - Notice Related Co-incidences

Tara giggled at Lee's grateful look. 'Your quest for knowledge shall be answered. Ok, rational stuff about the asking-thingy. You know, we said earlier, that if our interest changes, a previously insignificant event can become Significant? Well, **asking for specific things** does exactly that. It changes and **directs our interest towards something specific, which we can then actively look out for. So rather than just looking at any old event and wondering if it could be wondrously Significant or not, all we need to do is check if it's related to what we've asked for.**'

'That makes sense,' Lee's Rational Mind was back on board.

'Great. Now, let me use the job example slightly differently this time. Imagine you're not happy in your job. By actively asking for a new one, you become more aware of associated or related events. **It's like sticking a huge red arrow onto the request you just made in your brain. If something comes along now, which has anything at all to do with that red arrow, little red lights will be flashing**, right?'

'So, asking helps us to notice stuff,' Lee recapped.

'Right. **Also, simply by asking, we have put a question out for The Little Guys to receive. They can now go and chat with all their mates up there to figure out how they can work together to ensure that we're made aware of all the Signs and Co-incidences lined up for us, and then, with combined efforts, They can show us the way to a new job.**'

'Easy peasy,' Lee slapped his forehead. 'So, if somebody would have offered us a job *before* we asked for it, we may or may not have noticed the advert. We could easily have missed a hint to a fabulous event. But now, as we have *asked* for a new job, we *actively* look out for anything that comes our way that relates to that job. Fabulous,' Lee finished, then his forehead wrinkled again, 'But that doesn't rule out that I could still follow insignificant Co-incidences that lead nowhere, does it? It still leaves me open to suddenly regard everything as Significant.'

'You're right, but this is just the beginning. **At this stage you might still follow dead-ends or be confused about the Significance of an event or a Co-incidence. But don't worry**, you are still practising, right? Bear with me, there are many ways of how to get better with all of this! And I'll give you lots of tips and *how*-to-s. **The items on the list we wrote earlier are the initial stepping stones to actively work with The Guys and Co-incidences, so if you bear with me, you'll understand really quickly how to tell the weed from the flowers.**'

'I'll just have to practice the virtue of patience.'

Lee shrugged his shoulders, crossed his legs the other way round, let his hands sink onto his knees, his thumb and middle finger of each hand touching at the tips, forming a big circle. He straightened his back and looked at Tara virtuously and patiently. The only thing missing was a big golden halo over his head. His demeanour had the desired effect. Tara laughed. It was good to hear her laugh. It was comforting to feel close to another woman, so soon after Kate.

Lee remembered how he'd wondered earlier if he could use the Intuition and Co-incidence stuff to help him get over Kate faster. Well, just hanging out with Tara seemed to do the trick just fine. Of course he hadn't forgotten Kate, but Tara was inspiring, exciting and funny. Just what he needed right now. A picture flickered past his Minds eye. Him and Tara, with a little daughter.

"Wow, stop!" he caught himself. "Stop right there! Where the hell did that come from?" his Thoughts fell over themselves. He'd only just met her, and anyway, he could do with a bit of a break from the dating game. Spend some time on his own. Yes. Digest his four-year relationship with Kate. A friend. That's what he needed right now. A beautiful and intelligent friend. After another second, he unfolded his legs, placed them carefully back in the road, opened his notebook and said,

'Let me just jot down a quick summary.'

'Sure,' Tara's gaze washed over the busy street, the trees, the people, her Being focussed and aware.

Lee scribbled for a little while, put his pen down and read out loud:

To _increase the hit-rate_ of the number of Co-incidences we notice in the first place and then realise to be Significant, we need to:
* Understand how Co-incidences work
* Become more aware of what's going on around us, i.e. develop Mindfulness, be Here and Now
* Ask for stuff
* Follow Signs, Co-incidences and hunches that seem related to what we need and asked for.

'Well done,' Tara said when he was finished. 'The more of these steps you practice _together_, the more effective they become.'

Lee thought for a second and then said excitedly, 'Man, you know what I just thought? Does this mean that I always get everything I ask for?'

Tara knew this question only too well, but she also knew that it was still to early to really answer it properly. There were other things that had to be discussed first. 'That's really part of the _How_-to-talk-to-Them bit. Do you

Mind if we talk about that a bit later? Otherwise I'll get confused and miss bits.'

Lee nodded and made a note for later, just in case. He couldn't let that one slip, that one was just too interesting.

Tara watched bemused. He really wanted to know it all. Excellent!

Train Your Intuition - Analyse Past Co-incidences

Lee looked over his notes. 'I agree with everything we talked about so far, but I can still see it all going belly-up when we try to decide if a Co-incidence, a Sign or an Intuition is Significant or not.'

'Ok, let's tackle that once and for all,' Tara grinned. 'If you think about it, what do you find most difficult in determining if you should follow a Sign, or if something is Significant or not?'

Lee thought for a few moments, trying to give Tara his major problems in a nutshell. 'Mmh, not so easy', he realised, 'it's difficult enough to think about it for myself, but to actually put it into words for another person to understand seems even more difficult.'

'I know what you mean. I used to have the same problem. But it's good to practice talking about these things - and it *does* become easier the more you do it.'

Lee nodded and managed to shape his Thoughts into a coherent sentence, '**If I have a feeling that something is Significant, my biggest obstacle is that most of the time I don't know if it's a real Intuition or if it's my head making stuff up.** You know, if it's inventing stories, making itself important. **I guess the bottom-line is that I don't know my Intuition very well at all, and because of that, I don't allow myself to trust it.**'

'**That's why you have to start to *actively* work with your Intuition. You need to get to know it, understand what it feels like and how it differs from normal everyday thinking.**'

'If I could do that, I could increase my 'hit-rate' substantially,' Lee said with interest.

'Very much so. Want some more stuff for your list?' Lee nodded and wrote the bullet points Tara dictated to him underneath the heading he'd written earlier.

Understand how Co-incidences work and Learn about your Intuition:
* Analyse past Co-incidences.
* Look at the nature of Signs.
* Look at key events and key turning points in your life.

- Understand chain reactions.
- Find out which Signs you missed and Why.
- Notice patterns in the Signs you're getting.
- See how things have fallen into place.
- Look at how you followed the Signs.
- Look at the hunches and Intuitions themselves.
- Look at how you became aware of an Intuition.
- Look at your state of Mind *during* an Intuition.

When Lee finished writing, Tara began to explain, 'To really understand our Intuition inside and out, we need to understand how we use it in the first place. To do that, we need to look at a number of things at the same time. We need to understand how Co-incidences manifest themselves in our lives; we need to learn about cause and effect, i.e. become familiar with TSC and how it works; we need to learn to see the 'strings' as we explained earlier; and we need to become more aware of Nowness. On top of that, we need to examine how our Intuition fits into the big picture.

By doing all of that, we learn to distinguish *real* messages from all the other things going on in our heads and around us.' Lee's smile began to spread as Tara continued, 'The first step is to *analyse past events, situations and Co-incidences*. We do that by *looking back* on events in our lives where we thought, 'Man, that was really *lucky*.''

'Yeah, I have lots of those,' Lee interrupted.

He ran his fingers through his hair and scratched the side of his head. For a split second Lee thought he saw Tara looking at his arms. Well, the T-shirt he wore, did show off a nicely shaped pair of biceps, he smiled inwardly.

'Great, you won't be short of analysing material then,' Tara went on as if nothing had happened. '**You can take any** one of those **lucky situation**s **and look at *what actually* happened. First, ask yourself, if there were any *obvious* Signs in that situation**. If there were, that's great. You're already a step ahead, you recognised them. **But if no Signs stood out, you need to uncover and examine *all* the stepping-stones you took towards that particular lucky Co-incidence.** To do that, you need to have a look if there was anything, anything at all, that could have been a Sign. Anything that led you along the path, anything that made you go down the particular route which led you to your lucky event.

To aid you in doing that, it helps to look at the *nature of the Signs* you've been given. As I said before, The Little Guys are pretty crafty. They can and do think of a million and one ways to give you messages and Signs. Signs can be anything, a newspaper article, a word on a match box, a conversation, an interaction between two people, the way somebody moves or talks, a licence plate number, a book title, a poster, literally anything.

To find Signs, you can also look at the *key events* and *key turning points* that made your desired event happen. When did things begin to change for the better and why? Then check if there was a sign at that moment.

Then take an event where it was obvious that you *just missed* a lucky event. A moment where you say: 'bummer-that-was-so-close,' Check if there were any *Signs* which you didn't notice or which you ignored or which you maybe *just missed*. A Sign, which in retrospect, turned out to be significant. Check why you ignored it. Why didn't you see it? How involved were you in the Co-incidence? Could you have maybe influenced it and thus the result?

During this examination the Signs usually become pretty clear, sometimes you have to look a little harder though. Remember the *chain reactions*? **You need a pretty good memory and good observational skills to notice how some events and Co-incidences are linked.'**

'I can already see how much detail there could be. I think I'd just write it all down,' Lee said.

'That would help a lot, I used to do that too. Once you get a grip on this stuff? Once you get an overview and get to the bottom of all this? It'll blow you away. Co-incidences are absolutely ingenious, they're so meticulously arranged.'

Lee was baffled, 'This is good stuff, Tara.'

'I know, isn't it brilliant? And it gets so much better,' Tara promised, her eyes full of life. 'The next step is to have a look if you *notice patterns in the Signs you perceive*.'

'What kind of patterns?'

'Well, some people are particularly perceptive to *visual* clues, other people to *verbal* clues, others again to the behaviour of their peers. **Basically see where you get your Signs and your clues from. Figure out what worked for you in the past**.'

'Cool. I can think of a million examples already,' Lee was impressed.

'Fabulous. **Once you start getting into it, you wonder how you could ever not have known about it. It's so obvious, so common sense. And the more you practice, the clearer it becomes**.'

'Yeah, I can see that,' Lee smiled at Tara, who was literally glowing with enthusiasm. "Sparkly. That's what she is," he thought, as Tara had already begun to talk again.

'By doing this stuff, you start to see the Big Plan, the Strings. *You'll begin to see how cause and effect fall into place*. You'll see how Co-incidences, people, time and events worked together, how TSC overlapped. It's truly fascinating how obvious things become. It's like somebody suddenly opens a curtain in front of you and slaps you in the face, screaming: "Wake up! *See*, will you?!"' Tara grinned at the memory of *just that* happening to her. 'Can you take more?' she asked, full of energy.

'Of course,' Lee nodded.

Tara went on without hesitation, 'Once you are aware of all of the Signs, you can look at *how you followed the Signs*. Did you follow them Consciously or unconsciously? Was there a Sign which you didn't follow? Was it because you didn't notice the Sign or was it because you had a battle with your Rational Mind? If so, at what moment did you falter? Did you dismiss the Intuition straightaway? If so, why? Or did you think about it for a while? Did you try to figure out if it was an Intuition or not? If so, what was the Thought process in your head and what made you dismiss it in the end?' Lee gaped at Tara's waterfall of glorious ideas that never seem to stop. '*Doing all this, helps you to notice that you might have had a hunch, an Intuition, but that you didn't follow it.* **Looking back, you'll realise that if you *would* have followed that Intuition, that you might have gotten what you needed faster or easier,**' Tara paused. **'The aim with all this analysing is basically to get to know your Intuition and to figure out why on earth you didn't follow it, if you did noticed one, but ignored it!'**

'And from that, to know better for next time!' Lee said amazed.

'Precisely.'

Lee scribbled busily and then said, 'This is really useful. **I get to know situations in which following my Intuition was the key towards a great outcome, which in turn gives me immediate reassurance that following my Intuitions actually works.** This is fantastic. **I get to know my Intuition better, because I begin to figure out and understand what Intuitions are in the first place. Once I'm familiar with that, I'd be able to tell Intuitions apart from my head making stuff up.** This is magic!'

Lee was very pleased. The conversation. The new knowledge. Life. The lot. All positively fantastic! Tara's spirit certainly seemed to rub off. He couldn't believe that he was sitting here smiling and laughing, when he'd only just split from Kate. But he felt good. Strong. That's what they mean by: "Taking your Mind off things", he grinned.

'You can go even deeper than that,' Tara said cheerfully. 'After analysing each situation, you can *examine the hunches and Intuitions themselves*. The little pangs you had,' Tara snapped her fingers, 'the *split second* when you knew that something Significant was happening or was about happen.

Whether you actually followed the Intuition in the end or not doesn't matter for this examination. What is important though, is to **figure out *how you became aware* of the Intuition? What was it like?** Was it a strong pull to do something? Was it a gut-feeling? Did you feel drawn to something? Was it an automatic reaction? Was it an idea that just popped into your head? Was it a feeling, a Thought, a flicker of knowledge, a whisper of recognition? How did the hunch come to you? How did it feel like? How strong was it? How obvious was it? What form did it take - words, pictures, feelings, Emotions?'

Lee just nodded, too astounded to speak. His Mind was going over a million examples at the same time. God, she was right, he could see the patterns, the feelings, the tugging. Crazy! It was so obvious.

Tara continued unruffled, 'The last step, that helps you to get to know your Intuition better, is to **look at your *state of Mind during* an Intuition that turned out to be Significant**. Was your Mind relaxed? Weary, anxious, curious, stressed, calm, busy? Was it quiet? Once again, with a bit of practice, you'll **notice a pattern**.'

'Click, click... more stuff falling into place,' Lee said, his face concentrating hard. '**Once I've established the State of Mind in which I'm most receptive to notice and follow Intuitions correctly, I can then remember** that pattern, **that state of Mind, for the future**,' Lee's rational statistics Mind leaped with joy. '**I could even start to play with *re-creating* that state of Mind to *actively* improve my future ability to notice Intuitions**. Wow, I'm gob-smacked. I'm so clever,' he smiled broadly, showing a strong set of teeth, with a little crooked one at the bottom.

'You're truly awesome Lee,' Tara said, meaning it. She had sat cross-legged the whole time, but now, slowly and deliberately, she straightened out her legs, bent forwards and stretched out her back. The slit at the side of her skirt showed a little of her leg, the colour of honey. She sat up again, oblivious to the little appreciative flicker in Lee's eyes. She rearranged her pigtails that had fallen forward during her exercise and picked up where she had left off.

'**By observing and analysing your Intuition and your Mind themselves, rather than just the situations, that's when you really get to know your Intuition and hunches inside out.** Like this you really get to know when your head is interrupting or making stuff up - and hey presto, no more wood, just trees,' Tara blasted out more facts. '**To learn to listen to your Intuition is like relearning how to think. It's thinking through Hunches and Intuitions rather than through your Brain with your Thoughts.**'

'I would compare it to learning how to sing,' Lee said. 'When you sing, you use different parts of your throat and your mouth, than when you talk. You even use your lungs differently. You still make sounds, but they are different to when you talk. Hopefully better,' he winked. 'To acquire a well trained voice takes practice and some getting used to utilizing parts of your Body differently, but after a while, it becomes second nature and you wonder why you ever struggled,' Lee offered.

'Good example. And you're right. It's the same with relearning how to think, however, instead of getting to know our voice, we get to know our Mind.'

'Uh, could we work through an example of mine? To practice it once? That'll be really useful. That'll be easier to remember than trying to make sense of my notes,' Lee suggested.

'Of course. Example ahead.'

He already had one in Mind, 'A few years ago I needed to get information about some Tax stuff to fill-in silly paperwork. I was in a café and a man sat at a table opposite me. For some reason I had a feeling, just for a split second, that I should talk to the guy about those papers. But I didn't. My Mind told me that it would be silly to do that. I even laughed at myself. I mean, what would he have thought if I would have walked up to him, just like that, out of the blue, and asked about Tax stuff? I felt too uncomfortable to approach him. Believe it or not though, in the end it turned out that this person *did* have the information that I needed. That's it, that's the story.'

'Cool. That's a great example! Let's examine it. First, you need to realise that you had a gut feeling, which turned out to be a Significant feeling, but you didn't follow it at that moment in time. You already did that. You noticed a seconds worth of I-need-to-talk-to-that-guy, right?' Lee nodded. 'You also already know *why* you didn't follow that Intuition.'

'Yeah. I felt stupid to go up to him and say: "S'cuse me mate, would you happen to know where I can find out about Tax refunds for foreign travel?" I mean, it's not really one of the everyday subjects you'd talk to a random guy in café about, is it?'

Tara nodded and asked, 'I agree, but to be honest, if you would have just asked him, what would have been the *worst* thing that could have happened to you?'

'Well, he could have ignored me or maybe laughed at me or maybe thought I'm a weirdo.'

'Ok and how likely would that have been?' Tara asked.

'Not very I guess. But it could have happened.'

'Well, of course it could have, but it could have also turned out to be just fine, right?'

'Sure.'

'It's such a shame that we always expect the worst. That truly spoils stuff, you know? It's because of that fear, that we really miss out. Sometimes we just have to jump over our shadow and go for it, and if somebody laughs?

Well? So be it. Laugh with them! If they ignore you or if they think you're a weirdo, well, so what? If that's the worst that can happen...?'

'I get the point,' Lee agreed. 'A bit of embarrassment would have been tops on the list, but it's not as if I would have died or anything.'

'Exactly. So, lesson number one: **Next time you get such a feeling, overcome your fear and just go and ask. Just try, just for the fun of it**.'

'I like that idea, "just for the fun of it",' Lee smiled. '**Man, that would take all that stupid self-imposed seriousness out of it. Thank you for that! Shit, it can be fun, can't it?**' Lee laughed at his own silly conditioning.

'Of course it can! If you choose it to be, that is. I personally got myself into all sorts of weird and wonderful situations like this. It's more entertaining than television any day!' Tara grinned.

'You really mean that don't you?' Lee was taken aback by how easily Tara had adapted big Cosmic stuff to her very own personal liking. It was brilliant.

Tara's big smile was his answer.

'By the way, how did you find out, that the guy in the café could have actually helped you?' Tara wanted to know.

'Now that was the weirdest thing,' Lee grinned. 'The man's friend turned up with a huge folder with 'Tax' written on it and they started a longwinded discussion about a document in it. So, at that stage, I just got up and asked.'

'You're kidding, a folder with 'Tax' written on it? That's hilarious! That's as fantastic an example as I've ever heard one. Fabulous. You know, that's the other reason why playing with Intuition and Co-incidences is so much fun. I mean a 'Tax' folder? That's just absurd!'

'Oh God, that hadn't even really clicked,' Lee shook his head. 'It's like! Helllooo! How big a Sign do you need?' He rolled his eyes skywards. 'The Guys must have died of laughter - or frustration for that matter. I can just imagine Them up there discussing the situation,' Lee put on a deep voice, 'You know what fellow Guys? Let's just stick Lee's nose right in. Let's give it to him in big fat red capital letters - TAX!' he shook his head in disbelief. Lee felt as if he just had a little glimpse into a world of magic and fun, a world that had always been around him, but which had so far gone noticed. A world with glitches in the matrix, a twilight zone where things were not quite what they seemed, or actually where they were *more* than they seemed...

'Isn't it funny? Anyway, so you *did* ask in the end?' Tara probed.

'Yep. Once I'd seen the folder, it had been kind of obvious,' Lee wiped the tears of laugher out of his eyes. 'By then it was easy to go and talk to him.'

'Because now you had a reason, and you wouldn't embarrass yourself anymore,' Tara deducted.

'Right. He had his head in a folder with 'Tax' written on it in huge letters,' Lee giggled again, 'and *he* could see that too. So, my asking wasn't so weird anymore - to neither one of us.'

'Ok,' Tara concentrated visibly, 'therefore **the first reason why you didn't talk to the guy, despite the fact that your Intuition told you so, was that you felt that you needed a reason to talk to him?**'

'Yes,' Lee said simply.

'Actually, if you really think about it, you did have a reason.'

'I did?'

'Sure. You wanted to find out about Tax and your Intuition told you so. But you felt that that wasn't good enough as justification.'

'Well, no. I mean, how do you ask when it's just plain weird, but your Intuition nags you to get on with it?'

'Easy. Why not just go up to him and say: "Sorry, you don't happen to know anything about Tax, do you?" If he would have said: "No," you could have always said something like: "Worth a try," or you could have been truthful and told him that you felt drawn to talk to him, and that you didn't know why. That's honest. Honesty goes a long way.'

'Just like that? Out of the blue?'

'Yeah. **That's the nature of Intuitions! They come out of the blue. You can't explain them, they're just there. From out of nowhere. We need to learn to trust them and to act on them confidently. That's why you need to do the past analysis we've talked about.**'

'To learn what Significant Intuitions feel like and to trust them,' Lee marvelled.

'Exactly. Then all you need is a bit of guts to act on them,' she beamed at him with a flawless, beautiful smile. 'Now try and remember what state of Mind you were in, when you had that feeling and what *kind* of feeling it was.'

'I was pretty relaxed,' Lee tried to think back. 'As far as I remember I was drinking coffee and read the paper, but at the same time, I did have this nagging question about the Tax stuff in my head. When I saw that guy, it was like an order in my head: "Go and talk to him". It was a really strong feeling of certainty. But I guess, beforehand, overall my Mind was pretty quiet. Relaxed.'

'Great. Now that you remember the state of Mind you were in, take the event even further back in time. There was more than one Co-incidence, wasn't there?'

'More than one Co-incidence? What do you mean?' Lee was intrigued.

'The guy in the café wasn't the only Co-incidence,' Tara said as if she'd been there herself. 'What about *why* you sat down at a table where you could see the dude's folder in the first place? And what about you being in that particular café at that moment in time, rather than somewhere else?'

'Oh wow,' Lee was beginning to get a glimpse of the enormity of the insights that were opening up to him.

'I know! Now we're talking *real* Cosmic stuff! It still amazes me when I do this analysis,' Tara said with excited joy. 'So, *why did* you go there? *What* made you go to *that* café, rather than another one? Again, do the same analysis as before. Did you have a hunch, a feeling, a longing for a coffee in that particular place? What? You can take this as far back as you like, leaving your house, going down the street and so on.'

'Phew, I don't think I can remember all of that,' Lee said wearily.

'That's fine, really. I couldn't either when I started out with all of this. Analysing situations in so much detail is still new to you right now, but the more you do it, the more you can remember, and with practice it becomes really easy, until after a while, it becomes second nature and it just happens automatically.'

'I guess you can't get any easier than automatic, can ya?' Lee said with a smile. 'Until it happens automatically though, I guess I'll just have to help my Brain by writing things down, then I can also keep going back to my lists and add bits I didn't remember the first time around. As the details are so important here, it'll help me make sure that I don't miss anything.'

'Oh yes, and sometimes the hints are oh-so-subtle,' Tara said knowingly, wriggling her index finger at Lee. 'I used to write things down all the time, *everything* that I could remember, then I would leave it for a while. I never liked sitting down and wrecking my brain, that's not fun!' She winked at Lee and was rewarded with a big smile in return. 'Instead, I'd just read through my lists from time to time, and while I did that, things would pop back into my Mind naturally. Whenever I remembered little details during the day, I wrote them down, as and when they came up. By doing this, my memory was trained all by itself.

That's the good thing about doing it this way, you see, **the analysis can fit *into* your life and *around* it, just the way you wish. You don't have to change your life to do any of this. You stand in the post office queue, you don't have anything better to**

do, and you leisurely think about a past Co-incidence. On the bus you make a couple of notes. It's effortless that way,' Tara pointed out.

'And more effective,' Lee said.

'Yeah, and taking it easy works so much better. Forcing it just doesn't do the trick - *and* it's no fun.'

'I can't argue with that. Easy as opposed to difficult? Well, you can sign me up for that right away, sweetie,' he said light heartedly.

Lee was grateful for the repeated reminder to really *enjoy* working with The Guys. **Did he hear her say, *"Play with The Guys"*, at some stage? Now there was a Thought. *Play* with the Universe. Not revere it, not pray to it, not make it all complicated, but *play*. Play and be in simple and healthy awe of the sheer magnificence of it all.** He knew already that this knowing alone, was enough to change a lot in his life. It was as if he now had permission to just laugh about it all, about his indecisiveness, his inability to dare to talk to the Tax guy, and about the ridiculous obviousness of the Signs once he saw them. It was brilliant. Amongst all of his new realisations, he heard Tara's voice.

'And while you're getting the hang of it, keep in Mind why you're actually doing all of this in the first place. It's not a competition or anything, it's simply about becoming more aware of the Signs around you and training your Intuition. Sure, at the beginning, you might still miss out on some hints, you might follow a Thought rather than an Intuition, you might even get yourself into the occasional embarrassing situation. But hey, that's half the fun and anyway - you can learn from it.'

'That's exactly what I was just thinking,' Lee said.

'Great Minds think alike, what can I say!' Tara's face glowed as she continued her previous notion, 'And anyway, to counterbalance any of the situations where you're *not* getting it quite right, there will be lots of times where you *do* get it right. You might get yourself into fascinating conversations with people you would have never met otherwise. In fact, you'll find yourself in all sorts of other bizarre and wonderful situations. Play with it, jump into the deep-end a few times and test your feelings and Intuitions. The more you do it, the better you get. **The more you dare, the more fun you have, the more your Mind gets blown with the crazy, inexplicable reality of your Intuition.** It works so well, it's spooky sometimes.' Tara made a slightly weirded-out face and then grinned sheepishly, 'But man, it's all so good. Ridiculously good.'

'Oh boy, I can only begin to imagine,' Lee couldn't wait to examine, to learn, to play and to scream with laughter.

'You might think you can imagine,' Tara said ominously, 'but wait till you're actually really doing it - like *all* the time. It will seriously blow your brain *and* your imagination…'

Lee smiled at Tara's enthusiasm, 'No worries, next time when I think that I have an Intuition, I will *definitely* act on it, just to see what happens. You know? Experiment!'

'Fabulous, that's the spirit! You won't regret it. Welcome to the other side!' Tara sing-sang, with an enchanting glow on her face. '**Make sure to keep in mind though that it's not just about talking to other people, but that it's also about doing things or going places or leaving somewhere or staying behind and so on. It's about following *anything* that your Intuition might tell you.**'

'Yeah, anything! Phew. You know, even though I've already done some kind of Co-incidence analysis before I met you, what you're talking about takes everything I ever did so much further. You actually suggest for me to examine the Intuitions *themselves*, rather than just the events. You even suggest that I examine the events *leading up* to a Significant Co-incidence. That's really cool,' Lee considered that statement for a moment and then said, 'Just take today for example. The events that led us to meet. I mean, I'm not even supposed to be here. I'm supposed to be at work, but I locked myself out. Then I thought I'd walk to my friend's office five miles out of town to get my keys, but somehow ended up walking towards the park instead. Pretty ridiculous,' Lee remembered the early morning's events. 'And talking to you? Man, I followed a big-time Intuition there. Come to think of it, a number of them actually.'

'Same here,' Tara smiled.

'Really?' Lee asked dubiously.

'Well of course. I've been doing this stuff for a while, you know?' Tara said without pretence. 'I knew that I had to talk to you as soon as I saw you. Oh, and actually, I talked to you first,' she laughed, not in the least bit self-conscious.

'Ok, ok, you beat me to it,' Lee laughed with her and added with a cheeky undertone, 'But you're a professional!' Tara laughed. 'But seriously, I know that my feeling to talk to you was so strong, that if you wouldn't have got in there first, I would have approached you sooner or later. There really didn't seem to be much choice in the matter.'

'Well sweetie, I'm pleased to announce: you're getting good at this already,' she angled her face to one side and looked at him directly, with that solid, grounded, yet utterly outrageous look of hers.

When Tara looked at Lee, he sat upright, attentively like a little school kid, but his Body and his posture betrayed that notion. He looked strong and sharp. He soaked up new information easily, internalised it and compared it with what he already knew. And, what was best, he could see the silly side of it all. She could do with a playmate, she thought.

Looking at him, she remembered her own first steps into the world of Co-incidences and Intuitions. No teachers, no theory, only curiosity and a strong will to find out how the Universe worked. She remembered the confusion and frustration, how she'd never been quite sure if *her* Mind was making things up or not. She never really had anybody she could have talked to about this stuff either. She'd done it all on her own, through sheer tenacity, curiosity, and of course the analysis of many, many situations and Co-incidences. She had examined and trained her Intuition until she knew it inside and out. **The more she practiced, the more proof she got that following her Intuition worked and that as a result, her Co-incidence hit-rate increased. With time she'd begun to see patterns in her feelings, her moods, her actions and thus in her Intuition. The more patterns she found, the easier she managed to distinguish her Intuition from her Mind.** It was exactly like she had said to Lee earlier, after a while, it was all so obvious that she began to wonder how she could have ever missed it.

Tara quickly told Lee what she'd been thinking and then added, 'To get there though, you really do have to *do* it. It doesn't just happen.'

'I understand that. Gotta do it. No pain, no gain and all that,' Lee nodded.

'Oh, check, check, hang on, if you do it right, there shouldn't be any pain, just fun and gain. If you want it to be painful, it will be, but if you want it to be fun? It will be that! Always remember that!'

Lee nodded making an important mental note not to forget.

'Another thing that's useful until you get lots of experience, is to **analyse examples together with friends if you can. Tell each other what you felt and thought. Point out important stepping-stones, bits of Co-incidences and Signs to each other. It can be ever so useful to have somebody else point out the tree in the forest for you, and you for them. Discuss how each one of you would interpret the events or Intuitions. In this way, you can learn from each-other's experience, which speeds up the process for everybody**,' Tara finished off.

'Great idea,' Lee said satisfied, slumping back against the lamppost. This pavement was getting a bit hard for his liking. They'd been sitting here for ages. 'By the way Tara,' a Thought had popped into Lee's Mind, 'how far down the line are you with this stuff?'

Tara thought for a second. 'I guess I know my Intuition so well by now, that I can tell it apart from my Mind pretty much every time.'

Lee raised his eyebrows in disbelief. Tara held his gaze steadily. Nope, no showing off there. She really meant it.

'Additionally,' she continued, **'I've made a *personal commitment* to myself, to follow *every* Intuition, no matter how weird. I literally just do it. I don't think about it anymore**. Well, I sometimes still comment: "Oh wow, that's an interesting Intuition", or: "I wonder what happens next", but I don't let that stop me from *acting* on an Intuition anymore. Actually, when I come to think of it, **most of the time, I don't really think about it at all anymore. Most Intuitions are just put into action automatically**.'

Lee was slightly sceptical of the sheer possibility of this being true, but Tara seemed to think it was completely natural. "It's certainly alluring enough to at least try," he thought to himself.

'What's it like when it happens automatically?' he asked finally.

'It's mind-blowing, incredible and amazing. Let me give you an example to show you how extraordinary it can get. I was walking along one day, just a few years ago, wondering where to have lunch. I decided to go the Italian restaurant down the road. On my way to it, my suddenly Body stopped. Literally, without any reason, my feet wouldn't move anymore. I was so surprised. I looked up and said: "What?" waiting for The Guys to answer. I caught myself doing that, and giggled. There I am, rooted in place, talking to myself - what a sight. Anyway, my feet turned around and walked back to a little café I'd been in only once before. And there they were! A bunch of my friends, and a woman who I didn't know! She was only in town for a few days, and boy, did we have to talk to each other! It was amazing. We met up every night till the day she left to exchange stories and ideas. She was one of the first people back then that I could bounce my new ideas off. The meeting was so ridiculously significant that we kept commenting on how cool it was.'

Lee was soaking up the words. **Past experiences, events and feelings slowly tumbled into a magnificent cosmic order, just by listening to Tara. It wasn't like anything concrete, anything that he could put his finger on specifically, it was more like a web of realisations and recognitions that was being woven. Steadily and strongly. They were the kind of realisations that you got when you were subconsciously aware of something and then somebody pointed them out to you. Realisation when everything suddenly clicked into place. When your brain cells were rearranged in a**

new order, which was new and exciting, yet grounded and familiar.

'Those examples are really useful, all sorts of stuff is making sense here,' Lee said, 'care to give me another one?'

'Sure, how many do you want?' Tara joked, picked one from the edges of her Consciousness and began to describe it cheerfully, 'One morning I was cleaning out my apartment and found a whole load of notes on Chinese Medicine which I didn't need anymore. I hadn't looked at them for ages and I knew most of the stuff by heart anyway, so I decided to throw them away, but the second I had them in my hand they seemed to shout: "Put us in your bag".

Needless to say, instead of chucking them, I put them in my bag. I knew that it was odd to act on that Intuition, I mean, what was I going to do with the notes in my bag? I knew that I had no idea why I was doing it, but hey, I had an Intuition, so who was I to argue, right? My curiosity was aroused.'

'Oh man, I'm beginning to see why you said that your Intuition blows your brain *and* your imagination. **I can also see why your personal commitment to follow each and every Intuition is so useful. It makes sure that you really go for it**.' Tara nodded, Lee grinned. 'Man, is that really what goes on in your head?'

'Yeah, it is. **It's hilarious when you catch yourself out and observe the arguing in your own head, you know, knowing how strange it is what you are about to do, but knowing that you'll do it anyway - that you *want* to do it anyway.**

Anyway, back to the example. During the day I had entirely forgotten about the notes, until I got onto the train. A seat next to a young woman in her early-twenties literally screamed at me to sit on it. It was such a strong feeling that I walked over and sat down next to her. As soon as I sat, the notes bounced up and down in my Mind, loud and clear: "We want to be with her". I didn't even hesitate. I took the notes out of my bag, handed them to her and just said: "You might like these". The girl looked at me slightly wearily, as strangers always do when you offer them something, but still, she took the notes and looked at them. Slowly her jaw dropped. It was the most comical thing you could ever imagine. Her eyes were as big as a cow's and I could hear her gasp.' By the look on Tara's face, she obviously enjoyed the memory. 'Then she asked me: "How on earth did you know that I'm into this stuff?" I said that I didn't, but that I had just felt that she should have the papers. When she realised that I wasn't a freak, she finally relaxed and in turn was getting really excited. She said that this information was exactly what she'd been trying to find for ages. Just that morning she thought how desperate she'd been to find out more and that it was really time for some answers to come along.'

'That's ridiculous,' Lee said aghast.

'I know.'

'And there's no chance that that could have just been a weird Co-incidence, because you knew *beforehand*!'

'Exactly.'

'Wow.'

'I know. Actually, there's a part two, this one was a double-whammy. The girl got the info she needed and she also asked me why I didn't feel weird about talking to her. We ended up chatting about similar stuff to what you and I are talking about right now. Needless to say, she'd been asking the Universe for just that conversation.'

'Are you serious?' Lee held his head in over exaggerated disbelief.

'Of course. And as it's often mutual, I learned a bunch from her too.'

'So you were part of each others Co-incidences,' Lee stated attentively.

'Right.'

'Now there's a good story if I've ever heard one,' Lee liked the way Tara linked theory with some good solid examples out of her own life. It made everything so much more real for him; it somehow validated his own experiences in this new, weird and inexplicable realm as well.

'It's fascinating to see how many lucky Co-incidences seem to be foretold by Intuitions,' he said finally, 'my Tax example and your Chinese Medicine papers. Man,' he paused in surprise, 'I just realised something else. Phew, there are so many points where the chain could be broken.'

'Which chain?'

'The chain of Intuitions and Signs. If you think about all the Intuitions and Signs that could have been missed or ignored? It makes the Mind boggle! You could have ignored the idea of cleaning your apartment that day, you could have thrown the notes away, ignoring the Intuition of putting them into your bag.'

'You're getting the hang of this far to quick,' Tara said appreciating Lee's quick Mind.

'Thanks.' Lee continued on a roll, 'Then, you could have walked rather than taken the train. Then you could have chosen a different carriage of the train, and then you could have sat somewhere else, not next to the girl, and finally you could have not spoken to her and not given her the notes. Oh bloody hell,' Lee moaned, 'how can you ever get it right? How can you ever follow all those hints and not miss half of them?'

'Well, *you* already did it, didn't you?' Tara smiled knowingly. 'You already made your way into the café where the Tax dude sat, all by yourself, or not?'

'So I did,' Lee was taken aback.

'You even already knew that you had to talk to the guy in the café, right? It was clear. There wasn't any effort involved!'

'Good point. Well, spare the small detail of the minute time delay to wait for his mate to turn up with the give-away folder.'

'Well, yeah, details,' Tara grinned. 'But in the end, you *did* talk to him, so you somehow *already* followed the Signs, right? **Sometimes we just get it right by accident, just like you did**,' Tara said.

'I had a friend who listened to his Intuition without ever even having heard of the fact that you could *actively* play with it,' she remembered another example.

'Well now it gets exciting. Tell me more?'

'A while ago I met a few wonderful people. We had only known each other very briefly, but we all got on like a house on fire and we were amazed by the incredible connection the five of us had. It wasn't that we just *wanted* to spend more time together, it was rather that all of us felt that we *had* to spend more time together. It felt like part of a bigger plan - to all of us. And, being good Intuition-followers,' Tara winked at Lee, 'we made plans to go away for the weekend, to spend some quality time together. As we got into the jeep, one of us suddenly remembered that he was supposed to meet a friend of his that evening. He felt incredibly guilty, because if he was going to come with us, he was going to stand up his friend. He didn't know what to do. His Mind was racing so fast that a decision had become impossible.'

'What happened?' Lee asked curiously.

'Well, I asked him what he really *wanted* to do, from the bottom of his heart. He said that he didn't know, that he was too confused. I asked if he would, just for a few minutes, stop thinking about what he thought he *should* be doing, or what he thought everybody else wanted him to do, or even what other people might think of him - *then* what would the first answer be that came into his head? What would make *him* happy?

He was still thinking, I could literally hear him 'uhm-ing' and 'ah-ing,' so I interjected: "It's still your head, you're still thinking, it's not your Intuition. What is the *first* thing that pops into your head, your *first* reaction, without reasoning the pros and cons?" He said: "Oh, ok, ehm". He was still using his head, so I just kept on saying: "No head, use your heart. No head!" I prodded him gently. Suddenly he said really annoyed, "Stop bloody saying that will you? I know I need to come with you, I just feel so guilty to cancel on my friend". As soon as he realised what he had said, he understood. His heart had told him that he wanted to come. In fact it had told him more than that, it had told him that he *needed* to come. I just grinned and gave him a hug. He had listened to his heart. He had managed to switch off his crazy, mad and confused head and listened to his Intuition. He *had* to come with us and he knew it. The weekend turned out to be second to none.'

'No surprises there,' Lee grinned.

'Yep, and it doesn't stop there. He called his friend, explained what had happened and apologised a thousand times. His friend actually came to join us a few days later. When we asked him how he felt about my friend cancelling on him, he said that he was initially upset, but that he realised from talking to my friend how important this weekend was for him, and who was he to stand in the way of somebody's happiness.'

'Cool.'

'That's what I thought. Do you want the rest of the story?'

'Of course!' Lee propped up his elbows on his knees, rested his chin on his hands and looked at Tara expectantly.

'I also asked the guy what happened in his head when his friend called him to cancel. I asked him if he thought that he should let his friend go with us, or if he had some kind of feeling, you know, an Intuition.'

'You didn't!'

'Of course I did. **That's how you find out about stuff. You talk to people, you ask questions about this stuff. You do the reality checks.** You find out if they had Intuitions, how *they* felt like, even if they followed any Signs.'

'Fantastic. And? What did he say?'

'Funnily enough, after he had stopped laughing at my question, and after I had told him that I was serious, I asked him to really think about it. When he did, he said that he had somehow known that my friend wouldn't come to see him that evening. He was surprised to realise that he had strangely already prepared himself for it.'

'No way.'

'Yep. Needless to say that we also had an interesting conversation about Intuitions afterwards.'

'Nuts. That's all I can say. Great nuts though,' Lee laughed.

'Fabulous. Now, if you want to get involved *consciously* to get better at identifying your Intuition and make it all less of an accident, all you need to do is keep on practicing the analysis I explained earlier, get to know your Intuition better, and of course, most of all, play with following *all* those hunches, no matter how ridiculous they are.

You know Lee, you're doing better than you give yourself credit for. You even picked out all the right areas to analyse all by yourself. Once you have examined a bunch of situations like this on your own, the way your

Intuitions feel and the way they make themselves known to you will become more and more obvious. And, hey presto, next time when you get *that* feeling, you *know* that it's an Intuition. You really don't have to be Superman to be able to do this. It's just practice. And **before you know it, it's not really a question of *missing* an Intuition anymore, it's a question of making sure you *follow* it once you've noticed it, by making sure that the Mind doesn't rationalise it away.**'

'Which is exactly what I did that day with the Tax dude. I saw the red flag my Intuition waved at me and I happily ignored it.'

'Exactly. Now let's make sure that you don't ignore them anymore, shall we?' Tara offered.

'That would be fantastic.'

Lee nodded slowly as Tara said, 'Dude, your life is about to change.'

'Phew,' he sighed quietly, 'I think it already has.'

Lee re-arranged the lamppost in his back once again and silently reflected on the past few hours. This was new territory to him. He had never really spoken, let alone thought about the majority of Tara's ideas before. Granted, he'd touched on some of them, but most of his theories had been gobble-di-gook to his friends. There had been some wild theorising, but no hands-on stuff. Nothing practical. Nobody, including himself had really had any concrete experience to back up their ideas. The blind had been leading the blind. But now with Tara, everything felt different. Tara was confident in her statements, she actually *knew* these things to be true, not from theory, but from her *own experience*.

Lee was amazed to discover a surprising ability to combine his own knowledge with her ideas without effort, and to immediately apply them to his experiences. He had noticed how Tara would start a topic and everything seemed to simply slot into place with his existing Thoughts and theories, or knowledge that he suddenly had from out of nowhere. It was simply amazing how his brain automatically took the ideas just a little bit further every time. This was new. This was cool. "And what's more," he thought, "all this practice is so much better than just getting theory. This is hands-on stuff. No more fairytales!" Thinking about hands-on stuff, he really couldn't sit any longer.

He turned to Tara, 'You know, if I have to sit another minute on this pavement, that lamppost shall grow into my back and my bottom shall sprout roots.'

'Oh, you poor thing,' Tara grinned, rubbing her ankles. 'I know what you mean. I think the pavement is now permanently tattooed into my skin. Gosh, I had no idea we'd be talking this long.'

'Well, besides my Body being comfort-challenged, this conversation has been absolutely incredible,' Lee held up his hands with all fingers stretched out and said, 'Tara, ten-points.'

Shakes, Waffles, Chocolate

'**M**mh, I wonder what I can do with all those points I'm scoring here,' Tara said cheekily, looking dreamily into the sky.

'Shakes, Waffles, Chocolate, all the heavenly goods are for your taking,' Lee said without really knowing why.

Tara's eyes widened, 'Woha, that sounds right up my alley. I'm famished. I can't believe we're still sitting here, it must be well past lunchtime. How about grabbing some of that sweet stuff you just talked about and a drink? *And* a couple of chairs?' she added as an afterthought, 'In fact, I know a lovely café just around the corner.'

'Fabulous idea!' Lee said, patting his empty stomach, 'I'm absolutely starving. Oops, I just remembered something. You know when I locked myself out? Well, I don't have any funds to my name right now. Kind of embarrassing, sorry.'

Tara shrugged and said, 'Oh don't worry, I'll buy you lunch. You'll just have to pay me back in kind later,' she winked at Lee naughtily and burst out laughing.

'Oh yeah? And what might that entail?' Lee grinned back at her equally mischievously.

Tara gathered herself, 'Well, bearing my endless jabbering about God and the world would do just fine. But obviously,' she added, 'You don't have to.'

Lee laughed, 'It'll be my pleasure. I would love to redeem your brownie points in return for a good meal.'

Both of them grinned broadly as they walked down the road in silence. They reached the little café after only a few minutes. It was a quiet, comfortable looking little place, and Lee devoured the smell of truly heavenly sweet stuff that wafted through an open window. It reminded him of the tearooms his Granny used to take him to when he was a little boy.

When he saw the Specials menu for the day in the window, he laughed out loud, 'Tara, you won't believe this, but the Specials for today are: "Heavenly Feast - *Hot Vanilla Waffles, Chocolate Ice Cream, Mocha Shake*".'

'Well, I guess, we're in The Guy's favour today,' Tara giggled.

'This is so funny. I have no idea why I suggested those things earlier. I just had this flash of myself, in a café, just like this, about five-years-old, eating myself stupid on this stuff. I'm so impressed. With you around, I seem to be able to pick up on The Guy's hints really easily,' Lee observed.

'Yeah man, we seem to be working well together.'

They held each other's glances just a moment longer than necessary.

'Yum,' Tara licked her lips, 'lets go in.'

'Who are we to refuse?' Lee mumbled, lead Tara up the steps and gentlemanly held the door open for her. 'We're obviously supposed to be having that. *All* of it, that is.'

'Oh yeah!' said Tara, excited like a little girl, 'I tell you, this place is out of this world, it has *the best* gooey sweet tooth fillers in the whole wide Universe! Wait and you will see!'

'As with all of your stuff?' Lee said smiling.

'Absolutely. And as with all of my stuff,' Tara playfully pointed out while waving her index finger at Lee, 'you *will* see that it *is* all true.'

'It wouldn't surprise me in the slightest. Well, here comes your first real test,' Lee chuckled as they walked towards a table in the far corner and sat down.

'An easy one to pass,' Tara said, exchanging smiles with the elderly woman who had just appeared at the counter and promptly shuffled over to greet Tara. 'Tara, good to see you again. With a victim for my culinary sins, I see? Fabulous.'

Tara got up to hug her, 'Hi Angela. Angela, this is Lee, Lee, Angela.'

Lee couldn't help himself but get up and also hug the short, grey-haired lady. Angela felt warm and soft. Lee had always been a tactile person and he strongly believed that a hug a day kept the doctor away. Or something like that.

'Nice to meet you Angela,' he said.

'Nice to meet *you*. Tara's friends are my friends,' Angela chirped and then added invitingly, 'Looking at you, you need the works, don't you?'

'Knowing as always. Yes please, times two. Double-Choc Ice Cream for me, please. Lee?'

'Same here,' he said approvingly. Double-Choc was his favourite. Tara had read his Mind once again, he thought bemused.

'The Special today is just too perfect to be true, Angela. Gosh, we're in such need of a chocolate overload to replenish our talking cells! How did you know?' Tara asked with a knowing smile.

Angela interrupted excitedly, 'I know! It's great isn't it? I've only just put up the board. It came to me only about half an hour ago. Loud and clear, I mean, how could I refuse? But let me go and sort you lovelies out,' she turned and walked slowly, ever so slowly, with steps ever so small, back behind the counter.

Lee looked confused and asked Tara quietly, 'She didn't actually know, did she?'

Angela had overheard the comment and whispered, a hand held in front of her mouth in an angle as if to protect the words, 'Of course I did! Tara hasn't got the monopoly for talking to The Fairies you know?' she turned and walked casually into the kitchen with a girlish grin on her face.

Lee's jaw had dropped by then. 'She knows?' he asked flabbergasted.

'Of course! Lots of people do!'

'And she *does* it?'

'Of course! Lots of people do.'

'Really?' Lee asked, surprise written all over his face.

'Of course!'

'Great, always the last to know!' Lee shook his head.

'Well, not quite the last, unfortunately.'

Carefully turning around to make sure that Angela had safely disappeared into the kitchen, Lee grinned broadly and whispered, 'And she calls The Guys her 'Fairies'?'

Tara shrugged her shoulders, 'Yep, that's what works for her. Everybody calls The Guys what works best for them. 'Friends', 'Guides', 'Fairies', 'Dave', 'Bluey', anything.'

'That's so funny, who the hell calls The Guys, 'Dave?''

'A friend of mine,' Tara laughed. 'One day when he thought about what to call them, he joked: 'I could just call them Dave'', and somehow that stuck.'

Lee nearly died laughing, 'He calls The Guys, Dave. That's hilarious. I though 'The Guys' was funny, but 'Dave' takes the biscuit.'

'Well, it certainly always puts a smile on his face when he talks to them.'

'I guess that can only be good,' Lee laughed loudly. 'Tara, how many people know?' he suddenly asked very seriously.

'Lots of people know. Lots of people out there work with The Guys, although they might call Them different names such as Spirits, Gods, other Entities, the Cosmos, Helpers.

Unfortunately, a lot of people that work with The Guys have rightly or wrongly been described as silly Hippies, Loonies, Dreamers, Weirdoes, Special People or people with special gifts, believers, Gurus, followers, and so-on and so-on.'

'True, and there really *are* some raving fruitcakes out there. We can't deny that,' Lee said frankly.

'Of course,' Tara nodded. 'I agree, but **I also think it'll do human kind a world of good to realise that not all of the people that do things differently are mad, that they just happen to have a lot of curiosity, determination, discipline and a bunch more middle-fingers-up to conventionality, tradition, boredom, fear and laziness than the average person. And some of those people actually have a bunch of really useful things to say.**'

'Point taken,' Lee grinned at Tara's bluntness.

Until the sweet goodies arrived, the two of them sat in comfortable silence. All they heard was Angela banging her magic cooking utensils in the kitchen.

Still smiling, Lee pondered about the last few hours' conversation. He playfully mocked himself, "Of course, silly me, lots of people talk to their Souls, lots of them talk to The Guys, lots of them do this stuff, and they call them Paul, and Fairies and freaking Dave! Silly me! Of course! Man, how could I not know? Well, how the bloody hell should I have known? This is the first I've heard of it. But hey, better late than never. Cheers Dudes!" he said to himself, paused for a second, and then burst out laughing. He laughed and laughed, tears filling his eyes.

'What?' Tara asked, but only got another belly full of Lee's deep and roaring laughter. 'What?' Tara asked again, this time with a more urging curiosity.

'Oh God, you won't believe what just happened. I think I just named The Guys,' Lee rubbed his eyes.

'You did?'

'Yep. Just like you said, it just came out.'

'And? And?' Tara probed impatiently.

'It's 'The Dudes'.'

'You're kidding.'

'Nope.'

'That's hilarious.'

'I know. But it fits perfectly. The Dudes works for me. It's familiar and casual. Hey, it's The Dudes!'

They both laughed so hard, Angela had to come to see what was up. To their further amusement, after telling Angela, they heard her giggling in the kitchen for the a good long while afterwards. Lee looked out of the window, with a smile still on his face. He'd been lost in Thought for a while, when Tara waved a plate of steaming waffles in front of his face.

She spoke softly in a tempting voice, 'Food feast to Lee, food feast to Lee! Sugar resources need replenishing. Required to tuck in now!'

'Oh, sorry,' he hadn't noticed that Angela had put the plates right in front of his face, the Double Chocolate ice cream already slowly melting.

"The Dudes. I love it," he grinned to himself one last time, as Tara began to devour the presented chocolate treats.

After the first few spoonfuls she asked, 'You're not really that surprised that Angela knows about The Guys, are you?'

Lee wasn't so sure, 'I guess, talking about it and theorising about it, and then suddenly realising that this stuff is actually real, and that other people are really doing it, are two different kettles of fish.'

'No talk about fish in my pastry haven,' Angela said merrily, placing two huge glasses of Mocha Shake in front of each one of them. The glasses were frosted over, the shake dramatically piped over the rim of the glass like little ice cones. A special recipe of 'Guy's bar', a long, long time ago. 'Get your hands on these while they're cold.'

'You really know what two growing people need,' Tara said hungrily.

'Sorry to be the bearer of bad news sweetheart, but you are far beyond the *growing* age,' Angela said with theatrical concern.

'Mentally growing, dear, mentally growing,' Lee gargled, holding his hands in front of his stuffed mouth.

'And spiritually, dear, and spiritually,' Tara said, imitating Lee's facial expression so well, that they all burst out laughing.

The older couple at the small window table was just leaving. They waved at Angela, 'The cheque is in the little basket on the table, as usual. See you tomorrow.'

'Sure, have a wonderful afternoon Doris. Take care of that rascal dog or yours Danny,' she called after them, as they slowly left, carefully negotiating the steps with their walking sticks.

As they were the only customers in the café now, Tara asked, 'Why don't you sit down for a mo', Angela?'

'Sure, I'd love to,' she said, sat down next to Tara and began to chat away.

Quick as a flash, Lee was off with the fairies again. The proverbial ones, rather than his Dudes. Actually, with an ex-fairy called Kate to be more precise. Kate somehow had managed to sneak back into his Thoughts. She was good at that. His heart sank just a tiny bit, as he remembered her. How she felt, her smell. But then, could he have had any of these cosmic conversations with Kate? Fat chance.

Lee was so far lost in his Thoughts, he barely noticed when Tara carefully picked up a hair from his arm, pulled it gently and whispered to him.

'Yoohoo… anybody at home? Lights are on and all that?'

Lee jerked slightly in surprise, slotting back into the Now. 'Oh, sorry, I was a little distracted there. You know, it's funny, I always thought I was on my own thinking like this. People always took me for a little peculiar when I started to question the Universe. And now I've already met two people like me in one day!'

Angela reached over the table and gave Lee's hand a quick squeeze and said gently, 'Well, you're not alone, sweetheart. And believe me, it becomes even more fun once you meet like-Minded people,' her face lit up. 'But now, don't let my sweet heavenly creations get cold or hot or melt or whatever. I haven't laboured over them with all my love, to see the fruit of my hard work go to waste. So, ready, steady, spoons go,' she got up and disappeared back into her little Den of cookery magic.

'Endearing. I've never used that word before, but that's what Angela is: Endearing,' Lee whispered.

'I know,' Tara said with a affectionate look on her face. Lee could tell that Tara loved this woman very much.

'Silence! Eat!' they heard Angela shout from the kitchen.

'Yes ma'am!' the pair said in unison, catching their eyes in laughter as they heard Angela giggling in the other room.

Silence descended over the café, as Lee and Tara didn't breathe until every last crumb and every last drop had disappeared. When Angela came back, she looked at the crockery with the satisfaction of an appreciated cook. 'Polished, that's what I like. You are allowed to lick the plates, you know?' she added with a broad smile.

Lee and Tara held their stomachs and shook their heads, 'No more, no more.'

'Well, because it's such a lovely day, I'll let you off,' Angela smiled and began to clear the table.

'Fantastic food Angela. Pure bliss! Chocolate heaven! Thanks,' Tara praised.

'Yeah, brilliant, credit where credit is due,' Lee agreed.

'The pleasure was all mine,' Angela was delighted.

When Tara got her purse out to pay, Angela waved her hand and said with a knowing undertone to her voice, 'Don't worry, you can pay next time. I'd love to see you both again,' she winked at Tara a little bit too secretly.

'Thanks Angela. I'll be back soon, maybe I'll bring little Jack next time, he hasn't seen you for a while,' Tara said warmly.

'Oh, your little brother, I'd love to see him again. He loves my blueberry doughnuts you know,' Angela added proudly for Lee's benefit.

'That doesn't surprise me in the slightest. I'm sure you'll see me again too.'

'I should hope so,' she smiled.

'Thanks again.'

'No problemo. Have the *best* day!' Angela said, waving them off.

Tara whispered quietly, 'Isn't she lovely? No doubt Angela picked up those trendy words from her multitude of young friends. "No problemo', so sweet.'

Once outside, something clicked in Lee's brain. He looked at Tara in disbelief. 'You are not going to tell me now that Angela knew that I didn't have any money on me, will you?'

Tara just shrugged her shoulder, smiling sheepishly.

'Of course,' Lee said matter-of-factly, 'silly me!' he clasped his hands over his head. 'Woha, this surely is getting mad. Far out man,' he muttered, trying to get this mad new world straight in his Brain. His Rational Mind was putting up quite a dance in his skull, but his Intuition knew better. It was all good.

'Wanna go to the park?' Lee asked.

'Great idea,' Tara agreed. 'It'll be lovely there now. Much better than the middle of the road,' she added smiling.

They ambled along slowly, unhurriedly, digesting a belly full of chocolate. Luckily it wasn't far.

Once in the park and within minutes of planting themselves under the shading branches of a massive old Oak tree, they found themselves back in deep conversation.

PART 2

3   What's Going On In Our Mind?

The Interfering Mind - *Really* Telling Your Mind From Your Intuition

> *"The Intuitive Mind is a sacred gift*
> *and the Rational Mind is a faithful Servant.*
> *We have created a society that honours the servant*
> *and has forgotten the gift."*
> *- Einstein*

'Man, life can become so much more intense with all of this stuff,' Lee said.

'What do you mean intense?' Tara looked up.

'It seems that mind-blowing stuff suddenly happens all the time. And, well, it's kind of intense to have your Mind blown all the time. Especially if you still have to listen to your Rational Mind all along, telling you that you're crazy.'

'That's true, but that feeling only lasts a little while. It's a bit overwhelming at the beginning, but the more you do it, instead of getting freaked out, the more you'll begin to laugh about it. You'll just shrug your shoulders, smile and think: "Of course, The Guys, or The Dudes,"' she corrected herself with a giggle, '"arranged that. Of course people know. Of course others are doing it." Once you get your head around the fact that it's real and that it works, even though it's far out, even though you can't explain it scientifically, it's actually a lot of fun.'

'Well, I'll certainly keep playing, that's for sure. It's so funny though that Angela knows too,' Lee smiled at the memory.

'Yeah, she's the best.'

Lee nodded, laid down in the grass and stretched himself out. 'Ahh, this is nice.'

Tara watched the contours of Lee's moving Body through the material of his shirt. He had crossed his hands behind his head as a pillow, which naturally showed off the shape of his arms. "I'm just looking," Tara grinned to herself as she sat cross-legged again, and covered her legs with her skirt. It was her favourite position. It was comfortable, her back was straight and she could breathe easily.

Funny how both of them had left the café, assuming that they would spend more time together this afternoon. She liked being around him. He was in his power. He knew himself. He was strong, yet sensitive. A nice combination.

'Ok then, blow my Mind! I'm ready,' Lee interrupted Tara's Thoughts.

'You sure?'

'Absolutely,' he opened his eyes and looked at her invitingly.

'Mmh, where did we stop? Before chocolate and Fairies?' Tara cleared her Mind and switched to 'receiving'. It was much easier than wrecking her brain trying to remember. As always, the words came easily and effortlessly through her Being.

'Oh yes, the Tax-book example. We said that **noticing a hunch or Intuition is only the first step,** right?'

'Right.'

'**The *next* step would be to make sure that you're actually acting on it, that you *follow* it**. That's the tricky bit,' Tara picked up where their conversation had left off before their extreme chocolate fix.

'Thus **we need to learn how to stop our Rational Mind from interfering and rationalising away any Intuitions we have**, right?' Lee spoke from his own experience just a little earlier.

'Precisely. To do that, **you need to get yourself to a stage where you know your Intuitions so well, that you know without any doubt when you had one. Unless you're one hundred percent certain about it, right from the split second you noticed that particular Intuition, you've already lost.**'

'Really? It goes that fast?'

'Oh absolutely. You can try it! **It's nearly impossible to class a hunch or an Intuition as Significant or not, by trying to figure it out with your Mind**, by simply thinking about it.'

'Ah, yes, that'll be the typical ehm-was-that-an-Intuition-or-not conversation in my head,' Lee remembered.

'Exactly. And how confusing are those?' Tara remembered her own trial and errors.

'Utterly. **Once I start, I already know that I will drive myself crazy with it, there's no way out of it anymore. It's a constant back and forth, yes, no, yes, no, without a chance of resolution. Once my Mind gets hold of it, that's it, my Mind never comes up with a straight forward answer with regards to the Intuition department.**'

'Because that's not it's job,' Tara said with emphasis. 'The Mind is not designed to understand inexplicable stuff like Intuitions, on the contrary. It can't understand them, so it tries to rubbish them to try and get rid of them as fast as possible. We live in a rational world and our Mind constantly tries to *understand, know* and *explain*, but unless it can see or touch something, it will never believe that it exists. For the Mind, an Intuition is the ultimate curiosity, the ultimate pain in the neck. An Intuition is a feeling that comes from out of nowhere, seemingly at random. The Mind didn't ask for it, it just sort of appears at its own whim. Intuitions can't be seen or touched or grasped logically - but hey our Mind tries anyway. Our Mind tries to rationalise an Intuition, it tries to question it, understand where it came from and what the hell it's trying to tell us. But when you come down to it, the Rational Mind doesn't like Intuitions, because no matter how hard it tries, it cannot understand them! And that disturbs the Mind. Therefore, failing to get a satisfactory explanation, it's in the Mind's interest to get rid of an Intuition as quickly as possible. **As a result, the Mind either ignores the Intuition or it plants serious doubt by coming up with all sorts of reasons why something was or maybe wasn't an Intuition, why something was or wasn't, or even simply shouldn't *be* Significant. Either way, in the end we're so confused that we don't trust the Intuition anymore and certainly don't act on it**.'

'And that's why we don't want that ehm-was-that-an-Intuition-or-not discussion to start in the first place,' Lee said, sat up and looked at Tara.

'Exactly. **Therefore, it's much more effective if you can get to a stage where you just know, one hundred percent, *that's* my Mind, and *that* was an Intuition. Then the entire stupid Mind discussion becomes unnecessary in the first place**.'

'That'll be my dream. That's what I always wanted to be able to do!'

'And you will be able to shortly.'

'Oh yes!' Lee grinned happily, while his Rational Mind shook it's little head exhaustedly, feeling defeat coming on.

'And little do you know that that's just the beginning to sooo much more,' Tara taunted sweetly holding her gaze steady.

'Why am I so glad that you always say that?' Lee lifted his eyebrows in amusement.

Tara grinned. 'Lets give you more then, shall we?' As Lee nodded, she continued with ease, 'So that was the Intuition bit, and now? **Well, once you've familiarised yourself with your Intuitions, *it's time to learn the same things about your Mind*. You can learn *how* it thinks and *what* it *feels* like when it thinks.** You can learn about the situations when it stresses, goes mental or quiet. **You can get to know your Mind and Thoughts inside and out, backwards and forwards, left to right and back again**.'

'Ahh, and cha-ching, the penny dropped,' Lee caught an imaginary coin out of the air. **'When we know both our Intuition *and* our Mind inside out, it's child's play to tell them apart**. It's obvious.'

'Tadaah! See? It's common sense,' Tara said joyfully.

'I think it might be list time,' Lee said, grabbed his notebook and read out the bullet points, as he wrote them down.

Telling your Mind from your Intuition:
* Noticing a hunch or Intuition is just the first step.
* The second step is to stop our Mind interfering, ignoring and rationalising our Intuitions.
* We want to get to a stage where we're one hundred percent certain if something was an Intuition or not.
* We don't want the ehm-was-that-an-Intuition-or-not conversations in our head - there's no point to have them, as we'll never get a satisfactory answer.
* Past Co-incidence analysis helps us to get to know, familiarise and trust our Intuition.
* Now we need to do the same with our Mind.
* When we finally know both our Intuition and our Mind inside out, it's child's play to tell them apart.
* Yippee!

'Fabulous sweetie, well done. Especially that last point,' Tara chuckled. 'You're such a darling.'

'Thanks,' Lee looked straight into her eyes. He loved the colour of her eyes. Blue green. Startling. Effervescent. Unusual.

The Two Minds

Tara redirected his attention easily, 'Intuitions are fascinating, but the Mind is no less curious. Are you ready to get to know your Mind?' Tara asked with an extra sparkle in her smile.

'As ready as I'll ever be,' Lee sat up and stretched his back.

'Great,' Tara said joyfully, 'let's understand *how* the Mind works. A long time ago, I tried to explain the nature of the Mind, and I came up with a description that works really well for me. It might not be scientifically correct, but I think it's easy to understand.'

75

'Easy is the way to go, go ahead,' Lee said expectantly.

Tara began, 'I described it this way. Our Mind has two parts to it. There's our Conscious Mind and our Subconscious Mind. **I'd like to stress upfront though that the Terms Subconscious and Conscious Mind are not supposed to comply with any current scientific or psychological terms. I use them in my own way, with my own explanations and definitions, alright?** I've tried to make up my own words, but in the end I decided that these ones just fit. I think that's important for you to know. If it's ok, I'll explain them as I go along, how's that?'

'Sure, that's cool,' Lee approved.

'Great. So, even though the brain has many different functions, for our purpose we'll just be talking about the *analysing* and *rationalising* function of one part of it, and the *receiving* function of another part.' Lee looked slightly lost, which prompted Tara to give an example to clarify her Thoughts, **'Have you ever had a situation where you just knew that something wasn't quite right, but you didn't know why?'**

'What, a feeling like, I-don't-like-this-place-or-this-person, without a concrete reason? Sure.'

'That's your *Subconscious receiving* an *Intuitive* message,' Tara paused for a second to let that sink in. **'Our gut-feeling, our Subconscious tells us that something isn't quite right, but then the Conscious Mind comes in and analyses that message, trying to find rational explanation for it. If it can't find any, it tells you, 'Don't be so silly, everything is ok,** and presto, your Mind just ignored an Intuition.' Lee nodded and Tara went on, 'So, to be able to observe this *arguing* process *while* it's happening, you need to get to grips with the intricate workings of *both* of these brain parts. **When you get to know each part of your brain inside-out, then you can *choose* which one to listen to.'**

The Warehouse of The Mind and The Radio Transmitter

'**O**h, have I mentioned yet that The Guys talk to us through our Intuition?' Tara wondered out loud.

Lee's brain clicked into place once again, 'Yes, kind of. Oh, hang on, you just said that our Intuition gets received by our Subconscious Mind. Ah, and therefore, The Guys talk to us through our Subconscious Mind,' Lee was engrossed.

'Full points. **Our Subconscious is our own *personal* source of wisdom, our connection to The Guys.**

'But because of the interfering Conscious Mind we have lost touch with the Subconscious part of our Mind and have thus forgotten to trust its messages,' Lee finished Tara's sentence. 'So, let's learn how to tune in again,' his fingers turned an invisible radio button, while he made distorted crackling sounds.

Tara imitated a bad radio channel, coming in and out of tune, her muffled voice, getting louder and quieter and breaking up. Then suddenly, in a loud and clear voice, she announced, 'In this afternoons programme? Tuning advice coming up. Listen up dear people on Consciousness FM.'

They both laughed.

'I'm all ears,' Lee declared, wanting to know more.

'This is all my own theory again, ok?'

'I get it Tara, don't worry about it. Get on with it,' Lee said with exaggerated impatience. He winked at her.

'Ok, the way I explain this to myself, is that the brain is just a 'receiver', and our Souls, our True Selves, The Little Guys, are everywhere, inside and outside of our Body, maybe they are in a different dimension or physical space, we'll never know, but wherever They are, They are running a radio station, constantly transmitting Signals and messages to us. We receive these messages with our Subconscious Mind in the form of Intuitions or other intangible communications, which I'll explain later.'

'I thought Intuitions are gut-feelings. Shouldn't we receive them in our Appendix or something?' Lee joked.

'Ah, maybe *that's* the world's downfall! Too many people had their Appendix removed!' Tara fired back quick wittedly. 'But guts aside, imagine your Mind to be a huge Warehouse with a Back Yard, a Front Yard, a Warehouse Manager and a Fork-lift Truck.'

'I thought it was a radio transmitter.'

'It is, bear with me. I'll explain.'

Lee smiled in amusement. He loved the weird analogies Tara made up to explain her theories.

Tara continued by giving Lee a list of bullet points outlining the most important functions of the Warehouse *and* the Radio transmitter, promising to explain them in more detail, once they were written down.

The Warehouse and the Radio transmitter:
* Our Mind is like a massive *Radio*. A Radio with an attached Warehouse, a Back and a Front Yard.
* *The Guys* are the *Radio Station*, which sends out the Radio Signals.
* *The Guys Messages* are the *Radio Signals* or Waves, the *Intuitions* which our brain receives.
* The *Brain* is the *Back Yard*. The *address* where The Guys sends the Signals to.

- The *Subconscious Mind* is the *Warehouse*, of the Mind, where all the Radio Signals are stored or pass through on their way to the Front Yard.
- The *Conscious* Mind is the *Front Yard*. It's the *space* where Thoughts can be looked at and examined or rationalised against your conditionings, values, morals and reference points.
- The Conscious Mind, the Front Yard, has a manager allocated to it, which organises the various parts of our Mind as required. The Front Yard Manager, is the little voice in your head that calls the shots, it's our *Conscious Awareness*. It's the part of the Mind that decides what needs to be thought about, which observes or oversees what's going on in the Conscious Mind. The Front Yard Manager is *Conscious Attention* given to the boxes that he receives in The Front Yard. Conscious attention means that you are *actively aware* of your Thoughts.
- Your *Conscious Thoughts* are the *boxes* that are being delivered into the Front Yard and are *currently being looked* at by the Front Yard Manager.
- Background Thoughts, are any boxes that have been delivered into the Front Yard, but are *not currently being consciously processed*. They are the Thoughts that go on in the background without you really noticing, yet they can create a disturbance in the front Yard by their sheer presence.
- The *Fork-lift Truck* is the *Memory*, which picks up boxes out of the Warehouse and transports them to the Front Yard (Subconscious to Conscious).
- The *DNA* holds the necessary information to make all of this happen in the physical Body.

Lee looked over his notes and thought for a moment to get these descriptions clear in his head. 'Phew, that's complicated. Let me try and get my head around this. Basically, all Radio Signals have to arrive at the Back Yard and get stored in the Warehouse. The Manager sends the Fork-lift Truck into the Warehouse to pick up the boxes he requires and bring them out into the Front Yard.'

'That's right,' Tara was impressed how easily Lee internalised such complicated explanations. 'In Mind language, this means that The Guys send out Messages which arrive in our Brains. They are received by and stored in our Subconscious Mind in a box called 'The Guys Messages,' ready for the Front Yard Manager of the Conscious Mind to request the information through memory.'

All other information that we soak up subconsciously during our day, including our ordinary daily Thoughts that we're not accessing at any point in time, are stored in the Warehouse, or are causing a disturbance in the Front Yard,' Tara added.

'Check,' Lee said.

'Now it becomes interesting,' Tara said mysteriously. 'Sometimes, when we think that the Front Yard Manager is not working, the Fork-lift Truck switches to autopilot, and without the Front Yard Manager being aware of it, the Truck continuously brings random boxes, all sorts of junk it has unearthed, out of the warehouse and dumps them into the Front Yard. The very organised Front Yard Manager isn't used to things coming into the Front Yard without following his processes, especially if he hasn't asked for them, and he knows that without his organised schedule, those random boxes can cause a hell of a lot of congestion and confusion in the Front yard.'

'Ah, I see, that's the chitter-chatter, all the Background Thoughts in our heads, that go on all day long, all the nagging interruptions that prevent us from Listening to and following our Intuitions,' Lee deduced.

'Exactly,' Tara agreed.

The Warehouses At Birth

'**A**t birth, the warehouse of the Mind is empty, but for a few boxes with survival code. Then, the warehouse only has one room and there is no Front Yard yet. The Conscious and the Subconscious are in one and the same area. The Front Yard Manager not yet started his job, so everything still works on autopilot, but that's ok, as there are no boxes stored yet that could cause any disruptions.

Also, as there's nothing stored in the Warehouse so far, there is nothing in the way of The Guys' Signals passing through. They can move straight into the Warehouse and to the Conscious Mind, without any interruptions, just the way the Cosmos intended. The Conscious Mind, 'uses up' the Signals instantaneously, just like a Radio 'uses up' Radio Waves. The Messages don't get stored in any way and the Warehouse stays clean.'

'Does that mean that if the Warehouse would stay like that, then The Guy's messages would go straight to the Conscious Mind and get acted upon straight away, without delay, thinking, or rationalising?' Lee clarified.

'Exactly. As babies we fully rely on the messages of The Guys - our Intuition. We scream when we're hungry, regardless if it's a good time or not. We pee because we need to, no matter if the nappies are in place or not. We just do it. We don't question the messages, we don't judge them, we just live by them. We don't know any different. And They look after us just fine.'

Lee burst out laughing, 'Well, we might starve to death, if nobody feeds us, but at least we are happy,' Lee grinned. 'I get that, but you know, some people might just call all that 'just living' reflex.'

'True. We can argue about semantics, but when we come down to it, what we call it doesn't really matter. The point is, that **a baby hasn't** developed a Conscious Mind yet, but it lives subconsciously, wholly oblivious to such things as stress, Thoughts, and with that worry, fear, unhappiness or boredom. It just doesn't know those things yet. It kind of just hangs-out and screams when it's hungry.'

'Now that's an interesting one. It doesn't *know* worry, fear, unhappiness and boredom *yet*,' Lee repeated thoughtfully. 'That'll imply that we learn those things.'

'Of course. And while we're busy learning that, we forget how to listen to our Intuition.'

'Oh bummer.'

'That's one way of putting it,' Tara giggled.

Lee watched her face light up. 'Thinking about it,' he said, 'kids often speak to spirits and imaginary friends, don't they? They ask questions, get help, advice, even comfort and protection against the-ghost-in-the-cupboard. You know what? I think kids talk to The Guys all the time. Well,' Lee added slightly annoyed, 'until the parents tell them to "stop dreaming", or "forget about that nonsense", or "grow-up".'

The Warehouse Growing Up

'**S**ad but true. We are taught from an early age to not to pay attention to The Guys' Messages. Instead of trusting Them, we learn to question Them with our Rational Mind, and slowly we begin to overrule our Intuition with our logical conditionings.'

Both of them were taken aback for a moment.

Lee shook his head emphatically and said, 'And all that in the name of progress, civilisation and growing up. Great.'

'Yeah, ironic isn't it?' Tara added with a bitter smile. '**The good news is that even though we stopped listening when we grew up, The Guys never stopped talking to us. In the vague hope that maybe one day we will listen again, they relentlessly kept delivering Their messages and Signals to the same address, the way they always did.**'

'That's reassuring.'

'I know. **Anyway, when we're babies, we're blissfully ignorant and live happily with our empty Warehouse, fully tuned in. As we grow up, we start to fill it up with boxes, which are crammed full of all the things we've learned over the years. All our knowledge, our conditionings, growing-up guidelines, ideals, Thoughts, Emotions, feelings, memories, people, events,** behavioural patterns, our past experiences, our current life-style, future-plans, friends, work, family, fears, doubt, judgements and questions, all packed into huge boxes, which all end up in the way of The Guys' Signals.

The Separation of Subconscious and Conscious Mind After Birth

Tara drew a deep breath, 'A few months after birth, the Warehouse goes into overload. It can't cope with all the stored boxes and all the new ones that keep coming in. Therefore, a separate space is created for the Conscious Mind, the Front Yard, and a Manager is employed to help organise the chaos. The Front Yard Manager has just started his full time job.'

'We have just become *'Aware'*,' Lee pointed out, 'there is suddenly *'someone-at-home'*, someone that can oversee the mess.'

'Exactly! The Front Yard Manager is now in charge of selecting which boxes are picked out of the Warehouse jumble, and of organising the Front Yard.'

'Phew, I'm not surprised that he gets confused and mixed up, poor lad,' Lee emphasised.

'Yeah, and it gets worse,' Tara grimaced. 'The older we get, the more and the bigger the boxes we add. We clog up the Warehouse with all this stuff, until it gets so congested that The Guys' Signals get so lost in the jumble, that they hardly get through anymore. At that stage, it's nearly impossible for Them to communicate with us any longer. And,' she added sadly, 'it doesn't get any better either. **Every few seconds our environment adds a whole load of new boxes into the Warehouse. Every second our brain gets more and more congested, without the Front Yard Manager having any real control over it. The Front Yard Manager, our Conscious Awareness, gets so swamped, it can't be *clear* any more, so it gets confused. That's when we get stressed, snappy and short-tempered, when we worry too much or generally think too much.'**

'So that's when the Front Yard Manager has to look at so many boxes that are being delivered into the Conscious Mind, that it can't be present and Now anymore, right? Simply because there's just too much going on?' Lee deducted wisely.

'Exactly, well thought! And **with all that craziness, over time, the Front Yard Manager becomes exhausted or lazy. Either way,**

he stops *trying* to keep order and cleanliness. Eventually, he forgets that such a state, or even the possibility of such a clean, orderly and peaceful state even exists.'

'Shit, we forget that Nowness is even real!' Lee was shocked.

'Right,' Tara said with emphasis. 'To top all of this, while all of that happens, the Front Yard Manager also stops to actively work with the Subconscious Mind all together, simply because he's just too busy running around the Front Yard.

In the end he never goes into the Subconscious Warehouse at all anymore, and finally he forgets what's even in there.'

'And now he just relies on vague memory, the whims of the Fork-lift Truck,' Lee was disturbed at what this meant.

'Yep, and ultimately, all of this continuously removes us further and further from The Guys,' Tara summed up.

Lee gasped audibly. He was beginning to understand how his brain worked. How it worked without him really having any impact on it at all.

'Well, there's more too,' Tara said, smiling innocently, twirling one of her braids.

'Let's have it,' Lee said courageously.

'Obviously the Front Yard Manager is completely overworked, and just as anybody in a high-pressure workplace could, he makes heaps of mistakes. He's got quite a job,' Tara pointed out.

'Gosh, chaos and mistakes, how do we live with all of that? Yep, it certainly looks as if he's bitten off more than he can chew,' Lee was stunned.

'He surely has, but it wasn't his fault. All of that turmoil wasn't in the initial job description, you know? The original plan, since the Front Yard was build, was for nothing to get into the Conscious Mind without the Managers' orders and approval. It's a great concept, but it didn't have a Plan-B build in. You know, a backup plan for when the workload gets out of control, when the Manager can't cope and makes mistakes, when he's on a break, or when he just can't be bothered anymore.'

'That's when the Fork-lift Truck just goes and does whatever it wants to, right? When Thoughts wander of uncontrolled on their own accord?' Lee clarified.

'That's right. But you know, even if the Manager *is* on duty, even when he *does* pay full attention and tries to work attentively, there can still be mistakes.'

'How's that?'

'Simple. To deliberately remember facts, the Manager needs to send the Fork-lift Truck of Memory into the Warehouse to find the right box and bring it out front. But sometimes the Truck can't find the right box. There's just too much chaos to oversee anything, too much junk in the way.'

'I know that one,' Lee drummed his fists against the sides of his head. 'I know that information is in there somewhere, but I'll be damned if I can remember it, if I can get it out,' he groaned.

'That's when your Fork-lift Truck aimlessly drives around the Warehouse with its order to find a specific box. If it can't find the box it's supposed to get, the Truck has a few options. It could come back out and say: "Sorry, no have", or it could bring out a different box. You know, one either related to the subject (which would be common sense), or it could just bring out any random old carton that takes its fancy, just because it looks interesting,' Tara said. 'If it's really cheeky, it could also come back out and just make something up about some imaginary box.

I guess,' Tara shrugged her shoulders, 'it's a bit like surfing the Net. You can get really lost in all the information. Same in the Warehouse. We get distracted, our Thoughts wander off from the subject at hand. We daydream.'

'I think my Truck gets lost all the time. Half the time I really have no idea where some of my silly Thoughts come from,' Lee laughed.

The Unknown Subconscious With A Big Impact

'Yeah, that happens. Silly useless stuff comes up all the time, on the other hand though, has it ever happened to you that you knew something that you didn't know you knew?' Tara grinned at her complicated sentence.

'Yeah, especially over the past few hours actually,' Lee breathed out strongly.

'Ok, then how would you explain that scenario with The Two Minds example?' Tara prompted.

'I guess it would mean that the Manager doesn't know that the information is in the Warehouse, but sends the Truck off anyway, just on the off chance that it could find something,' Lee paused. 'Or maybe the fork lift truck just stumbles across something clever by chance and brings it out. '

'Yeah, but how can that happen?' Tara probed.

Lee thought, his eyes slowly widening. 'Oh, shit, **that means that we stumble across boxes, which we didn't even know existed in the first place! They have been placed into our Subconscious without us noticing**! Shit, Tara, that's scary. **We have stuff within us, which we don't know about. We didn't *invite* it in**,' Lee looked horrified.

'I know, isn't that mad? And believe it or not, those boxes, have an enormous effect on our daily lives, our Thoughts, Feelings and Behaviour. Sometimes we are miserable, sad or unhappy, but we don't really know why. Well, the reason is often in one of those boxes somewhere, stowed away in the Subconscious Warehouse.

These boxes are full with all sorts of stuff that influences us: Society's rules, laws, regulations and expectations, other people's influences or opinions of us, past experiences, Emotions and impressions which have been stored there, negative and positive. Even the ones we think we've dealt with in one way or another, often still lurk on the fringes of our Subconscious, somewhere in the far off corners of our Warehouse. The negative ones seem to be especially persistent.' Lee gasped at the realisation, while Tara continued, '*All* **boxes, known and unknown, make up our personality, our self-image, our Behaviour, Feelings and our reactions. The boxes stored in our warehouse are *who* and *what* we are! So, obviously, some good old spring cleaning wouldn't go amiss**.'

'What do you mean by spring cleaning? How can you spring clean the Mind?' Lee was intrigued.

'Well, sort it out, clean it up. **Check what's there, take out old stuff, put in new stuff. Deliberately**,' Tara said purposefully.

'That sounds great. Got any housewife's tips as to how to spring clean our little friend?' Lee tapped his forehead.

'Sure,' Tara laid back, rolled onto her front and propped herself up on her elbows. '**First we have to find out what's stored in the Subconscious Warehouse. Once we know what's in there, we can start to play with it, change it, re-label and restack boxes for easier access and so on, and of course throw out what we don't want. We do that by learning to actively look at the Subconscious again, by reconnecting with it**,' Tara suggested.

'Yeah, but that doesn't come natural to us, does it? I'd say that most of us haven't actively looked at their Subconscious Mind in a long, long time. And even if, I think, people have conditionings and problems that are rooted so deeply in the abyss of their Subconscious, they have no idea how to get them out. I for a start wouldn't know where to begin. I'd have to learn how to do that right from scratch,' Lee said.

Ok, What Was That Again? A Quick Summary

'**B**efore we go into that though, could you just give me a few minutes?' Lee requested thoughtfully, 'I'd just like to summarise a bit to help me keep on track, ok?'

'Sure,' Tara said, laid comfortably back on the grass and quietly watched Lee scribbling in his little book.

He was shuffling pages back and forth, as his pen busily danced across the pages. All along while they'd been talking, Lee had been writing like a madman. He managed to take notes while listening, thinking, understanding, marvelling, agreeing and talking, all at the same time. His old school teachers would have been proud of him. He looked over all the bits he'd underlined in his notebook, wrote them under one heading and after a while he began slowly, 'Wow, we have talked about so much stuff, it's unbelievable,' he said, and continued to read out his list.

What goes on in our Mind?
*   We have talked about Co-incidences and our current problems with following them.
*   We imagined how great it would be to actively work with Co-incidences, rather than just be at their mercy.
*   We said that The Guys are aware of everything that will happen and that they can guide us.
*   To understand how The Little Guys talk to us, we need to understand how our own brain works.
*   Together with the Radio Warehouse of the Mind, we discussed the function of our Subconscious and our Conscious Mind.
*   The Little Guys talk to us through our Subconscious Mind but we have forgotten how to listen to Their guidance, help and advice.
*   We don't know our Subconscious Mind anymore.
*   We've forgotten what's actually in it.
*   A whole bunch of unknown boxes and conditionings influence the way we behave, think and feel.
*   A lot of our thinking happens involuntarily in the background, without us really being aware of it, or being aware of it, but being unable to stop it, preventing us from being Now.
*   We can't remember how to observe our Mind or take inventories.

'Ten bonus points for attentiveness and summary skills. Yep, that's the gist of it,' Tara sat up, clapped her hands and bowed deeply in admiration.

Lee made a sweeping gesture with his hands and said with a kingly tone to his voice, 'Be at ease, humble servant, be at ease.'

Tara stood up and playfully stepped backwards, continually bowing, mumbling, 'Thank you sir, at ease, thank you sir.'

With a royal belly full of laughter, Lee summoned her to return back to her seat.

Once leaning back against the tree, Tara looked at him, her happiness lighting up her face. 'Seriously though, your lists are great!'

'I'm fairly proud myself, I dare say,' Lee smiled back at her. 'Writing has always helped me think, understand and even order my Thoughts. Somehow, as soon as I write things down I remember them. Photographic memory I guess. Or maybe my Fork-lift Truck is just one of the older models. My memory is hapless unless I write it down,' he grinned.

Tara laughed, 'Well, I'm glad you do remember it long enough to write it down. Actually I'd like to copy all of that at some stage, if it's ok.'

'I'd be truly honoured,' Lee said proudly.

Tara laid back onto the grass again with verbal exhaustion and said, 'I don't think I've monologue-ed like this ever, in my entire life.'

Lee gave her a reassuring pad on the shoulder, 'Don't worry, I mean, I am doing a fair bit of monologue-ing myself, so I think we're even. And anyway, I love talking to you. This is all so amazing and my horizons are truly blown away. So, seriously, please don't stop talking. I could chat to you all day.'

'Careful what you wish for,' Tara said daringly.

'Ok, I wish for more - and now please, thank you, if you don't Mind!' Lee pushed Tara playfully.

4   Working With the Mind

Reconnecting With the Subconscious

'Your wish is my command,' Tara leafed through the notebook until she found the 'Significant-or-not-list', and pointed at the last two items: Listen-to-Them and Talk-to-Them. 'This is what reconnecting with our Subconscious enables us to do,' she said. 'Now, let's make another list just for those two points, shall we? I'm beginning to find your lists really useful to structure my Thoughts, you know?' Tara handed the notebook back to Lee.

Once they finished another bunch of bullet points, they were both as excited as each other. Each point was as fascinating as the next. Lee held up his notebook triumphantly and like an actor reciting a script, read out their handy-work. 'The chocolate inspired Minds agree on the following next steps:

How to prepare ourselves to Listen and talk to The Guys again - Reconnecting with the Subconscious:
- Get to know your Mind.
- Clear out the Subconscious Warehouse (to allow The Guy's messages to pass through again).
- Talk to The Guys.
- Learn how The Little Guys talk to us.
- Listen to Them.
- Ask Them questions, and of course, Listen to the answers.

'Besides the sheer fabulousness of the list, I liked the 'chocolate-inspired' thing,' Tara giggled.

Lee laughed, 'I think with the sheer amount of sweet stuff we gobbled down earlier, my inspiration will last for quite a bit.'

'Well, let's not drop the ball then.'

'Well, I'm waiting,' Lee tapped his foot impatiently.

Know Your Mind - How We Think and Where Our Thoughts Come From

Tara dove straight in, 'The first point on the list actually covers quite a lot of stuff, and it might take a while to talk about, but don't worry, I will get to the other points in time,' Tara re-read the list briefly. 'Now then, point one deals with **how we prepare ourselves to listen to The Guys and Their messages again**. We do that by getting to know our Mind and clearing out the Warehouse.' Tara paused for a moment and then continued, 'Logically, **to notice anything new, we need to know the old first. Unless we know what we've already got in our warehouse, anything new won't stand out**, right? Therefore **we need to get to know all the existing boxes and all of the Thoughts in our Mind inside out. We need to take an *inventory*. Know what's** there. Backwards, upwards, left-to-right, tipsy-turvy, and back again. **Once we know all of that, we can actively begin to work with it and clean it up**.'

'Makes sense. Once everything is nice and clean, anything new that comes in, like messages from The Guys, will stand out a mile,' Lee pointed out.

'Exactly. So, how do we do all that? **First we have to get to know our Mind. We have to understand how it works, *what* and *how* we think, and what *disturbs* the Mind**.

Once we know the *content* of our Mind, we need to learn *how* we think, *where* our Thoughts come from and *how* they build up on one another. By doing that we learn to turn all Background Thoughts into Conscious Thoughts, simply by becoming *aware* of them. This means that nothing in our brain happens anymore without us knowing about it!'

'Wow, what a concept. Oh, that would also means that we could observe the arguments between our Intuition and our Rational Mind, right?' Lee said, while he quickly added some notes to the list he made earlier:

<u>Know your Mind:</u>
* Learn to know our Mind - Subconscious and Conscious.
* Know the *content* of our Thoughts.
* Learn about *how* we think.

Turn all Background Thoughts Into Conscious Thoughts

Looking over his list Lee said, '**Mhh, I've never really thought about knowing the contents of my Thoughts. I guess I just assumed that I know *what* I'm thinking and *when* I'm thinking it. But then again, I know that I have caught myself mulling things over and over in my head for ages, without knowing that I was doing it. So, I'm *not* always consciously aware of the going-on's of my Mind**. Oh shit, Tara,' Something suddenly dawned on Lee, 'the   turning-all-the-background-Thoughts-into-Conscious-Thoughts   bit could be really scary. Man, I really don't know if I *want* to be consciously aware of millions of useless Thoughts, that are flitting around in my head all the time. I think that would be total and utter mental overload. I think I'd probably be quite happy with them staying in the background,' he added as an afterthought.

'I understand that, but don't worry,' Tara reassured him, 'that's what the spring-cleaning is for. After taking the inventory, you can look at the boxes one by one and chuck out any boxes you don't need or want anymore. Like this you can weed all the crap out of the Subconscious Mind. We'll go into more detail a bit later if you want to.'

'That'll be great. Yes please,' Lee's worries dispersed, but he made a mental note to make sure he got more information on that. His eyes flew over the other points on the list. Cool, he would learn about *how* he thought.

Mmm, strange though, **didn't everybody think in the same way? He'd never really considered that there could be options in thinking**. Thinking just happened…, or did it?

'Are you keeping up young man?' Tara interrupted Lee's Thoughts, smiling at him openly.

Lee looked up and returned her warmth, 'Sorry, there was just another mission on planet Bla to be absolved, but I've just landed back in the mother-ship.'

Tara put on a deep husky voice and said, 'Glad to hear it Skywalker, do you need to rest or can you continue on our mission?'

'The martyr in me is set to continue - give it to me!' Lee said, holding one hand against his forehead in exasperation.

Obediently, Tara took the pen and added another few points to the list.

Know your Mind:
- Take an inventory of the Subconscious Warehouse.
- Turn Background Thoughts into Conscious Thoughts by becoming aware of stored boxes.
- Spring clean the Warehouse and clear out unwanted boxes.

5   Meditation, Learn to Observe Your Mind

Hippie-Shit

'**Ok, to do all that getting-to-know-your-Mind business, we need to reach a new level of Consciousness, a different state of Mind, where that is possible. A state of Mind where we can quieten our mental chatter to such an extent that we're able to observe it. A state where the background Thoughts cannot take over**, where we can control the influx of boxes into the Conscious Mind, and where the Front Yard Manager is one hundred percent 'ON'.' Tara winked at Lee, knowing that this was something he was keen to understand. '**This state is reached with Meditation**.'

'Oh great, I knew there had to be a catch. I knew this was going to be Hippy-Shit,' Lee moaned.

'What do you mean, there had to be a catch?' Tara asked surprised.

'Well, all this esoteric stuff *always* leads back to Meditation. Everybody has tried it, but hardly anybody seems to be able to do it properly

- or for that matter, to keep it up long enough to actually get results. I sometimes wonder if it's just a hype.'

Not in the least bit offended Tara asked, 'Before I explain anything, let me ask you first what you think Meditation is?'

Lee thought for a while, but found it difficult to come up with a proper definition, when he suddenly saw a picture in his Mind and decided to just describe it, 'I guess I associate Meditation with certain groups of people: Hippies, people searching for illumination, Buddhists, show-offs and wanna-be's, 'Trendy's,' people with Stress, Yoga fanatics, people wanting to escape from reality, or people wanting to have an excuse to sit in a corner and do nothing. I see somebody sitting in a cave or a special little place with incense and flowers and stuff, eating nettles and raw food, going, "OOOMMM". I see little groups of people telling each other to be Love and Light and the Daughter of the Sun or of the Moon. People calling each other Indian names or things like Silver Star and Ocean Wave.

Lots of people see Meditation as a fad, a phase, entertainment for people with flowers on their pants, they don't take Meditation seriously. Most people regard it as this big special thing for a selected few, seeking enlightenment. Other people even regard it as part of a religion or cult. Others believe that it's this magical tool that transforms their lives. Others again, believe it's only good for relaxation.

Meditation has become such a cliché. Lot's of people say they meditate, but they don't seem to be any wiser, calmer or happier than myself. So I wonder - why bother?' Lee drew breath and then asked self-consciously, 'Does this sound silly?'

Tara smiled, 'Actually, I think that was a pretty good summary of how most people nowadays view Meditation: Hippie-Shit.'

Lee burst out laughing, 'Hippie-Shit? Oh Tara, you're brilliant! That's going to be one of my favourite phrases in the whole wide world,' he laughed so hard, his sides were hurting. He made some pretty passable OMM sounds, handed Tara a daisy, that he'd picked out of the grass, and tried to look all serious, sitting cross-legged.

Tara was hardly able to speak, she had to laugh so loud. She so wished she had a camera with her. This really was one for the books.

In between spurts of laughter she managed to squeal, 'Now, even though I agree that this is the way a lot of people regard Meditation, I don't agree that this is what Meditation actually is all about. I whole-heartedly believe that Meditation needs to be de-mystified.'

'Sounds like a plan. Demystify ahead, sweetie,' Lee said still laughing. 'It won't be easy though, I've been conditioned well.'

'Well, let me try,' Tara said boldly.

'Be my guest,' Lee sat up, leaned against the tree and pulled Tara a little closer to him.

Meditation De-Mystified - It's Just The Beginning

'First, **it's important to understand that Meditation is for** *everybody*, **not just for a special group of people, and that it has benefits for** *everybody*, **not just for people with halos, orange robes or shaved heads. And you can do much more with it than just relax.**'

Lee's head bobbed up and down rhythmically to Tara's statements.

Tara went on, 'Meditation is a means to achieve many things. Many different schools teach many kinds of Meditation with different aims, for fun and for serious stuff. If we know how, **Meditation can be a near-magical tool to help us sort out our lives, solve present and past problems, remove anxiety and anger, and generally become calmer and more balanced people. We can use Meditation to get to know ourselves, the way we behave, think and react. The list is endless. And of course we can use it to enter Nowness and talk to The Guys, to get help and guidance, answers to questions, help with the Co-incidence stuff, and some other little magic tid-bits. And to top it off, it's all really good fun**!'

'Well, sounds a million times better than what I've ever heard about Meditation,' Lee said nonchalantly with a little grin curling the corners of his lips.

'I'm glad. You know, in the Western World, Meditation is most commonly used for deep relaxation, to quieten the Mind, and to 'switch off'. That's all that's being taught or publicised. And yeah, breaking out of the vicious cycle of our Minds going round and round, even if just for a short while, is pure bliss for lots of people. Many use Meditation just for this purpose alone and are incredibly happy with it.

What a lot of people don't know though, is that clearing the Mind, ending the ceaseless chatter of our brain and entering a new realm of silence is just the *foundation* **for much more. It's just the** *beginning*. **They don't realise that they are only doing the very first step on a whole colourful staircase. The potential of Meditation is vast. Once your Mind is relaxed, you can start to use it and** *play* **with it. And that's where the really interesting stuff kicks in.** Even talking to The Guys is only a small part of it. It's up to you how far you want to take it.' Lee's mouth opened slowly with anticipation, but Tara went on unperturbed, '**Meditation is the dare you have to go with, to be able to play with some seriously weird and wonderful far out stuff. And the good news is, that once you know**

what you're doing, you don't even have to do the formal Meditation practice anymore, you don't have to sit in a corner for hours on end, you can fully incorporate it into your everyday life. Anytime. Easy. And before you know it, one door after another will open up for you. It's just the coolest! Yippppeeeeeeeee...,' Tara shrieked, throwing her hands into the air.

'*Now* you're talking,' Lee's face lit up. He was still a little sceptical, but Tara sure made it sound like fun.

'And it *is* so much fun,' Tara read his Mind.

Nowness and Mindfulness

'**B**ack to needing to reach his new State of Mind we just talked about. Well, with Meditation you'll get two for the price of one. **The first is** *total emptiness* **of the Mind,** *Nowness*, **the state where there are no Thoughts at all. The second is the ability to** *observe* **our Mind and everything that's going on inside of it, which comes through a state of Mind I call** *Mindfulness*. **A lot of the Warehouse stuff we've talked about is done with Mindfulness, by observing and thus getting to know the Mind, doing the Inventory etcetera, whereas talking to The Guys and Listening to Them, is mostly done with Nowness - by actually shutting up.**'

'Yep, **we can't Listen when the Mind's talking**,' Lee said wisely.

'Precisely. Both Nowness and Mindfulness are tremendously useful in their own right, each one teaches us heaps and each has huge potential. Let me give you some more details on each one of them.'

Nowness

'**S**o, Meditation is normally used for relaxation and to quiet the Mind,' Tara begun.

'To achieve Nowness,' Lee stated alertly.

'Exactly. Or at least as a state on the way towards it. The constant chatter in our Mind is our Thoughts. And that's exactly what we want to play with in the first steps of Meditation. May I?' Tara pointed at the notebook.

'Sure, go ahead,' Lee said, opened it for her on a blank piece of paper and passed it over.

Tara placed it on her lab to have a more solid base and begun to draw a horizontal line with a dot in the middle of it.

'The bit to the left of the dot is the Past, the dot itself is the Present, and the line to the right of it is the Future, ok?' Lee nodded his head attentively and Tara continued, '**Thinking can only happen when we put our attention onto the Past or the Future. In the Now, Thoughts don't exist.**' Lee looked at Tara blankly. 'Well, try it,' Tara suggested, 'Try to think of anything *not* in the Past or the Future.'

Lee scrunched up his eyebrows, glanced first to the left, then to the right, then back at Tara with a puzzled look of astonishment on his face.

'See? It's impossible,' Tara said. 'You can even try to describe anything you see or feel right now, but you will see that as soon as you start to describe it, even as soon as you open your mouth, the moment is already over. It has become the Past. All thinking can only ever describe something in the Past or in the Future. **Even if we're describing an object in front of us right now, we'll never be able to catch up with describing the present, because each moment, once you grasp it enough to put it into words, is already finished again. Even a split-second ago is already the past.**'

They sat in silence for a couple of minutes when Lee finally said, 'Tara, that's amazing.' He thought a bit longer and then said, 'So, **to stop your Thoughts, you have to find a way to just be in the Present. You have to stop thinking about the past or the future**. That actually makes sense.'

'So it does. With Meditation you can reach a constant experience of the Present, the Here and Now, and Nowness, which is what I call the dot here,' Tara pointed to the drawing. '**With Meditation you are constantly in the Present. That's why it is so incredibly powerful. Your Mind stops, your Thoughts stop, it's where you can begin to Listen**. But lets start at the beginning, with Nowness for Hardcore Relaxation.'

Lee pulled a face. 'Can't we dive straight in? Can't we just go to the exciting stuff?'

'Actually, it's all pretty exciting if you do it properly, so bear with me. Also, every step builds upon the other, and missing out on the foundations would just make the later steps unnecessarily difficult. So it's easier and more fun to start at the beginning, which in this case is Relaxation.'

'Uoh, spoil sport. If I have to...,' Lee gave in quickly.

'Guess you do, sorry,' Tara said even quicker and sat back up in her favourite position.

Lee reminded himself to concentrate as he caught his Mind drifting. It was such a beautiful day and the sunrays that passed through the leaves of the big oak tree played with Tara's hair, making it sparkle like the rest of her. "Talk about Mental overload," he grinned to himself. "This is certainly a good exercise in that Mindfulness thingy," he noted. Listen, Listen, hair, Listen, skirt, legs, Listen, Listen. It was hilarious to observe his Mind, especially when the subject was so enchanting.

Little did he know that Tara was feeling the same way.

Meditate to Relax - The First Step On A Staircase of Fascinating Uses

'Whenever I talk about Meditation for Relaxation, people often say things like: "I don't need to Meditate to relax, I walk or swim or run, cook, listen to music or whatever", and I agree. **I agree that different people can relax in many different ways, some being a lot more sociable or enjoyable than sitting quietly in a corner.**'

'Yep, I'm one of the listening-to-stupendously-loud-music-and-dance-around-the-room, or go-to-the-park-for-a-walk-kind-of-Meditation-for-Relaxation man,' Lee smirked. 'Works for me every time.'

Tara grinned, imagining Lee doing just that, 'Yeah, that seems to work for loads of people and it's a wonderful way, **but a well practised Meditation can relax you on a much deeper level than any of the other activities ever could.**'

'Care to elaborate?' Lee asked with a business-like voice.

'Sure. **During a well-practiced Meditation, all there is, is You. Pure, empty, relaxed, calm, content, blissed-out. It is a feeling that is nearly indescribable. You feel as if you've had a good night's sleep in just a few minutes. You feel rejuvenated. Your Mind is strong, clear, powerful, fresh and sharp. You feel fantastic, physically and mentally.**'

'Mmm, sounds kind of useful. May I introduce: Meditation - the Power Nap,' Lee thought out loud.

Tara grinned, 'That and more. Much more. **You see, taking a break from our everyday Thoughts, even just for a short while, gives us the distance we need to be able to look at our lives and Thoughts more objectively.** It works wonders for problems, worries and things we've gone over and over in our Mind. During a Meditation, answers to our questions and confusion come as if all by themselves. Effortlessly. No tedious thinking necessary.'

As she spoke, Tara noticed that the last few signs of Doubt were finally taking their leave from Lee's face. She went on happily, 'And that's just the beginning. **Sometimes only taking a few minutes everyday for yourself, without any external entertainment like TV, books, music, food or other sensory impressions for that matter, can create a magic feeling. It's time just for you. Time where you're not doing anything, *anything* at all, or better, where you *don't have* to do anything at all...**'

'Mmm, interesting. I never really thought about it that way. **I always thought that I'm not doing anything when I'm watching TV, but of course, I *am* doing *something*. I'm watching the telly.** That's a good point actually. Mmm, **I think I hardly ever do *'nothing,'* no-thing at all.** There's always something to do like read the paper, make dinner, bills, books, meet somebody, plan something, prepare something, think about something, anything. I guess I'm always busy one way or another. Ha, even if I'm sleeping I'm usually dreaming. Sneaky,' Lee grinned.

'Yes, it's funny, isn't it? We always take time to do lots of stuff, but we hardly ever take time to spend just with ourselves. There's always something outside of us, drawing our attention away from *Us*.'

'That's true,' Lee agreed. '**But I think that a lot of people wouldn't know what to do with themselves, if they just sat, not doing anything. They'd just be tremendously bored, and some might even find it scary**,' Lee said half-jokingly.

'Actually, **that's more true than you think and that's why it's important to know that Meditation is so much more than just sitting in a corner and not doing anything. In fact, it's truly Mind-boggling and even exciting**.'

'Like how?'

'Well, how often have you driven yourself crazy thinking about a problem at work or at home? How often have you nearly gone insane with worry or trying to solve a problem or decide something? How many times could you not go to sleep because your Mind was still far too awake to even think of sleep? **How many times have you dreamed how wonderful it would be to just switch all that jabber off? Stop your worries, problems, work, kids bills, partner, fears, jealousy, anger, status, pretensions, insecurities, self-doubt, Ego...**'

'Ok, you've got a point.'

'I know,' Tara said matter-of-factly. '**All of that stuff stops when you are 100 percent in the Now. In that space, none of these things exist - *as thinking cannot exist in the Now*.**'

'Yeah, right, and as soon as you stop your Meditation, all those things just smack you right back in the face again,' Lee blurted out.

'Exactly!'

'What?' Lee was taken aback. Did he just happen upon a flaw in Tara's flow?

'Well, if you don't follow Tara's special recipe, that is,' Tara winked. Lee grinned. 'Actually, you just hit an important note, a misconception which I feel people should know about. The point is that **Meditation should not be used as a tool to escape the real world. That would be nice, but what's the point if the world catches up with you again as soon as you stop**?' Lee gestured agreement. 'And **that's why I'm talking about a *different* kind of Meditation. A Meditation, which can be used to *actively* change the way the outside world affects us, and how problems affect us.** I'll talk about that a bit later if you like, once we're done with the basics,' Tara added.

Lee made a quick note into his book, to make sure it was covered later: "Dealing with problems in the with Meditation, with Nowness". "What about getting over ex-girlfriends?" his little friend, the right-shouldered devil, gently whispered into his ear. "Later," Lee thought, "I will get to that." The little devil put his fork aside and sat down - he was content to wait, knowing he wouldn't give up. It did notice though, somewhere in the back of it's devilish little head, that Lee didn't Listen to him as much as he used to.

'Anyway,' Tara said, and the little devil on Lee's shoulder puffed up in smoke, '**during Meditation and thus in Nowness, thinking and memories don't exist, therefore your Warehouse is thoroughly clean. Nowness is pretty much as close as we'll get to The Guys. It's a straight connection, because in the Now, we become One with the Universe again**.'

'Whoa, big words,' Lee said.

'So they are, and they'll get bigger,' Tara said with an auspicious look on her face. '**Once you reach the state of Nowness, you can tap into all the Cosmic Knowledge you want to. All you need to do is ask questions**.'

'And you get answers?'

'Of course! That's the point of asking, isn't it?' Tara said smiling vivaciously.

'What can you ask about? Give us a little taster?' Lee asked excitedly.

'You can ask about all sorts of stuff, whatever you need - help, guidance, answers, you can even get a little more adventurous,' Tara paused.

'Yes?' Lee probed curiously.

'**I have known people who have taken the asking-thing to the extreme**. They've tried asking for *everything*. For solutions to complicated physics questions, the well-being of friends and family member, directions, train times. You can ask for anything you like.' Lee's jaw threatened to drop again. 'You can ask to see people through Astral Travel, know things with Psychometry, where you can tell things about people by holding an object of theirs, or you can ask for help to heal people. Basically you can do whatever you want to. **This is the extreme end of the scale and many people will never get into this, not because they can't, but simply because they're not interested in trying or persistent enough in practicing.** As I said before, the long and short of it is that Meditation for the sole purpose of relaxation and quietening the Mind is just the tip of the iceberg. There is so much more, it's ridiculous.'

'Yeah, sounds like it. Wow, Tara, I had no idea.'

'I know, most people don't. It's a shame really, because it can be so much fun.'

After a second of contemplation Lee asked, 'Mmm, I always thought that stuff like Psychometry and Astral Travel was just for, well, what's the word for it... - special people?'

'Nicely put,' Tara grinned.

Lee shrugged self-consciously, 'Thanks. But you're telling me that all you need to do is be in Nowness?'

'That's right. Let me give you an example from when I heard about Psychometry. I was intrigued and asked a friend who was reading a book about it how it's supposed to be done. My friend explained that he put an Intent out there by asking for certain information from the object, then he would meditate while holding the object in his hand and he'd Listen to what came up. I tried it, and it worked.'

'It did? Just like that?'

'Yeah, I thought it was pretty cool myself. I held a friend's headscarf, asked for information, went into deep Meditation, reached Nowness, and just Listened. After holding the scarf for a short while, there it was, like a little film. Totally mad.'

'You got your answers in a film?' Lee asked in disbelief.

'Yes. I literally saw pictures in my Mind's eye.'

'Now that's impressive.'

'Impressive, but piss-easy,' Tara said 'and it got even better. When I told the owner of the scarf what I had seen, he couldn't believe that I had perfectly described a scene from his childhood - the scene, his feelings, his Emotions, the lot. Having done that I had immediate reassurance that what I had seen was real and not just my head making things up.'

'Very important. Otherwise you can make yourself believe all sorts of things,' Lee appreciated to be always reminded how down to earth Tara was.

'Precisely. My friend was surprised though, because he'd been the one reading the book. He really wanted to learn it but still had difficulty with it. Without being bigheaded, I told him that I wasn't surprised - the book was like 300 pages long, you know something like: '1001 Easy Steps To Psychometry'. So funny that people never see the contradiction in titles like that.' Lee laughed at Tara's cynicism. 'The book was ever so complicated, and the way I saw it, it didn't explain one of the most important things, that Meditation in this case meant Nowness.'

'No Thought-clutter in your Mind.'

'*No* clutter, *no* Thoughts, not even *expectations* of what you're trying to do, like: I-want-to-receive-stuff-about-this-necklace or I-wonder-what-messages-I'll-get. These are Thoughts too.'

'Oh wow, we're talking *really no* Thoughts.'

'Right. To be in Nowness, you need to be *totally* empty. Your Warehouse needs to be absolutely clean, so that the messages won't get obstructed by heaps of boxes. Only then can the information come through with ease. But don't worry,' Tara anticipated an objection, 'with practice you'll be able to tell messages from your Thoughts anyway, and you don't have to be in the perfect Now anymore. But at the beginning, Nowness is pretty much a prerequisite.'

'Good to know. So, what did your mate say to all of that?'

'Well, after I explained things he went home and tried it again. After a few days, once he got the hang of it, it worked for him too. We talked about it quite a lot afterwards and during one of our conversations we tried to find out why he still took a few days to do it, whereas I had done it immediately. We realised that when he was clearing his Mind he didn't notice one thing. His Mind was clear, all but for one thing - the *trying*. He was *trying* to get a message.'

'And *trying* is a Thought too?' Lee ventured.

'Precisely. Trying-Thoughts filled his head the whole time and stopped him from being empty, in Nowness and on *receiving*. Once he managed to stop those Thoughts and entered Nowness, it all happened as if by itself.'

'That's amazing. And you get the messages like a film?'

'I did, yes, but people get messages in different ways. You might see something in your Mind's Eye like a film, you might just know something, or you might get words, individual pictures, sounds and feelings. There really is no right or wrong. But when you get it, it's obvious. It's like something you've never experienced before. It's pretty cool.'

'This is fascinating, what else can you do with Nowness?' Lee moved a little closer, he wanted all the details.

Tara waved her hand to convey the enormity of that question. 'I know of people that know the meanings of Tarot cards, simply by meditating on them. You ask a question, go into Nowness and automatically tap into the Cosmic Knowledge Bank. No need to read the book that comes with the cards.

I could go on forever, but you know as you already said, when you get down to it most of the esoteric things work the same way. You put the question or the Intent out, reach Nowness, and then shut up and Listen. No matter how complicated people like to make it in all those fantastic books and courses, this simple way has always worked for me and my friends. And be assured, we are all just ordinary people,' Tara added, just to make sure Lee didn't think again that this was only for 'special people'.

'Mmm, you just mentioned **Astral Travel**? Just to quickly clarify Tara, do you really mean the stuff where you leave your Body to go and visit other places?'

'Yep, that's it. **All I had to do was meditate and concentrate on the friend that I wanted to visit, went deeper and deeper into my Meditation until I reached Nowness, and then watched what came up. And, it worked. I saw what my friend was doing and where. I even called him afterwards to double-check.'**

'You didn't,' Lee said laughing. 'You called him?'

'Well, **of course I did. Otherwise it would be cheating, wouldn't it? How would I've know that what I saw was real if I hadn't checked**?' Tara said.

Lee laughed even louder. Before he could comment, Tara already reeled off the next example.

'Meditation also allows you to get involved with a lot of the Energy Healing arts. Again, it's all much easier than many people make it out to be. All you do is put out the Intention to heal or help a person, then, if you can, you touch them or lay your hands on them. If you can't, you just keep their image in your Minds Eye, and then you enter Nowness. As you reach Nowness, you become one with the Cosmos again and the Cosmic energies flow through your Body into the other person. Hey presto, Energy Healing.'

'And you can do that?'

'Sure. It's not just for Jesus, it's for everyone!'

'Wow. I'm impressed.'

Tara shook her head vehemently, 'There really isn't anything to be impressed about. I'm not special, anybody can do this, trust me. Simply Be Now and do it.'

'Phew, I'm not so sure about that, Tara.'

'Well, there are lots of people out there doing it and they're teaching it to anybody who wants to learn it.'

'And it's that easy?' Lee asked still a little sceptical.

'Once you can reach Nowness it is, yes. **Once you can reach Nowness, *anything* becomes possible, even if you haven't read lots of books or done a lot of courses.** Many people will tell you that it's much more complicated than that, but that's business. Oops, sorry, I mean of course that's *their* business,' Tara added sarcastically. 'Of course, as with everything, there are tricks of the trade to become better at what you do, and of course, everybody does things their own little way, but no matter how complicated they care to make it, if you read between the lines,' Tara's voice trailed off as she jotted down a few points into Lee's book.

Esoteric things often boil down to:
- Knowing how to do it - and I have given you the basics.
- *Trusting* yourself that you *can* do it.
- Putting out an Intent, asking for it and focussing your attention to the task at hand.
- Then stop thinking and Meditate to reach Nowness.
- Shut up and Listen. Keep yourself open in Nowness and your Mind uncluttered - no Thoughts. No trying or expectations either.

'My Mind is truly boggled,' Lee said once Tara was finished. 'Man, I can't believe it's all really that easy.'

'Strangely most people don't. It's so weird, we live in a society where we're always led to believe that everything has to be difficult. But it's not! Of course, unless you try, you'll never know. Chicken and egg.'

'Good point. I don't know about anybody else, but my appetite is sufficiently whetted. I will try, believe you me.'

'Great,' Tara said enthusiastically. 'You won't regret it.'

'Excellent stuff, lady!' Lee slapped his notebook shut.

How Long Does It Take? - Tell Me, Tell Me

'**T**hinking about it, I need to put you straight on something,' something important had just popped into Tara's Mind.

'Oh yeah? Is the bubble going to burst now?' Lee held up his hands in a self-protective gesture.

'No, don't worry. All **I wanted to stress one more time, is that all this stuff is easy *once* you're able to reach Nowness, and you're able to *maintain* Nowness. If your Mind is still cluttered,**

you won't *hear* anything or only with great difficulty, and to reach a level of Meditation that deep requires a bit of practice.'

'Check. Got that, ma'am,' Lee saluted, touching his temple with his right hand.

'Good. Sorry, I just want to make sure that you don't go and try this stuff tonight and then get pissed off or disillusioned if it might not work,' Tara said caringly.

'Don't worry,' Lee said, dismissing Tara's comment light-heartedly.

Suddenly Lee rummaged through his jeans pockets, eventually fished out his mailbox keys, just to announce in a mysterious voice that his neighbour Ted had touched them and that he was now going to use his instantaneously acquired Psychometry skills to find out what Ted was doing. He closed his eyes, clutched his keys tightly to his chest and shouted, 'OOOOMMMM.' After a second he opened his eyes again, frowned angrily, threw the keys into the grass and complained loudly.

'Damn it, I knew it wouldn't work,' he crossed his arms, frowned and looked incredibly pissed off. What a spectacle.

'Oh stop it,' Tara screamed with laughter, as she ripped out grass and threw it at him. She was hardly able to look at Lee, because every time she did, he threatened to pick up the keys again. It was one of those moments, when hysterics take over and there's just nothing that can be done about it.

Still laughing, Lee said, 'But seriously, you already know me too well. I would have probably tried it tonight, you know?'

Tara smiled knowingly. 'Don't let me put you off though, by all means *do* try it!' Tara said encouragingly. 'Weirder things have happened, and maybe you're a natural. Just be kind on yourself, and don't give up if it doesn't work right away, that's all I'm saying.'

'Fair enough,' Lee agreed. 'Actually, come to think of it, **how do I know if I am good enough at Meditation to start with the more 'far out' things we've talked about**?'

'**It's not really a matter of being *good enough*. It's more a matter of *Emptiness*,**' Tara pointed out. 'It's pretty obvious though. I mean, if you're meditating and your Mind is cluttered and full with Thoughts, you're obviously not there yet, right? But if your Mind is clear, empty, sharp and relaxed, at least for a little while, then you're in Nowness and you can start playing. With a little practice and observation, you'll realise pretty soon which state your head needs to be in to be able to Listen. As a bottom line, the clearer your head, the easier and more effective the Listening becomes.

At the end of the day nobody can be in your head, nobody can tell you when you're there. You need to find out when you're

ready for yourself and play around with it until you get results. I'll explain more about that later. **But so far, if you follow the basic guidelines, and keep asking yourself after your practice if there were still any last remaining thoughts left, it's easy, and you'll figure out for yourself what you need to do in your head,**' Tara promised.

Without delay Lee made a little reminder note into his notebook and then asked, 'I guess how long it takes to reach Emptiness and thus Nowness, will depend on each individual person anyway, won't it?'

'Right. Some people need to practice more than others. Some do it immediately, some take weeks, some months. **Most people expect instantaneous results. We think that sitting in a corner and stopping to think, should be the easiest thing we ever did. When that expectation isn't fulfilled, when it doesn't happen instantaneously, people give up without really having given it a chance. We don't understand that Meditation is a** *skill* **that needs to be** *learned*. **We can't just sit in a corner and expect to meditate right away. We need to practice it, like everything else,**' Tara said.

'True. **We would never expect to play guitar overnight.** I have experienced that myself the hard way. I know that to become half-way decent, it takes years of practice. Sure we can strum around a bit, but to really be able to *play*? That takes a while.'

'Exactly, and it's the same with Meditation. **Meditation is something that has to be done rather than just talked about.** But man, get started and it'll blow your Mind!'

'Ha, just by looking at your face when you say that, I get a pretty good idea that it's worth sticking around to find out more.'

'Oh boy, it is,' Tara said unreservedly.

Lee pushed himself off the stem of the oak and lay down on his belly, his chin on his hands.

Meditation - Incentive Summary

Tara laid down on her side, propped up her right elbow and cradled her head in her hand. 'Ok, that was just a very quick, hardly-do-it-justice-run-down of what the potential of Meditation is. But still, how is all that for incentive?'

'Getting there,' Lee grinned. 'Actually Tara, I think it's notebook time again. I made lots of notes while we were talking, could we just go over them for a sec?'

'Sure, go ahead.'

Lee put the little book in front of them and read out the list:

Meditation is good for:
- Deep relaxation of Body, Mind and Spirit - true chilling.
- Pure, empty, relaxed, calm, content, blissed-out, fresh, sharp, clear, powerful, feel fantastic, physically and mentally.
- Meditation gives us the distance to be able to look at problems or worries more objectively - answers and solutions come more easily.
- In the Now, Thoughts don't exist.
- Meditation can *actively* change the way the outside world affects us.
- Meditation can change the way we look at problems in our lives.
- Our Being opens and we become more receptive to messages from The Guys.
- We can talk to The Guys and also Listen to Them.
- We can get help and guidance for our lives and answers to lots of questions.
- We get to sort out our Warehouses.
- We can tap into all the Cosmic knowledge, the Collective Consciousness.
- We get to play with the Cosmic Toys out there. Including far out stuff such as Healing and Psychometry.
- Through Nowness we become One with the Universe again.
- We generally become more chilled and relaxed.

'I think this is a pretty conclusive list,' Tara said appreciatively. It was reassuring to see that her Thoughts still made sense in somebody else's notes. 'Some of the topics obviously need more detail, but we'll fill in the gaps later if you want to. At least for now you've had a taste of what's to come,' Tara promised temptingly, 'if you want more that is.'

Lee didn't have to answer. The look on his face revealed all.

6   Meditation Pitfalls

Instructions, Techniques and More Incentives

'**Y**ou know what puzzles me with all of this?' Lee wondered out loud. 'If it's all so cool, how come that so few people actually practice Meditation? No matter how enthusiastic people are at the beginning, no matter how much they believe that it's good for them, most people don't keep it up. People rarely manage to integrate it into their everyday lives. I mean I'm talking from personal experience. I'd really love to start meditating again and I want to talk to The Guys, but…' Lee's voice trailed of.

'But what?' Tara asked carefully.

'But Meditation has been a thorn in my side for a while,' Lee said grudgingly.

'Why?' Tara probed.

'Well, a couple of years ago, a lot of my father's friends started Meditation for stress-busting purposes. They didn't stop talking about it for ages and I had become curious. I tried a whole bunch of different classes, but never quite got into it properly,' Lee finished.

'The age-old problem,' Tara said knowingly. 'You're not the first and you sure won't be the last.' Lee looked relieved. 'Tell me more about *why* you felt it wasn't for you?'

'I guess it all seemed like too much effort to get involved in.'

'What do you mean?' Tara was curious to hear Lee's story, giggling to herself **how funny it was that people always found that doing *nothing* was too much effort**!

'I just found it impossible to find classes and teachers that I liked and felt comfortable with. Teachers that I could relate to or was prepared to pay the money they asked, they were really quite expensive,' Lee grumbled, remembering his frustration. 'On top of that, there were so many different kinds of Meditation around, I would have needed a degree to get my head around all of them, just to try and figure out what they were all about in the first place,' Lee rolled his eyes. 'I remember being so spoilt for choice and drowned in information that I didn't understand, that I simply didn't know where to start. There was visualisation, concentration on physical sensations, individual Body part relaxation, imagining nice feelings, sceneries, colours, concentrating on stuff with lots of Indian names that I still don't know what they mean, I could imagine to be an animal, have guided Meditations, send love to the world, concentrate on Chakras, Kundalini or various energies, or I could just breathe. The sheer range of techniques, practices and schools of Thought made it impossible for me to make a choice, I was totally dumb struck.

I initially thought that Meditation would be straightforward, it's to stop thinking, right? Well, it didn't seem to be that simple.' Tara was listening attentively as he went on. 'It would have been a total hit-and-miss scenario to try and find something suitable. I mean, what if I would have kept picking the daft ones? No wonder people get fed up and stop. Actually, considering my experience, I'm not surprised that people don't even start to begin with. There's only so much time, effort and money we are prepared or able to put into things to try them out, especially with the little time we've got spare.' A tiny smile began to creep into the corner of Tara's mouth as

Lee continued without drawing breath, 'I was lucky that I had a bit of tenacity and in the end found a *method* that I was interested in, but then I hit another wall. It was really difficult to find a decent, down to earth teacher, giving instructions that I could connect with. Most classes I went to were so ridiculously fluffy, I couldn't even take them seriously. It was all 'love and light,' or they were all about this Guru or that Guru, some were so whacked-out I just wanted to scream. Some classes were utterly airy-fairy, without any foundation. But to be honest? Most of them were either so dry and boring that I could have fallen asleep after the first five minutes or they were so full of theory and information, that they were far to complicated to ever get the hang of it. Seriously, some Meditation techniques? I had to concentrate so hard to remember what to do next, that I never got to relax,' Lee grinned. 'I mean, what's the story with that?' Lee finally relaxed his vocal cords.

'Wow, you really *did* try, didn't you?'

'Eh, yeah. Sorry, I guess I needed to vent a little,' he shrugged his shoulders self-consciously.

'Boy, it sounds like it,' Tara had begun to giggle.

'Needless to say, I stopped.'

'Yeah, I'm not surprised,' by now Tara laughed loudly. 'And you know what? I agree with everything you've said.'

'You do?'

'Of course I do. You pretty much described exactly what a lot of people go though when they would like to start to meditate, including my own initial experience. Luckily, most people only have some of those problems though, not *all* of them,' Tara shook her head, still laughing. 'Obviously there are also the lucky ones that find the perfect teacher right away, but I really do agree. You've described common problems.'

'Oh thank God for that,' Lee let out a sigh of relief.

'You know what? I'd even take it further.'

'You're kidding, worse than that?' Lee asked with disbelief.

'Yes. **I've also had lots of problems with the content and the quality of the teachings themselves**.'

'Really?'

'You better believe it. **My experience was that many teachers got too hung up on the methods and the process, rather than focussing on the goal.** It was all rituals and not much practical use. And to top that, **few schools or teachers taught or even *knew* about the potential beyond relaxation**. So there was always limited incentive right from the start. **I also found no teachings on how to measure intangible progress and results, what the practice pitfalls could be or even how to deal with our continuous problem to practice every day.** Lots of people have these problems, but nobody seems to teach about them. **I always found it odd, that for the most individual thing on earth, people's Minds, there doesn't seem to be any *tailored, personalised* instructions available.**'

'I know, that's exactly what I thought too. Isn't that weird?'

'Yep, agreed. Additionally, I found that all the techniques were often made so much more complicated than they had to be. **All people need to kick off and to continue is to be excited about the goal, encouraged to practice, be able to measure and notice their progress and of course, to have interesting results. The instructions have to be practical and easy to follow and understand, so that *anybody* can follow them *anywhere, in all of life's situations.*** If they are not - people will stop. It's not rocket science.'

'I so agree. I mean, what's the point in teaching something if people can't integrate it into their everyday lives? If it's complicated or difficult or takes up too much time, only the most determined will continue. The rest will drop out,' Lee suddenly grinned. 'It's funny that you agree with me. I thought you'd start preaching how I got it all wrong and that I just hadn't met the right teachers and that your Guru really is the best.'

'Ha, you don't know me then,' Tara said and smiled at Lee's wonderful honesty. 'Well, first, there are obviously great teachers out there with many satisfied students, and it works for them. With regards to the Guru? I don't have one. I just listen to everyone and then make up my own thing. I believe in learning, guidance and teachings, but not in following other people's ideas regardless. That works for me, but hey, something else might work for somebody else. And now my disciple, now you may kiss my feet,' Tara leant back and wriggled her bare feet in front of Lee's face.

Lee grabbed them, pulled them to his side and started tickling them. Tara squealed, trying to free herself, but Lee held on. 'Full marks for trying, you had me tempted there for a second,' he grinned.

'I give up, I give up! You can be your own guru,' Tara yelped.

'Now that's better,' Lee gave her feet one last tickle and tenderly placed them back on the ground.

'Do *you* want to be *my* guru?' Tara laughed now that she had her feet back.

'Watch it, young lady,' Lee threatened to grab one of her feet again.

Tara pulled them away quickly and protectively wrapped her arms around her knees. 'You could be the Guru of Tickles. What a great name that would be.'

'Mmm, Guru of Tickles, I could get used to that name,' Lee joked, leant forward, grabbed Tara by the waist and began to tickle her again. His quick movement had caught her off-guard and with her arms still around her knees she was like a little ball, unable to defend herself.

They giggled and laughed, until Tara finally begged for mercy, 'Oh Guru of Tickles, be kind to me and let me catch my breath.'

Lee let go of her, poised himself and put on a self-important facial expression.

'Oh boy, you do make me laugh,' Tara's eyes were filled with tears of laughter.

'It's mutual sweetie. It's mutual,' Lee said, his gaze steadily holding hers.

Are We There Yet? - Measuring Intangible Progress and Results

This time it was Lee who went back to business first. 'You said something interesting earlier,' Lee remembered. 'You mentioned that you didn't find any teachings on how to measure intangible results? Now that would be a good idea.'

'Yeah. It's such an obvious one, but no information was to be found when I looked for it!

Let's assume that you were lucky enough to find a great Meditation that you like. It's supposed to change your life, you're excited and you start meditating. **You get really into it, and then you realise that *progress* and *results* seem to be kind of wishy-washy and your progress-orientated Western Mind can't figure out if you're getting any better or not.'**

Lee laughed, 'That's so true. I never knew if I was getting anywhere.'

'Same here. **The reason why people don't know, is because it's all going on in our heads and therefore the progress and the results are intangible.** Nobody can be in our brain and consequently nobody can tell us: "Ok, you're there now", or: "you've progressed well with that bit", or: "You're about *this* good now...",' Tara held her hands about a meter apart. Lee chuckled. Tara continued boldly, 'It's funny really how everybody, after having meditated for a month or so, asks the same typical questions. We look at our physical self and ask, 'Ok, how has this changed me? Has my life changed yet? Am I happier yet? Are all my problems sorted yet? Am I enlightened yet?' Well, it doesn't always work that way. And that creates a problem for most of us.'

'Yeah, I agree. In our world hands-on proof and results are ever so important. We are reluctant to continue or even begin anything if we can't expect visible results. What's the point if we can't see the progress pretty much straight away, right?

I remember when my father's friends discussed their progress, they all felt uncertain about the real impact Meditation had on their lives. **It felt that even though they had noticed a change within themselves, they were still reluctant to attribute it to their Meditation practice.** "Maybe it was the stomach pills after all," my dad had said, "or the new car... or was it the Meditation?" **They always felt that they needed some kind of physical evidence, which they never got.**'

'That is why we need to know that the results and the Signs of internal change are different from other external skills that we learn,' Tara emphasised. 'This is where semantics are important. **The results and Signs of progress and the impact on our lives are *intangible*, but that doesn't mean that they are *non-existent*. It's just that when we start out, they are so subtle, that we often overlook them. But if we know *what* to pay attention to, *what* to look out for, then we'll realise that actually, we *do* get pretty obvious results all along.**

Let me give you an example. I compare Meditation with learning to play an instrument, such as the guitar, like we mentioned earlier. When we want to learn how to play the guitar, we're usually not put-off by a few weird people that play the same instrument, right? There's always somebody who we can admire, somebody to aspire to.'

'Yeah, of course, nobody would *not* learn the guitar just because the only thing the local busker ever plays is freaking 'Knocking on Heaven's Door',' Lee laughed. 'We'd just ignore him and aim for Hendrix or Clapton instead.'

'Exactly. We know *why* we want to learn the guitar. We can listen to some great music and say, that this is exactly how we would like to play. The incentive is obvious, we don't have to take anybody's word for it. Once we begin to practice, the results and the progress we make, are obvious too. They are tangible and practical. We can hear what we're doing straight away and if we practice enough, we can obviously see ourselves improving. Hence we get an *immediate sense of achievement*. Well, that's the theory at least.'

Lee laughed, 'Like from being truly crap, to being able to play Ba Ba Black Sheep.'

'And then Mozart.'

'Yeah right, or not...,' Lee waved his hands in a dismissive gesture and reminisced, 'I remember the first chord I ever learned. Man, I was completely besotted with it, running through the house, strumming this one silly chord over and over, standing in front of the mirror pretending to be Hendrix. I tell you, I was God's gift.'

Tara imagined Lee in leather clobber, with sunglasses and a microphone, torturing the strings of an electric guitar. She laughed. But then again, tight leather pants… She dismissed the Thought with a grin.

'And of course, what's more, with those skills, once you've fine tuned them a little, you can actually *be* somebody, you have something to *show* for. You can *measure* your skills with others. With Meditation you don't get any of these physically obvious things, but you get many other satisfying results and signs of progress,' Tara said, still light-heartedly battling with the vision of Lee's behind in leather trousers.

'And they are?'

'Easy. **If you learn about all the *different stages* of Meditation, you'll be 100 percent aware of the progress you're making, of the *changes* within yourself and the effect Meditation has on your life. You just need to know what to watch for, what to expect, what happens to you and your Mind during each stage, what can be achieved, what the pitfalls and the problems are that you could encounter, and of course you need to know about the aims and results that come with each stage.**

The key is that we have to take responsibility for our own progress. We need to stop doubting ourselves and get some confidence in our own judgement. I'll explain all that stuff in as much detail as you want to, including all the tips and tricks, when we start to talk about the individual steps on that fabulous staircase of Meditation. Ha, and once you get started, you can even wear your leathers,' Tara grinned and blushed a little.

'Yeah, and do the 'OMMM' on the electric,' Lee laid down an animated sit-down air-guitar performance.

No Buts - Just Do It

Suddenly a small shadow crossed over Lee's face, a frown ever so slight. Tara noticed it and asked tentatively, 'What's up?'

'We have talked about all the issues I had with Mediation, except one.'

'Oh yeah? Which one?' Tara asked without hesitation.

'It's the actually-getting-around-to-doing-it. The incorporating-the-practice-into-our-daily-lives thingy. Nobody I met ever addressed *that* point.

Tara laughed, 'Oh, I so know what you mean.'

Lee gave her a thankful look. It felt comforting that Tara had the same experiences and the same problems he'd had.

'I love this bit,' Tara smiled, '**it's absolutely hilarious to hear the excuses people come up with, as to why they can't find** *five* **free minutes a day to meditate. They all say that they really want to do it - but**. "*But*, I have to watch this telly programme first. *But* I have to clean my shoes first", - which we would usually never do, "***But* I have to do the dishes or look out the window or put that spoon back into the drawer, or call someone - and maybe, if I think about everything else just a little bit longer, maybe that dreaded Meditation thing will go away**".'

Lee laughed out loud, recognising himself in Tara's words. 'Oh boy, it's scary that you know me so well.'

'Ha, I don't know anybody, I just know myself,' Tara smiled. 'Believe you me, I've been there, and you know what? The only way of actually doing it is to…,' Lee's ears perked up, here came the magic answer he'd been waiting for. Tara repeated for special effect, '**The only way of actually doing it is to…** *just do it*!'

Lee's ears dropped. 'Oh no, that's not what I wanted to hear.'

'Well, what did you expect?' Tara teased.

'Oh bugger,' Lee said unhappily.

'There is no other way. *We* have to *just do it*, all by ourselves! No but-s or sooner-s or later-s. Now and You!'

'I guess you're right,' Lee squirmed, 'there is no easy option, is there? And,' Lee paused for a second, 'I guess either we understand the benefits and feel that they are worthwhile and decide to actually get on with it, or we decide the benefits are not for us, and we don't. But I can see that **there's no point to do it half-heartedly. That would be a waste of time right from the start**.'

'That's my boy. We really have to stop pussyfooting around Meditation. People always come up with these silly excuses: "I know I should, and I know it's good for me, but I can't", or: "I don't have the time". You know, it's all rubbish. **If you** *really want* **something, and that's** *anything* **in life for that matter, not just Meditation - bloody well go and do it and stop whinging! Stop blaming the situation, the process, the world, yourself or others. Go and make it happe!** If we would only get as far as off-our-backsides more often, a lot more would get done, and we'd moan much less too.'

Lee grinned. It was hilarious how we excused ourselves not to have *five* minutes! Tara was right, she had described him to a 'T'. He always came up with an entire library full of yes-but-s. And the funniest thing was, that he believed those excuses. He knew. He'd done it. How come he hadn't really *consciously* realised this before she mentioned it? Had he just not admitted it to himself, or had he not even noticed? Whatever, Lee shrugged his shoulders, it was true.

He suddenly burst out laughing, 'Oh my God Tara, I have a 'But' problem,' he laughed even louder, 'One 'T' though, mind you. Man, what a realisation. I really *do* have a 'But' problem. I can't believe I never noticed that before.'

Tara felt her own enthusiasm rising up in her, 'You can't believe it, and neither could I. I've been there. And you know what? Once you begin to meditate and you start to get to know your brain more, these little insights will come to you all the time. You're suddenly in a forest where you can see *every single* tree, and you wonder how you could ever not have seen them.'

'I don't know how I would cope with realising that I've been blind all my life,' Lee said. 'Not only not seeing the trees, but not even knowing that the freaking things even existed!'

'Sweetie, I'm sorry to say, the But-thing is only the beginning,' Tara whispered with an apologetic tone in her voice. '**I mean, think about what it says about us if we can't even make five minutes for our own well-being**?'

Lee stroked his chin thoughtfully, 'Mmm, yeah, it's pathetic really. Man, what's five minutes? I could easily find five minutes while the kettle boils or the Pot-Noodle soaks! But strangely I still always think, that I don't have the time. This is ridiculous!' he shook his head in disbelief.

'It is, isn't it? The trick with *everything* we need to do, but somehow always find something better to do, is to *just do it*. **There are two tips that help to beat the 'But'.**'

'Let's have the tips to beat the 'but', baby,' Lee could hardly contain himself.

They both grinned at each other as Tara continued, 'The first one is to never even *begin* to think *if* we want to do it or not. As soon as we start to give ourselves an option to get out, we *will* take it, it's as simple as that! As soon as we think: "umm... I should be meditating, but maybe, I could do it later," we will *not* do it. **As soon as we start to *think about it? We* will not do it**.'

'The Mind busily rationalises things away again, it doesn't want to be redundant,' Lee remembered.

'That's it. The solution to that is as simple as it comes: *Physically move*!'

'What?'

'The solution is to *Physically* **get up, stand up, sit down, do whatever you need to do to get yourself into a meditative situation or position. *Then just start*. No thinking involved. And then you JUST DO IT!** It takes some practice, but it works a treat. **The**

more you train yourself, the more all of this becomes an automatic reaction. The whole thing just bypasses your brain. You just do it.'

'Oh my God, Tara, this is ingenious. **The Physical Body movement counteracts the Rational Mind. By the time the Mind has kicked in, we're already moving, getting ready and before we know it, we've started.** I could use this for anything, not just Meditation: "Umm, window cleaning, yes but - no but! Just get up and do it!"' he got up and pretended to clean a window. 'And hey presto - clean windows. It'll work with everything, bringing out the rubbish, doing bills, cooking - and all that, despite the utterly stupid programme on TV that we'd usually just have to see. Just physically get up, get the window cloth and start!'

'Exactly. Like this it's nearly as if the things that you dread doing, do themselves. **You see, it's our brain that stop us from doing things! If we would use the five minutes we normally spend thinking about excuses *why* we *don't* have the time to meditate, or *why* we can't be asked to sit down, and would just *do* it instead, then stuff would actually get done!** Tadaaaa!' Tara leant forward and gave Lee a quick excited hug.

'I think we should do pep talks for multinational companies, you know!' Lee chuckled as he grabbed his notebook to scribble some more notes.

The Secret to Doing It, is to:
*   Decide that something is worth doing, that we really *want* to do it and that we actually *want* to *stick* with it - there's no point in doing it half-heartedly. It's either 'Yes' or 'No.'
*   Then, Just Do It.
*   Never begin to think if you want to do it or not.
*   Don't think about it.
*   Don't contemplate it.
*   Don't find excuses.
*   Just Do It!
*   Physically move. Stand up, sit down, move and start.
*   No But-s.
*   The physical Body movement counteracts the Rational Mind.
*   After a while it becomes an automatic reaction.
*   Use the five minutes you'd normally spend thinking about excuses to just *do* it instead.

It's All About Your Own Timing

'**B**ack to Meditation itself,' Lee said, 'let's say I'm actually *just doing it.* I'm standing in my living room, or better I've just sat down, and I have decided that *now's* the time to meditate and I'm ready to start. Now, how long do I need to sit for? Do I really only do it for five minutes?'

'Well, that depends who you listen to,' Tara said. 'Some teachers say that we should go and meditate for an hour.'

'One whole hour? Are you serious?' Lee butted in. 'Whose got time for that?'

'Well, exactly,' Tara said reassuringly. 'Sitting for an hour at the beginning works for some people, but it discourages most.'

Lee slapped his forehead in relief, 'Thank God for that. I nearly just packed up and left. Man, even just sitting still for a hour is nearly impossible for me, let alone meditating while I'm at it.'

'That's probably true for most or us. In my opinion, we should take it as easy on ourselves as possible, at least until we're well and truly ready to experiment. Anyway, it's not a competition, is it? **Start with five minutes or so and slowly increase it. But *make sure to do it Everyday*!** Do five minutes everyday, until you feel that you're getting more comfortable with the practice and the sitting itself. That can take anything from a few days to a few weeks. **When you feel like moving on, you can start to experiment with increasing the time.** 10, 15, 20, 25, 30 minutes and more. The aim is for your sitting to be long enough for you to experience the benefits of Meditation, a calm Mind or Nowness, or on the other hand to practice the exercises that I will talk about later if you want to.

Try not to extend the length of the sitting too much too early. That'll just drive you mad and frustrate you. Rather try and do what actually feels right, comfortable and manageable. Push yourself, but don't overdo it. That way you become more confident and experienced the gentle way.'

'Sounds great,' Lee agreed and then asked persistently, '**Is there an ideal length of Meditation one should aim for though**?'

'I could give you a time, but to be honest, **it just depends on how much time you personally need to still your Mind. If you only ever manage to calm your Mind after 14 minutes, it'll be a shame to stop after 15, just because I told you 15 minutes is the ideal time.**'

'Makes sense. If I find that I need 15 minutes to chill out, I should meditate longer, maybe 20 minutes.'

'Exactly. **On the other hand, if you can just turn a switch and you're there after just two minutes, then the total Meditation time could potentially be much less**.'

'Got it.'

'It's up to each person to find out what the best time is for them. We need to observe ourselves for a while, observe how long the individual stages which I'll explain take to complete, and find our own optimum-Meditation-time by ourselves. Instead of using a time somebody else told us, we can begin with that and then just tweak it now and then to fit our needs. **It's better to do it this way, it's a tailor-made approach, rather than a bog standard one out of a text book which might not suit us**.'

'Sounds great. **Everybody's head is different, so it only makes sense that it might take different lengths of time to quieten the thinking machine**.'

'Exactly. **Another consideration, which should play a role in selecting the duration for our practice, is our lifestyle**. You asked earlier: "Whose got time for that?"' Tara imitated Lee's outraged tone of voice from earlier. **'If we only have 10 or 20 minutes everyday, then** *that's* **what we can play with, end of story, no matter what anybody else tells us**.'

'You've got the right attitude,' Lee nodded appreciatively. 'I like that. I can work with that. And, even if some people tell me it's not enough, it doesn't matter. **It's better to do that, than not do it at all**.'

'Yeah. **It's useful though, once we figured out what timing is good for us, to try and be as consistent with the durations as possible and to not keep changing it every day**.'

'Why is that?' Lee asked.

'Because it agitates our inner clock. If we change the time for every Meditation, our inner clock gets confused and fidgety. If we stick with the same time for a while though, our inner clock gets used to it. We internally learn how long 15 minutes is or ten or whatever. And we can sit peacefully without our inner clock worrying if the alarm clock batteries might have run out.'

Lee laughed at Tara's antics, shaking her watch, holding it to her ear, all while keeping her eyes tightly shut.

'It's important to know that every day is different too,' Tara went on. **'On some days it's easy to meditate and on some days it's not so easy. Some days it might take five minutes to be deeply in Nowness and on other days we might still be struggling after 15 minutes. It happens**. Some days the Fork-lift Truck is just busier than on others. **It depends on our mood, how much we've got**

on our Mind, how relaxed we are physically, how comfortable we are in our environment and so on and so on. **No matter how easy or difficult it is, try to stick to your time and don't get upset or angry if it's a bit more control on one day than on another.** There's no point in doing that. **All it does, is spoil the fun and make it more difficult.**'

'Yeah, **because then, on top of all the other Thoughts, we'd also have to fight the Thoughts that tell us that Meditation is too difficult and that we're useless,**' Lee laughed.

'Well put. Therefore, instead of doing all of that, just accept it as a day where Meditation is not so easy and then stop thinking about it and go back to Meditating instead! As simple as that. **Just keep on going as best as you can.**'

'I think I can do that,' Lee said contentedly. 'What about you Tara, how long do you meditate for?'

'It depends. I started out with five minutes a day, twice a day, and then I increased it to 10, then 15, then 20. I found that for myself, 20 minutes twice a day was very effective and still manageable in my sometimes very busy life. If I would have tried to do more, I would have put myself under unnecessary pressure and stress. Sometimes, when I felt that I needed longer and time would allow it, I sat longer.

'When I worked, I usually got up 20 minutes early and did it just after my bathroom activities. In the evenings I did another 20 minutes straight after coming home. Doing that used to chill me out no end. All the stress of the day would just fall off me. I even started to put my feet into a bowl of warm salty water. It felt like my own personal SPA for 20 minutes everyday after work. It's truly wonderful. After a while you begin to *crave* it. It's just the first few days where you're battling with your Mind.

I made sure that I meditated everyday, twice a day, and I made sure that I never did less than 20 minutes. On the weekends I usually did 30 minutes. If for whatever reason I could only do it once a day or only 15 minutes, not because I didn't fancy it, or I couldn't be asked, but because I genuinely couldn't, tough, I just did what was possible. As you said, doing a little is better than doing nothing. I stuck with that routine for a long time. Now that I have a bit more time in my life, I find that a half-an-hour is the perfect time. That gives me 10 minutes to start to chill out and calm my Mind, another 10 minutes to get into it, then another 10 minutes of deep Meditation or exercises. I don't time myself, but that seems to be the way it turns out.'

Lee had listened closely and summarised, '**Basically the gist of it is to be realistic, to be disciplined but not anal, to set achievable goals and stick to those.**'

'Precisely. It's also good to know that **it might be a little uncomfortable at the beginning when you first sit and are-just-in-your-head, but you'll get into it, trust me. You'll soon begin to feel how every minute gives you balance, strength and power**. And anyway, once you begin to observe what's going on in your head, the practice itself becomes so interesting, enlightening and really good fun, that you'll probably want to increase the time anyway. And once you can reach Nowness,' Tara added as an afterthought, '**in Nowness, time doesn't exist anyway, no future, no present, no Thoughts. When our Mind is clear and empty like that, we loose all concept of time anyhow**. Sometimes it feels as if you've just started and the alarm clock already rings. When you're in a really deep Meditation, twenty minutes are over in no time.'

'You really like this stuff, don't you?' Lee said, feeling Tara's commitment.

'Well, yeah. Meditation isn't a chore for me anymore. I love doing it. It gives me so much it's impossible to describe.

And you know what's best?' Tara's face shone brightly, '**With practice you don't even need to formally sit down anymore! You can just do it on the bus or the train or wherever, even while cooking**. Actually, if you just do it all the time, your Mind would be so clear, that The Guys could talk to you whenever They wanted to,' Tara looked dreamily. '**Once you get to that stage, Meditation has become a part of your life**, just as brushing your teeth or eating. The more you get into it, the more you meditate and the more you're in Nowness, the more the benefits become part of your everyday life. Your whole life kind of becomes one long Meditation.'

Lee was flabbergasted. 'Whoa, hang on right there! What - you mean you meditate all day?'

'Yes and no. It's more that **we begin to slip Meditation into our daily routines**. Whenever you have a spare minute with nothing to do, you go through some exercises. In a queue, while mowing the lawn or doing the dishes. **With practice, you can meditate anywhere, anytime. Like this you can experience that calm, peaceful and balanced feeling all day long!'**

'I'll take your word on that one,' Lee said, taken aback, flopping himself back against the strong bark of the tree behind him.

'**I understand that this might sound a bit much right now, but wait until I tell you about the exercises and wait till you've**

had your first conversation with The Guys. You'll change your Mind so quickly you'll never want to stop,' Tara said confidently.

'Can't wait.' Lee was excited, yet a little doubtful. He knew that to get his real proof, he would have to try it for himself. He actually had to *do it.*

Tara suddenly grinned broadly, 'Oh man, I just remembered a funny story for you about how I used Meditation to help me in a real life scenario. When it got hectic at my previous job, I used to nip to the ladies' room, sit on the toilet lid and meditate for a few minutes to chill-out. There's nothing better for training your concentration than trying to ignore the toilet flushing next door,' she laughed at the memory.

'Or trying not to freak out your fellow workers by shouting OOOMMM at them from behind the cubicle door,' Lee said laughing loudly.

'I wonder if that would be a sack-able offence,' Tara wondered, one finger on her lip, her eyebrows raised.

'Your Honour, this young lady disturbed the inhabitants of cubicle D to G with loud nasal sounds... Man, Tara, did you really do that?' Lee grinned.

'Of course I did. Well, not the OOOMMM bit, but yeah, I did sit on the toilet lid to meditate. Did wonders; I tell you. I would emerge, bright, sparkly and ready for anything.'

Lee put on a high-pitched voice and screeched, 'Catch me, I'm the spring, fluffy and irresistible,' he flapped his arms like a fairy.

Tara laughed out loud, 'Yeah, something like that.'

'I bet your colleagues wondered what on earth you were doing in the ladies' room, when they saw you came out of the door with your eyes half-closed and a little smile on your face,' Lee put on a very, very chilled look, narrowed his eyes to little slits and grinned.

'Just out of curiosity, what was the longest you ever meditated?' he asked.

'I think my longest sitting Meditation was three hours.' Tara noticed that Lee was taken aback and therefore added, 'You know, it's actually really good fun to experiment with marathon sessions. Set the alarm clock for a silly time, like an hour or two. Even though I'd recommend to stick with regular lengths for your usual Meditation time, it's fun to challenge yourself from time to time, you know, experiment and experience what Meditation can do for you. Your Mind might go crazy for two and a half hours, but the last half hour might be absolute bliss. You can also learn a lot about your Mind by observing it going crazy... Longer sittings are not necessarily better than shorter ones, but longer sessions can give you *different* kinds of experiences and some of them are extremely cool,' she winked at Lee slyly.

'Tara, you must be the first person I've heard use the word Meditation and cool in the same breath.'

'That's because I know that it is! I tell you, the first full hour Meditation I did absolutely blew my Mind. But, until you do it, you have no idea what your Mind is capable of, and it'll all just be pretty words.'

Lee longed to experience these things himself, 'I think I would have my *standard* time that I'd do all the time, and then my occasional *play time* where I can experiment.'

'Play time. I like that. That's a good way of doing it,' Tara smiled.

'Hang on, let me just do justice to my role as scribe-for-the-day,' Lee said and began to write.

Common Difficulties with Meditation:
- The perception we have of the kind of people that meditate.
- Lack of *incentive* - because we don't understand the real potential.
- Lack of easy, straight forward *instruction*.
- The practice we chose doesn't suit us.
- Difficulties with measuring Intangible progress and results - incomplete instructions.
- Lacking confidence in our own judgement about improvement.
- Until we *experience* it, we will never *really* know what it's all about and how we can personally benefit.
- Lack of *persistence* - it *does* take practice, like learning any other skill.
- Being too hard on ourselves, pushing ourselves too far too soon, and getting frustrated rather than having fun!

The Timing Thingy:
- Start with five minutes - Every Day.
- Slowly increase the time, till you find your *own* optimum-duration due to your abilities.
- Find the time that suits yourself, your progress and your lifestyle, rather than pressuring yourself with unrealistic goals and getting frustrated when you can't keep them - or even not enjoying the meditation because you feel rushed!
- Be persistent but not anal.
- Experiment with longer durations, just for the hell of it.
- Incorporate Meditation into daily routines and eventually into your whole life.
- Joyfully look for the fun, the cool and the far-out stuff to come along.

When Lee was done, he handed Tara the little book. Tara read over the first list, 'Great summary. If we're aware of these pitfalls *before* we even start, then it's easy to avoid them in our practice. It makes it easier to kick-off and then *stick* with the practice. And the second list helps to make our lives much, much easier.'

7   Meditation the Gateway To A New Consciousness - and Lots of Fun Stuff

The Warehouse and Meditation

'I think it's time to talk about how to actually do this Meditation thing, what do you think?' Lee asked.

'Agreed. I think it would be useful to begin the how-to bit by explaining what actually happens in our warehouses when we meditate.'

'Good plan,' Lee approved.

'Great. Let's go back to the Warehouse example then. When we meditate, the Fork-lift Truck is on holiday, it has left the premises, and nothing is being brought out to the Front Yard anymore. The Front Yard Manager takes a little time to sort out the Front Yard, to get things in order and cleared up, and can then sit down and enjoy the emptiness. That's Nowness, when the Conscious Mind is silent, when there's no activity in the Front Yard at all. That's **the first step, quieting the Mind.**

By learning how to do that, we begin to clean and empty out the Warehouse for the duration of the not-thinking. And with practice we can permanently transform it into a tidier, more peaceful place.'

'Sounds wonderful,' Lee said longingly.

'It is. **Once the Mind is quiet or at least much slower, it becomes more useable. Now you can begin to learn how to send the Front Yard Manager himself into the Warehouse to have a look around, observe what's stored in it and do a good inventory.'**

'Which means we get to consciously have a look at the Subconscious Warehouse, the stuff that influences our lives in the background,' Lee added.

'Exactly. While the Manager is doing the inventory, he continuously takes notes of what he sees and finds. Like that, he gets an overview of all the things that are stashed in the Warehouse: Thoughts, Emotions, feelings, Conditionings and so-on. Once he's done the inventory, he have a *choice* about to what to do with all the boxes. He can choose to examine them and get to know more about them, he can store them for later, or he can just acknowledge their existence. He can even do a bit of spring-cleaning, you know, make order, tidy up a bit, chuck out some boxes, repack or label them.

It becomes easier with time. **At the beginning when you start to meditate, there are millions of boxes piled up everywhere, without any order whatsoever. It's all a total jumble. As you can imagine, it will still be a little tricky to walk around the warehouse without stumbling, and taking an inventory will seem like an impossible task. But with practice, the Manager begins to oversee the chaos and starts to make sense of it. After a little while, he will know all the boxes inside and out. He will know which boxes are important for our lives and which ones aren't. If they're not, he chucks them out, and the others he neatly stows away for future use**. End of story.'

Be Comfy

'**I** understand the theory about what's going on in our warehouse when we meditate,' Lee said, 'but **what I still don't know is how I actually make the Manager do all that stuff**. So, I am sitting in my living room, rearing to go. What do I do?' Lee sat cross-legged again, just about to sneak in a little 'OOOOMMM,' when Tara already began to explain.

'When we begin to meditate, **we want to have as few distractions as possible**. Therefore, try and find a quiet space that will naturally help you to chill and calm down. **In quietness, we only have our Mind to battle with and that's already hard enough. Once we've got some experience and confidence, we can throw ourselves into the big world of Mind-distractions and meditate anywhere, anytime.** But until then, having people talking around us, having the TV on or having other tempting things around us is distracting and makes Meditation unnecessarily difficult. From my own experience, different people find different environments relaxing. Believe it or not, I've had some of my best Meditation in Trance music clubs. Sitting in a corner of the dance floor, people everywhere, the beat thumping. It helps to keep me focussed.' Tara added, 'Strangely, in an environment like that, I'm off with the fairies in no time.'

'Or rather off with The Guys,' Lee grinned. 'I can so imagine you doing that. Sitting in a club meditating. Only you,' he laughed.

'Well, you called it play-time. And you're right, that's exactly what it can be! It is loads of fun to play with all sorts of weird and different things. **Try to meditate at different times, with friends, together with animals or plants, in different places, in woods, by lakes, at parties, in holy places, at the beach, on the bus, whatever. They**

all feel different and they all give you different experiences. It's fascinating how different your Body and your Mind feel when you subject yourself to varying external influences. It'll make you very aware of how other people and places affect us all day long without us even realising. It's good to become conscious of that.'

'Yeah, I can see *that!*'

'Anyway, back to the beginning. All the Hippy stuff like soft music, candles and incense is optional. I like it sometimes, but not all the time. When I have the time and inclination, I do the lot, just because it's nice. But you don't need it. As I said, before you throw yourself into hardcore on-the-bus stuff, it's nice to practice in a more mellow environment. Just sit down comfortably, in a quiet room, on a chair or cross-legged on the floor. Whichever position you choose to sit in, make sure that you can maintain it for the duration of the Meditation and that you can keep your spine straight. When you sit cross-legged make sure your legs are comfortable.'

'So that I don't have to have my legs amputated due to blood loss after the first session, right?' Lee finished Tara's sentence, making an awkward stretching movement with his legs.

'Yeah, because that would be a shame,' Tara said compassionately.

'You said that I'd have to keep my spine straight, why is that important?' Lee asked.

'There's a whole long answer about energies flowing up your spine and stuff, but the basics are that Meditation is simply easier and more effective when we can breathe well. If we sit slumped over like a sack of potatoes, our lungs are squashed, our pipes are bent, and then breathing is more effort than it has to be. If we sit nice and straight, breathing is effortless and more natural. Try it.'

Lee slouched and tried to fill his lungs with air. He didn't get very far and it was quite a bit of effort. Then he sat up and breathed in deeply.

'Phew, like a breath of fresh air. Yep, I see what you mean.'

'Sitting with a straight back is also much easier on the spine.'

'Like this?' Lee straightened his spine stiffly as if he'd swallowed a stick.

'Not quite. May I?' Tara motioned at his back.

'Sure,' Lee said and moved a little closer so that Tara could reach better.

Tara moved her hands over Lee's spine and his front, pushed his hips a little forward, his lower back out just a tad, straightened his upper back a little and pushed his whole upper Body slightly backward, until the natural curve of his spine shone through.

'There. Now you're straight.'

'That doesn't feel very straight,' Lee looked down on himself.

'I know. You're just not used to it. To me it always felt as if I was leaning backwards a bit. But I was straight.'

'I see,' Lee said doubtfully.

'Do you want to know an easy way to help you find your natural straight spine position?' Tara offered.

'Of course.'

'Follow me. First breathe in *fully* into your belly by pushing it out, then pull the breath all the way up into your chest, don't strain though, just do it naturally.'

Lee complied and his spine automatically straightened.

'Now relax the muscles but hold onto that position.' **Tara stood up and gently pressed both of her hands onto Lee's head, 'Now imagine that I'm an elephant sitting on your head.** Try and feel my weight in your coccyx, the spot where our tail used to be if you're into Darwin. Feel the pressure of my hand travel all the way from your head, through your spine, right down into the floor.

The only way you can carry all that weight comfortably and effortlessly is, if your spine is perfectly aligned. If your spine is bend forward, backwards or sideways at any place, if I would increase the weight, your back would break at the spot where it's bent. Try it,' Tara pressed a little harder.

Lee bent forwards, 'Whoa, yep, that's effort, I'm using all the muscles I have to push you up.' He bent backwards and sideways with the same result. He then closed his eyes and worked his way up his spine from his butt, trying to feel a strong connection between the pressure on his head and the ground beneath him, without any kinks or bends.

'There, that's it,' Tara suddenly said. 'Oops, it's gone again. Did you feel that?'

'I think so. Just for a moment, it felt strong and effortless to carry your weight on my head. Let me try again.' He shook his spine a little to loosen up and tried again. 'There it is,' he said confidently. He managed to retain the position a little longer this time. 'I know what you mean now by being *perfectly aligned*. Mad that you can feel that as well.'

'I can feel the floor through your head when you're properly aligned. It's solid. When you're not aligned, you wobble,' Tara pointed out. 'You can play with this standing too. You know, **I pay attention to this alignment all day long. I constantly check my posture. If more people would just know and practice this simple thing, most of the Western World's back problems would disappear, you know the famous 'computer-backs'?'**

'Yep. I think I'm still doing it, right?' Lee still felt the connection.

Tara glanced at Lee briefly. She knew how the energies of a person felt and looked when they were connected and physically aligned. They had this extra little glow to them, an extra bit of sparkle, an extra strength and internal power that came from freely opening up the energy channels in the Body rather than bending and squashing them.

'So you are,' she said proudly. 'There you go, that's your natural spine position, where all bones are resting on one another, no muscles are used, no strain, no effort. I find this posture is usually easiest to maintain when you lean back ever so slightly, but it might be different for you, maybe try it though. You can also have a friend help you from time to time. If you feel tension anywhere then it's not right, so do it again. Play with it. Sometimes it might help to put a rolled up sweater or something under your bum to lift your spine a bit.' She looked around and found a thick branch and made Lee sit on it. 'Not as comfortable, but it's good enough to show what I mean.'

Lee sat on it and crossed his legs again. 'Ah, yes, I can feel that. That's good, that relieves my knees a bit too,' Lee said gladly.

'Good. Oh, if you get fed up with the pushing sensation on your head, **you can also imagine somebody pulling your head upwards by your hair**.'

'Charming,' Lee grabbed a bushel of his hair and yanked his head upwards.

'A bit more lovingly I would have imagined,' Tara laughed.

'Ah I see,' Lee *felt* in his Body what Tara tried to tell him, 'like this it feels a little as if my spine is pulled upwards and my butt is lifted of the ground ever so slightly. Yeah, I can feel my back straightening that way too. Cool. I get it.'

'Excellent! So, remember this when you meditate. It really helps to pay attention to your spinal alignment throughout your Meditation. It makes the whole experience much more comfortable. As always, it can take a bit of practice. At the beginning you might feel a little uncomfortable because you're not accustomed to it, but you'll get used to the new posture in no time, and your back will begin to feel better all the time, even when you're not meditating. You can help yourself by also checking your posture throughout the day. Over time this new straight back will become your default way of Being.

As always, be aware but not anal. If at some stage you can only meditate hanging upside down from a trapeze, bent to one side, well, so be it.'

Lee was already looking for a branch above him to hang from, when Tara caught his intention and cuffed him playfully in the side.

'Oh, no, don't even think about it. I don't want *that* on my conscience,' she laughed and was rewarded with a big smile.

What to Do? Meditation Steps and More

'So, now you're sitting with your back straight. You might like to close your eyes to help shut out any visual distractions.'

'Why is it so important to have the eyes closed?' Lee asked.

'Cutting out visual impressions helps enormously to shut out the outside world. Did you know that we get more sensory stimulation from our vision, than from any other sense, and with that the most distraction?'

'Mmh, but what about the Buddha figures? Most of those are shown with their eyes downcast and just ever so slightly open,' Lee interjected.

'You're right, but they're *professionals*!' Tara laughed. 'You can try that if you like, but it's usually more difficult, especially at the beginning.'

'Fair enough.'

'Shall I give you a list of the main steps, so that you'll have some kind of idea of what's coming?'

'That'll be great.'

'It might look like a long list, but don't worry, you'll tick off the points before you know it, and you don't have to do them all in the same sitting either. And anyway, once you get the hang of it and experience the sheer fabulousness of it, you'll be so curious you will want to explore more and more anyway.'

'No worries. Now amaze me,' Lee opened his notebook and waved his pen with anticipation.

They stuck their heads together and after a few minutes, Lee read out the completed list:

What to Do?

Meditation - Nowness
0 - The world is your oyster.
1 - The breath thing - Physical Relaxation.
2 - Continuous concentration or sharpening the Mind.
3 - Catching yourself out - Learn to consciously interrupt your Thoughts - Mental relaxation.

Mindfulness
4 - Mindfulness.
5 - Meditate during daily activities and with other people etc.
6 - Time for laughing - observe your Thoughts, retracing and contemplation.
7 - Observe your feelings and reactions.
8 - Notice how you talk to yourself.
9 -Through all of this, get to know *how* you think.

Then we can begin to talk about the new Dimensions for Meditation:
10 - Nowness through Mindfulness.
11 - Deal with Big Thoughts.
12 - Deal with Emotions, Behaviour, etc.

And then afterwards, you'll have a good basis to understand how to:
13 - Listen to your Intuition again, your Subconscious, your Soul.
14 - Listen to the Little Guys.
15 - Talk to Them.
16 – Know the world is an even *bigger* oyster.
17 - Play with the Oyster and have some fun.

'Entertainment gurus eat your heart out, I don't think you can get much better than that,' Tara announced proudly.

'I can see now why most people are only on the first step of the Meditation staircase that you mentioned. I had no idea. Man, looking at this list, relaxation is only *the first three* steps out of *seventeen*, if you count the oysters that is.'

'That's it, Einstein.'

'Albert, my dear, please, you can call me Albert,' Lee offered modestly.

Tara giggled, 'Ok then Albert, people in the Western World, usually don't know about the other stages and they usually stop after the first three. It's such a bummer, because the other steps open our Minds so much more. We make such unbelievable discoveries about ourselves, other people, our environment and even bigger, the Universe, it's breath taking!'

'Go on,' Lee probed.

'By doing these steps, we *really* get to see what's going on inside of us. With our Mind, Thoughts, Emotions, Behaviour and Reactions. We get a better insight into life in general, our dealings with other people and many other things. And of course, we get to communicate with The Guys.'

'Just by sitting quietly in a corner,' Lee said still slightly baffled.

'Just by sitting quietly in a corner,' Tara confirmed. '**For the beginning it's best to stick with the order on the list to familiarise yourself with the individual steps. It's particularly good to get the three basic steps down pretty well, so that you have a solid foundation. After that, once you know what you're doing and you've got a feel for how the steps build up on one another and complement one another, you can do whatever you want. You can only practice a few steps, you can swap and change them around and truly make the process your own. Take it easy on yourself. Do it slowly and keep in Mind that if you** don't feel comfortable with an advanced step, don't worry, it doesn't mean that you can't do it, it just means that you might have to go back and practice the previous step a bit longer.'

'Check,' Lee ticked off the air in front of him with his index finger, 'Satisfactory answer as always. Please continue.'

'No matter what the goal of any Meditation is, relaxation is the first step that has to be mastered. It normally begins with physical relaxation, and for that, sitting down and closing our eyes is usually a good start, that will have an immediate *physically* calming effect on us.

During step two and three we learn to slow down our Thoughts and eventually stop them, which is the goal for *mental* relaxation. Once we've done step three, we are meditating and should be able to reach Nowness. All the other steps are about how to use Meditation to it's full potential, how to play with Nowness and with our newly acquired calm, clear and sharpened Mind.'

'Can't wait,' Lee said with excitement.

<u>The Breathing Thing - Physical Relaxation</u>

'Let's go through the steps. Actually, why don't we call that list the *'What to do?'* list? That will make it easier to refer to it in the future.'

'Great idea.'

'Cool. Now, in the first few stages of Meditation, we learn how to relax, to stop thinking and how to reach that state of Nowness we talked about earlier. The first comment people make after their initial five minutes of Meditation, is usually about how bizarre it is, that learning how *not* to think seems at least as difficult as learning how to think in the first place.'

'Oh yes, I know about that one!' Lee remembered.

'Luckily, there are some tips and tricks to help make that first experience easier on ourselves. **A really important thing to understand before we start to meditate, is that we will *not* stop thinking by just *deciding* to do so. You can't just decide to *think* your way out of Thoughts. You can't *think* Nowness. No matter how much you want to switch off the Mind, the *wanting* itself is still *thinking*! Your Mind will want to go on thinking about not wanting to think.** If you catch my drift.'

'Caught. Sounds like the Psychometry dude that kept *trying*,' Lee connected the dots.

Tara nodded, then suddenly giggled, 'Do you want to know how people look like five minutes into their first Meditation? It's a little bit like this,' Tara pulled her hair, hit her temples with her fits and shouted, 'Stop you silly Thoughts! Stop I say! Silence, concentrate, be quiet, oh no, there they are again. Hush, will you stop? Yep, you there, Thought, get out, get ooouuuuttttt!!!' she composed herself again and looked dead straight at Lee, whose jaw had dropped visibly. 'This was a small demonstration of how many people torture themselves,' Tara giggled. 'And as you can see, it's not fun.'

'You don't say,' Lee looked amused.

'Well, there's obviously a better way of doing this.'

'I sure hope so, otherwise I won't have any hair left by the end of it,' Lee protectively covered his head with his hands.

Tara picked up Lee's notebook and looked through it until she found the page where they had **drawn the Nowness-dot with the Past and the Future lines** earlier. She pointed at the dot and said, 'Remember? **We said that the dot is Nowness**?'

'The bit where we don't think about the past or the future?'

'Yeah, that's it. **To meditate, we can just concentrate on that dot**.'

'Uhoh, that sounds hardcore,' Lee shook his head.

'For some that works a treat and that's all they need to do - hey, presto! They're in Nowness. They're meditating.'

'But for most of us that's difficult, right?' Lee asked hopefully.

'Yep.' Lee let out a sigh of relief. 'Try it though, it might work wonders. **For a lot of people it's easier to *divert* our attention to something *different* than our everyday nagging Thoughts.** A very common method is to choose an *object* to focus our concentration on. They are usually called Meditation Objects, and they are usually either a Physical object or a Mental one. A physical Meditation Object could be the flame of a candle, flowers, pictures, crystals etcetera.'

'Hippy-Shit,' Lee sneaked in quietly.

'True, but despite that, it works for lots of people. I personally find that focusing on a physical object is too distracting, mainly because I have to practice with my eyes open. When I stare at an object, besides the fact that I find the constant blinking irritating, sooner or later, my vision becomes blurred and as a result, so does my Mind. Slowly, Thoughts start to creep in, as my eyes start to become aware of things on the peripheries of my vision, and as I notice things, I inevitably start thinking. I begin to describe the objects with my Thoughts or go through some nice little word associations related to it, and hey presto, I'm at the weekend party or the dinner with my friends. But, that said, I know of people that love it, so play with it, see if it

127

works for you. Due to the possible distractions though with Physical Meditation Objects, I prefer *Mental* ones instead.'

'What, like Visualisation?' Lee asked.

'Yes, for example. You can visualise all sorts of things. A black dot, a white light, a warm summer's day, a nature scene, a meadow, a waterfall, a ping pong ball, anything. For me personally, visualisation of scenes doesn't work too well either. When I imagine these wonderful, idyllic pictures, the person that pissed me off for the last week usually sits right underneath my beautiful tree or next to me on the back of my fabulously visualised eagle. But hey, maybe it's just me,' Tara grinned.

'Ha, that's so funny,' Lee laughed.

'Yeah, but not if you're trying to get away from them!' she shook her head, smiling. '**Some people like to visualize that they are a bird or a wild horse. If you can stick with it, all these basic visualisation fulfil the purpose of giving you a nice blissful experience and if that's what you're after, then that's great. But the thing is that with these methods, you'll never get past that particular experience. They will not get you to Nowness. Concentrating on delightful, peaceful and pleasurable images might enable you to relax, and divert your Thoughts to the scene at hand, but it doesn't enable you to *stop* thinking**.'

'Ah, I see. We are using our imagination to create the picture, and that of course, is thinking.'

'Exactly. Naturally Visualisation and Mental objects have their place, and for specific objectives they can be very useful or even just fun. I mean imagine, you could visualise anything you'd want!'

Tara had that wickedly playful sparkle in her eyes again that Lee loved so much. Lee grinned as she carried on.

'**The long and short of it is that once you start, you'll see pretty quickly that the later stages of Meditation are not possible when you're trying to think of a waterfall at the same time**.'

'Oh yeah, I remember, the main prerequisite for getting back in touch with our Subconscious and therefore The Guys, is to totally clear the Mind.'

'Exactly, **therefore there are a couple of methods that are more suitable than visualisation. Some people find it easy to just meditate or concentrate on Emptiness. I mean the *feeling* of Emptiness, rather than the *Thought* of it. Not Emptiness as the opposite of full, where empty is something undesirable, but rather Emptiness of the Mind, Emptiness of craziness and hectic. It's focus on Peace, 'Letting Go', clarity even purity. It's like concentrating on the space between the Thoughts**.'

'Wow, that sounds amazing.'

'It is, and it's the way I meditate mostly now, but as it's a little like concentrating on the dot,' Tara pointed at the drawing again, '**a lot of people find it difficult at the beginning to muster up such concentration, therefore there's a way to keep the wandering Mind focussed in a different way**.'

'Great, let's have it.'

'This way is all about **using your Breath as the Meditation Object**,' Tara began. 'You see, **if your Mind is kept still and rigid, because it's not used to it, it will desperately try to wander. But if you focus your Mind on a moving object like your breath, that tendency to wander is being pre-empted, as your attention is already moving. Therefore, following the in-and-out movement of your breath aids your concentration**.'

'Ah yes, that would make sense,' Lee nodded. 'And on top of that, concentrating on our Breath allows us to close our eyes and we don't need any Thoughts to stay with it as we can just observe it. It's also kind of handy, because we always have it with us, so we can use it whenever we like. No setting up or rummaging around for props required,' Lee thought out loud.

'Bingo.'

'Mmm, yeah,' Lee looked upset, 'unfortunately that's how I tried to meditate the first time around,' he said, remembering his first few attempts at Meditation. 'I thought that it should be simple and straight forward, but I found it ever-so-difficult to concentrate on my breathing for any length of time. Actually, when I think about it, even though it sounds silly, I think I always felt that I didn't really know *how* to concentrate on it.'

'That doesn't sound silly at all, that's a problem a lot of people have when they begin. I have a little trick though to help your concentration to stay on your breathing, give it a go.'

Lee sat up straight and hopeful and waited for instructions.

'Now, follow the *feeling of the movement* of your breath with *all* of your *attention*, but *not* with your *Thoughts*,' Tara instructed.

Lee closed his eyes and breathed.

'*Feel*, rather than *think* the air coming in through your nose, *feel* the *movement* of your breath down your windpipe and into your belly. *Feel* your belly inflate with air. You can even deliberately push your belly out a bit.' Lee followed dutifully. 'Then, follow your Breath back up again. As your belly deflates, the air moves back up the windpipe and out of your nose.'

He opened his eyes. 'Wow, that's complicated.'

'Actually, it only sounds complicated because I'm trying to put it into words. In simpler terms, the air goes down, inflates our Body and then goes the same way back up deflating the Body. It's the natural movement of your breath.'

Tara had sat up straight and demonstrated the flow of the air with her hands moving up and down her Body. When she was done she encouraged Lee to try again. After a couple more tries he grabbed his pen and wrote:

Breathe:
- Into nose
- Down windpipe
- Into stomach
- Stomach inflates
- Stomach deflates
- Up the windpipe
- Out of nose

'Ok, now do this again, but once the air arrives in your tummy, instead of breathing out, try and breathe *in* a bit more and observe what happens.'

Lee closed his eyes again and Tara observed his belly rising, then Lee huffed one extra time to suck in more air and automatically his shoulders raised and his chest expanded. 'Ah,' Lee observed, 'interesting.'

'Yeah, this is the extra step a friend of mine added to the basic breathing routine, which I found really useful. **We breathe in and feel the air coming in through our nose, down our windpipe and into our stomach, and we feel our stomach inflate. Now we breathe in even deeper until our chest inflates as well. Then we breathe out by deflating our chest first, then our stomach. In the end you get a bit of a wave-like motion going**.'

To give Lee a more visual impression, she sat herself upright, put one hand onto her stomach and one onto the upper part of her chest. As she breathed in deeply, the hand on her stomach got pushed outwards as her stomach filled with air. Next the hand on her chest got pushed outwards as her chest expanded. Now both of her hands rested on inflated air pockets. As she breathed out of her chest first, the hand on her chest sunk, followed by the hand on her stomach as she finally breathed out of her belly. She repeated this motion a few times, with Lee following her with his hands on the required areas of his anatomy.

'Ah, I get it. It's really useful to put the hands on the stomach and the chest - it helps to remember the sequence.' Lee continued breathing for a while. 'Mmm,' Lee breathed contentedly, 'you know, **by breathing this way, I feel that I can breathe in a lot longer and a lot more air compared with how I breathe normally**. Gosh, I really notice the difference,' Lee said, while he continued the exercise. It really *did* feel good. Calming, soothing.

'I know, it's quite amazing, isn't it?'

'Yeah,' Lee reluctantly opened his eyes. 'It does feel strange to breathe into my stomach though.'

'I know that always feels weird when you're not used to it, but that becomes second nature after a while.'

'Fair enough. I wonder, why does breathing into your stomach allow you to draw in so much more air? That doesn't really make sense, does it?' Lee asked. 'I mean, what does the stomach have to do with your lungs?'

'Actually, it does make sense. Check this one out,' Tara sat up for another demonstration. 'Breathe out,' Lee obliged, 'and now try not to breathe in deliberately, but keep the back of your throat and your windpipes open. Now, push your belly out.'

Lee followed the instructions with a surprised look on his face, as he felt himself breathe in noisily.

'See?' Tara smiled, 'By pushing your belly out, air gets sucked into your lungs automatically. Effortlessly. Now, relax your belly.'

Lee did and felt himself breathe out. 'Oh wow, that's amazing,' Lee said, repeating the process a few more times. 'I had no idea. **I'm breathing automatically, just by moving my stomach**.'

'Yeah, cool, isn't it? Breathing this way makes perfect anatomic sense. Your lungs sit in your chest cavity just above your diaphragm. If you push your belly out, you push your diaphragm down which makes more space for your lungs to expand and fill themselves to their full capacity. When you only breathe into our chest, your lungs can never expand to their full capacity because the diaphragm is in the way below them,' Tara finished her biology lesson.

'Wow, this is incredible. How come they don't teach *this* at schools?'

'Beats me. It's the natural way for humans to breathe, we've just forgotten.'

'We've forgotten a lot, haven't we?' Lee said with a sigh.

'True, but that's why we're here. To remember,' Tara said sincerely. 'When you begin to breathe like this,' she paused to breathe in deeply, '**when you suddenly begin to fill your *whole* lungs with air again, rather than just the fraction that you're used to, you automatically draw more Oxygen into your system than you'd normally do**. If you're new to this and you do this for any length of time, you can feel slightly dizzy or light headed because your brain is just not used to so much goodness. Make sure not to over-breathe and keep checking in with yourself to ensure that you feel alright, especially at the beginning. **Don't suck in as much air as you can with every breath. Instead,**

take it easy. Breathe deeply and slowly. You know, just breathe normally. If you do feel funny in any way, just ease off on the amount you're breathing in or just breathe your normal way again and concentrate on that breathing instead. Once your Body gets used to the new kind of breathing routine, you can use your lungs to their full capacity. Remember that to reach Nowness it's not necessary to breathe in as much as you can, it's enough to just concentrate on your slow and calm belly breath, no matter how deep.'

Lee nodded and added another few points to his list:

Breathe:
- Into nose.
- Into stomach.
- Into chest.
- Out of chest.
- Out of stomach.
- Out of nose.
- Pushing out the stomach drops the diaphragm, which helps to extend the lungs fully. It's the natural way of breathing.
- Breathe deeply and slowly.
- Don't over-breathe.
- Take it easy.

'So, to summarize, for the *first* step of the Meditation Staircase, you can do stomach breathing, or stomach/chest breathing or just breathe normally. In the end it doesn't really matter, as long as you breathe deeply and slowly, and continuously follow your breath with your attention.'

'But, if you can breathe normally, why did we just go through the exercises?' Lee asked confused.

'There are a three reasons, first because procedures helps you concentrate.'

'Because it takes more concentration to pay attention to a new breathing technique, compared to just observing what you normally do. Makes sense,' Lee deducted attentively. 'Clever,' he grinned.

'Second, **breathing this way also supports concentration because the brain gets more Oxygen. The more you use the whole of your lungs, the more Oxygen the blood around your lungs can absorb, and of course that blood, with all that lovely fresh Oxygen, goes to your Brain**.'

'Ah,' Lee deducted easily. '**And the extra Oxygen wakes you up, makes you more alert and enhances your concentration**.'

'Precisely. And on top of that, third, **by breathing deeper and fuller, you pump more air, and thus more oxygen, into your** blood, **Brain,** *and* your *whole* metabolism - your *whole* **Being sparks up**. If you would just sit there for five minutes and breathe deeply like that? You'd get as much Oxygen into your Body as if you'd do gentle exercise. And all that just by sitting on your bottom and breathing. Isn't that great?' Tara clapped her hands excitedly.

'Truly. **Sounds like an instant cure for low blood-pressure, chronic fatigue and concentration problems,**' Lee deducted. '**I guess a lot of people breathe so shallowly that they don't use their lungs to their full capacity, which in turn limits their Oxygen intake.** And due to the general lack of exercise, they don't get any regular Oxygen bursts through that either. Mmm, yeah, **I can see how our energy would be much lower than it could be. We've let our lungs turn into a wasted resource, that's one of the reasons why so we're often lethargic and tired.** You know what? We should bottle proper breathing. We'd make a fortune,' Lee grinned.

'Agreed wholeheartedly,' Tara said. 'Actually there's a fourth reason for stomach breathing. **By breathing into your stomach, you breathe into the centre of your Body, which strengthens your Core, your Inner Centre, the place where you are perfectly balanced. Our Body and Mind stay calmer when we breathe into our stomach, than when we would** *only* **breathe high up into our chest**. Try it,' Tara suggested. 'First slowly then faster.'

Lee started breathing, first only into his chest, then only into his stomach, adjusting the speed as instructed. When he was done, he observed, '**If I just breathe into my chest, my breath is shallower and it's easy to breathe really fast, even to hyperventilate. Whereas when I breathe into my stomach, my breath somehow becomes automatically calmer. Also, it's more difficult to breathe really fast. Belly breathing altogether feels more**, more..., I guess *centred* **is the right word for it**.'

'Well done, that's exactly it. Stomach breathing centres us. Let me demonstrate,' Tara pulled Lee up onto his feet, and stood opposite him.

Lee smiled to himself, wondering what passers-by must think, but he didn't care, he loved all the little hands-on demonstrations.

'Breathe really deeply high up into your chest and carefully hold your breath,' he heard Tara say.

Lee did as he was told and Tara gently pushed him. Lee fell over, landing on his butt, exhaling with a spurt. 'What did you do that for?' he asked bewilderedly, scrambling back onto all fours.

'I'll show you. Come, get up again,' she held out her hand and pulled a slightly concerned Lee back onto his feet. 'Ok, so now breathe really deeply again, but this time *only* into your stomach and then hold your breath.'

Lee did as he was told, gently bracing himself against another fall, and as expected, Tara pushed him again, a bit harder this time. Lee, to his surprise, stood rock solid.

Tara grinned and asked, 'See?'

'Cool demonstration. Full marks,' Lee stemmed his hands into his sides. As he looked warmly down at Tara who was a little shorter than him, he noticed the little that Thought had managed to push it's way into his warehouse: "She's the perfect size, she'd just disappear in my arms." Lee grinned, had the Manager store the box away for later use and concentrated again on the matter at hand.

'So, if I breathe into my chest, I'm out of balance and can be toppled over easily,' he said, 'whereas if I breathe into my stomach, I *feel* more mentally centred and grounded. I'm also *physically* more centred because I breathe into my centre of gravity, my belly, which actually physically puts my two feet firmly on the ground. That's why I didn't get pushed over. That was great, Tara. I don't think I will forget that one in a hurry, at least not as long as that bruise flourishes on my bottom,' Lee said with a wince.

'Yeah, sorry about that,' Tara said apologetically.

'No problem, it's all in the name of wisdom, right?' Lee rubbed his bum. 'I'm sure I can live with a couple of bruises if I learn about balance in the mean time.'

'I promise I won't make a habit out of it,' Tara said sheepishly, looking up at him from under her eyelashes.

Lee creased his forehead and said with a stern undertone, 'I should hope not, young lady.'

'I can kiss it better,' Tara playfully bent forward, but Lee skilfully jumped out of the way.

'Nice try. Maybe later,' Lee laughed like a teenager.

Tara happily joined in. They stood looking at one another for a moment, breathed deeply and brought their Thoughts back into order. Slowly they sat down again, facing each other.

Tara was the one to break the silence, 'Let me wrap up the breathing thing by saying that **your Mind and your Breath are closely linked. Your Mind can influence your breath, and in turn, your breath can influence your Mind. If you observe your breathing throughout the day, you can learn a hell of a lot about your State of Mind**. You'll notice that when you're sad, you breathe shallower. When you get angry, pissed off, upset or worried, you'll start to breathe faster and normally higher up in our chest.'

'Ah, I just thought of something clever,' Lee interjected. '**If I want to calm myself down, all I need to do is breathe into my stomach, because breathing into my stomach, my centre, will calm and ground me**.'

'Exactly! Once keeping your attention on your breathing becomes second nature throughout the day, your whole Being becomes much calmer and relaxed all round.'

'It's mad how something as simple as good breathing can have such an amazing effect on our lives. Grounded, centred, and concentrated. And all that due to a bit of decent breathing and some extra Oxygen,' Lee marvelled.

'Yeah, right, and that's just on top of all the fantabulous Meditation-mind-blowers that we haven't even touched on yet. Speaking of which, let's get back to the staircase.'

'Oh yeah, the staircase,' Lee opened up the '_What to do?_' list in his book and looked at Tara.

'So, you're sitting down and you're breathing properly. Now all you need to do for the first step on the list, is to follow every breath with your Mind, your whole attention, breathing deeply, calmly, and comfortably. **By slowing down your breathing, your heartbeat slows down, which will calm your whole Body. When the Body chills out, so does your brain and your Thoughts slow down too.'**

'**But even though the brain activity slows down, the brain doesn't get sleepy due to the extra Oxygen, in fact it becomes much more alert. The brain is immensely calm and peaceful, but still fully alert and aware**. That's ingenious!' Lee added.

'Yep, clever isn't it?' Tara said appreciatively. 'At the beginning, when you try to concentrate on your breathing, Thoughts often still creep in, and that's normal. The aim of the first step is not necessarily to stop _all_ of your Thoughts, but rather to _slow_ them and thus _relax_ your Mind and Body, which is a necessary prerequisite for the next few steps.'

Lee and Tara sat in silence for a while, looking up at the clouds, thinking about all the wonderful things this world had still in store for them. Tara suddenly looked up and said sincerely, 'Lee, I just wanted to say that it is a joy to talk to you.'

'Oh, thanks,' Lee said, surprised. 'Same here. Ha, where did that suddenly come from?'

'Well, I just thought how nice it is that you really listen to what I'm saying, no matter how new or different it is. You have common sense, you can draw your own logical conclusions about stuff you've never heard of or spoken about before, and you have your own ideas. It's just refreshing.'

'Well, gee, thanks,' Lee said, 'I guess I just haven't lost the ability to wonder as Sophie would say.'

Tara giggled at the hint to the lovely book 'Sophie's World'. 'Yeah, and that's nice to see. **Many grown ups have forgotten how to wonder.**'

'**I think I'll never really grow up in that respect**,' Lee said happily.

'I'm right there with you, dude. **Total silliness and child-fullness - but not childishness, mind you, coupled with the wisdom of the ages. Perfect combination I'd say. It's happily skipping on the line between Superconsciousness and Stupidity.**'

'Skipping on the line between Superconsciousness and Stupidity? I like that! A lot,' Lee grinned broadly.

She sparkled at him. In her eyes he could see the little girl, the beautiful woman and the wise crone, all perfectly balanced in that wonderful creature in front of him. He closed his eyes and shook his head barely visible and smiled inwardly, 'Cheers Dudes.'

Continuous Concentration

Tara caught the dreamy look on Lee's face, but felt that it was right to continue talking, 'Anyway,' she started gently, 'for the second step, we'll start to concentrate on our breathing for a specific amount of time. Using an alarm clock can be really helpful.'

'An alarm clock? Whoa, I could imagine that to be a bit of a shock. I mean, picture this, you're off in LaLa land, and suddenly there's an alarm clock buzzing in your brain. Doesn't sound too pleasant somehow,' Lee stuck his fingers into his ears. 'But then again, I remember the possible problems with the inner clock thing we spoke about earlier, so I guess an alarm clock would be a good idea. You know, I think I still have a really old alarm clock somewhere. It only ever rings a couple of times and it doesn't wake me up in a million years, but for Meditation it would be perfect. Great, that's sorted then.'

'There you go, that was easy. Once you've set your alarm clock, it's all about Continuous Concentration on your breath.'

'Ugh, Continuous Concentration - two dreaded words. That's the one I don't look forward to. I've always had a terribly short attention span. My mum and my teachers always used to say that I couldn't sit still for two minutes - and I really couldn't. I still can't really,' Lee bounced up and down to emphasise his point.

'Don't worry, it isn't that bad. **You can train your concentration and your attention span as you can train everything else.** Just take your time and be easy on yourself. It will come with practice. And guess what?'

'It can be fun?' Lee guessed expertly.

'How did you know?' Tara played innocent.

'Just this feeling,' Lee's voice trailed of theatrically.

'It really isn't that bad. Trust me, I'm a doctor,' Tara said with a creepy undertone in her voice.

'Ahhhh, infuse me with your wisdom, oh keeper of the Hippocratic Oath,' Lee said sticking out his tongue.

Tara took an imaginary pill and placed it on Lee's tongue. 'A pill of wisdom for the honest seeker of Truth,' she said with a mysterious voice. 'Ok now, while we wait for the pill to take effect, you don't have to do anything but sit down and concentrate on your Breath - in and out. Into your nose, down the pipe, into the stomach, chest, and so on. Just sit there and keep on doing it. Lets do it together, shall we?'

For a few minutes they breathed. In and out, nice, gently, deeply and slowly. Both had their hands on their stomach to let the movement under their hands aid their concentration and help them remember the breathing sequence.

After a few minutes, Lee tried a tentative, 'Riiiiing, riiiing.'

'Ha, excellent, I didn't even have to tell you that the pill had a built-in alarm clock,' Tara joked. 'How did it go?'

'Well, I concentrated on my breathing for about thirty seconds, then I kind of forgot, started to think a lot and then I thought the five minutes should be over,' Lee said honestly.

'That's pretty much what happens to everyone when they start out.'

'Oh, I'm sure you say that to all the boys,' Lee grinned widely and very cheekily.

'Only because it's true,' Tara patted Lee's arm reassuringly. 'But seriously. It does. We want to sit and concentrate for five minutes, but we realise rather quickly that actually we've been doing pretty much everything else *but* concentrate on our breath. Our Mind stopped noticing it long ago. Then we try again, but this time, we *really* concentrate. Very probably, by the time the alarm clock rings again, we realise, that once more, all the stuff in our brain was much more interesting than our breath. Then, we get fed-up and give up.'

'Oh God, that is so true,' Lee laughed out loud. 'It's hilarious how predictable people are, isn't it? Well, including myself,' he added humbly.

'I know, it is funny, but in this case it's also sad, because **this lack of attention during the first five minutes is unfortunately often**

**the beginning and the end of people's encounter with Meditation.
And that's not really giving it a fair go, is it?'**

'Yeah, I agree.'

'Well, until we train our attention, the first few times will always be challenging. But that's normal, so don't worry. **Even for me, after all these years, some days are still easier than others.**'

'I don't know if that's very reassuring.'

'Well, it just means that **with practice, our overall Meditation ability, if I can call it that, will get better every day. But as I said before, some days, our Mind is naturally busier, and on those days it just takes a bit more resolve, that's all.**'

Meditation is Like Surfing

'**A**ctually, Meditation is not just like playing guitar, it's also like surfing,' Tara said.

Lee could literally see a light bulb spark up above Tara's head, as she stretched herself, got onto her feet and stood on an imaginary surfboard, her arms stretched out wide to either side. She wobbled a bit.

'At the beginning, you can't surf the waves of the Mind to save your life, in fact you can't even get on the board, let alone stand on it. You fall off a bunch of times, swallow a bit of salt water, enjoy a short swim, chuck out your Ego and pull yourself back up onto the board, slowly, deliberately, but you keep falling off, having to start again, and paddle, paddle a lot, then - again, on, off, on, off,' she stepped from side to side, pretending get on and off her surfboard. 'By following instructions and with a bunch of trial and error you'll learn. With the right frame of Mind, you'll even enjoy the actual practice itself, no matter how wet you get! That's the best bit if you can get to that. **If you can enjoy the path rather than just the destination.** That makes the whole affair so much more enjoyable.'

'Enjoy the practice itself,' Lee repeated thoughtfully. He had never enjoyed it, he had always beat himself up because he couldn't stop thinking. He'd never even thought of *trying* to find something positive about the practice itself.

'And then,' Tara continued unperturbed, just when you think that you'll never be able to do it, one day you wake up, get on that board and you surf. Just like that,' she stood up straight, with her face turned towards the sun, a happy look of satisfaction in her eyes. 'Suddenly, out of nowhere, something just clicked and you got it - and from then on it's effortless.'

'That's actually really funny, Tara. You won't believe it, but I surf and I know exactly what you're talking about,' he smirked. 'I know that staying on the surfboard is never easy at first and a lot of people get fed up and give up, but some of us keep going. It takes persistence and practice and then, it's magic!'

'There you go! It's the same with Meditation. **You step on and fall off the surfboard of Meditation, trying to find the balance between Thoughts and Emptiness, trying to catch each wave of silence without falling off into the sea of mindless brain chatter.**'

'Mmm, good way of putting it, albeit a bit corny,' Lee tapped Tara's arm jokingly.

'Ha, I've got some more corniness for you: When we surf through our Meditation, we learn how to *observe* all the distracting winds and disturbing waves.'

'Which are the boxes, the Thoughts, Emotions and ideas, everything that has been stored in the Warehouse since we were born, right?'

'Yeah. With time we get to know all the winds and waves i.e. the boxes inside out, we understand where they came from and why they are there. We become one with them and nothing can surprise us anymore. We can ride some, ignore some, learn from some, and get rid of others. It's our choice,' Tara said.

'As long as we keep getting up on that board every time we fall off, otherwise we'll never get anywhere,' Lee said expertly. 'It can be done and it can be fun. Lots of people do it, even when the weather is freezing!' Lee shivered in memory of some of his autumn surfing adventures.

'Brrrr, yeah, I always wonder how they do it,' Tara shuddered. 'Luckily Meditation is not that physically hardcore. **But as with surfing, once the basics of Meditation are accomplished, it's just a matter of fine-tuning your skills, practicing certain moves, become better, more daring and experiment until it becomes second nature, and eventually, managing to surf all afternoon rather than just half an hour.** That's when the fun really starts,' Tara sat down again. 'It just takes a bit of determination and some good instruction.'

'And a couple of bruises,' Lee looked at Tara, felt his bruised butt and said with a smile, 'Actually, you know, surfing really is like more like Meditation than you might think. You know, when you surf, once you're out on those waves, it takes *all* of your concentration, your whole and total focus to stay on that board. Once you think or get distracted, you usually fall off. Mmh, it seems that Meditation requires the same focus and determination as any *skill* you'd want to learn.'

'Very true. You know what's quite ironic? **Usually at the exact point where you get fed up with Meditation and throw in the towel, that's when you've just mastered the first stage of Meditation,**' Tara pointed out.

'Oh yeah? How's that?'

'Well, **you've just realised that Meditation requires concentration and that you simply don't have that kind of concentration yet. So instead of packing it in and saying: "I can't meditate", we should say: "I can't concentrate very well - yet". So, to Meditate, we need to *train* our concentration.**'

Lee repeated with a monotonous voice as if reciting a mantra, 'Want to train concentration. Want to train concentration.'

Tara laughed. 'Actually, it doesn't even have to be that intense, it's not as if the concept of concentration is new to us. Even just pouring a cup of coffee, reading the newspaper or a book, writing, calculating, driving, even talking, it all requires concentration of one kind or another. We're actually concentrating on stuff all day long, but we don't really think about it anymore. We already concentrate continuously, too.

'***Continuous* Concentration Meditation is like driving a car. Can you remember how hard you had to concentrate just to remember to let the clutch come sloooowly? As soon as your concentration lagged just for a second, you stalled,**' Tara laughed and rolled her eyes, remembering her initial struggle with a VW Bug. '**Whereas now, you continuously concentrate automatically, simply because you know what you're doing and because you've practiced it.** Easy. So, if you can drive, you're already doing the continuous concentration thingy to some extent.'

'Great,' Lee loved that fact that he finally had a reference point to what he was trying to accomplish.

'Oh, and there are more hints and tips on how to continuously keep your attention on your breathing.'

'Thank God for that, because getting used to that clutch nearly killed me!' Lee cringed, remembering his own initial struggle with a Golf GTI - with power steering no less. He hoped the Meditation thing wasn't going to be quite that tricky.

Catch Yourself Out

'So,' Lee began, '**I have done the five minute test and have realised that I can't concentrate long enough. I've said my I-want-to-learn-to-concentrate mantra.** Now what?'

'Well, **in step three you try to *catch yourself* out when your Mind drifts off. Catching yourself, means that you *notice* when your Mind is wandering off, when you start to think.** Oh, and obviously, the aim is to try and catch yourself out *before* the alarm clock rings,' Tara added cheekily. 'The first few times you'll probably sit there, thinking about God and the World, and not notice that you've drifted off. That's fine and normal. Then one day, as if by magic, you'll *notice* that your Mind has wandered off. **Then, all you need to do is bring your attention back to your breathing - in and out, in and out.** And then, when the alarm clock rings, there's the first feeling of success. Yipee, congratulations! **You have just become** *aware* **of your Thoughts. You have noticed for the first time that you were thinking** *while* **you were doing it. Not afterwards. This is a crucial experience, because this new awareness gives you a** *choice,* **the choice of what to do next.** You now can decide what to do with your Mind. You can either decide to go on thinking that Thought or you can divert your attention back to your breath again. **For the first time you are in the driver's seat, rather than being driven.'**

'**Instead of having constant turmoil in our heads, we can learn to stop it.** That certainly sounds appealing,' Lee raised his eyebrows.

'Yeah, it does. Now, with practice, you notice your Mind wandering of more and more, and the time spent with your attention on your breath becomes longer and longer and your thinking becomes less and less, and with time you learn to clear your Mind from everything but your Meditation Object - the Breath. You learn to concentrate on just one thing, your breathing. Nothing else. Empty. Silence. Peace. Surfing effortlessly.'

Gently - Thinking Creatures On The Sofa

'That sounds wonderful, but how do we stop ourselves from getting angry when it doesn't work straight away? What about the perfectionists, the people with high expectations of themselves?' Lee asked, remembering his own misplaced goals.

'It's ironic, because **getting angry about** *not* **fulfilling your expectations, actually makes it** *more* **difficult to meditate. If you get angry - your Mind not only kicks off a thinking loop of angry Thoughts, which clutters up your Mind, but also due to the anger, your Body becomes upset as well, your breathing speeds up, becomes erratic and chesty and all the nice relaxation work you've done goes down the toilet**. And, on top of that, **you'll have to start all over with calming down your breathing, let alone your Mind. By becoming angry, you've just made things tougher on yourself. If you remained calm on the other hand, your Mind will stay calm and so will your Body. Meditation is much easier if we don't get angry, upset, fed up, irritable or scold ourselves.'**

'Yeah, makes sense, but **how do I do that**? I mean, it's kind of a natural reaction to have these Thoughts: "Oh, I'm stupid", "I just can't do it", "Oh no, I don't believe it, my Mind has just wandered off *again*", "I can't even do not-thinking", "why is this not working?"'

'Well, **what did you do when you learned to surf**?' Tara asked simply.

Lee thought for a second, 'I guess **I ignored those Thoughts and focussed on trying to keep my balance instead. And of course I didn't let myself be disheartened, I just kept on doing it.**'

'There you go. You already know what to do. **You do the same thing with Meditation**. Well, nearly.' Tara looked Lee straight into the eyes and asked, '**All those feeling you've just described, the: "I'm stupid", "I can't do it", and so on, what are they**?'

Lee stopped for a second, slightly distracted by all that blue-green which was directly focussed on him, then it hit him, 'Thoughts. Shit, Tara, **they're Thoughts**!'

'Tadaaa. **And what can we do with Thoughts?**'

'**We catch ourselves out. We notice that we're having them and then we *choose to divert our attention back to our breathing***. Oh my God Tara, I just got it. Any Thoughts, any Thoughts at all, even the I-can't-be-asked or is-the-time-over-yet Thoughts, or I'm-stupid-that-I'm-still-thinking, they are all Thoughts! Man!'

'Exactly and we treat them exactly like all the other Thoughts. We notice our Mind has wandered and calmly and gently bring our Mind back to our Breathing,' Tara repeated once more. 'No need to beat ourselves up about it. In the Now there is no anger, no frustration or being stupid.'

'That's so simple.'

'It *does* takes practice, but yes it is simple once you get it. All you need to do is continue until the alarm clock rings. And you're done for the day. Checked-off step three,' Tara checked off the air in front of her with her index finger. 'And if you really want to, you can do it all day long.'

'All day long? Phew.'

'Not such a big deal really, you just **catch yourself out all day long, whenever you have an I'm-stupid Thought, a worry or some silly feeling, anything that you don't want in your head. Just notice it and go back to your breathing. Gently, easy, no anger, just breathe away jealousy, worry, stress** ...' Tara waved her hand gently to emphasise her point.

'I like that,' Lee was fascinated once again. '**Gentleness and ease. Be tender and kind to yourself, just because it's nicer than beating yourself over the head. *And* it's more effective**. Great.'

'Precisely! You know, that little creature in our Brain?' Tara tapped her forehead. 'It's just trying to do it's job, right? And to do that, it thinks.

That's what it does, and it'll be damned if it's going to stop doing that, just because we suddenly decide that that's what we want, right? We can't just sack it. It won't have it. So, we need to gently and tenderly train it to take a rest instead. You know? Chill out a bit. Take a holiday. It's all about gentle persuasion rather than force. It's more like, 'Oops, you're working again darling, why don't you just go and sit on the sofa, I make you a nice little cup of tea. Relax. Put your feet up.'

Lee grinned at the Thought of seeing his Thoughts relaxing on the sofa with their feet up.

'And after a while,' Tara described the picture in her head, 'the little workaholic will realise all by itself that it's quite nice to have a break from time to time. Meditation teaches the little creature to get used to and accept temporary redundancy.'

'Ooh, that is so sweet. I'm just imagining this little creature on my sofa taking a nap, a cup of tea steaming next to it.'

'Yeah, it might look sweet to you, but wait until it wakes up again,' Tara said with a warning tone in her voice.

'Shhhhhhh,' Lee grinned with his index finger in front of his mouth.

Watch Out, It Has Left the Sofa!

Lee flicked through his notebook and said, 'Ok, we've discussed that we should catch ourselves out and why it doesn't make any sense to get angry if it doesn't work immediately. Mmm, **what about some practical tips on how to do the catching out thing?** How do we notice that the little guy has woken up, jumped off the sofa and started working again?'

'Good question. There's something that really works,' Tara said mysteriously.

'Sounds intriguing.'

'Well, **before we meditate we have to put out an Intent.**'

'Put out an Intent?'

'Yeah, **you either say out loud or in your head that you want to catch yourself out when you begin to think. You have to really part that curtain of fuzz in your hand and** *consciously* **say that this is what you are going to do.** When I say consciously, I mean don't just say it as a fleeting Thought, like: "Umm maybe when I have some time I could possibly try and catch myself out", or "Oh yeah that'll be an idea sometime. Mmm what about dinner?". No, I mean that **you have to use** *all* **your attention, concentration and focus on it, when you say that you're** *going to* **catch yourself out.** *That's* **putting out an Intent**.'

'Got it.'

'That Intent then sits in your Subconscious and triggers itself off from time to time and gives you a little prod: "Yoo-hoo, you were supposed to catch yourself out, now is a good time!" In short, from time to time there'll be a big fat red flag saying: "Hello, sorry, but you're thinking darling!",' she smiled. **'Until you do it automatically, you can renew the Intent before every Mediation. It's also a good idea to renew it at random times during the day, to plant it deeper and deeper into your Subconscious.'**

'And the more I get in touch with my Subconscious through Meditation, the clearer my Mind becomes, the easier it is for the Conscious Mind to pick up the Intent, and therefore in turn, the easier it is to get in touch with my Subconscious again, and so on. Oh my God, it trains itself! Once you kick it off, it doesn't stop! That's amazing.'

Tara didn't say anything, she just smiled that knowing sweet little smile.

The Last Thought, Sneaky Little Bugger…

'Oh yeah, by the way, **you know, the comment that you have in your head the second you catch yourself out?'**

'What, the oops-I'm-thinking-again comment?'

'Yes, that one. *That's* a Thought too, and to be in Nowness we would want to try and get rid of *that* Thought as well.'

'Phew, hardcore.'

'Not really. It becomes an automatic response in no time, and after a while there's no thinking involved in the catching out process at all anymore.'

'Full on, Tara.'

'Actually, it gets even more full on, want to know?'

'Of course!'

'There's one *very* last Thought before Stillness.'

'Another one?'

'Oh yes, and it's a right sneaky little bugger. It's when we think that we are finally in Nowness? When we think we're in total thoughtlessness.'

'Well, what is it?' Lee asked impatiently.

'It's the Thought or the voice congratulating ourselves that we're finally meditating! That we're finally silent, that we're finally in Nowness. Ah, no you're not!'

Lee burst out laughing. 'Are you serious?'

'Oh boy, I am. I only noticed it after years of meditating. There I was, sitting happily during my first whole hour of meditating, when I suddenly heard this voice, clear as a bell: "Oh great, this is nice and silent now. Oh wow, you've been meditating for nearly an hour, you're doing so well today. Phew, Nowness feels great. Mmm, my Body feels wonderful". And on it went, the whole time! Gosh, it was such a shock, when I heard it for the first time. I just couldn't believe that I hadn't noticed it before.'

'You're kidding. And noticing *that* took you *years?*' Lee asked doubtfully.

'Well, nobody told me that that voice existed and I just never noticed it. I tell you, the Mind really does mysterious things. But the point is that you know now that this voice exists and that you can watch out for it right from the beginning.'

'Which will make my life much easier than yours was,' Lee said appreciatively.

'Precisely.'

'Any tips on how to get rid of that last sneaky little bugger?' he probed.

'It's always the same answer. Only one word: *Breathe*,' Tara took a deep breath and held it, 'and breathe even more,' she raised her eyebrows and squealed while trying to breathe in even deeper.

'Of course, silly question,' Lee grinned and quick as a flash lunged forward to tickled Tara's sides, while her cheeks were still filled to the brim with air.

She screamed out loud as all the air in her lungs gushed out in one go. She dove forward and tried to tickled him back. Lee pulled up his knees to shield his sides and grabbed Tara's hands to stop her from doing any damage. Then, with one swift movement, he let go of her hands, grabbed one of Tara's bare feet and tickled it thoroughly, with her trying to pull it back in vain for several seconds. They continued to tickle each other until their stomachs hurt so much from all the laughing, and a truce had to be called.

It was always nice to empty the brain from time to time, Tara thought, preferably with some hardcore silliness. **She knew that it was never good to get too serious about anything, because that would be boring, right? She always made sure to remember the fine line between Super-consciousness and Silliness, and she rode that edge with style**.

Once recovered and regularly breathing again, Lee said happily, 'So, **Breathing is always the answer**.'

'Yep, and when we finally get rid of all those Thoughts, including all the naughty little last ones, then we're in Nowness.'

'I so want to be able to do that. Can I just have a minute?' Lee asked.

'Sure.'

Lee closed his eyes and with all his Being concentrated on one sentence: "I *will* catch myself out when I'm thinking. I *will* catch myself out when I'm thinking". He repeated it to himself a few times, realising that he was saying it with all the sincerity he could muster up, and that he actually really meant it.

Then, a picture flashed past his mind's eye. There she was again. Kate. Right on cue. She certainly had been a recurring Thought. "Ha, nothing like immediate practical application!" Lee thought in high spirits. He really wanted Kate out of his head, at least all the stressful bits. It was over and there was no point keeping in keeping her on the sofa with that little creature up there in his head. Lee cradled his forehead gently, imagining the thinking creature and Kate having cups of tea, their feet up, happily chit-chatting along. "Resolve, Intend," he said firmly in his Mind. "I *will* catch myself out when I'm thinking about Kate and *will* concentrate on my breathing instead." He sincerely repeated it again a couple of times and finally he opened his eyes again.

He appreciated the fact that Tara never asked where he went when he went silent. If he wanted to talk he would, if not, he didn't need to. Tara made him feel respected. Respected when he chose to be in his own head, doing whatever it was he needed to do. He smiled at her.

'Ready for more?' Tara asked when she saw that Lee was back.

He nodded slowly, 'Yes please, ma'am.'

'Now, you keep catching yourself out, until you can easily do it for about five minutes. Then you slowly increase the time. You can do that a minute at a time or more, whatever suits you best. While you increase the time, you always need to remember that the easier you are on yourself, the less likely you are to get upset or fed up. It's not a competition as to who can increase the time fastest or who can perfect Meditation in the least amount of time. You're doing it for yourself, not for anybody else. As with surfing, after a while you might even get to like the practice itself and enjoy the new experiences.'

'No matter how short that joy may be at the beginning,' Lee said quietly, seeing Kate on that wretched sofa again.

'But that joy is ever increasing, eee-ver increasing,' Tara flung her arms out wide apart,'

She always made him laugh. For a split second he saw Tara sit with Kate and the creature on the sofa, "No way, that's enough," he shouted at the three of them in the safety of his Mind. "I don't care about that being gentle business, out, out!" The picture in his Mind burst into a million little pieces and disappeared just in time for him to hear Tara asking him a question.

'Do you want to write down a quick summary?' she asked cheerfully.

Lee nodded, firmly focussing on his breathing, and for a few minutes the two of them went over the main points they had just discussed.

With this third step we learn:
• To consciously interrupt our Mind and our Thoughts, which is a very powerful tool to master.
• To do this at regular intervals or whenever our concentration moves away from our Meditation Object.
• To notice when our Mind is running away with us, which gives us a choice - to stop it, change it or to continue.
• A 'new' kind of concentration, Continuous Concentration.
• To experience a new calm, peace, quietness and emptiness in our Mind (Tara added, 'This can have many, many uses, which I will talk about later.').
• To make friends with that creature on the sofa.
• To learn to even catch out the last sneaky little Thought in our head.
• To enter Nowness.

Once they were finished Tara said, 'There are many, many more exercises to sharpen and improve our Mind, but for now, this will be enough.'

'Alrighty, so, what's next?'

This is Where Most Meditations Stop

'Actually that's a good question, because there is more, but **this is where most Meditation methods stop. We're chilled, we're physically and mentally calm, we've slowed down our Thoughts and maybe we've even stopped thinking. If that's enough for us, all we need to do is keep doing it, change or increase the duration from time to time, and enjoy the amazing effects it'll have on our lives.'**

'But that's not what *you* have in Mind, is it?' Lee was already getting flashes of his new and improved life. Calmer, chilled, relaxed, having stopped all these Thoughts - and certain people - that went round and round in his head, again and again, driving him mad. Just that, sounded totally amazing.

Catching Out For Real

Lee was pleased with the realism and common sense Tara had introduced into Meditation for him. She was the first person he'd met, who had not only addressed the possible difficulties and pitfalls, but who had also given practical tips on how to avoid them. He was surprised nobody else had ever explained that to him. In fact, why didn't anybody ever talk about the problems they were having? Did people just not know, or didn't anybody have any problems? Unlikely. Were they just pretending that they didn't have any? Possible. Maybe because they're embarrassed that they can't do a simple thing like not thinking? But that would be silly. Anyway, it didn't really matter what other people did or thought or why. What was important what *he* did and what *he* thought.

And he thought, that the method Tara talked about, seemed much more relaxed and practical than anything he'd heard of before. Lee felt a new confidence grow within him. With Tara's explanations, tips and incentives and with a bit of determination, he thought he might be able to start again, and this time - stick with it. He might even finally sort out his head, he thought longingly, when realisation hit him: he was going to start to meditate again - wow. He would have never dreamed of that a few days ago. And now? Now it just seemed the most natural thing to do. Funny how things changed, he thought. This time, he'd be easier on himself though. Tara was right, it wasn't a competition. Everybody needed to learn in their own time. He would do five minutes every day for a while and when he felt ready, he'd slowly increase the time. This gentle, easy way definitely suited him a lot better. He suddenly laughed as he remembered when he lost patience with the little get-together on the creatures couch only a few minutes earlier, he grinned. Well, there'll always be some exceptions, Lee grinned to himself.

He still couldn't get over how glad he was to have met Tara. Not just because she was absolutely beautiful, but because of what he was learning. This conversation was so different to any he'd ever had in his life. Not only because of the content, but because of how strongly it all resonated. It seemed so much like remembering something he already knew, rather than learning something new. He didn't really have to think about what he was saying or which questions to ask, he just seemed to know. It was all so clear in his Mind. It was as if he'd found a box in his Warehouse that he had forgotten about, and now, having rediscovered that box, it felt like an old friend, it felt familiar. He surprised himself with how logical his own conclusions had been, how interesting the ideas that had come into his Mind from out of that box. Sometimes they felt like somebody else's Thoughts *and* like his own at the same time - and right now he was observing *both* of them!

'Oh man,' Lee suddenly said out loud. When Tara looked at him in surprise, he decided to share what he'd been thinking.

'You're just getting in touch with your Subconscious again, the bit of it which The Guys talk to you through, that's all,' Tara replied once he was done explaining. 'You're tapping into the Collective Consciousness we talked about earlier, and what's more, you have the confidence to examine it and to really look at it and use it. Go with it, buddy,' Tara said encouragingly. 'Actually, that's really important,' she stressed, 'because a lot of people get scared by the sudden clarity and knowledge that catching out and the whole Meditation business brings. But there's no reason to. Just go with it. Let it carry you into a new and different world.'

'Yeah, I'm up for that. I'm just wondering where that box came from, there's so much fascinating information in it. It's so bizarre that I never noticed it before.'

'And *you* couldn't believe that it took *me* years to notice the last sneaky little Thought,' Tara teased.

'Phew, yeah, point taken. I guess there's a lot of stuff within us that we don't know about yet,' Lee said carefully, the sheer magnificence of that remark was only beginning to dawn on him.

'You're right, and there are a lot more cool boxes where yours just came from!' Tara said with a beaming smile.

Suddenly, without him really noticing, Lee's Rational Mind switched itself on again. A renewed uncertainty welled up in him as he thought: "Yeah, right. Getting in touch with the Collective Consciousness. Cool. Weird. Cool. No weird!" and then suddenly: "Oops, hang on there. Stop. You're thinking." It's as if a little red flag was being waved around in his head. *That* red flag! Whoa, he had just consciously caught himself out. **He had jumped out of the cotton wool of his head just for a second, and had observed his Thoughts. Ha, and now he was observing the Thought that was observing his Thought. How cool was that?** Yes! He was doing it. Already! Fabulous. Man, where did all that suddenly come from? Well, he did do that Intent thing earlier. But, it had been about catching out Thoughts about Kate, hadn't it? What the heck. Oh Goodie, it actually worked! But no way, that was crazy, was it possible to work so quickly? This was mad. Lee grinned broadly. He was beginning to like this more and more.

He took a deep breath, making sure that he breathed into his belly first and then his chest, and smiled even broader as he realised that he had just been commenting, with more Thoughts, on how cool it was that he'd caught himself out. Aha! The last sneaky Thought Tara had talked about earlier. Hilarious. There it was, everything they had talked about, right in front of him. If he'd been meditating now, all he'd need to do was to go back to his breathing. But actually, why not do it anyway. She had said he could do it all day long, right? This stuff was great. He was getting it!

But hang on, what had the Thought been, that had started all this off? Mmm, go back, he told himself. Remember, remember, remember, ah, yes. Cool and Weird. Well, why was getting in touch with the Collective Consciousness weird? Oh wow, he was still sceptical! Despite all this fabulousness he realised that he still had doubt, he was still worried that it was all going to turn out to be Hippy-Shit. Man, he had no idea that he still thought that way. Surprise! Now then, there was another interesting box. And gosh, this was even more interesting - Lee tried to keep up with all the realisations that were flooding into his Consciousness - his Conscious Thoughts were contradicting the way he was reacting and thinking subconsciously! He didn't think that he was sceptical, but he was! What was *that* all about? And hang on, where did those Thoughts come from that were observing and commenting on all of the going-s on in his head right now? It was like an '*Observing* Consciousness.' Man, and what about the Consciousness that just asked *that* question?

Lee furrowed his forehead, it was all getting a bit intense. Examining his own Thoughts *as and when* he was thinking them? Now that was new! He looked up at Tara, puzzled, but she was happily staring off into the distance, giving him time to think. He smiled, as his Mind gently waved a little red rag on a stick at him, "And another flag! My Thoughts just changed the subject to Tara. Man, does it ever stop?"

As Lee observed the new phenomenon in his brain, little by little he began to accept the new kind of conversations in his head. Slowly, ever so slowly, a knowing little grin began to creep across his face. Things in his life were about to change on a far bigger scale than he'd ever imagined.

In his Mind, he walked over to the little thinking creature and plonked himself down on the sofa right next it, "Nice cuppa, darling. Nice new perspectives too." He plumped up the pillows, put his feet on the coffee table and snuggled up. Nice. The little creature curled up next to him, vast asleep. His Mind was empty and quiet. Lovely! Ha, and there it was again, Lee nearly fell of the couch, that last sneaky little Thought again..., the Thought of how lovely it was on that sofa. He smiled and breathed even that last Thought away.

He opened his eyes and carefully tapped Tara's shoulder to let her know he was ready for her to continue.

PART 3

8   Mindfulness To Chill All Day Long

Mindfulness All Day Long

'**Y**ou will have noticed,' Tara began in her usual relaxed manner, 'that everything we've talked about so far is geared towards clearing your Mind, because to be able to chat to The Guys, the emptier and tidier your Mind is, the better, right? Well, **Meditation** does exactly that. It **not only allows us to spring clean our Mind, but it also enables us to *keep* it clean**.

On top of that you will have also noticed that **Meditation is not just a quick fix for a run-away Mind, but that it's also a profound and fundamental tool, with amazing long-term effects.** I thought I'd say that once again, just because it's so important,' Tara honed in.

'Absorbed and stored for future use,' Lee labelled the box carefully.

'Great. Now, **besides sitting in a corner, there are other ways to quieten and clear our Mind. As I hinted earlier, we can be Mindful during absolutely *everything* we do: Thinking, planning, talking, walking, doing the dishes and so on.** Now, **you can either focus on your *breath*, or you can mindfully observe and fully concentrate on the *activity* you're doing, which means that you concentrate on the actual activity itself and *nothing* else but *that* activity. With all your Mind, all of your Body and all of your concentration and Awareness, you do *that* one thing and nothing else.**

Let me give you an example. You're eating, and *all* your Thoughts are engaged in tasting, chewing, etcetera, and *nothing* else enters your Mind. If you walk or run, that's all your Mind does, it runs. NOW, in the Present. There are no distractions. Everything you do at that moment in time has your *fullest* attention, there are no stray Thoughts. **All of your Awareness, all of your Consciousness is directed on what you're doing *right Now*, in the Present Moment.** Doing that, is like exploring a new world.'

'Oh right, I should have known that this little world isn't enough for you,' Lee's eyes sparkled at the promise of more cool stuff.

'Oh, it's enough for me, believe me, and you know what? **By being Now, this fabulous world becomes even cooler! In the Now, *every***

151

moment is new! *Everything* **is amazing, beautiful, exciting, fabulous and wonderful. You're like a child again, you see everything with** *new* **eyes,**' Tara said. '**And the best thing is that you can have that, all day long!**'

'Hit me with the list, let's have more of this!' Lee pre-empted eagerly.

'Man, I've got you trained well,' Tara giggled. 'It's a great list too. Every item on it can help you to be more Mindful during the day and it'll open you up to lots of fascinating realisations and experiences. Listen up, here it comes.'

Mindfulness on Daily Activities:
- On daily activities (we just talked about that).
- Humming.
- Talking to ourselves.
- Focus on our Senses.
- Observing how our Body functions   .
- Mindful Interaction.

'Sounds interesting,' Lee said nibbling the top of his pen, 'earlier we focussed on our Mind, now we're going to focus on activities, our Body, and on interaction with other people. Good, that's pretty much got everything covered then, I like it.'

Humming

'**E**xcellent, that's what we like to hear! Let's get to the first point on that list. Humming. I love this one,' Tara said merrily.

'What kind of humming are we talking about here? Is it humming a song,' Lee hummed a little tune and bobbed his head along with it, 'or humming like a bee?' he asked and fairly effectively imitated the rumbling buzz of a bee.

'Good question,' Tara grinned, especially when Lee made big bug-eyes, 'actually, I'd recommend just humming one monotonous tone.'

'Oh, why?' Lee's bug-eyes disappeared in wonderfully acted sad resignation.

'Because it's more difficult to be Mindful when you hum a song or your hum isn't steady. Also, somehow melodies trigger pictures and feelings in our Mind, which make us think. But you know my standard answer...'

'Play around with it and find out what suits me best?' Lee guessed expertly.

'Full points. Now, the way it works, is to hum one a monotonous sound whenever your Mind goes mad.'

'Would I hum like this?' Lee jokingly hummed a ridiculously low tone, 'or like this?' he hummed as high as he could manage, which turned out to be a terribly screechy first soprano.

'Have mercy, have mercy,' Tara grimaced and stuck her fingers into her ears. 'It's neither one of those! At least I truly hope not,' she looked at him sternly as not to dare him to start again. 'In fact, every person has their *own* tone. Have a go, just hum any tone. A normal tone!' she added quickly with a smile. 'Don't think about it - just begin humming for as long as you can. Then very slowly, make the sound lower and deeper or higher and lighter. By fiddling around like this for a bit, you will find a sound that feels more comfortable than any of the others, which will feel more laboured in comparison. That's the one you hum. You can obviously hum whichever tone you want to, but this one sound is the most effortless tone and can therefore help you relax the most.'

Lee obliged and began humming again. First fairly high, then low, then more closely to his speaking voice, then he continued for a few seconds, going up and down and then finally settled on one sound. 'Ah, I think I've got it. I know what you mean with the one effortless sound. OOOMM,' he hummed it again and abruptly stopped. He nudged Tara's arm and grinned broadly, 'Oh, you cheeky minx, you managed to sneak in an OOOMM after all! I didn't even notice. You *are* trying to turn me into a Hippy.'

'Well, kind of,' Tara giggled, 'but at least you don't have to sit cross-legged, you don't have to wear flowers, you don't have to hold your fingers in weird ways and you don't have to do it loudly, and actually, it doesn't even have to be OOOMMM. It could just be the MMMM bit,' Tara said innocently.

'Ok, ok, I'll let you off,' Lee laughed, 'and anyway, besides how stereotypical the OOMM-ing is, I do have to admit that it seems to be great at keeping Thoughts at bay.'

'It is. It only works if you hum consciously though, you know, not just in the background while you're thinking of other stuff.'

'Goes without saying,' Lee nodded.

'In fact, you can make it even more effective if you try and breathe into your stomach while you're humming, exactly as we have done during Meditation. That will get as much oxygen into your system as possible, which gives you all the benefits we discussed earlier and on top of that, it allows you to keep humming longer with each exhalation, but also while you walk or exercise, without losing your breath. With practice you can keep the tone longer and longer without any effort at all, no matter what you do.'

'Ah, I can see the logic! Very good. By holding the humming sound longer, our breathing slows down and becomes more deliberate, which in turn relaxes the Body and Mind. It's soothing. And it's foolproof, because I can't forget humming, can I? I mean, I'll hear if I stop humming, right? So it'll be piss-easy to stay Now,' Lee said confidently.

'Oops, sorry, reality check,' Tara held up her hand. 'Actually, you'll still have to catch yourself out, because you can very happily forget to hum.'

'Oh yeah? Cloud-head returns? Bummer,' Lee said beat.

'Afraid so. You know, I really got into humming at one stage. I hummed continuously during my waking hours for a week, whenever I talked or ate, I hummed in my head.'

'You did? You hummed for a week? Shit, what does that do to you? Phew, I can't even begin to imagine the concentration needed for that. I can't believe you actually do stuff like that. I mean why?'

'Well, just to try out what it's like. What it feels like, what it does to you. It's mad, but it feels amazing. It's like you're buzzing the whole time. Physically and Mentally. Your Mind is so empty, you think you've shifted into a different dimension. You can't even imagine what something like that feels like, until you've tried it. It's crazy.'

'But a week?'

'Fair enough, a week is a bit extreme, but I like to experiment, I always try and find out how far I can go. Gently, obviously.'

'And while having fun!' Lee grinned.

'Self-evidently,' she winked. 'Nowadays, I only do it if I feel that my Mind is really going nuts. Humming helps me chill when I can't calm down otherwise. Oh, did I mention that Humming has a whole bunch of other benefits?'

'Go on?' Lee beckoned her to continue.

'When we hum, our vocal cords vibrate, and actually, our whole Body vibrates ever so subtly.'

'Yeah, but for that you don't need to Hum, do you? Wouldn't just talking all day do the trick just as well? That'll get your vocal chords going too, or not?'

'Good thinking, and yes that's true, but humming and talking have different vibrational frequencies. Talking goes constantly up and down, whereas humming hits the one perfect regenerative frequency for Mind and Spirit, continuously.'

'Two in one. Mind food *and* Spirit food. Bingo!'

'Actually, three in one,' Tara corrected him with a smile, 'just as a side bonus of the humming thingy you can heal and positively influence your Body too.'

'You're kidding.'

'No, honestly. Try it when you have a headache for example. Hum and adjust the level of tone, till you gently feel the vibration of your hum in your head where it hurts and keep it going for a while. Consciously and persistently *feel* the vibrations. Feel the vibrations loosen up the blocked energies and clear them out. It's a fascinating little trick.'

'Always useful when you can't find the Paracetamol,' Lee said slightly doubtful, but hey, he thought, it's always worth a try. He made a note: 'Humming/Paracetamol,' - just to make sure that he actually would give it a go. You never knew.

'The further down you go on your Body, from below the chest downwards for example, the more difficult it is to feel the vibrations. With practice though, you can even feel them in your lower abdomen and further down,' Tara said, a cheeky smile spreading over her lips, 'and if you want to go really hardcore, you'll find, that there are sounds you can make, which can be felt in all parts of your Body, right down to your little toe!'

'Great, I might be able to itch some stuff by humming if I can't get to it with my hands,' Lee giggled playfully.

'I can tell that you're going to have fun with this stuff!'

'Tara, I was joking.'

'I know you were, but wouldn't it be great to try?'

'Tara, you're unbelievable.'

'Nah, just curious.'

'You'd actually do that, wouldn't you?' Lee shook his head.

'Of course. I mean, what a great thing to be able to do! Can you imagine, your leg is all in plaster and the knitting needle just can't reach and you sit there humming? Whatever next?' she laughed.

'And there is more, isn't there?' Lee asked, knowing the look on Tara's face.

'Of course, there's always more,' she smiled at him wickedly.

You Are Not Your Thoughts! Talking to Ourselves - Here Comes the Straight-Jacket

"All sorts of thoughts were battling for the use of his vocal cords."
- Douglas Adams

Tara didn't disappoint. She tapped Lee's notebook and said, 'The second point on the list is Practicing Mindfulness by talking-to-yourself. That basically means that you talk-out-loud *every single* word you're thinking and at the same time, *Listen* to yourself talk. You really make a point of *hearing* that voice in your head.'

'That's what you do with Mantras, isn't it? They keep the Mind clear by being repeated and Listened to over and over again. The Mind is so busy, that it can't do anything else,' Lee remembered his journey to Tibet where people walked around all day long muttering Mantras. They really do that, today, and have done for eons!

'True, Mantras are a great way to stay Mindful, and they really work, but I'm talking about something else right now though,' Tara said with emphasis. 'I'm talking about being Mindful of *what's going on in your head*, and *Listening* to *every single Thought* you have, rather than just *one* particular sentence.

The aim is that, **if you *Listen* to yourself talk, you begin too see that one part of your Mind is occupied with talking and another with *Listening*. The more you do this exercise, besides getting to know the *content* of your Mind because you're constantly Listening to it, it also *trains the part of your Consciousness which is detached from the chatter in you brain. It makes you realise that you are not your Thoughts!'***

'Wow, that's cool!' was all Lee managed to say. He waved at Tara to take a few minutes break while he mulled over the last few sentences. "There's a part in your brain that *observes*. *You are not your Thoughts*," he repeated to himself. That was *big* stuff! He felt butterflies in his stomach, he breathed deeply. **If he wasn't his Thoughts, then *what* was he? *Who* was he?**

Lee took a moment to look at the sky, the grass, the pond in the distance. His Mind was empty. He closed his eyes. Was that who he was? **An observer without any comments in his head which described what was going on inside and outside of him?** He kept his eyes closed for a little while longer, allowing himself to *feel* that feeling. Just *feeling* it *without thinking* it.

When Lee finally opened his eyes he felt dazed. His Rational Mind had a lot to deal with today. His mental world was being turned upside down, but he observed that he was fine with it, he knew it felt good, that it *was* good. He felt strong, **his *Being* felt strong, getting finally what it had known was out there, what it had been waiting for all these years. It was as if it had been woken from a long, long sleep and slowly begun to remember.**

'You ok?' Tara asked more out of politeness than anything else. She knew the look on Lee's face only too well. *Remembrance*. It was powerful, yet slightly bewildering when you were not used to it.

'Yeah, I'm fine,' Lee shook his head vigorously to clear the muddiness. He breathed deeply until renewed vigour flooded through his veins and oxygen sparked up his brain. He was ready.

'Yeah, I'm cool, where were we? Talking-out-loud?'

'Yep,' Tara said gently, quietly, '**talking-out-loud is also a fabulous way to show us *how* we think, because we don't usually think in *words* or whole and nicely structured sentences**.'

'We don't? How do we think if not in words?'

'**We think in *concepts*, sudden realisations and in pictures.** Give it a go, observe your Thoughts, while you think...,' she paused and then said with emphasis, 'America!'

Before Lee knew what was happening, he thought about America and presidents and the Statue of Liberty and the Empire State Building and LA and Hollywood, it's entire history, past and current, politics, food, movies, film-stars, it was all there, *all at once*! Tara was right. There were no words. **It was more like millions of impressions and knowing-s flying at him and past him from everywhere.** Amazing. **A lifetime of information in a flash.** He laughed.

'See?' Tara interrupted his Thoughts. 'Just one word triggers vast amounts of Thoughts, and all that at lightening speed. Can you see that your mouth could never keep up if you'd tried to talk *that* out-loud?" Lee grinned. 'Try it, try to keep up with that while you talk, just for fun,' she dared him.

'Oh, no way!' Lee was amusedly by the sheer prospect of such an undertaking.

'Oh, yes way! It's a fascinating little peek into your head. Really! When I did this for the first time, I couldn't believe it. I had no idea how *fast* I was thinking until then. No matter how hard I tried, I couldn't keep up with my Thoughts, I simply couldn't talk fast enough.

It was fascinating to observe how my Mind jumped aimlessly from association to association, then from subject to subject and how desperately my tongue tried to keep up. It was absolutely hilarious. Most of the time I was just rambling about God and the world, mostly not making much sense.'

'So the point is to try to verbally keep up with Thoughts *while* they unfold?' Lee wanted to clarify.

'Exactly. So, to summarise everything so far, **you can learn from Listening to the *content* of your Thoughts, you can learn about *how* you think, you can meet the '*observer*', you can laugh at the sheer hilarity of what comes out of your mouth, and you can do something else. You can also learn to *slow down* your Thoughts, which then ultimately helps you with stopping them too.**'

'Aha?'

'**The trick is to keep catching yourself out when you think faster than you can talk, and then to slow your Mind down by focussing with all your might on** *Listening to your words, rather than thinking new ones*. **The aim is to slow down your Thoughts so much, until you** *can* **actually keep up with your mouth! With practice you can learn to slow them down dramatically, and as a result, your Mind becomes more peaceful.**'

'Unfathomable.'

'Until you try it yes,' Tara said candidly. 'Can you see the difference between talking out loud and thinking?'

'Sure. Thinking *always* happens, but often we're not aware of it, because a lot of it happens *subconsciously*, so our Consciousness misses a lot of it. Whereas, when we actively talk-our-Thoughts-out-loud and simultaneously *hear* the voice *and Listen* to it, we become consciously aware of *all* of our Thoughts – or at least most of them.'

'Precisely. **By doing this, we notice the Thoughts that we're talking out loud** *and* **the ones we can't keep up with** - they're usually the interesting ones,' Tara smiled. '**To add to all the Thoughts we're thinking about a particular subject, and of course all the associations that come with it, our Mind also** *prepares* **the next twenty Thoughts including all it's sidelines and options**,' Tara said.

'Craziness,' Lee was aghast.

'I know. This exercise gives you a very special insight into your head. It allows you to consciously notice some of the *preparing*. **It's like normally we just see the advertising board, but we never get so see the actual board meeting that plans it.** Well, **by talking to yourself, you get yourself a first class seat in that boardroom**.

You'll see pictures flash past your Mind at lightening speed, concepts, arguments, entire worlds off judgements and opinions, and all that while you're talking about something completely different. On top of that you'll become aware of the vast numbers of Mind associations for every single individual word you *are* talking-out-loud.

You could be talking about America as a fabulous country to travel, and within a split second your Mind also reels of your entire knowledge and opinion of it, plus of course all your other background Thoughts that might be going on, which never make it to the tip of your tongue. You can talk and think about so many different things at the same time it's ridiculous.'

'Man, our Minds *are* busy.'

'Aren't they just. And it goes further than that. You might see a picture of a situation, which in turn might then give you a particular *feeling*. Your head then goes on interpreting the feeling. *More* background Thoughts, impressions, concepts, which you can't keep up with, but you can at least begin to become *aware* of them with this exercise. It really is great, somehow when you talk out loud, you notice all these things.'

'Fascinating,' Lee said amazed. 'Such a simple thing to do with so many things we can learn from it.'

'It truly is. But, I tell you, even though I've told you *some* of the things you'll observe, nothing can describe what it's *really* like. You'll realise that you indeed have a little creature up there that happily does whatever it wants, regardless of what we want it to do,' Tara tapped her forehead. 'And it does so at a million miles an hour, using up ridiculous amounts of our energy for things that are mostly nonsensical useless crap - and all that *while* we're watching!'

'The creature has no shame!' Lee butted in. 'Nuts.'

'Yep. More?'

'Sure.'

'You'll also realise within seconds of starting this exercise, how unbelievably annoying the sound of your voice is. Within seconds you'll bore the pants of yourself. I mean, it's not like you're talking to another person, you're talking-out all of your Thoughts, and they're *stupid*! **Imagine another person talking to you, constantly repeating themselves over and over again, going over the same stuff again and again, jabbering on and on, and all that *really* fast!** That person comments, on everything, and I mean *everything*. It'll drive you bonkers in no time. And you know what? This happens in our heads all the time, we just don't notice it because we're not paying any attention. Our Conscious Mind does a fabulous job to block these background Thoughts, but when we talk out loud, these little details get amplified to the nth degree and really home in the point.'

'Sounds intense.'

'Oh rubbish, it's hilarious, try it!' Tara waved her hand.

'What, now?' Lee raised his eyebrows.

'Sure. No time like the present.'

'Ok, but, I think I'll need some privacy for this one,' Lee got up and turned, he didn't want to get caught talking about Kate.

'Oh, you spoil sport,' Tara laughed, waving Lee goodbye as he walked a few paces away. She heard him mumbling for a bit and then laughing and laughing and laughing. After a few minutes he came back and sat back down with a reddened face and a huge smile.

'And?' Tara prodded him impatiently.

'This must be one of the most positively entertaining things I've ever done,' Lee was still catching his breath. He ran his fingers through his hair, massaged his scalp for a second and rubbed his face to relax the laughing muscles around his mouth and eyes.

'Go on, go on! Tell me, tell me, tell me!' Tara nudged his arm.

'That was crazy! I had to stop talking, after just a few minutes. It was driving me insane! The constant ridiculous chatter, so clear, so loud, it nearly drove me bonkers! I was so desperate to stop, all I wanted to do was breathe and meditate, it was unreal. This exercise can really drive you barmy, it's mad to notice how much we think and how stupid most of it is - and how utterly irrelevant! And those preparing Thoughts you were talking about? I've never experienced anything like it! You're right. Words *don't* do it justice. You really have to live through this for yourself. I've just had a valuable lesson, thank you. I just experienced first hand that my brain really has a life of it's own and that it thinks all by itself. And it's ruuuuubiiishh! God, the crap in my head,' Lee pulled his hair. 'If they didn't cart me off to the loony-bin after they caught me Humming for a week, they'd sure change their Minds, when they catch me talking to myself,' Lee grinned.

Tara laughed, 'Yeah, you might have to pick your environment to practice this one safely.'

'Yeah, I think so too. Actually, **couldn't I just talk-to-myself-in-my-head?**'

'**Sure, if you do that though, it's important to really *talk* to yourself in your head**, you know, as if you'd be talking to another person, telling them everything you're thinking. Doing that silently is usually more difficult though,' she drew Lee's attention to some of the pitfalls.

'Why is that?'

'Thinking **quietly and thinking loudly, is very similar to reading quietly and reading out aloud. When you read something quietly, your Mind can rush over lines very fast and words can get fuzzy or lost in speed**. You might think that you're concentrating wholly on your reading, but actually you might've just read a whole page, without taking any of it in. It's the same with thinking quietly. You often won't notice that you've stopped paying proper attention, unless you're really good with the old catching out thingy. If you'd have talked-out-loud or read the same page out loud on the other hand, you'd have more of a chance to really become aware of every word and you'd notice much easier if you zoned out.'

'Fair enough,' Lee could see the sense in that.

'The more we practice the more we manage to slow down our Thoughts and the more we manage to verbally keep up with them.'

'Great. We realise Thoughts are stupid, we slow them down and we become Mindful, all at the same time! Gosh, this stuff is so clever.' Lee quickly scribbled:

This exercise helps us to:

* Observe our Thoughts because we're Listening to them.
* Realise that we're thinking lots of rubbish.
* Slow down our Thoughts.
* We become Mindful.

Lee put his pen down. Both of them laid down on their sides in the grass, facing each other, their Minds still focussed and sharp, ready for more. They checked in with each other to make sure that they wanted to go on. It was a mutual affirmative: Yes.

Focus On Your Senses

Tara took the notebook and checked the 'Mindfulness-on-daily-activities list' to pick the next point, 'Ah, yes. Another enjoyable way of practising Mindfulness is by focussing on our five senses. You know when I said earlier that you rediscover the world every day when you're in the Now? Well, this is the bit where that happens. We use our sense of touch, smell, taste, sight and hearing to constantly stay Mindful in our every day life.'

'Ok?' Lee wanted more.

'**Our senses are relentlessly in action and constantly feed input into our brain, usually all at the same time! It's far too much information for our Mind to process, so most of it usually becomes a blur and doesn't register consciously. If we concentrate on our senses Mindfully, we pay attention to one individual sense at a time, and that sense alone. We shut off everything, but that one sense.** For example we hear, and I mean *really* hear it. Hear *everything*. *Hear* the wind, the traffic, people, music, dogs, insects, everything. Then *smell* everything, then see everything, see the wind in the trees, the leaves, the grass, then *feel* it on your skin and in your hair, etc. **Sense by sense, experience your environment. You will become aware of the world around you as you have never before**.'

'That sounds great, and it's easy to do all day long. I can do it out in nature, in the office, in a noisy town, in the supermarket queue, anywhere,' Lee said.

'That's when it's the most fun, when you're out and about. Listen to the noise, smell the smells, see the chaos, really *feel* people shuffling past you. You can focus on impressions close by or far away. You can **slowly scan every inch of the world with each of your senses, one after another**. You can Listen to sounds in various distances. I tell you, once you

161

do this, you'll notice the amount of sensory input your Consciousness has been missing.'

'I can only begin to imagine.'

Lee instantly noticed an astonishing selection of sensory input that he hadn't been aware of before, simply by shifting his focus onto truly hearing and then seeing - Tara really was lovely, hearing, seeing, ... he grinned. She'd make a wonderful storyteller, Lee thought. He loved it when Tara got excited. Her face was so expressive, it brought everything she described to life.

'By focussing on your senses and just *feeling* **them, rather than** *thinking* **them, you slip into the Present,'** Tara went on being her usual animated self. 'Have you ever seen one of those music videos, where the singer walks through a busy town in slow motion and the world around him seems to have sped up? Well, that's how it feels sometimes. By being Now, by *really* seeing, hearing and so on, you feel as if you're suddenly in a different dimension, everything is much clearer, much more intense. Colours, beauty, nature, all of it. **By becoming a conscious and Mindful** *observer***, we become a** *part* **of the world with our whole Being, rather than the world just passing us by when we're not looking.** That's when we *really are* in the *Now*! The space where it *all* happens, and with practice, we can have this experience all the time.'

'Wow.'

'Yep. And what it can do to you and your life is without words,' she went on with spirit, '**suddenly the world around you explodes in sensory delights. Take eating for example. With Mindfulness, all your Thoughts and attention and concentration is** *only* **on tasting and eating food.** Try it without any distractions, on your own, no telly, no book, nothing to divert your Mind. Just eat. Suddenly you *taste* the food - I mean *really* taste it! **You taste** *every* **bite,** *all* **the spices, you notice the consistency, feel your tongue moving through the food, the strength of our teeth - bloody hell- it's like you've never eaten before. Imagine having a bath like that....!'** Tara's eyes trailed off in delighted memories.

At the suggestion of a bath, Lee's eyes had become shiny and excited like a little child's, 'Wooha!! A bath, with bubbles! The hot water, covering my Body, getting hotter with movement. All my skin's getting tingly. Wow, taking baths and doing it Mindfully? I'd feel the water, move my toes and hands really slowly, dip my head under water - and feel it play with my hair! Listen to the bubbles burst. Smell the water... all five senses - individually. Tara, that sounds so cool! I mean, yeah, it's Hippy-shit and I don't know how the lads at the pub would get on with this, but I don't care, I think it's great. I can see how interesting life could suddenly become. Total sensory overload in fact, and, oh man, it's *everywhere*!'

'Isn't it great? I tell you, **this is an entirely new experience. If you are fully in the Present with *all* your *doings*, a new world opens up. You suddenly notice things you'd never have before. Each moment in your life becomes so much fuller and glorious and you'll wonder how you could've lived in such a bubble for all those years to have missed *This*! You begin to appreciate tiny little things so much- I mean how much bliss can a bath bring you? Can you even imagine making love?'** Without realising she held his gaze a second longer than needed and quickly stumbled on, 'Totally? Mindfully? Uoooohh. **I mean, preposterous, just the Thought of it,'** she continued unperturbed. **'*All* activities become new and interesting and exciting. You never get bored anymore. I mean, how can you, when there's always something *new* to discover with your senses?** All those amazing things that are always around us, but which we've always missed with our cloudy heads? You suddenly do everything with a big smile on your face - which also happens to infect others,' Tara added, pointing at the world around her.

Lee nodded, 'Every action would be as if I'd be doing it for the first time. I'd see every moment like out of the eyes of a child, which has never had a bath or a run before. A child which has never driven or cycled or eaten or danced or listened to music. Oh God, the Thought of listening Mindfully to my music collection gives me Goosebumps!' Lee smiled widely, 'Oh boy, this is so easy and so amazingly wonderful – living in the Now. And all for free! **I can see how our ordinary world suddenly changes around us, simply because we're actually paying attention. Living in the moment rocks**, Tara! If you ever want to practice together...,' his voice trailed off as he winked at her innocently, not in the slightest hinting at anything.

Tara grinned back at him, equally innocently, 'You'd be surprised how many incredible things are splattered along our little paths, the world is full of them, believe you me!'

A curious smile overcame Lee's lips, 'Ha, you know what I just thought? I'd love to try to focus on *all* my senses, *all at the same time*! Man, I wonder what *that* would be like,' he sat up, closed his eyes and began to play.

Tara burst out laughing, 'And you said that I was full-on with this stuff? See how tempting the experimenting is? Just for fun? Just to see what it does? What it's like?'

Lee nodded as his smile widened, but kept his eyes closed. By the time he opened them again, his face was glowing.

'That was truly ridiculous. That was like some mind-altering substance experience. Woha, that really blew me away. It's actually quite difficult to *feel* all your senses at the same time, you know? But boy, I think I got a couple of little flashes of it, what it *would* be like. Whooohoo!'

'Isn't it great? There are endless things to play with.'

Tara sat up, she felt joyful and full of beans, as it had become her nature. As she had made herself to be. Today there was some extra excitement in her Being, she could feel it clearly. She had found a play buddy! Lee loved to experiment as much as she did and he was as fascinated as she was. This was getting better by the minute.

She smiled happily, 'Oh, and **besides all the fun stuff, concentrating on your senses like this, also trains your Mind to become Mindful, to be Present, to be in the Now *and* it stops the clutter of Thoughts in your Brain**.'

'Amazing,' Lee said breathing elatedly. "Oops, deep belly breathing!" - the red flag in his Brain whacked him gently. As he slowed and deepened his breathing, his Mind and Thoughts calmed down instantly - just a warm feeling of contentment remained, with a tiny bit of excitement mixed in there somewhere too.

He noticed with interest that Kate was slowly disappearing out of his head. Something, which had as much to do with his new ability to catch himself out when Kate took over his Thoughts, as with the sparkly Being besides him. The art-of-distraction, he thought to himself and smiled.

Observe Your Body

'The next point on the list,' Tara pointed at Lee's notebook, 'is **Observing your Body and being Mindful about *what* your Body does and *how* it does it**. Let me give you an example. Back at my house, we have a little front garden and from time to time the leaves in the garden need to be swept up. A few days ago, it was my turn to clean up. I was tired, I was hot and I really couldn't be bothered, but I had to do it,' Tara looked exhausted just talking about it. 'But instead of moaning about it, I saw it as an opportunity to practice Mindfulness. I started to observe my Body sweeping. I observed my muscles, the weight shifting back and forth on my feet, my knees and my spine, I observed my posture and looked if I could detect any tension in my Body. I learned so much about my Body that day, that I nearly started to enjoy the sweeping,' Tara giggled. 'Anyway, **observing your Body is a great thing to do all day long.** You can observe the *way* you walk, the way you stand, sit, run, drink, write, go up the stairs, how your legs move or your arms, how your teeth, tongue and jaws interact while eating, how you read, how you lounge on the sofa while watching telly, whatever, anything. Just observe *exactly* what your Body does and how it does it. *Feel* **it, don't think it. Don't** *describe* **the feeling with words, just** *feel* **the sensations**,' Tara ended another one of her little monologues.

'Like that *every* activity could become an opportunity to observe, learn and practice Mindfulness and be Now, and of course to get out of my head. **What's best, I never have to set special practice time aside anymore because it can just be part of my everyday life**, there doesn't have to be formal Meditation practice. Now *this* really rocks!'

'Spot on. **Mindfulness, Nowness, Meditation, it's all about** *Living* **Now - not about sitting in a corner.**'

'This is why I like your approach Tara. It's hands on. Not hairy-fairy. It's practical, do-able and as an extra bonus, **I finally have a way of making my little pet hates more interesting**. Changing the sheets on my bed, tidying the house, bringing out the rubbish, cleaning windows, driving to work, they'll all take on a new dimension. I've never driven to work while completely focussing on my senses, *really* seeing everything around me, not being distracted with Thoughts in my head, *really* paying attention to my surroundings or my Body for that matter - well, and the road of course,' Lee grinned. 'I love it.'

The Mind's Effect On Our Body

'**Wait till you start to observe how your State-of-Mind affects everything you do physically, that's even more interesting!**'

'Eh what?'

'I mean to observe how your actions change with different moods, in different situations, with different people or with what you think. You can have a right giggle about that. If you're angry, you walk fast and stompy, you slam doors or bang pots and pans, maybe even drop stuff,' Tara got up and acted out various scenarios. 'If you're happy you're relaxed,' she let her Body hang comfortably. 'If you're pissed off, your Body tenses up,' she stood stiff like a stick. 'Feeling cocky, insecure, feeling tired, sad, happy, whatever, they all have an effect on our Body and how we move it,' her Body tensed, relaxed, shifted, bend and bounced, matching to the adjectives that flowed easily out of her mouth. 'We can observe and learn from it. We might notice that if we're hungry, angry or upset we become Mindless, we don't pay attention to where we're stepping and as a result we might stumble and hurt ourselves - especially if we're barefoot,' she bend forward and tickled Lee's big toe. 'If we're halfway aware, we'll at least learn a lesson. It's not that we're clumsy, it's just that we're not paying attention! Next time when we're stumbling, we can catch ourselves out and slow down - our Mind *and* our Body!' Tara was in a flow, 'Maybe you're sweeping the yard and you suddenly realise that your left shoulder hurts during a particular motion or your back feels uncomfortable or whatever. Then during the day, you Mindfully observe any posture that aggravates it. You can now consciously start to change the way you sit or bend down or sleep, or maybe even determine what caused the pain in the first place.

You can observe how your Body reacts to different kinds of food, sleep patterns, drink, stress *and* the way you think. **The more you notice the impact of different patterns on your physical and mental well being, the more in tune you become with your Body and your Mind. You begin to *know* that it really is good and important to look after your Body with the right food and exercise. You'll understand from the core of your Being that it's beneficial to look after your Mind by being Mindful and in the Now, to stop, observe and learn. It's not because somebody else tells you or because you read about it. You'll know it for yourself, first hand. And by becoming aware, you can *choose* to change things - just the way you want them to be.'**

'Check. Taken in and digested,' Lee said, rubbing his belly.

Tara paused a moment and then added cautiously, 'I think you're cool with this anyway, but still, I'd just like to add that it's important not to become fanatical about any of this stuff. You know, **playing, experimenting, even taking some things to the extreme is great, but always remember, it's all supposed to be fun**, right? So, **keep in Mind, that all this is a means to an end, it's not an end in itself. It's just an interesting tool to help you become more aware, more Mindful, and while we're doing that, learn a little about yourself and have a giggle.'**

'Thanks for that. Yeah, that *is* important to remember, it'll keep my feet solid on the ground and not lift off,' Lee made a tiny gesture of flapping wings with his fingers.

Mindful Interaction - Meeting People Mindfully

'**M**mh, I just thought of something,' Lee said, 'I can see all this stuff working fine when I'm on my own, but how does it work when there are other people around?' Lee started to stumble and fall about, leaning against an imaginary bar counter, pulling up one of his eyebrows and slurred, 'Sorry lads, give me half an hour, will ya? I just have to go and do my Be-Now-exercise, so don't Mind me for a bit, ok?'

Tara laughed at Lee's scarily authentic imitation of a Lager-loud.

'Naa, I somehow don't think that would be socially acceptable,' he grinned.

'I'd dare to agree with that - if you do it like that anyway,' Tara laughed. 'But seriously, remember? You don't have to go away to play, you can be Mindful *during* all actions, including interactions with the world around you.'

'And that'll include talking to my mates,' Lee stated simply.

'Of course,' Tara said, picked up the pen and handed it to Lee.

'Woha, I see a list coming on,' Lee said and opened his notebook.

'Actually, have a look at the last point on your previous list.'

Lee looked through his book and found the entry Tara was talking about: 'Mindful Interaction'. Together they wrote a list for just that headline.

<u>Be Mindful during interactions:</u>
- Observe y*our Behaviour* during interactions.
- Observe y*our Mind* during interactions.
- Get to know the way *you react* to others and interact with others.
- See how *others* react to you.
- Observe others.
- Become sensitive to interactions between other people.
- Be Now.

'Got it. All there,' Lee said satisfied and flopped back into the grass.

'Excellent. **Now, being Mindful while interacting with others can teach us nicely about a whole bunch of things**, even if you're in a pub with a bunch of drunks,' Tara winked at Lee remembering his earlier performance. '**First we get to know our *own* actions in a group better, how *we* think, behave and react when we're amongst other people. All we need to do is *catch ourselves out* and Mindfully observe what's going on and thus become aware of the unspoken Signs and messages within us**: Are we animated? Are we loud? Are we shy? Are we the centre of attention? Are we not really involved? Are we dominating the conversation? Are we listening or are we distracted? Are we having a conversation or a monologue? Are we funny? Serious? Are we always trying to make somebody laugh? Are we aggressive? Angry? Happy? Do we snap at certain people? How does our way of interacting change with different moods? Do we behave differently with family, friends and strangers? With people we love or don't love so much? People that irritate us? They're all fascinating insights.'

'Man, **I can see my brain going into total overload with all this new information. How am I ever supposed to concentrate on** a conversation with all of that stuff going on top of it?' Lee asked shrugging his shoulders.

Observing, Not Judging

'**G**ood point,' Tara enjoyed that nothing ever went past Lee. '**To be able to do that, it's important to simply notice and *observe* yourself and others, what's going on or what you're saying, and *not* to *judge, analyse* or *compare* or use any other related Thoughts**,' Tara took a deep breath after this mammoth sentence.

'Mmh,' Lee's brain switched into the next gear, 'because **as soon as we judge, we start to think. Judging requires a Thought process of comparing, of opinions and decisions**. Therefore, before we know it, we get into a loop of Thought's, and that's exactly what we want to avoid,' Lee deducted easily.

'Precisely. So, **besides the fact that judging yourself or even somebody else isn't very nice, by just *observing*, rather than *judging*, we can stay Mindful and in the Now *and Listen* to the conversation all at the same time,**' Tara grinned at the pun. '**And all that because instead of making up stories in our head about what we hear or what we believe things around us to be like, *we just see and hear what actually is*. It's like holding a mirror in front and around us and observing what we see without any comments in our head.**'

Lee nodded, 'It's just about getting to know *how* we are and how others are, without thinking or judging anything to be good or bad or cool or not for that matter. We just observe. If somebody is agitated or angry, we don't judge it as bad, we just notice it, observe it. Cool get it.'

'Exactly. **Be sensitive and be aware. This stuff is not about going around and judging or labelling people. It's not for Mind games and trying to figure people out**,' Tara said with a warning undertone.

'But it's to help us practice to *become aware* and *Mindful* of every little detail in our environment inside and outside of us, in every moment in time, without creating any more Thoughts,' Lee finished Tara's sentence.

Tara held up her thumbs, 'Full points.'

Observe The Mind While We're Interacting

'**You'd be surprised by the amount of crap you think of,** *while* **you're talking to people,**' Tara grinned, '**I always used to believe that I don't think about other stuff when I talk to my mates. I mean I'm** *talking* **to them, how could I be** *thinking* **of something else, right**?' Tara paused dramatically.

'Wrong?' Lee's ventured.

'Absolutely. That's what I thought until I *actively observed* my Mind during a conversation with a friend. It's crazy, how we think that we are Listening to somebody, when actually our Mind is off on one as usual. I sometimes wonder how we can follow a conversation, with our brains giving a *constant* running commentary of it. It comes up with endless *word associations*, judgements, completely unrelated stuff, basically the whole shebang we've just talked about, just for fun, to try and be helpful or to just utterly confuse you.

Our Mind has to try and Listen to the conversation and understand it, battle with distracting Thoughts, and on top of all of that it has to deal with all the sensory input we're getting every single split second. We might notice something out of the corner of our eyes: "uh, what was that?" - bang, there's a Thought. "We're hungry" – a Thought. We just picked something out of our teeth that tastes odd - bang another Thought,' Tara grinned, 'A smell, a sound. As soon as we notice it, the Mind has already created a Thought.'

'Or a million more like it,' Lee said whistling through his teeth.

'Yeah exactly, the Mind begins to associate and compare what it has just noticed with something else, bang, bang, bang, more Thoughts and so on and so on. **If we don't catch ourselves out, the Mind looses itself.** "Yeah, that pair of trousers was really great," - Thought, "Shampoo, soap, Cornflakes. Uh, nice bottom," - Thought,' Tara grinned. 'Are we drinking our beer faster than our friend? - a Thought. We wonder what the time is – a Thought. "Time for a bathroom break," – a Thought. "Did I switch the iron off? Dogs, cats…,". **Believe it or not, all this happens** *constantly while* **we think that we're paying our undivided attention to Listening to our friend.**'

'Scary, but I can think of a million and one occasions where exactly that has happened,' Lee said surprised.

'Yeah, and it happened right now.'

'How do you know?' Lee looked perplexed.

'Did you noticed how quickly you just gave me that answer?' she looked at him with clear and steady eyes. 'To tell me so quickly that you can think of a million and one occasions, you must have compared what I said to your own experiences all along while I was talking! Which means you did exactly what I just said. Gotcha honey!' Tara grinned playfully.

'You're right! Man, you're quick! How can you pick up on all of that stuff?'

'Practice,' Tara shrugged her shoulder. 'Well, and I pay attention.'

'Practice what you preach!' Lee said with respect for Tara's presence in his voice. 'Well,' Lee breathed out heavily, 'it seems that if we don't focus our brain, it's the genius of multi-tasking.'

'Yeah, or rather Jack-of-all-trades-but-genius-of-none,' Tara's sharp Mind was in full form. 'But, once you're aware it's easy to play with. When your Mind runs off, all you need to do is catch yourself out and instead of chattering in your Brain, bring your attention back to the Now, and *Listen* instead.'

'Until I'm off again.'

'Yep.'

Observe People in Conversations and How They React To Us

Lee glanced at the list, 'Cool, ticked off. The next point is: 'observing how *other* people react to *us*'.'

'Oh yes, that'll be Mindfully observing *other* people while we talk to them,' Tara said. 'So this one is about *other* people now. Check out if they are calm or fidgety? Do they fiddle or shuffle? Do they stare? Are they paying attention? Are they tired? Bored? Intimidated? Indifferent? Do they get a word in edgeways when others talk? Do they listen to us? Do they ask questions? Are they alert? Interested? Observe their Body-language, their face, eyes, hands, how they talk. Do they behave differently to us than to others? Observe every facet of how they interact between themselves.'

'I think I usually do that anyway,' Lee thought out loud. 'Mmh, but maybe not really consciously.'

'Well, the conscious bit is what changes everything. Eeeeverythiiiing!' Tara demonstrated chirpily with a bunch of lively hand gestures.

'Yeah right. It has to be conscious,' Lee said with emphasis, 'otherwise how can we make sure that we just observe instead of judging and interpreting others' Behaviour in all sorts of weird? We wouldn't be able to catch ourselves out and just get paranoid instead.'

'Very important. We need to observe what's actually there, not *think* what's there.'

'Observe, don't judge. I can already imagine being called freak-boy, when I'm sitting in a corner of the pub or at home, observing and staring at my mates,' Lee grinned.

'Ha, I love how you always get straight down to the extreme. If you want to be freak-boy, be my guest, but **you can do all of this, without anybody actually noticing**. You can still be part of a group, you can still have a conversation, laugh and joke like you'd normally do, it's just that you stay *consciously aware* of what's happening around and inside of you, *while* it's happening, instead of being in your head thinking stuff. **There's no need for staring or being any different than you normally are.**'

'Good-bye freak-boy,' Lee said sadly, waving to no-one in particular.

'Good-bye freak-boy and *hello* Conscious-boy!' Tara laughed.

'Oh, alright then, you win,' Lee gave in easily.

'You know, **by paying attention we start to notice and become familiar with the *more subtle* ways of people's interactions. We become more sensitive to the way people relate to each other with language, with unspoken words, with Body-language, actions and lots more**. A kink of the head, a leaning forward or backward, different ways of speaking, tense or relaxed movements, raising of an eyebrow, nervous ticks, hand gestures, that sort of thing. Observe, do people behave or communicate differently when are they are angry or agitated or open or closed or argumentative or shy? How do other people react to their environment and other sensory input? You could maybe even learn something from them - but that's just an extra option,' Tara said casually. '**With practice we'll be able to easily read the relationships and energies in a room and between people.**

Becoming aware of our fellow Beings in this way, therefore makes our own interactions much easier and much more fun. If we can become aware of the fact that somebody is irritable or angry, we might be able to tread a bit more carefully. On the other hand, maybe there's a really shy person, who never gets a word in edge ways, maybe it'll be nice to give them some space to butt in? It's absolutely spellbinding to even just *look* at different situations and people, at various times of day or places and to just observe. **You'd be surprised to see how much you can learn, just by being aware of what's *really* going on - Now.**'

'Yeah dude, know what'z'a *really* goin' on in de hood man, sorted geezer,' Lee curled his fingers into the thumb-little-finger-sign that the really cool dudes do, and waved his hand up and down to make it more authentic.

Tara shot him a big smile, which was retuned heartily. She curled her own fingers in the same way and met Lee's hand in mid air as the approving gesture.

Within all the smiles a wonderful feeling of elation crept up Lee's spine. This was amazing - the discovery of the internal Universe! Then his Rational Mind switched itself on again: "This is all a bit to good to be true, isn't it? Why would you even want to stop thinking in the first place? I'm doing a good job, aren't I?" Right on cue Doubts, fears and scepticisms crept in. Then - click, his Intuition switched itself on loud and clear: "Red flag. Lee? Hello? Don't be so bloody stupid, you know that it makes sense!" He laughed at himself. With a start it dawned on him that his Awareness had already changed, after just a few hours. He was observing his Thoughts! He even just noticed that his Rational Mind was contradicting the way he actually felt. His Mind was trying to convince him that how he really felt was wrong. Strange, strange world... Lee looked puzzled, then grinned again, sat up straight and breathed. Effortlessly his Mind and his Being cleared. Strong, Powerful, Alive, Happy. Clear. Yes!

Tara noticed the changes on Lee's face. She loved the way she could see him think, how his forehead wrinkled, and oh yes, that eyebrow, expressively dancing up and down with every Thought, with every question. She'd always had a weakness for animated faces. Especially faces that could smile like that - and eyes that could sparkle like that, she thought dreamily. They really had the most beautiful colour. She usually liked blue eyes, but Lee's were this brown, this deep dark brown, awake, piercing, yet so gentle and loving, and they had these little green crinkles in them. He smiled at her. Little did she know that Lee already knew all about the different shades of light blue and green in *her* eyes.

PART 4

9 Play With Your Mind, Getting to Know Your Mind

Mindfulness to Observe Your Thoughts

Tara gently shook her head and remembered what they had been talking about. 'Thoughts. Oh yeah, now comes the fun bit.'

'God, more fun? How will I ever cope?' Lee joked.

'Surrender dear, surrender to fabulousness,' Tara threw her arm into the air, let herself fall forward onto her belly and hugged the grass.

When she looked up again, to Lee's relief, she didn't look as if she'd lost it, but she looked content, happy and present.

'Up till now,' Lee slumped down next to her, equally on his belly, **'we've talked about quietening our Thoughts and observing our Body, actions and reactions, our interactions with other's and their interactions with us and other people. With all the other examples we've gone through, I'd say that by now we know our Mind pretty well.'**

'Exactly, and now is the time to begin to *play* with it! A good start would be to Mindfully observe our Thoughts. It's a little bit like the talking-out-loud thingy, but also different. This is where Mindfulness and Meditation begins to get really interesting, even exciting. **It's about *actively* observing our Thoughts.'**

'You're kidding,' Lee blurted out.

'Eh, no. Why?'

Lee laughed out loud, 'Because I think that I just did that! Just a few minutes ago. I observed my Thoughts! And I noticed myself doing it earlier too.'

'Are you serious?'

'Yes I am, and I don't think I've ever done that before today. I mean I have analysed ideas and stuff, but not my Thoughts *themselves*,' Lee said. He told Tara about the experience he had earlier.

'Wow, that's so cool,' Tara grinned when Lee finished telling his story.

'Yeah I know, but it's also bizarre. It really *is* like *observing* what you think, rather than just thinking it. It's like standing outside of your head and looking in, observing what's going on in there, laughing at your own stupidity. Talking about funny.

Oh man, there was something else, I just remember, I noticed that my feelings and my Thoughts were contradicting each other, isn't that ridiculous? Gosh, if we can't notice the contradictions in our own head, I'm not surprised that we all get so confused. I mean, how are we ever supposed to sort things out in our lives if we don't even notice that kind of stuff within ourselves? It was certainly news to me. Funny, I knew that what my heart was telling me was right, but still my Rational Mind wouldn't stop talking, even when I told it to! It really does get interesting once you observe what's gong on up here,' Lee tapped his forehead. 'I guess, you can either get freaked out or overwhelmed, or you can just laugh about it, it's your choice. In the end they're all just Thoughts anyway, and most of them are stupid!' Lee said with emphasis.

Tara smiled brightly, 'Oh, you have no idea just *how* stupid they are, until you've *really* checked them out,' Tara clapped her hands with excitement.

'I guess that's what you meant with your we-don't-need-external-entertainment-as-it's-all-within-us comment,' Lee remembered.

'Might have done,' Tara smiled mischievously.

'Well, let's have it.'

Mindfulness to Analyse your Thoughts (Time for Laughing, Observing Your Thoughts and eh, Puppies)

'**O**k, just in case you hadn't noticed, we've just ticked of step four and five on the '*What to do?*' list.'

Lee rummaged in his notebook till he found the appropriate list. He ticket off step four and five and looked at the sixth step. 'Oh great, it's Time-for-Laughing,' he read out loud.

'So it is. For the sixth step, we go back to observing our *inside* world, rather than the outside world. The sixth step begins by going through the initial three Meditation steps we talked about earlier, keeping your attention on breathing in and out continuously and catching yourself out whenever your attention wanders.'

'Gently, gently, just making sure we don't get fed up,' Lee waggled his index finger in front of Tara's face.

'Exactly, but now we do something slightly different to before. Now, **every time we catch ourselves out and notice that our Mind has wandered, instead of bringing our concentration back to our breathing and thus to Nowness, we have a quick look at the**

Thought we've just had - this is where it gets really outrageous. Do you fancy seeing what *really* goes on in your head? How little control we *really* have about what's happening up there?' Tara tapped her temples with her forefinger. '**It's kind of the same, but also different to talking-out-loud, cause the emphasis is on recognising the hilarity, rather than trying to keep up verbally**. Wanna play?'

'Go for it,' Lee requested.

'Ok, try and think about just one thing for a few minutes.'

'Like what?'

'Anything,' Tara waved her hand in dismissal.

'I'll think of a weekend away I'm planning,' Lee said and silently added in his head: "Which, due to Kate's absence, will now be slightly different than originally planned".

'Great,' Tara said enthusiastically. 'Take a few minutes and consciously think of that weekend and *nothing* else. I tell you when to stop.'

'That's it?'

'That's it.'

Lee was surprised, that seemed too easy, he wondered where the catch was. 'Yes Ma'am,' he said obediently, a small smile playing at the corners of his mouth.

Just before he closed his eyes to concentrate better, he noticed that Tara had this knowing look on her face again and an amused twinkle in her eyes. "An intriguing combination," his stomach told him. Anyway, what was he going to think about? Oh yeah, the weekend away. He laughed at the fact that he'd forgotten his exercise subject, and had been sidetracked, even before he'd started the exercise. And again, the weekend. After a few minutes in silence, Lee burst out laughing. Laughing a lot seemed to become a habit. He loved it.

'This is hilarious!' he said. 'This is totally unreal! This is absolutely ludicrous. I can't believe that I never tried that before.'

'Go on then, what happened?' Tara asked eagerly. 'What, what?'

Lee was still laughing, 'Man, I had no idea. You're right, this is so funny!'

'Well, are you going to tell me or what?' Tara poked Lee impatiently.

Lee tried to pull himself together, 'First I remembered that I wanted to go to the countryside to hike and that I wanted to do that at the end of the month. Then I thought about the train ticket I needed to get and not having to get one for my ex-girlfriend. All of that still made sense.' While he was talking he could already hear his Mind scolding himself for mentioning his ex-girlfriend, but he tried to stay focussed. 'Then, probably having had a word association with the word train, I suddenly remembered a time when I took the Euro-star to Paris a few years ago, how the coffee had been so bad and how I got delayed and how I should have taken the plane. And then my Mind just went off. I remembered about a million flights I've been on, pictures of holidays flashed past my Mind. And yes, Italy, and the food I had in Rome, and did I invite Mum and Dad this Wednesday or next? Puff: The Rolling Stones. Puff again: Cheese. I mean, I have no idea where these Thoughts came from and then suddenly there were Pandas! That's when I just couldn't go on. I mean for freak's sake! Pandas? That was the weirdest thing. I have absolutely no idea where they came from. I caught myself out and went back to the holiday. The scary thing is that all that distraction happened so fast I nearly didn't notice that I hadn't been thinking about my holiday. But hey, I'm becoming an expert, so I *did* notice,' Lee said proudly, yet slightly frazzled.

'See what I mean?' Tara grinned.

Lee shook his head with awe, 'Man, besides the entertainment value that I just got out of that, I also *really* understood something. You said before that we will never really *know* anything, unless we *experience* it first hand? Well, it's true. When you told me earlier about the silly Thoughts we have in our heads, I thought, yeah, of course, I know that. And sure, throughout the previous exercises I got a pretty good idea, but this one takes the biscuit. I tell you, I had no idea, how ridiculous my Thoughts were really going to be. So many were total rubbish, they just didn't have *anything* to do with planning my holiday! Such gibberish.

I mean, I noticed that already when I talked-out-loud. **I noticed that a lot of Thoughts didn't make sense or were completely unnecessary, but now I noticed that we can also think about complete crap, *while* we think that we're actually concentrating on something.** Gosh, the little creature up there never stops,' Lee rested his index finger on his forehead. 'It came up with stuff that had nothing whatsoever to do with the subject that I actually wanted to think about. That's just silly.' Tara nodded her head vigorously while Lee continued, 'And you know what? **The cheeky bugger goes on *while* I'm observing it. I mean it actually goes on talking about Pandas while I'm standing right there looking at it.** Outrageous! As you said before, that little creature has no shame. **I don't even want to know what it's doing when I'm *not* looking.** There must be hundreds of unrelated Thoughts one can have in just one minute. I had no idea that my brain can get distracted so easily. There are all these little side Thoughts that just pop up from out of nowhere. I mean Pandas?' Lee was on a roll, 'It's like playing with a dog and her litter of *puppies*.

The mama-dog is the main Thought and the puppies are the distractions in our Mind, the word associations that create seemingly unrelated Thoughts and the Thoughts that process sensory input and so on. Let's say that our aim is to give the mama-dog attention, bla, bla, holiday, bla, bla, yep holiday, but then all the little puppies come waggling along, climbing all over us, chewing our legs, biting our pants, wanting attention. So, we give them some attention, of course we do, they are cute, right? And it's not as if they're politely asking for attention, they're *demanding* it! I mean, they're chewing my friggin' leg! So what am I supposed to do?'

Tara's face was radiating, 'What a fantastic example! Puppies! I love it. What a perfect way to describe it! I know exactly what you mean. And you know what? On a bad day? There are puppies *everywhere*. They come at you left, right and centre, all bouncy and jappy, seeking attention - all day long,' Tara grinned widely. She was really enjoying herself. 'They are crafty little sods too. They only take a split second to disturb your concentration - and either you notice them and go back to your main mummy dog Thought or − whoops - you don't. Lost in fluff. Or rather in fur,' Tara grinned.

'And another Mind- Diarrhoea-victim coming through on the scatterbrain-express,' Lee pressed both palms together horizontally and with a zooming train noise let them whiz from one side of his head to the other and back. He scratched his chin, 'Now that I've become aware of all this, it seems even more unbelievable that we never notice any of this stuff in our head. We all welcome each and every one of those stupid little puppy Thoughts into our heads. It's all: "Oh, hello little one, oh, aren't you cute?", or: "You're interesting too, let's spend some time with you", or: "oh and yes, you could be interesting too", or: "and you there, what about you?" And off we go,' Lee said mockingly. 'So funny, I thought that I can just think about one particular thing and that thing only, but I've just proven to myself that I can't do it. And what's more, my brain is constantly thinking - and I mean *constantly*, even if I think it's *not!*' he threw his hands into the air and let them drop into his lap again, stunned. 'Phew. But, I guess, the answer is always the same. To stop this dog story, all we need to do is catch-ourselves-out, notice that we're playing with one of the puppies, rather than with the mum, and bring our attention back to mummy-dog, the main Thought. Awareness, breath, attention, focus.'

They looked at one another in silence, letting the conversation sink in for a moment. Lee was flabbergasted, excited and tingly all over. He had this strange butterfly-feeling in his stomach that he usually got when he felt big stuff coming on. He looked at Tara who smiled even wider than before. Oh God, there was more.

Retracing Our Thoughts, Triggers, Contemplation and the Insight Thingy

Tara dove straight in, 'With your weekend trip example, you didn't only *observe* the Thought though, did you? You also did something else,' she hinted.

'I did?'

'Of course. You did something to remember *all* the Thoughts that you had.'

'Oh.'

'Can you remember how you did that?'

Tara wanted to go deeper as always and Lee was more than happy to do so. He pondered a few seconds, trying to remember. 'I think I was so Aware of what was going on in my head, that I noticed all the Thoughts unfolding *as and when* they came. I kind of noticed how one Thought build up on the other one. I was *observing*, following my train of Thoughts *while* I was thinking it. Even though it was so fast that I nearly missed it altogether.'

'Right. What you did there, was kind of step six-B, which means you're a step ahead,' Tara praised Lee, pinning an imaginary medal on his chest.

'I am? Excellent,' Lee pushed out his chest, looked down and admired his medal.

'Yeah, because people are often not able to see the Thoughts unfolding as they come yet. **They usually notice that they lost their mummy-subject and then have to try to remember the previous Thoughts. For that they have to learn to retrace their Thoughts.**'

'Ok, I might have done something like that to actually, but it was an accident rather than a deliberate act. So, tell me more about retracing Thoughts.'

'I'd love to. **It's a good thing to play around with at any rate, because retracing your Thoughts gives you free access to your Thoughts, and it trains your memory no end.** Retracing Thoughts is basically like step six, just instead of looking at the Thought you just caught yourself out on, you try to remember what you thought about before, and before that and so on.'

'Sounds tough.'

'Not really. It's just practice. To train your retracing ability you can begin with trying to remember everything you did during the day. You know, try and remember *everything backwards*, from the moment you're in now. How did you get to where you are at that moment in time, what did you eat, drink, who did you talk to, when did you get up? It's like trying to remember your dreams, first it's impossible, then hazy, then suddenly crystal clear. With practice it becomes pretty spot on.'

Lee sighed, 'Man, I can already see that following Thoughts will take as much concentration as trying *not* to think.'

'It just seems tough because we're directing our concentration *inwards* rather than outwards and we're not used to that. But again, nothing a bit of practice can't fix.'

'All those puppies. This is like 101 Dalmatians.'

'I know. That's why it's so important to practice step one to three, till you're really comfortable with your inward-continuous-concentration. And the more we get to know our Mind, the easier it will be to tell apart from our Intuition, the easier it will be to get back in touch with our Subconscious and the easier it will be to chat to The Guys.'

'Oh God, I've forgotten about The Guys.'

'Are you serious? That's why we're doing all of this isn't it? All the fabulous benefits you're getting here, no matter how life changing and Mind blowing, are nothing compared to what's still coming! More?' Tara asked which a cheeky look on her face, already knowing the answer.

'Oh yes, please,' Lee said readily, nodding his head up and down avidly.

A thick strain of soft, deep brown hair fell over his forehead. Lee thoughtlessly brushed it back, just for it to stubbornly fall back. Tara tried not to lean forward to touch it. She loved tousled hair. Tara smiled to herself, took her own medicine, retraced her Thoughts and continued.

'Now, why does retracing your Thoughts help with the Intuition thingy we talked about earlier? Well, do you remember where you had to analyse past Co-incidences and figure out if you had an Intuition beforehand, what it felt like and stuff?' Lee nodded. 'There you go, now you can go back in time and retrace Thoughts to the origin, right back to the Intuition! Learning to retrace your Thoughts, can also be tremendously useful to find out the origin of your Thoughts, to see where they came from, you know, what actually *triggered* them in the first place.'

Another switch flicked itself on in Lee's brain, 'Oh wow, I can see where you're heading! That's really useful! We could see *why* we have certain Thoughts. We could learn so much about ourselves by doing that. We could see that certain situations or people create certain reactions or Thoughts within us. For example: "I'm feeling self-conscious – uh, stop, where did that Thought come from?"…da, da, da, retrace, retrace? "Ok, that person over there looked at me disapprovingly, - stop, analyse - I felt self-conscious and behaved differently – stop, wonder, why the hell would I to do that? Why on earth would I be self-conscious. Does my Rational Mind contradict my feeling again? Or vice versa?"' Lee laughed, he'd never spoken his Thoughts out loud like that before, it was so funny, so clever. He continued, 'Normally such Behaviour or Thoughts would have been an automatic reaction. But now, if I can catch myself out, I have a *choice* - I could stop the Thought or go on with it. Whatever I want to,' Lee finished.

'Woha, stop right there, you've already started on step six-C.'

'I have? Which one is that?'

'Contemplation of Thoughts.'

'Ha, aren't I the clever one,' Lee grinned.

'You are. It's quite impressive actually. You traced the Thought about feeling self-conscious back to where it came from and then you contemplated as to *why* you felt self-conscious in the first place.'

'Ok, so just to get this straight in my head, the *observing* is where we just look at a Thought, but don't comment on it. But *contemplation* means thinking in great depth about something, doesn't it? Is it like studying the Thought and reflecting on it? Is that the way you use these terms too?'

'You've got it.'

'Hang on a sec if you don't Mind,' Lee made a quick note into his notebook:

Step 6 - Play with your Mind:
- Observe Thoughts
- Retrace Thoughts
- Contemplate Thoughts

While Lee was writing, something occurred to Tara. She patiently waited till he was done and then said, 'Just so that you know, I'm not talking about any old contemplation though.'

'Of course not!' Lee laughed and looked expectantly at Tara.

'I'm serious. **I'm talking about *conscious* contemplation, *conscious* analysing, *conscious* examining, being *fully aware* of the *entire* contemplation process *while* it's going on. Which means not loosing yourself in the analysing Thoughts.'**

'Ok?' That really didn't sound like *any old* contemplation to Lee, he grinned.

'The easiest way to start,' Tara continued, 'is to do short contemplating spurts at a time, and always bring your Thoughts back to your breathing fairly quickly.'

'What does fairly quickly mean?' Lee wanted to clarify.

'Quick enough so that you don't loose yourself in analysing or contemplating Thoughts, however long that means for you,' Tara said easily.

'I guess the point is not to replace lots of *unconscious thinking* with lots of *conscious analysing*,' Lee gathered.

'Exactly. So, look at the Thoughts, but don't drive yourself nuts with analysis. Look at it, learn, finished. All nice and consciously.'

'Ah, I see, **this time I have to catch myself out *during* the contemplation, to make sure that I don't get lost**. Makes sense.'

'Exactly. You'll have to find out for yourself, how long you can contemplate something before you're off with the fairies. It's different for everybody. **At the beginning it only takes a few seconds to get lost in Thoughts and it might take a while until you notice that you've lost it. Sometimes it takes seconds, sometimes minutes.**'

'Or until the alarm clock rings,' Lee added like a good student.

'Yep or that. Therefore, as I said, if you're still new to all this, it's best to only do very quick contemplating journeys, you know: look at the Thought or feeling, comment on it, and straight back to your breath. Like that you're easy on yourself, you'll have feelings of success and thus you don't get fed up. **The better your Continuous Awareness and Concentration gets, the more you can extend the contemplation time, simply because you can be confident that you can actually stay with it, without getting lost**,' Lee nodded appreciatively.

'Wanna hear what's going on in *my* head right now?' Lee asked Tara with a sudden intense look of concentration on his face.

'Absolutely,' Tara was curious to hear what Lee had on his Mind.

'Tara, this is really powerful stuff. Once I get the catching-out thingy down, I can do pretty much whatever I want with my Mind. I can observe my Mind unfold, I can trace it back to where it came from or I can take a snapshot of it at any moment in time. I can watch it, analyse it, contemplate on it, learn from it, piss myself laughing about it, the options are endless. All that simply by putting conscious attention on what's going on in my head, by dispersing the cotton wool, not giving in to four legged creatures and actually having an *active* look. Not only can I find out where a Thought comes from, I can also find out why is it there in the first place. I can accept it, question it's validity, I can turn it upside down, back to front, see all the ins and outs and even decide that it's stupid and that I don't really need a Thought like that in my head. And,' he added with a smile, 'if I don't want to do any of that, I just choose to get back to my breathing, and puff… it's silence,' the words came flooding out of his mouth. 'I can observe that certain Thoughts provoke certain **reactions** in my Mind. I can contemplate where they came from, why are they there, what triggered this particular reaction, maybe even if I *want* to react like that? If not, I just breathe.'

The more Lee thought about Meditation, the stronger his understanding rooted in his Being. 'It's like I'm talking to myself in my own head. I catch myself out. I get surprised that I actually *did* catch myself out and I notice that something new is going on in my head. I recognise that *all* the Thoughts in my head right now are in fact unusual, as I am aware that I don't normally *think about* my Thoughts. I decide to find out more and keep my attention on that analysis. I contemplate a bit. When my brain wants to think something else, I keep reminding myself to stay with the analysis, simply by focussed thinking about it. Hey presto – contemplation,' he paused to come up with an example to clarify to himself and Tara what he was talking about. After a minute or so he said, 'It's the same as if I would have to think about something at work. My Mind drifts off and I have to keep reminding myself that the weekend has not yet started and that I still have to do work, to shut up and concentrate. It's like off, on, off, on. And, I guess, the more I improve my concentration, the on-s become longer than the off-s,' Lee finished. 'Man, that was a right verbal waterfall, did you get all that?'

'Oh yes!' Tara said with emphasis. 'Thanks for sharing. It's so nice to hear what goes on in people's heads when they Get It! You don't need me to explain anything to you,' Tara bowed with her hands folded in front of her chest. 'You already know how to contemplate. And what's more, you're already doing it - and you're doing it well! A box labelled, wow-look-what's-going-on-in-my-head has just been dragged out of the deepest recesses of your warehouse and happily placed into your Consciousness; and it has a huge great big red label on it: "ha, surprise, look at me!" And it even stayed there long enough for you not only to notice it, but also to examine it *and* understand it. **A lot of people, when they get sudden insights like you just did, can't hold onto that box long enough to appreciate that there is something new happening in their brain, something outstanding, something really amazing, something that could be examined further.** With a lot of people it's more like: flick, it's there, uh, that's different, then again, uoh, I wonder when the bus comes, oh, dinner, and oops, look over there. So, trust me, you're doing really well. This is brilliant stuff, sweetie. **You really *want* to do it and you're actually doing it, that's what gives you the head start. A lot of people do the half-hearted approach and that just doesn't bring the insights that fast,**' Tara praised him with another one of those magical smiles. 'Ha, *and* you've been doing it without even knowing that you were doing it. Now darling, imagine what it could be like when you're doing it *deliberately*!'

'Just the Thought of it makes my Mind fly,' Lee looked up into the sky, his Mind boggled.

They sat quietly for a while, wondering if the people around them had any idea about the wonders they were carrying around with them, finely balanced on their necks. It seemed strange, it was all so near, yet so far, so unreachable to most, although it was right there, in their own heads. With everyone - all the time. God, us humans are so blind. As a mini break had arrived, Lee waved his pen and together they concocted another list.

Catching-ourselves-out:
- *Feel* the Breath, don't *think* it.
- Notice the existence of a Thought.
- *Don't* comment on it.
- Straight back to breathing.

Once we are confident with that:

Observing Thoughts:
- Breathe.
- Notice a Thought.
- Consciously observe train-of-Thoughts, as it unfolds. Only *observe, don't* comment.
- Don't get caught up.
- Back to breathing.

And last but not least:

Retracing -or- Contemplation:
- Breathe.
- Think.
- Catch out.
- Retrace the Thought to it's origin, by remembering previous Thoughts - or - consciously contemplate, reflect and analyse the Thought.
- Don't get caught up.
- Back to breathing.

When they were finished, they happily laid back onto the grass, their feet up against the oak this time, letting blood flow back into their brain. After a while Tara said, 'You truly are a Master summariser, you know?' 'Thanks,' Lee said, yawning discreetly. He was beginning to feel a little tired. His Master-Summariser's brain was slowly beginning to switch off. He hadn't even finished this Thought when Tara asked, 'I think I need a break, what do you think?'

'Shall I observe or contemplate the associated Thoughts? Or shall I rather breathe instead?' Lee looked amused at his own joke.

Tara nudged his ribcage playfully with her elbow, 'Whichever one you prefer.'

'Observed and contemplated. Result affirmative. Great Minds, what can I say. I'm starving and my head needs a break. What about some more food, are you hungry?'

'I could eat a horse, the chocolate fix has long worn off,' Tara held her tummy longingly.

'I know a little place down the road,' Lee suggested. 'I don't think they do horses, but they do a wicked Vegetable Soup and lots of fresh salad and bread, how does that sound?'

'Great. Where did you have in Mind?'

A few minutes later they found themselves in the Slug and Lettuce. A beautiful old English pub, with a great menu and a real chef to show for - not just a microwave attendant. They sat in the Beer-garden and devoured two huge bowls of the recommended soup, two door step slices of home made bread and shared a salad which was so colourful and full of weird and wonderful shapes, Dali would have been proud.

As it was such a lovely evening and the benches were comfortable and beautifully shaded by the trees, they decided to camp out in the Beer-garden for a while, rather than going back to the park. Both acknowledge the welcome change of sitting on chairs. Lee's knees were especially grateful. He wasn't used to all that cross-leg-ed-ness. Tara ordered another Orange juice and Tim another beer. A Bitter this time. He liked to try a different beer every time. It kept it interesting. He was never a great man of habit, far too boring. There was far too much out there to play with.

As Lee leant back against the chair, his back moaned thankfully. As he sat there and observed the hustle and bustle in the pub, a Thought came to him. It was amazing how alike they thought. He had to laugh. It was funny, he knew how Tara *thought*, but he had no idea who she *was*. He decided that the time had come to change that.

Some Personal Stuff

'**M**an Tara, we've talked since ten o'clock this morning. I know how you envision the Universe - in great detail,' he winked at her, 'but I have absolutely no idea of who *you* are. How come that you walk around during the day and can talk all day to a complete stranger?'

'I teach.'

'Teach what?'

'I teach children. All the way up from six to about eighteen. It's an alternative school and I'm lucky enough to be allowed to teach Consciousness Studies.'

'You teach Consciousness Studies to six year olds?' Lee was baffled.

'Yeah, and older. But, actually, the little ones? They already know most of it. With them it's more a matter of making sure that they don't *forget* while they're being taught all the other stuff.'

Lee had to stop himself from staring at Tara. 'Wow, what kind of a school allows you to do that? I've never even heard of a subject like that.'

'It's a Co-operative school. A bunch of really cool parents have come together on the principle of home schooling. But all it really is, is a school, where parents decide what they want their children to learn. They do have to comply with the regular curriculum, but they are free to add whatever they want. And hey, lucky for me, they added me. I absolutely love it there. The kids are great, the parents are even better and what's best is, I only teach four days a week and I have Fridays and Mondays off.'

'Do they let you turn up barefoot?'

'They do. Granted that was a bit of a struggle, but hey, I'm the eccentric lady teacher, teaching Consciousness Studies, what can they do?' Tara smiled one of her most charming smiles.

'I'm sure there was no way they could resist you,' Lee smiled back, equally charmingly. Tara shrugged her shoulders innocently. 'So, how did you end up there?' Lee wanted to know more. 'I mean that's not your normal off the peg kind of job, is it?'

'I created it.'

'Of course you did,' Lee laughed out loud. 'Why am I not even surprised? How on earth did you do that?' he shook his head incredulously.

'Oh, that's a long story.'

'Another one? We're still working on the story why-you're-being-looked-after-by-the-Universe,' he bantered light-heartedly.

'Well, not quite *that* long,' Tara smiled. 'I finished school, all A-levels intact, and went to London to be Au-Pair. I just wanted another year after school to decide what to study. I didn't have the money to go travelling, which is what I really wanted to do, so I thought, hey, London is cool, right? I'll get a room and food and all I have to do in return is be the big sister to a little girl. I can do that. Well, I got stuck in London. I loved big cities then. So after my year was up, I started a Business Degree.'

'Really? You have a degree in Business?' surprised

'What's so odd about that?'

'You walk around barefoot for a start,' Lee grinned.

'I was conditioned to want a *proper* job and career,' Tara stressed the word - proper, ' and to do everything *they* tell us to do. Society, I mean. So like a good human, I did. I studied and got a proper job in IT. After four years I thought, great, I have all the money, but no time to spend it. Time for a break.' Lee recognized his current experience in Tara's words. 'So, I quit my job, initially just for a year and went travelling, intending to return back to London afterwards. I mean everybody was talking about different cultures, belief systems and mystical practices. I just wanted to go and see for myself. Well, I went and saw.'

'What did you see?' Lee asked intrigued.

'Richness and poverty and countryside and people and different food and religions and bla, bla, bla, but most of all? I saw myself. I chose to travel alone a lot.'

'Wow, that's pretty brave, isn't it?'

'That's what I thought at the beginning, but a friend told me that it's not as scary as I made it out to be, and it wasn't. Lots of people do it, even women, it's quite common practice. You constantly meet lone travellers, it's sometimes even difficult to *stay* alone because you meet so many great people. But, even though I met and travelled with lots of people, I also chose to spend a lot of time on my own and in my own head. During that time, I figured out a lot of the stuff we've been talking about, and boy did I play with it. Endlessly. Needless to say, my perspective of things changed, or let's rather say: it exploded! I mean, you haven't even heard the half of it yet.'

'Well, I do hope that I get to hear the rest. So, what changed for you?'

'Well, for a start, my findings and experiments turned me from an unsatisfied, angry, confused and self-centred girl, into a caring, content and utterly happy woman. I'm really truly happy.'

'I can see that,' Lee said with an honest nod and an appreciative raising of his left eyebrow.

'Thanks. Anyway, over time, more and more people commented on my care-free and loving nature, and asked me to share some of my knowledge. So I did. One to one at first, then in small seminars. At one of my groups I met Lucy. When we got talking about her school, I asked her if she'd be interested in creating a subject on Consciousness. She loved the idea. We presented it to the parents and the kids and they all voted for me and asked me to join the school, and I'm still there.'

'Wow, you asked the kids too?' Lee was stunned.

'Well, of course, they have to listen to me all day! Actually, it was the kids that literally begged the parents. It always fascinates me how kids still know what's important.'

'Amazing. Actually, if you don't mind me asking, were you always - different?' Lee asked bluntly.

Tara giggled. 'Different? Well, I was always interested in the 'unusual', in inexplicable phenomena, in alternative approaches to pretty much everything. You know, the mystical side to life. If that's what you mean, then yes. I've devoured weird books since I was a kid. The Human Mind, Psychology and social studies had always fascinated me. I heard of

Significant Co-incidences just before I went on my travels. I was sold immediately. I wanted to learn more, but nobody seemed to be able to give me some straightforward answers, let alone instructions. What *was* available, was either all on a different wavelength, or so complicated that it was impossible for me to incorporate into my normal every day life. So I set out to find out more by myself. I asked questions, experimented and made things up as I went along, and luckily for me I ended up where I would have never even dreamt myself to end up and better! Somehow all the bits fell into place. The Guys, Intuition, Co-incidences, the Mind, all of it.'

'I guess you like your life then?'

'Like it? I love it. If I wouldn't, I'd change it!' Tara said without batting an eyelid. 'I have chosen a job I love and what's best, I get so much holiday, that I can still spend lots of time travelling, which never stops to blow my horizons. I choose my environment, my lifestyle and my friends. I live with a lovely housemate about 4 miles out of town in a small but beautiful apartment. It's close enough to town to party, but far outside enough to get some piece and quiet when I want it.'

'So, you're single?' Lee's mouth worked, bypassing his brain.

'Yep,' Tara said cheerfully.

"Cool," Lee heard himself think - or did he say it out loud? Tara still smiled at him without a discernible reaction, so, either she didn't hear, or he hadn't said it. Ah, whatever. Why should she not know what he thought? It's not as if it wasn't obvious. Strange, if he hadn't just split up with Kate, all of this wouldn't really be an issue. How come that he was holding back? That he somehow really didn't *want* to like Tara? "Uoh, doing a bit of contemplating?", his Mind squealed in delight. "Eh yes. And why not?" Shit, he was holding back. Why? "There should be a grieving period." Who says? Once again, his Subconscious and his Conscious Mind were of differing opinions. Now, *that* was at least one good thing to know. Mmh, **thinking about your Thoughts. Was that what people meant when they talked about dealing with stuff? Usually people just suffered didn't they? But they didn't really analyse what was going on inside of them, or did they**? Well, he had never paid a lot of attention to it. Not really. And anyway, this was different. **Not only had he begun to notice his Thoughts, he actually began to understand *how* he was thinking, which seemed to clear and sort things in his Mind all by itself.** And most of all, he'd somehow begun not to take himself and his Thoughts so seriously anymore. Suddenly he could laugh about stuff that would have usually driven him insane. Kate was gone and Tara was present. And he would enjoy it as much as he could. Right Now.

'So, that's me, what about you?' Lee heard Tara's voice from far away.

'Uh, sorry. I just visited LaLa land. Ha, *conscious* LaLa land though, I might add, if such a thing exists. It's all very interesting!'

'I'm glad it works for you,' Tara smiled.

'Boy it does. One realisation after another is pounding in on me. I'm loving it. It's all so helpful.'

'I know, isn't it amazing?'

'Yeah. You know what, could you give me just a second? I'd really like to quickly write a few things down.'

Lee opened his notebook from the back, that's where he always made personal notes. The front for general stuff, the back for personal stuff. He made a few notes to remind him of some of the things he'd realised today, especially with regards to Kate. He wanted to make sure that he'd still remember tomorrow. When he was all done, he slapped the book shut, and looked pleased with himself.

Tara had watched the intensity and focus on Lee's face while he'd been writing. She'd seen that look many times and she knew what it meant. *Processing*, she smiled too herself. He was doing it good and proper. He was waking up fast. And he knew it.

It took a few minutes for Lee to regain his presence with Tara and to think of his own personal story, his way through life.

'From when I was little,' Lee began, 'I was also fascinated with the paranormal and the weird and different, just like you, but my thing were Mathematics, Probability and Chaos theories. You know, how the concepts of Math underlie everything the world is and does, including us in it. Infinity and the Universe, explanations of dimensions and all sorts of stuff. Things that could be proven, calculated and discovered. People always scrunch up their nose at Math and I would have too, had I always only ever used it to calculate the cubic content of a box,' Lee said sarcastically. 'Man, the modern education system can really reduce a perfectly fascinating subject into complete and utter boredom.'

Tara laughed, 'Yeah, it bred any initial interest out of me in no time.'

'I know, common syndrome of bad teacher-itis or useless curriculum-itis. I was lucky though. During school I kept my interest up by reading whatever I could get my hands on, After I did my A-levels and began to study Applied Physics and Mathematics, I met Mr Blake, one of my tutors. He was great, he was totally into his subject and his research, the interesting side, mind you. He taught us the cool side of the subjects, including Sacred Numerology, Quantum Mechanics and all sorts of other incredible stuff. That's when I read Fritjof Capra's book 'The Tao of Physics'. The book describes how modern Science is closer to the esoteric than one might think. It's about how Science actually describes and sometimes mathematically proves a lot of ancient concepts.'

'Oh yeah, I've read that. That really is a good book.'

'You've read it? Great. Well, I had never really called myself a particularly spiritual person. Down to earth, rational, loving and caring yes - but not spiritual. Well, the book told me that I was. That's when I opened my Mind to new ideas and theories on life and began to think that there had to be more than getting up, going to work and partying. I started reading different books. New Age, Old Age, Religions, bla, bla, but in the end, the people around me, as well as the books that touched on the subject of happiness, or sorting out one's life, or discovering new and fascinating things, were all either too fluffy, really patronising, from a different century, completely unpractical for a normal everyday life, or simply mind-numbingly boring. I was looking for something new, something different, something exciting. Which I dare say, I have barefooted-ly stumbled across today,' Lee added with a twinkle in his eyes. 'Before I met you, I did find the odd bit of information and ideas in various books or conversations, but never anything really Significant. Well, that's not true. There have been Significant moments, but just small ones.

Unfortunately I never found a job that incorporated everything I wanted to do. I thought about the Professor thing and to lecture at my University, I would have had lots of time to do my own research, but there was just no money in it. To Mr Blake's great disappointment, I decided to go into Finance instead. I buy and sell Bonds now. I work in the city. I make good money, I'm more or less my own boss - as long as I make my quota - and I can use my mathematical brain to figure out good deals. I do kind of like it somehow. I use my free time to learn, read and research whatever I like. That was my compromise. I guessed it was better for me to do it this way. Sometimes when we make our hobby our work, that's what it becomes. Work. I know that I won't stay too much longer with my current job, but so far it served it's purpose well.

Come to think of it, I actually learned a lot from my job. About people in particular. My bullshit detector is so finely tuned now, it hurts. I personally and professionally don't like dealing with people who promise things and don't shape up, or people that make statements that they cannot back up. You know, people that are all Talk but no Do? Well, I can smell them a mile off, even over the phone.' Lee thought for a second, 'I'm strong on Integrity and Honesty. Samurai values I think. I want to be a good person, and a content and happy person. I'm actively working on that,' he added as an afterthought. 'Well, I guess that's me. Oh,' he suddenly remembered, 'and I'm single too, and live in a flat about 25 barefoot walking minutes from here, by that big Willow Tree, if you know it.'

'Oh, I do. It's a wonderful tree. I always thought somebody should put a bench underneath.'

'Yeah, to breathe in the fumes.'

'Destroying my illusions with sheer truth, shameful,...' Tara grinned.

'Sorry,' Lee laughed. 'I think our backgrounds explain a bit why we make such a great team. You have the first hand experience and explanations to all this Hippy Shit and I have the mathematical and rational background to pick it all apart and make you explain everything till my logical Mind is satisfied. And we both seem to be enjoying it.'

'Very much so. Well, do fancy some more of it?'

'Absolutely.'

Lee noticed that with his previous realisation, that he really didn't need a grieving period after Kate, he'd become much more relaxed around Tara. He was more himself again, rather than what he thought he should be. It was so much easier this way.

They ordered a couple more drinks, banana juice for Tara and lemon water for Lee, and slowly prepared their brains for more Cosmic stuff with Calcium and Vitamin C.

Observe and Contemplate Your Feelings and Other Gremlins

'**O**h yeah, I feel inspired again,' Lee stretched his back. 'That little break from the Cosmic stuff was necessary. I feel much better now. And man, I really needed some proper food, talking like this uses up calories like no man's business.' Lee leafed through his little paper companion for the '_What to do?_' list. 'Now then, cheeky step number seven, curtains up,' he announced.

'Pleased to oblige,' Tara glanced at the list. The next point was: Observe your Feelings and Reactions.

Tara opened up her Being to The Guys. She cleared out her Thoughts, breathed deeply and entered Nowness. She had trained herself to easily slip into it whenever required and most of the time it happened effortlessly. She had made a special point to be able to do it without weird-ing people out. She just closed her eyes for a moment, nothing else spectacular. Nowness was her best friend. In Nowness she could access all the right

information at the right time. Lee had called it Collective Consciousness. Whatever it was, it was pretty damn clever.

Rather than trying to *think* the right words and the right order for all the multitude of subjects they were discussing today, it was much easier to just let the right boxes arrive by themselves. The Guys usually did a pretty marvellous job. All she had to do was open her mouth and let the words flow out. Sometimes she surprised herself by how easy it was. She was sure that Lee would love it too, once they'd talked about it. If he wanted to, of course. But that was for later. Now it was step seven. Guys. Pretty Please.

The corners of Tara's mouth, once again, moved inevitably upwards, and her eyes crinkled as she began, 'Step seven is exactly like the sixth step, where you observed your Thoughts, but there's one a small variation. **You do all the breathing and catching out things just as before, but instead of looking at the Thought you've just had, you look at the Feeling you just had. Then you observe, contemplate or analyse it, just as you did with your Thoughts before.**'

'I gathered that that's what it was going to be, and it's brilliant! Checking out Feelings, great,' Lee marvelled.

'Yep, Feelings are a whole new world, all on top of the Thinking one.'

Lee closed his eyes and felt. It was an interesting mixture of relaxedness and tenseness. He thought of Kate. He still felt a little hurt, but also stronger, clearer *and* curious. "Interesting. This stuff has potential," Lee though and raised his eyebrows with respect. He opened his eyes and noticed Tara patiently waiting for him to finish his Thoughts.

'Ha, I guess, like with the sixth step, it's important not to loose yourself in Thoughts *about* your Feelings,' Lee grinned.

'Spot on. Same drill. Notice them, observe them, maybe comment on them or examine and contemplate them with your Mind, then bring your attention back to your Breathing,' Tara finished Lee's sentence and then added, 'This seventh step, can be done on it's own, *after* the sixth step or it can be *combined* with it. To combine it you'd look at *whatever* preceded the catching-out. Was it a Thought, a Feeling or was it something else altogether?' Tara waggled her head.

'What do you mean something else altogether? What else is there?'

'Well, I don't know what else you've got stashed in that warehouse of yours.' Tara leant forward and whispered into Lee's ears, 'Little green gremlins maybe?' she giggled. 'Just kidding.'

'You might not be as far of as you think. I guess amongst all of my boxes there are bound to be some gremlin-like Thoughts. 'But hey, I don't mind, I can breathe them away!'

Lee began to pump his cheeks full with air until he looked like a hamster. Tara laughed so much looking at him, she had to turn away, not to fall off the chair. Lee got up and pounced around her until he was in her view again. Just like one of the puppies seeking attention. Tara caught on and pretended to try and breathe him away, filling her cheeks in hamster fashion too. This time round Lee had to turn away from Tara, especially since she'd opened her eyes wide and began to roll them dramatically. By that people in the pub were beginning to turn their heads to watch their little game. Some were smiling, some looked away embarrassed. Lee and Tara grinned at each other and decided to reclaim their seats and behave like *normal* people. Whatever that meant. Well, the pub was nice and one wouldn't want to get chucked out, would one?

Notice and Analyse How You Talk to Yourself

Once they had sat down again all chaste and orderly, Lee readily read the next step on the renowned list. 'Ok, step eight is notice-how-you-talk-to-yourself. Do you mean the voice we're contemplating with?'
'That and *all the other* voices that are in your head. The catching-out voice, if there is one, the scolding voice, the one that tells you that you're not good enough or stupid to make mistakes, the voice that tells you that you rule, that you are God's gift and are doing ever so well, the voice that is doing the remembering or retracing or whatever. *Any* Thoughts or words in your head can have a voice. The voices can all be the same or they can be different.'
'Come again?' Lee was taken aback. 'I thought you'd be lucky to hear *one* voice. Now you're telling me that there are *lots* of them?'
'Well, yeah. Each person is different. Some have one, others have more. I personally only really get two or three. It's usually the same, unless it's really important. You might be the same or different, that's why I'm mentioning it. **To find out, next time you think, analyse a Thought, catch yourself out, or contemplate something, check if there is a voice in your head that goes with it. If there is, have a look at two things, first, the voice of the Thought *itself* and second, the voice that's doing the *analysing* of that Thought.'**

Lee looked at Tara and said slowly, 'Wow man, that's like - one level up,' he propped his elbows up on the table and laid his chin on his hands.

'What do you mean one level up?' Tara drank the last sip of her juice.

'Well, Thoughts are the *base* level and they can have a voice. Then observing those Thoughts is a level up, right? We observe what observes the Thoughts. So, we're observing the Observer and it's voice.' Lee sat up again, 'Then there's another voice observing that, and another observing that one and so on! That's cool, it could be endless! That's like proper super-consciousness!' Lee said as new pictures and ideas were quickly taking form in his brain.

'Exactly,' Tara picked up. '**Now, for all of those voices, check if they are always the same? Are they male or female? Is one of them your own voice?** Can you distinguish different tones of voice? Are they calm and rational or erratic and crazy? Are they talking in first, second or third person? Are they saying: "*I* need to do XYZ", or are they saying: "*You* need to do XYZ"? Are the voices using actual words or do you 'just know' a meaning in a kind of conceptual manner? Pay attention to the voices and how they change.'

'It sounds fascinating, but why is that important?' Lee wondered.

'Getting the voices down, can mainly be really useful because sometimes certain voices seem to be reserved for certain messages. With practice you can figure that out.'

'Oh, I see. **Let's say I would notice a voice, I could then make a mental note of what kind of thing it's telling me and if was worth Listening to. Then when it talks to me again, I'll know all about it.** That's so clever. Oh yeah, **that'll also help with my Intuition, right? If I can find out what kind of voice my Intuition uses to talk to me**?' Lee was amazed.

'Dude, you get full points. Yes, yes, yes and yes. That's it. Looking at the list, we've just covered step nine together with all of the previous points. Nine was: Get-to-know-HOW-you-think,' Tara checked off the two steps on the list.

'Fair enough. Incredible, what can I say. Seriously weird, totally far out and yet it all makes perfect sense.' A smile crossed his lips as he added, 'Just as we like it. Is this still as amazing for you as it for me?' Lee asked with an excited shine in his eyes.

'Oh, absolutely. Even though I've done this for years, it never gets boring. I still discover new things all the time. The insights and the amazement is literally never ending. That's why I love it so much.'

The WOW Journal vs. The Insight Diary

'Because it's never ending, that's why an Insight Diary is so useful,' Tara laid her hands on Lee's notebook. 'You know when you get a useful insight, when you *really* understand something or *really* notice something extraordinary? When you truly get something? Keep writing it down! It helps to make sure that those insights don't disappear back into the abyss of our chaotic box systems - and believe you me, that happens quicker than you think. Especially if new ones keep coming in,' she added as an afterthought and tenderly placed the notebook into Lee's lap.

'I guess that's what this little notebook has already become,' Lee picked it up and held it tightly to his chest. 'I do have to say though, that Insight Diary sounds super corny, can I call it something else?' Lee asked with a smile on his face.

'You can call it whatever you like my dear,' Tara said smiling in anticipation.

'Oh yes! What about WOW Journal? That's it. That I like!'

'And that's less corny?' Tara burst out laughing.

'Well, you get to talk about Your Little Guys, I get to use my WOW journal,' Lee grinned broadly.

'Touché,' Tara laughed.

'Actually, I always work like that. I always write things down. I can see how important it is with this stuff too.'

'It really is. You know, you might think that you've finished contemplating a particular topic, but then suddenly, maybe a month or a year later, it comes up again. Then you can check your WOW journal,' Tara giggled under her breath, 'learn, add, delete or change whatever is necessary to bring it up to date again. It's quite fascinating to have all your life changing insights in one place. **It's kind of like an evolutionary backup file**.'

'Darwin eat your heart out, here come the professionals,' Lee drummed on his notebook.

'Absolutely,' Tara gave her thumbs up.

'I think I'll also use it to write down Past-analysis of Co-incidences, Contemplations, and maybe even retracing steps.'

'That's a great idea. Don't solely rely on the book though. You'll also want to make sure that you train yourself to *remember* as much as you can, because you might not always have your journal with you.'

'Goes unsaid,' Lee ticked off a to-do list in his head.

'Oh, I nearly forgot,' Tara looked up in surprise. 'The WOW journal is also useful to help you stay grounded.'

'Grounded? How?'

'Well, this might sound weird now, but when you get to the really far out end of all of this? **Once you begin to play with Co-incidences and Intuitions and once you begin to talk to The Guys? Your Rational Mind can start to freak out a bit. It cannot understand, no matter how much it tries, and sometimes, it will make you wonder if something actually happened or not - if it was in fact real**,' Tara said remembering her own experiences.

'Ah, I see. But **if I wrote it down, I know that it was real. It gives me confirmation that it really *did* happen, no matter how much my Rational Mind wants to convince me otherwise**,' Lee opened his notebook.

'Precisely. And on top of that, it's not just our Mind, but also other people around us that can be sceptical towards our insights. They might tell you it's all rubbish, that you're going loony or whatever. So, writing things down from time to time, helps to reassure you that this stuff is alive and kicking and *very* real, no matter what anybody else says or believes.'

'Thanks for that. I will definitely keep that in Mind,' Lee said and put theory into practice straight away. He didn't need to be prompted to quickly write another note to make sure he wouldn't forget.

WOW journal:
- Write down realisations, Past-analysis of Co-incidences, Contemplations, Retracing Steps, afterwards or during as memory aid.
- Helps to stay grounded. Reassures that it really happened, no matter how strange.

It's Only Big If You Make It

'**I** love how easily you put everything into practice,' Tara mentioned. 'Some people find it a bit unnerving when they see the inside of their head for the first time. I guess it can be pretty gob-smacking,' Tara remembered her own experiences. 'Most people are not used to all that awareness of what's going on up there, they often find it difficult not to get lost in all those background Thoughts. They *judge* the Thoughts and even themselves, they become upset or angry. For those **people it's important** to be gentle with themselves and also **to understand that there's nothing new in their head**.'

'Yeah, good point. **You're not creating anything. You're only becoming aware of what's *already* going on in your head anyway**,' Lee said.

'Exactly and the other thing is that: **it's-only-big-stuff-if-you-make-it!**' Tara paused to let the importance of that sentence sink in. 'That's really worth keeping in Mind. **It's only big and unnerving if you *think* it is.**'

'Ah,' Lee effortlessly picked up Tara's train of Thought, 'Even those shit-this-is-big-stuff-Feelings are just Thoughts. Notice them, go back to your breath and they're neither big nor unnerving anymore.'

'Full points. If you can **remember that whenever it gets intense - not just with The Guys, but in your entire life - that'll help you not freak out** when it gets really far out later,' Tara pointed out. **'Once you start playing with the Mind stuff and with The Guys for that matter, it's really important to make sure that you're rooted and grounded in the physical world, that you keep your grip.** When I started all of this, I got really wow-ed out about it all. I constantly had to tell everybody about the weird and wonderful things that had happened to me, the marvellous Co-incidences, the mad stuff in my head. I couldn't think or talk about anything else. Don't do that! You seem to be pretty good with it anyway, but just in case it does happen at any stage? Just breathe and accept it as part of your new life, but don't go around making a nuisance of yourself like I did. I hope that doesn't sound patronising,' Tara suddenly thought out loud.

'Not at all. In fact I appreciate the concern and the tips. You never know what could happen once I'm all alone,' Lee contorted his face into a grimace. 'But seriously. I will remember this if and when necessary, and to give it special honours, I shall make a note of it,' he said and wrote on a separate page, in extra big letters:

It's only Big if you make it:
- Stay grounded!
- You're not creating anything new.
- Catch out and breathe.
- Observe.
- Take it easy.

'Do *you* ever still get freaked out?' Lee asked.

'Na, not really. I just notice what's going on in my head, chuckle and say: "Of course", or: "Thanks Guys", instead of being thrown off balance by the sheer magnificence of it all. They don't freak me out anymore, they just make me laugh. It's so funny sometimes,' Tara giggled like a little schoolgirl.

Don't Try to Make It Happen

'**I**'m know that I want to do this Mind stuff all day long, but it does still sound a bit daunting' Lee said.

'Actually, it's the easiest thing in the whole wide world. All you have to do is Nothing. No-thing. And I mean that in the least facetious way possible. Sure, it *does* take practice and for some it's easier than for others, but I noticed for myself that it becomes much easier once you learn to *Let Go of Trying* so hard to achieve Nowness.'

'More?'

'Well, just like surfing or juggling, you can't force it! A friend of mine described it nicely. He said that: **"You can't force yourself to be present, because that takes you into your head." If you do that, you *think* about being better or faster or more Now, rather than just *Being* it. *Trying* takes you *out* of the moment. *Being* present and *Being* Now is a result of Letting Go of your Thoughts, of allowing your Thoughts to drift away, and thereby *leaving* you in the present *naturally*.**

Basically, we have to stop being so hard on ourselves and stop criticising ourselves. Be sure that it will not miraculously happen, just because you *decide* it should. Nowness cannot be forced.'

'And anyway, forcing doesn't sound like much fun, does it? Forcing sounds like hard work and lots of effort. It sounds difficult,' Lee said.

'Exactly, and we don't want it to be difficult, do we? We want it to be effortless. And fun!

If we stop trying, we stop desiring and thinking that we should be better or faster and instead we're just *doing* it, and with that, we take ourselves out of the vicious cycle. To do that, we need to learn to relax our Mind and be more *patient* for our own sake. My grandmother always used to say: "Rome wasn't build in a day", and right she was.'

'Of course she was,' Lee grinned, 'Well, unless there's some truth to the Alien theory after all. They're supposed to have been able to move rock by sheer will power.'

'Yes,' Tara winked at him, and moved swiftly on, 'The trick is to be *playful* with this stuff. Play with it, observe, experiment! **Nowness happens as a result of a *natural* progression, a *natural* evolution. It *will* happen, with time, and we need to *give* ourselves that time. We can't *force* our way out of an *entire life times worth* of conditionings and self images**.'

'I guess it's like having walked on our feet all of our lives,' Lee wiggled one of his bare toes, 'and somebody would come to us and say, ok, from now on you have to walk on your hands instead. I mean, that'll take time too, right?'

'Exactly. We need to gently Let Go, re-learn the way we think, and gently persuade the little Gremlin up there to chill.' Tara touched her right temple. 'If we force it, it'll get stroppy. **Let go of the idea that we always have to *work* so hard on everything, that everything has to happen immediately, that we have to *make* things happen, when actually, all we need to do is gently remind ourselves of the Present and redirect our focus onto the Now. It's gentle but continuous practice, just like playing an instrument or surfing**.'

'Sounds wise.'

10 Practicalities

Lee looked at his notes and briefly recapped the conversation, when a more practical question popped into his Mind, 'Tara, what's the best way to practice all of these steps?'

'Oh, good point. Which steps you do, depends on what you want to achieve and what you are interested in. **If your goal is to calm yourself down, physically and mentally, to break out of the Mental Rat-race, to stop the Mind roller-coaster, then the first three steps will do just fine. The first three steps are the basics, the fundament of Meditation. They allow you to stop your brain from going nuts and with practice, help you to enter the state of Nowness.**

All of the next steps are fascinating extras. You practice those, if you're interested in learning about yourself and your Mind, if want to practice Mindfulness, or,' Tara paused dramatically, a twinkle flashed across her face, 'if you want to begin to play with The Guys.'

Lee's heart jumped for a second. Was it Tara's smile or was it the promise of meeting The Guys? Breathe. 'Cool. Oh, and should I practice the steps in any particular order?'

'Sorry, it's not a cop out, but the answer is: it depends. Let's say you'd want to practice a sitting Meditation, for that I'd run through the first three steps (to get super chilled) and then I'd pick one or two of the other steps to spice it up a bit. **For the beginning I'd recommend to go through the steps in the given order, just because they kind of build up on one another, but as soon as you got the hang of them, you can swap and change them in whichever way you want to.** You can do as many steps in one sitting as you like. It's up to you. There are no rules set in stone. Use your common sense.

Try and play with all of the steps eventually, as each one has fascinating insights to give you. Don't avoid new steps, just because they're new or different or because they break an established routine,' Tara warned. 'Try and give every step a fair shot. If it feels good, continue, if not, you can just go back to practicing the previous step a bit longer and then try again. There's no competition, you can do whatever you want to for however long you want to, in one sitting or through out the day.'

'Good that you say that, because when I initially saw that huge list of yours, I was a bit worried about how long it would take to do all steps. But this is actually do-able. And the best thing is that I can do all of that sitting in a corner or out there in real life. I can do as much or as little of it as I like. I think I'll still be busy for a while though, the sheer amazement factor will keep me going without Doubt. Fabulous.'

'Yeah, I think you might enjoy yourself,' the understatement easily came off Tara's lips. 'Just make sure not to overdo it,' she warned. 'Take it easy on yourself and remember never to take it or yourself to seriously. It's not about perfecting Meditation or any of it for that matter. There's no point trying to do that when you just start out, because whenever you think you know it all or you've done it all, suddenly, out of nowhere comes another fluffy Panda with a huge, great, big Sign stuck to his forehead saying: "Ha! Chew on this one sucker!"' she laughed. 'Just know right from the start, it's something you can practice your whole life. Your head will always think, and you'll always have new things to observe. So, there's no point in trying to win. Even though with time it gets less hectic and crazy up there,' Tara pointed at her head, 'it's a continuous flow of fascinating new insights and realisations, and the first sense of achievement comes quickly.'

No Need for Formal Practice Anymore

'**Y**ou'll be please to know that you can either wait until progress happens automatically, and it will sooner or later, or if you want to, you *can* speed up the progress a bit.'

'That's always good. Mmh, then again, I thought we can't *make* it happen,' Lee was confused.

'Let me explain what I mean. **Formal sitting-down-Meditation is great and it has an important place in our lives, but the point where all of this becomes really useful is, when we *actively* transfer all the skills we've learned to our everyday lives.** To *everything* we do, *all* the time. We can learn to interrupt our Thoughts *throughout* the day and if we want to, do all the same steps we would do during a formal sitting down Meditation. **When we begin to observe our**

Breath throughout the day, that's when we begin to incorporate Meditation into our lives and when we become *constantly* **Mindful.** Our Mind slows down, we don't go round and round anymore as we would normally do. We just notice our Thoughts, decide that we don't need them and go back to our breathing. **Throughout the day our entire Being becomes calmer, more relaxed and more laid back, as we don't flip out or worry so much anymore.** As different Thoughts, Emotions and reactions come up during the day, **as different issues arise when we relate with other people, do things, work, hurry, organise, we begin to actively learn about ourselves and our Mind**. You will get an abundance of Significant insights, which will give you the choice to change ingrained patterns of thinking, feeling, behaving and reacting. It really is a new world once you get out there - or *in there*,' Tara grinned.

'Now all you But-heads, no more excuses now!' Lee warned an invisible audience. 'We can clear our Mind at Will, *wherever* we are, and whenever we want to. Do we want the worry-Thought when the bus doesn't come? No. Back to the breath. Do I want to feel all nervous before the presentation? No. Back to breath.' The words flowed out of him as if by Magic, 'Do I want to get all fidgety because the line doesn't move? No. Back to the breath. Is it really a good idea to shout at that person right now? No. Back to the breath. Do I like that Thought about that lovely young girl over there? Well, yes I do actually. Sod the breath,' Lee said cheekily.

Tara laughed out loud. 'Oh Lee, I can see you're getting the hang of this.'

Lee grinned, 'Yeah, I think am, and I love the fact that I can do whatever I want to, rather than it being done to me. It's like finally taking control over *myself*.'

Be Your Own Teacher and Have Ridiculous Amounts of Fun!

'That's the nice thing about all of this,' Tara agreed. 'Once you've got the basics of Meditation down, **you become your own teacher. You can get tips, tricks and new ideas from other people, but you never have to ask anybody: "Can I do this?", "How do I do that?", "Can I combine these?". Just do it, try it, play with it, see what works for you personally. Every single one of us can get our own answers and insights.**

Teaching yourself by experimenting and trying stuff is a natural process as you become more curious. **You get inventive as you'll see how you can have fun with this stuff - simply because nobody**

tells you that you can't. This is why it is so amazing, because you can literally try *anything*! **Contrary to common belief, you can't do anything wrong, you can just learn.** Meditation and Mindfulness is your oyster and it can be used in whatever way you want to. You can choose to make it all serious, or you can choose to have some fun with it, and thus do it the easy way.'

Tara took a breather, Lee was still listening, his beautiful brown eyes looking at her with a mixture of amazement and wonder, yet with a deep inner strength and grounded-ness. She liked it when he looked at her like that. Actually, she liked it when he looked at her - period.

Tara smiled at her stray Thought, gathered her wit and went on, **'If something doesn't work, or,'** she added with a smile, remembering his brown eyes, **'if you get distracted, it doesn't matter, just keep doing it. Enjoy the process, observe your Mind while things are *not* working the way you want them to, and learn from *that*! Take it easy, be gentle, have fun!'** Brown eyes. Grin.

'Yeah, just like with surfing, with a bit of practice, one day it works, and nothing in this world can distract you anymore.'

'Unless you want to,' Tara added with a cheeky smile, catching a glimpse of the proportions of Lee's chest under Che Guvare's face. **'And actually, sometimes you might just want to get distracted. You know, just really go off on one? That's what I call Play-Time! Just looking and laughing.'**

'Are you serious?' Lee grinned.

'Oh, absolutely, **the entertainment value is endless**.' Tara was on a roll, 'Whenever you're bored? Just make up stories, spin a yarn, think of anything, simply to amuse yourself. You can do whatever you want to, with who ever you want to. It's fantastic! It's like all your dreams come true. When you get good at it, you can even imagine feelings with it too. Then sit back and enjoy the show - just for fun. **But** obviously,' Tara lifted a warning finger, **'always remember that that's what it is, a made up story. A show that you put on for yourself. It's not real. But as long as you know that, and you stay *conscious* throughout? Hey, you might as well enjoy it, right?'** she grinned.

'Oh man, I love you Tara, I can't believe the stuff you come up with. It's so nice to hear all this light heartedness in your approach, the joy and the fun.'

'Thanks sweetie. **Oh yes, the other useful and equally hilarious thing to do is, to randomly check into on your head during the day and have a look at what you've just been thinking about.** When you walk, cook, do the dishes, watch telly, drive, talk, do the shopping, anything, wait at the Check-out, sitting on the toilet. **The off-the-**

wall crap we think about during our normal day is just unreal. It's absolutely hilarious. We judge and think and compare and associate and jumble and go round and round and go off the subject and day-dream. **Observing your Mind when it thinks you're not looking, is like getting to know a completely new person.**'

'Yeah, I had a pretty good dose of that already,' Lee's previous escapades came back to his Mind.

'I tell you,' Tara continued temptingly, her excitement never running dry, 'if you start to check in throughout the day, you'll get an even bigger dose! You'll walk around with a big fat smile on your face, all day long!'

'And our Mind won't have a life of it's own anymore,' Lee added. 'It's *our* brain and *our* Thoughts again. The little creature up here,' he tapped his head, 'is not our enemy anymore!' his face lit up, 'We can join it on the sofa, have a cup of tea with it, laugh with it, tell each other stories or even spin a yarn together.

And when we catch ourselves out not to be Conscious, we can learn from our Thoughts, laugh about them or we can choose to enter silence in Nowness. This is fabulous Tara. It's like an all in one solution.'

'*Absolutely*. **And it's all about where we put our attention, our ability to learn and to recognise the total ridiculousness of it all!**'

'Very satisfied customer, very satisfied,' Lee grinned.

He was happy. He could already see real-life applications for everything they'd talked about. He could see past situations and past roller-coaster Thoughts clear as a bell in his Minds eye. **He saw flashes of how he Thought and behaved as a consequence, and how he could now choose to think differently** - or not of course. That was the beauty of it. He could *choose*! What a simple word, yet so life changing-ly powerful. It was such a fabulous toy to play and experiment with. **Tara had given the Hippy phrase know-thy-self a whole new dimension - over the last few hours his head had become his very own spiritual entertainment centre.**

Meditation as Reminder

'**A**ctually,' Tara tried to make herself a little more comfortable on the wooden chair, 'doing all this stuff during the day, is a constant self-examination of ourselves and our lives. **We can constantly make sure that we're happy, and remind ourselves that we can think whatever we want to, that we can *be* whoever we *want* to be.**

Actually, this might sound a bit weird, but Meditating and becoming Aware, can give us similar benefits to people who have experienced a serious trauma.'

'Ehm, if we're talking about a meditatively induced whiplash, you can count me out,' Lee held the back of his neck protectively.

'Not quite,' Tara giggled, 'I'm more talking about the change in people's lives that traumas can induce. **Accidents, serious illnesses, near death experiences, loved ones dying or important relationships ending, all of those often make people stop dead in their tracks and take a good look at themselves and their lives.** More often than not, they begin to have Thoughts like: "What if that would happen to me? That person was so young. I could have died. What am I actually doing with my life? Am I really making the best of it? Am I happy? Do I really want to be in this situation, job or relationship? Why am I not changing it? Why do I always allow this to happen to me? Why do so many things in my life repeat themselves? Why am I constantly behaving like this? Why is this bothering me so much?"' Lee nodded in recognition. **'Most of those people eventually realise that, in the bigger scheme of things, so many things that used to make them upset or mad, are actually quite pathetic and really not worth the trouble.'**

'Yeah, rule number one – don't fret the little thing. Rule number two – everything's a little thing,' Lee said poignantly.

'That's a good one,' Tara nodded. 'And that's exactly what people sometimes realise after a serious trauma. They suddenly understand that they haven't been living their lives the way they wanted to, that they've let silly things such as fear, Doubt, being lazy or comfortable hold them back from doing what they really wanted to do. They realise that life's too short to mess about with silly stuff and that NOW is the time to live.

Some of them change their lives drastically in a way that fulfils them and makes them happy. Some people really sort themselves out, they actively pull themselves out of misery or self-imposed situations and ruts. All of a sudden they find the willpower, strength and Trust to do so. Well, Meditation and Mindfulness can do the same thing. We get the same insights and we can choose do something about it.

With traumas *and* with Meditation, some people change forever, whereas others don't manage to hold on to their insights or their newly improved life. As soon as the trigger situation is over, they finished reading the book, people stop being Mindful and they suddenly get all wrapped up in their lives again and magically forget all about the fantastic realisations they've had.'

'That's so sad. All that hard work for nothing,' Lee pouted.

'I know. That's where everything that we've talked about can help. As I just said, with **Meditation, Mindfulness and Nowness, the** insights never stop, so we *can't* forget! **On top of that they remind us** *every* **single day, to make sure that we're 'ok'**. 'Ok' with ourselves, with our Emotions, Thoughts, our lives and fellow Beings. If we're not ok, it gives us a chance to notice and actively identify the reason, find out *why* deep down we're not 'ok', and most of all, why we're not doing anything about it.'

'Which then gives us a choice to get of our but-ts and find a way to change it.'

'Amen.'

Be Now And The Magic Hand Trick

'**O**k, I'm convinced once again. This is all fabulous. **Now then, how do I remember to do all of this all day long? I think I'd just forget to do it, Intent or no Intent**. I wouldn't even get around to being easy on myself, if I can't remember to do it in the first place.'

'Good point. **Actually, the *Doing-It*, is not the difficult thing, the *Remembering-to-Do-it* is,**' Tara said.

'Well yes. If I'd tell myself right now to be Now, to stop thinking, and to fully concentrate on my breath, the chances are that I'd be able to do it, especially with a bit of practice, right? So the Doing-it is not difficult - it's just that I keep forgetting. So, I need to find a way to remember. Any tips?'

'Obviously, you have to learn to catch yourself out and that's one way,' Tara said and Lee moaned. 'But don't worry,' Tara flashed another one of her knowing smiles, 'there's certainly a handy little crutch, a cute little trick that you can use.'

'Oh, thank God for that,' Lee let out a deep sigh of relief. 'You nearly had me worried there! So, what is it? Is it the most fabulous and easiest of the easiest tricks in the whole wide world?' Lee playfully tugged at Tara's skirt.

'Of course,' she said with a huge grin.

'What is it, what is it?' Lee squealed with exaggerated anticipation.

'You **write 'BE NOW' on your hand**.'

Lee looked dumbstruck, 'What?'

'You write 'BE NOW' on your hand. **That's your reminder**.'

'Oh my God, that's ingenious Tara, that's such a good idea. Why did I never think of that?'

'Out of the same reason that nobody else ever thought of it. It's just too obvious,' she grinned. 'Actually, I do it with all sorts of things, anything I need to remember. People laugh about it, but you know, it's the best reminder in the whole wide world, simply because **you see it all the time**.

Every time you pick up something, you see it, you write something you see it, you point, you see it. **All day long. Had I not done that, I would have gone days without remembering Nowness or being Mindful. What a waste of good practising time that would have been**. I change the message depending on whatever I want to remember. "Be Now", "Breathe", "Stop" or "Contemplate".'

   'God, I just remember something, you've got BE NOW written on your foot!' Lee grinned, reached under the table and grabbed Tara's foot, playfully dragging it into the light and onto his lap, examining the pen markings.

   Tara squealed at the tickles, 'Yep. I usually write it on my hand, but sometimes I like variety, otherwise it gets boring,' Tara giggled.

   'God, you really *do* this stuff, don't you?' he carefully set her foot back on the floor.

   'Oh, absolutely, what's the point of it if you don't do it? Now, what to do with your new markings? **Simply make a *strong commitment* to stop thinking about the past or future and just BE NOW, every time you see it!** *Consciously* put *all* of your attention, all of your concentration on that moment! Make a conscious effort to experience that moment as if it would be your last, live it to the full.'

   'Even James Dean knew about this stuff, he said: "Live every day as if it would be your last". It wasn't his quote, but he said it anyway,' Lee reminisced.

   'Yeah right, and then he died, silly twat. I hope that he practised what he preached - at least till then,' she said laughing.

   'Ha, that's probably why James Dean always wore those leather gloves when he drove his flash cars!' Lee said with a big grin on his face, 'We weren't supposed to see the massive 'Be Now' tattoo on his hand.' Both of them burst out laughing.

   'Sorry Jimmy Boy, we didn't mean to laugh at you, Rest In Peace and all that,' Tara said, desperately trying to sound ashamed and humble.

   Both of them drew a long breath and looked at one another.

   'Brilliant,' Lee said once again shaking his head. 'I can already see myself at work, with people freaking out left right and centre because I've got Hippy-Shit written on my hands,' Lee picked up his pen and pretended to write lots and lots of stuff all over his hands and wrists and lower arms. When he looked up again he still grinned, but then asked a little more seriously, 'Actually, that *is* a point. What about doing something a little bit less conspicuous? Like a sticker somewhere or a note on the fridge or a knot in a hanky?'

Tara knew what Lee was trying to get at, 'Yeah, I asked myself the same question. I played around with a bunch of things. From my own experience, first it needs to be something that you can have with you all the time. A note on the fridge is obviously not that useful.' Tara already saw the gleam in Lee's eyes, and quickly said, 'Unless you carry fridges around with you for a hobby.' Lee grinned, caught out. 'But then, even with items that you have with you all the time, you need something that will remind you, *every* time, without fail. **I tried it with a bracelet, a new ring, a scarf, assuming that I would remember Nowness whenever I look at it. But it didn't work**.'

'Why not?' Lee asked surprised.

'It's logical really. **After a while all those things became part of my everyday life, like my favourite pair of shoes. After a while you look at them, but you forget the message attached to them**.'

'Makes sense.'

'**Using the message *itself* is foolproof. It's never ambiguous and when you see it, you can't forget the meaning because it's in your face, simply, plainly and straight forward in letters**.'

Lee pulled an overly excited face, waved his hands frantically and squeaked, 'Me! Me! Hel-lo? Me, I'm down here, on your hand! Look at me! No, down here, juuuhuuu. 'Scuse me, 'scuse me! Please would you be so kind and breathe?'

Tara burst out laughing, Lee was so funny when he did stuff like that. She stared at him to following his orders and started to breathe as if she'd never breathed before. Her eyes were wide, her chest heaving up and down. Only when Tara nearly died of hyperventilation, did Lee sit back calmly, with a satisfied look on his face.

'I guess I can see how it works. You can relax now,' he smiled regally.

'I'm glad you approve. One more minute and I would have keeled right over.' Tara was out of breath, but smiled broadly. 'I know what you mean though. It might feel a bit weird to have something written on your hand and you might think people stare or whatever, but you know what? It's not as if it's a shopping list or something. It's different to have "Be Now" on your hand than stuff like "pint of milk, tampons and tomatoes". **And anyway it can get you into all sorts of interesting conversations, because some people ask what it's all about.** So, be prepared!'

'I think I am, just,' Lee said, wondering if he could ever be prepared enough to take this stuff out into the *real* world.

'But of course, only *you* can know what's appropriate or possible in your life. If you can't write anything on your hand, because of your job or whatever, just do it whenever you *can* do it and practice extra intent-out-putting and catching-out at all other times instead.'

'Cool.'

'But seriously, if you can? Do it! **Nowness can either just be another fad in your life, a phase, where it doesn't really matter if you remember it or not**; one of those you know? When it comes it's nice, if not, that's ok too - **or, you decide that your head is in the clouds and you want it out! And well, for that, you have to *remember* it – all the time - all Day Long**!' Tara said with emphasis. 'And the Magic-Hand-Trick works.'

'Because "the *doing* it is not the difficult thing, the *remembering* to do it, is!" This is so funny,' Lee chuckled again, 'I still can't get my head around this. **You have trained yourself to be continuously aware of the Now, by writing messages on your hand.** It's brilliant. Tara, you're officially mad and brilliant.'

'Thanks, I guess,' Tara grinned.

'Man, how on earth do you come up with stuff like that.'

'Well, I always used to write shopping lists on my hand, so I guess this was just a logical thing to do to remember something important. **Keep in Mind though that the message on the hand is only supposed to be a reminder, a crutch. The point is to learn to do it automatically and only use the crutch until you remember to do it by yourself.**'

'Do you still use it?' Lee wanted to know.

'Sure. Sometimes I use it to remind myself of old stuff again, and of course there's always new stuff. Here, let's do it right now,' Tara said, rummaging in her bag for a marker pen. 'Are you left or right handed?'

'Left,' Lee said and watched Tara write "BE NOW" onto his left hand in nice girly letters.

'Why does it matter if I'm left or right handed?'

'You want to see it as often as possible, don't you? If you're left handed, you'll use your left hand more and you'll automatically look at it more too.'

'Tara, you're so clever it hurts.'

'I do what I can,' she smiled humbly. 'It's just a lot of experiments and experience.'

Lee picked up his own pen and wrote a few sentences into his notebook, not without having seen the "BE NOW" on his hand again. He stopped briefly, checked in and breathed. It worked! The message had just reminded him to be Now. His list looked like this:

The Magic Hand Trick:
- The *Doing It*, is not the difficult thing, the *Remembering* To Do It is.
- Write 'Be Now' on your hand.

When she was done, Lee took Tara's right hand, he'd observed and noticed that she was right handed, and wrote slowly and deliberately - THANKS.

'Fantastic,' Tara said happily. 'What a fabulously, fabulous day!'

'Oh yes - and I'm sure there's more to come,' Lee said with conviction.

Chilling out Time

The two of them had been so absorbed in their little conversation, that neither of them had noticed that it had started to rain, that it was slowly getting dark, and that they were the last ones left in the beer garden. Everybody must have left or gone inside without them noticing.

'Oops, talking about day...,' Tara looked around with surprise. 'Isn't it strange, how time and the world around you, just seems to disappear, when you're fully engrossed in something? I don't think that I have taken notice of anything around us over the past few hours. It's amazing, nobody has even disturbed us. Nobody has come and asked us for a light or the time, nobody even came to clear the table. It's as if we're not really here. Bizarre.'

'I know, it's like we've been in this little bubble,' Lee looked at his glass that must have been empty for hours.

'By the way, it's getting a bit late, what do you want to do?' Tara asked. 'I think my Mind has had as much as it can take for one day. But I would really like to keep talking to you. Can we meet up again?'

Lee nodded, 'Definitely. Let's postpone until, mmh, what about tomorrow? With it being Saturday and all that?'

'Tomorrow sounds perfect,' Tara got up and stretched her legs.

'How early do you usually get up?'

'Depends if I go out tonight, but to be honest, I don't think I'll make it anywhere tonight, I'm dead tired,' Tara said yawning. 'I wouldn't mind making it early-ish tomorrow, if that's ok, because I'll have to go and see my mum for a late lunch, around three.'

Lee tried to remember if he'd made any arrangement for the morning, he hadn't. 'Sounds fine by me. What about nine o'clock, in the park again?'

'Done,' Tara smiled at him.

They got up, and walked over to the fence, where Lee gentlemanly opened the gate for her. After they had both walked through, they stood next to each other for a moment, about to go separate ways. They looked at one another slightly awkwardly not quite knowing what to do. Lee took the initiative to hug Tara. Just quickly. Like friends. As a thank you for a great day. No come on. Tara returned the hug just the same way. She liked it when people were tactile. A hug didn't always have to be a marriage proposal. It was just nice to feel close to someone.

"It's so easy and familiar with her," Lee marvelled to himself. There was no pressure. It was just comfortable being with her, hanging out. "I'm hugging a near stranger. I really *am* turning into a Hippy," Lee grinned as he waved Tara good-bye. He looked after her walking down the street, her long green skirt swaying around her hips, her bare feet touching the ground confidently.

Tara stopped, turned and called up the street, 'I'm really glad I met you.'

'Ditto. See you tomorrow!' Lee shouted back.

Tara smiled before she turned again and walked on.

Lee walked back home with a spring in his step. This time he was happy to walk barefoot. He paid attention to his feet, used his senses and observed how his Body moved. It wasn't a chore anymore, but an opportunity to observe himself.

Ambling along softly, he took some time to mull over his extraordinary day. **How terrible it had started and how amazing it had ended - even though, looking down at his feet, he was in the same position as he'd been earlier this morning. Strange how things change once your perspective changes, how you look at things**. He looked over the trees into the sky and gave The Dudes the thumbs up. He couldn't wait for the morning to come. He glanced at his watch. It was nearly half past nine. Ted should be back from work, but there was no need to rush. Ted was a night owl and there wouldn't be a problem with turning up late to get the keys.

Lee leisurely walked along the street, whistling. He enjoyed the walk, despite the fact that the rain was still drizzling. Today it seemed, nothing could phase him. It was just a perfect, perfect day.

When he arrived back home, he rang Ted's doorbell and crossed his fingers. Ted answered the door after only a couple of minutes. Lee was so relieved that he nearly gave Ted a hug, but quickly Thought the better of it. With Tara the hugging thing felt natural and normal, but with Ted? They were neighbours, they weren't even friends. It was more a mutual agreement that they looked after each others' keys and that was pretty much it. No hugging involved here. Instead, Lee asked how the new job went.

Ted answered with a gruff shrug of the shoulders, 'Ok I suppose. It's a job. Did you want your keys?' Lee nodded. Ted left the door open and walked back into his apartment. He had never been a man of many words. Lee liked him though. He had friendly eyes. And he was reliable. Well if he wasn't working that is.

Ted came back, handed Lee his keys and said, 'I'll wait till you've opened up, you can give'm straight back then. We don't want to have two sets of keys locked in that apartment tomorrow now, do we?' he laughed at his own joke, loosening up a little.

Ted had a point, Lee thought, smiling at his neighbour's efficiency. He quickly unlocked his front door, wedged it open with a shoe, turned around, gave Ted the keys back and said gratefully, 'Thanks Ted, you have no idea what you did for me today.' - " Especially by not being at home this morning", he added in his Mind with a grin.

'Ah, it's nothing,' Ted said, slightly embarrassed. He awkwardly shuffled back into his apartment and noisily closed the door behind him. Lee grinned. Ted was such a nice guy, but he wasn't blessed with any social skills whatsoever.

Back in his apartment, he frowned at the keys, which, as if nothing had happened, laid innocently on the kitchen table. Then, his brow softened, his eyes took on an other-worldly sparkle, as in a sudden impulse, he grabbed the keys, held them to his chest, squeezed them tightly and planted a fat kiss on them, 'Thank you, you little buggers! For a change I truly thank you for not being in my pocket!' he grinned again. Hugging strangers and kissing keys. Worrying. He laughed loudly.

Lee heard his stomach growl. He was starving. Talking and thinking had taken up a lot of energy. He decided on quick and easy junk food. He rummaged around the freezer and stuck his findings, a Full Monty Pizza, into the oven and went to the bathroom to have a shower. He felt better afterwards, but still exhausted. Mental work didn't only make hungry, but also very tired. He had no energy left for going out and instead, contently opted for a TV dinner and bed.

Lee was floating on the brink of sleep. The apartment was strange and empty without Kate and her clutter. She loved to have her stuff all over the place. He felt a pang of pain in his chest at the Thought of her. They did have a great time, didn't they? Oh, how he missed her... His Mind drifted off sleepily. Red flag. Red flag? Thoughts. Sure, there're Thoughts, but man, we've only just split up - it's only natural to think of her, isn't it? "Well," Lee's Mind continued sleepily, "let's have a look at the nature of those

Thoughts, just for fun." **He observed his Mind going on about how much he loved Kate and how she was The One and how he'd never find anybody else.** He woke up with a start. **"Never find anybody else? What a lot of rubbish!** Of course there'll be somebody else. There already was," he thought of Tara. "Well, kind of," he brought himself back to reality. Anyway. And Kate was The One? **Well, they'd fit well together, but there had always been little niggly things, right from the start.** They'd never talked much about their relationship or their feelings for each other. Kate usually kept her feelings and Emotions to herself, which he had found difficult, especially when there were problems between them. Lee had always been interested in esoteric and far out stuff, whereas Kate had trained to be a Western Medical Doctor and a lot of his alternative Thoughts hit a brick wall with her. He'd been very much into sports, camping and hiking, whereas Kate preferred to stay at home. So, **come to look at it, she was not really as ideal as his Mind was now trying to make it out to be.** The last Thought flickered past Lee's conscious Mind, just before the dream world took over: "God, I hope I won't dream of her all night."

Strangely he didn't dream of Kate, he dreamt of Tara. And The Guys. His dreams were lucid and unusually real. He dreamt of being a Warehouse Manager, doing inventories, finding weird boxes he hadn't ordered and tearing around the Front Yard in his Fork-Lift truck. He loved it. He felt like a little boy on an adventurous treasure hunt though his own Mind. When he found boxes that were scary or simply utterly useless, he'd just divert his Mind to his Breath or a playfully made up story and puff, the box would disappear. He talked to The Guys and They talked to him, giving him all sorts of tips to improve his life. He was becoming more carefree and playful than he'd ever been, all the while staying grounded and strong, because everything he learned, or rather 'remembered', was reinforced by strong common sense.

When Lee woke in the morning, the reality of his dreams was still strongly with him. They had left an interesting combination of peace and excitement in the core of his chest. He opened his eyes slowly, trying to make sure that he wouldn't loose the connection to the dream. He wanted to remember it.

It was five to eight. He'd woken up just before his alarm clock was due to ring. "My inner clock is not that bad after all," Lee mused. He leaned over the edge of the bed to fish his notebook out of his trousers. As he wrote a brief summary of his dream, he vaguely remembered some more details. **He'd also dreamt that he had a golden line painted on his Body. A line which connected his head and his chest. His Mind and his**

Heart. He remembered that he had felt his Body very intensely and that there'd been something about Emotions. But no matter how hard he tried to remember, he couldn't break through the Mist, which kept the dream world safe from waking intrusion, and which had once again descended back over his memory. Tough. It was time to get up anyway.

Lee put the book onto the night table, pushed the sheets away and stretched himself thoroughly. He got up and looked out of the open window. He could feel the sunrays on his skin. Great park weather, he thought. He got out of bed, went to the bathroom, washed away the sleep with a hot and cold shower, got dressed, same favourite jeans, black T-shirt, the tight one, gobbled down a couple of slices of Toast and a cup of coffee, packed a blanket and some lunchtime nibbles into a bag, made sure to put his keys and some money into his pocket - one didn't have to tempt fate - put his notebook back in his other pocket, and left the apartment within twenty minutes flat - leaving his shoes behind. Deliberately.

He was only halfway out of the main front door, when his brain shouted: "Dictionary!". Lee looked around him, then up, then down. "What?" "Dictionary!" It came again loud and clear. "This feels like the Tax-example," he thought to himself. It was a strange knowing, a certainty that this message was important. Weird, but hey, who was he to refuse? Even if just for the fun of it... He walked back up the stairs, went into his apartment, found his little electronic dictionary in the desk drawer and left his home yet again. Once outside, a broad grin crossed over his face, as he stopped, looked up and asked, "Anything else?" His request was met with silence. "Oh well, worth a try," he laughed to himself and wandered down the street, walking carefully, paying attention.

Despite extra deep breathing, his brain still felt a little foggy. Another coffee would probably do the trick. He grabbed a couple café latté at the little breakfast place on the way and arrived at the park about fifteen minutes early. He spread out the blanket underneath the big tree, leant the spare coffee he'd brought for Tara safely against the trunk and laid himself down. He didn't mind waiting on his own for a bit. He closed his eyes and soaked up the early morning sunrays. It promised to be another fine day.

Lee woke to a deep voice and somebody tapping his left shoulder.
'Excuse me Sir, could you give me a light please, and eh, could you also tell me the way to the Zoo? And I want some spare change please. And for heaven's sake, why are you not wearing shoes?' By that time, Tara laughed so loudly that she could hardly finish the sentence.

Lee looked up at her. She was wearing a long, yellow dress, the simple cut emphasized the curves of her Body. 'Well proportioned', Lee thought. He'd never liked the skinny ones. He smiled, wriggled his bare toes at her, got up and hugged her.

'I thought I'd get the disturbances out of the way first thing,' Tara giggled and sat herself down. 'Great, a blanket, what a good idea. I'm impressed, you're prepared today.' She made herself comfortable next to Lee, seemingly unaware of how her dress revealed just the right amount of leg. 'Did you have a good evening last night?' she asked brightly.

Lee yawned and passed one of the cups of coffee to Tara, 'Here you go, just in case you like one.'

'Oh, great. And brown sugar, excellent, thanks,' Tara stirred her coffee, 'Purrrfect'.

'Start as you mean to go on I say,' Lee slurred. 'Man Tara, I was so tired last night, I had some food and went straight to bed. I started to watch a film, but I didn't even manage to keep up for the first five minutes. I was nearly comatosed by the time my head hit the pillow. What a wimp.'

'Well, if you are a whip, then so am I. I did exactly the same thing. I came home last night, had a bath and then had dinner with my roommate Charlene. She was such a superstar, she had cooked for the both of us and I ate lots, despite our pigging out session at Angela's and at the pub.'

'I know what you mean. I ate a whole pizza. Family size!'

'Pig!' Tara laughed, silently thinking that he must be doing something to stay in shape like that.

She'd always had a weakness for tight T-shirts on men. It showed off their upper arms. Lee wasn't muscle man, but he was nicely toned. Fit came to Mind. She liked guys that looked after themselves. Without being fanatic about it, mind you. She pushed the Thoughts aside and cheerfully continued to talk about the previous evening.

'Charlene asked me a million and one questions about my day. In the end I was so tired that I nearly fell of the chair. Only then did she allow me to go to bed. It was lovely though, she'd even bought wine. So nice. When I asked her what the occasion was, she just said: "Is Friday night good enough?" She's such a sweetie. When I finally went to sleep, I was out like a light.'

'So, both of us are well and rested I gather. Excellent. Ready for more,' Lee winked. 'Oh, before I forget, here's the money I owe you from yesterday. Maybe you could pass it on to Angela when you see her next?'

'Oh, thanks for remembering, that's really thoughtful.' Tara made a mental note, with a little red flag, to remember to pay Angela back next time she would take her little brother to see her. 'By the way, do you have any questions about anything we've talked about yesterday?'

Lee Thought for a moment, slurped his coffee and then said, 'Na, I don't think so. To be honest, I haven't really been awake long enough to think about anything. But I'm sure that I pretty much asked everything I wanted to know as and when it came up during our chat yesterday anyway. So, I think I'm cool. But man, I just remember, I had an interesting and almightily fun dream.' Lee laughed all the way through the story of his nightly encounter, recounting how he terrorised the Warehouse with his Fork-Lift truck. 'I'm glad there aren't any policemen in dreams, I'm sure they would have arrested me,' he grinned. Tara was visibly amused by his nightly anecdote. 'If nothing else, the dream has left me hungering for more,' Lee patted his belly.

'Well, you can have that without a problem. Lots of it.'

'Great. Why don't I go over some of the last few snippets we talked about yesterday first, that'll get us back into the swing of things,' Lee offered.

'Fab,' Tara said.

Lee woke up his brain with the last few sips of coffee, savouring the sweet bit right at the bottom which was always his favourite, took a deep breath and send the Fork-lift Truck of Memory back into his Warehouse.

PART 5

11 Thinking, A Matter of Choice

Let Go of Individual Thoughts or Be in Nowness

Slowly the memories came flooding back and one by one became substantial enough for him to grasp. 'By practicing the nine steps on the '_What to do?_' list, we've looked at the _way_ we think, _how_ we think and _what_ we think. I noticed how the Mind roller-coasters on and on regardless, and of course, that I have precious little control over it, unless I learn to continuously concentrate and focus on one thing only,' Lee began. 'We talked about how certain Thoughts automatically create other Thoughts, how they kick off new chain reactions of associated Thoughts, and how they go round and round in never ending circles.' Lee was relieved to notice that the coffee and the sugar were beginning to do the trick. The fog was beginning to clear. 'With practice, we can become aware of Thoughts and Feelings that are always with us, and which make us miserable, angry or insecure and we can begin to deal with them, by doing an Inventory and a good old spring clean. Besides making our life easier, becoming aware of what's in our Warehouse helps to make sure that these Thoughts and Feelings don't stay part of our Subconscious Mind and affect our lives without us knowing. Additionally,' he said, 'de-cluttering our Mind makes it easier for us to listen to The Guys,' Lee cocked his head to one side and stroked a hand over his head to return a tousley mop of dark brown hair back into its rightful place.

'I think, if I look back at all of it? **One of the biggest things I've learned, is that I have a _choice_ of what's going on in my head,**' he tapped his temple. 'I've got a choice about what to do with all the Thoughts I become aware of. I can contemplate them, learn from them or even stop them. I can think of something else, or clear my Mind by being Mindful or focussing on Nowness instead.' Lee could feel the coffee bubbling in his brain. 'I've experienced how many of my Thoughts are useless crap and how much rubbish is in my head, rubbish which doesn't even make sense. It's just there, driving me nuts and taking up my energy. Stuff like thinking about cigarettes for the last twenty minutes, I mean what? I've given up about 6 months ago,' Lee explained. 'Or food or a project at work, even though it's my day off, or the problem with my colleague, the broken lift, my relationships, anything. Literally the same damn thing again and again.

215

Thoughts that drive me nuts, go on my nerves and make me anxious! But now, if I want to, I can choose to Let Go of all those Thoughts.'

'Master student,' Tara clapped her hand. 'So, having realised the sheer stupidity and uselessness of most of your thoughts, I guess you wouldn't be bothered if a lot of them would disappear?'

'Absolutely not, I'd welcome it,' Lee nodded affirmatively.

'Would there be some Thoughts in particular that you'd be craving to get rid off?'

'Oh, absolutely yes,' Lee gave the thumbs up.

'Do you want to start playing with those?' Tara asked.

'That'll be great,' he grinned at her, 'I love the way you say *playing*. That sounds so much more fun than *working with* or *dealing with* them.'

'There's no point taking it too seriously,' Tara just shrugged her shoulders and winked at him. 'It depends what you want to do now. Do you want to stop *individual* Thoughts, or do you want to *Be Now, where ALL Thoughts disappear.*'

'Wow, there's a choice,' Lee waved his hand past his ear to scare away a big bluebottle that was buzzing around a little too close for comfort.

'It's good to be aware of the difference,' Tara pointed out. 'Most people begin to deal with individual Thoughts until they are able to reach Nowness. Some Thoughts are so distracting that they just have to be dealt with individually anyway. It'll change your life greatly just to be able to keep some of the ridiculous rollercoaster in your head at bay, but **most of the things we'll be talking about, can only be played with once you get to be comfortable in Nowness**. Well, **we've already talked about playing with individual Thoughts**, right? **Catch out, breathe**, and *that* Thought will be gone, right?'

'Yep,' Lee remembered how much easier the break up with Kate was now, simply because he wasn't giving it so much attention, because he wasn't wallowing in it as he would have normally done.

'Great. **Let's say that on the other hand you want to be in Nowness - period - for that you have to catch out *EVERY* Thought, and go back to your Breath or the *Feeling* of Emptiness. I personally feel that spending time in Nowness is much more relaxing and pleasant, than constantly having to fiddle with individual Thoughts.** Also, by trying to Let Go of individual Thoughts, in the end you're probably still thinking, just that you're thinking of something else. If that's cool with you, that's good, but if you really want to live in the space where *everything* happens? That's in the Now. And in the end, *ALL* Thoughts distract you from being Now.

Which option you choose depends how far you want to take it and what you want to use it for. **Also remember, as I said earlier, to get** to Nowness in the first place, you might have to tackle some persistent Thoughts individually. Those are the ones that just won't leave you alone, no matter how hard you focus on the Now, no matter how much you want to Listen to The Guys.'

As Tara drew breath, Lee saw to the first list of the day:

Thinking - A Matter of Choice. Let Go of Individual Thoughts or Be in Nowness?

- It depends what you want to do, if you just want to *stop individual Thoughts*, or if you want to *Be Now, where ALL Thoughts disappear*.
- To reach Nowness in the first place, you might first have to tackle some persistent Thoughts individually.
- In then end it depends on *how far* you want to take the capabilities of your brain and *what* you want to use it for.

Individual Big Thoughts and Illusions

'**O**k, let's first talk about the *really persistent Thoughts*, the Individual *Big* Thoughts in our brain. The ones that go round and round and round all day. The pushy, the naggy and the super pesky puppies. The ones that won't leave us alone, even if we try. The ones that drive us the most crazy, the ones that stop us from being Mindful and entering Nowness, the ones that are just too difficult to stop thinking about, the ones which affect our quality of life, our happiness and our Well Being the most.'

Lee nodded knowingly. 'Oh yeah, I know about those puppies, I've seen a whole bunch of them up here,' he tapped his temples.

'Great, so you'll have something to practice with,' Tara smiled. 'What's important to know is, that if we choose to, we can Let Go of *all* of them. Even the biggest Thought can be Let Go of, with enough *concentration, focus, determination and will power*. If you have all of those qualities, or if you are willing to learn them, you can *actively* change the way you think.'

'I'm all ears. Just don't stop now!' Lee knew how valuable this stuff was for him.

'I have no intention to, don't worry. Then again...,' Tara grinned mischievously, Lee shot her a stern look and she continued still giggling. 'So, the first thing to do is to identify the *most* persistent Thoughts that you have. Have a look in your head and pick out the four or five *Biggest* ones that keep coming back. **Let's say the most annoying ones, or the ones that cause you the most stress.** Playing with just four or five things like this, is easier than playing with too many at the same time,' Tara spoke from her own experience.

'Yeah, I can see that. With just four or five the Intent stays clear and the Red Flag obvious, whereas too many would probably drive me crazy all by themselves,' Lee said.

Tara laughed, 'You've got it. Then, once identified, look at those Thoughts, and decide if they actually get you anywhere. Do they change the situation? Do they do you any good? Are they maybe just plain silly? Are they thinking for the sake of thinking? Do they stop you from being Now? From listening to The Guys?' Lee remembered the Thought process he'd had about Kate last night, about never finding another woman, about Kate being The One. Yep, they had all been useless - and untrue for that matter.

Tara continued, 'For any of the Thoughts you identify as useless, you make a *conscious* decision, that you don't want them in your head and then you continuously and persistently **do the same old thing: intent, red flag, catch out, distract or back to the Now.'**

'So, **until I get the hang of staying Now, I can just play with distracting myself away from persistent Thoughts, by simply thinking of something else, right**? "What I want to do for dinner, my plants, a TV programme, friends, a holiday?" whatever. It's about *actively* and *consciously* diverting my Thoughts to something different. Because when we think of something else, the Thoughts that we don't want anymore, can't be in our head at the same time, so they are *out* of our head - no matter how big they are. Easy,' Lee was still amazed by the simplicity.

'Exactly. And you're right, it is easy, but only when you know what you're up against and how to deal with it.' Lee's eyebrow lifted in anticipation as Tara continued. 'You see, a Thought has a job to do, right? It's job is *to be in* your head. If you try to get it *out of* your head and to Let Go of it, it will keep trying to come back to do it's job, and believe you me, it will give you a good run for your money. Especially at the beginning.'

'That would be the puppies that keep coming back for my attention over and over again.'

'Right. Once you've diverted your attention away from the little puppy, that persistent Thought will be gone for about 2 seconds, and then it will be straight back, jap, jap,' Tara held her hands in front of her chest like paws and made cute little japing noises.

'Yeah, I know, pesky little buggers,' Lee took Tara's hands and carefully laid them back on her lap.

'Well, no matter how many times they come back, you just have to keep paying attention the red flag. If you persist with that, the *spaces* between the unwanted Thoughts will become longer and longer. With practice, they will stay away for a few seconds, then minutes and longer, until they don't come back at all or at least hardly ever.

The more you practice, the easier it is to Let Go of a Thought or to stay in **Nowness. At the beginning you actively notice a Thought and Let Go of it consciously. With practice that process becomes faster and faster, until you can literally catch a Thought the split second it touches the fringes of your Consciousness and it's gone. With more practice, this whole process becomes automatic, and the Thought just bounces off your Consciousness without even entering your Mind or it needing your active involvement. It's gone for good.'**

'And you can do that?' Lee asked.

'Yeah. Sometimes it's easier than others, but yes, I can. Sometimes it still needs my active attention, sometimes I might notice afterwards that something that would have normally been in my Mind, wasn't. It takes a bit of practice, and truck loads of focus and concentration, determination and will power. If you don't have those, or are unable to gain these skills with practice, you're going to have a tough time. **But even if you have trouble to Let Go of a Thought completely, you'll most certainly be able to reduce the *frequency* of it turning up and the *length* of it staying.'**

'And that's already going to make a world of difference,' Lee said enthusiastically. 'Oh, and if I'm playing with unhappy Thoughts, even if I can't be fully Now yet, by practicing to divert my attention to something nice instead, even just that can make my life much more joyful. I think I've had some successes with that already,' Lee remembered proudly.

'Yep, you truly are a superstar!' Tara put her hand on Lee's forearm and let it rest for a few moments. She paused for a second, 'I know I've said this before, but it's important enough to repeat. **When you play with a Thought, that's what you do. You *play*. No matter how *big* it is. You *dance* with it. You don't beat it with sticks, you don't scream at it, or shout or wrinkle your brow or become upset. If you piss them off, they come back harder, just to prove a point. So remember to always gently, ever so gently withdraw your attention**. Most of the time they won't even notice what's happening, and before you know it they're gone. It's play! Be easy on yourself. Doing this does takes practice. **Our natural tendency is to set goals, to want to achieve, to be rid of it *now*, to *try* to *make* it happen and if it doesn't work instantaneously, we're hard on ourselves and beat ourselves up. Well, doing that won't make the Thoughts go away any faster or better or easier for that matter. It's just less fun.**'

'And all of that anger and upset just creates more Thoughts, right?' Lee threw in.

'Exactly. So, stay calm, notice and divert your attention.'

'Without comments or judgements - just a peaceful diversion - thank you.'

'You've got it.'

'Could you talk me through an actual Thought process that would be in your head while you do all of that?' Lee already grinned in anticipation. He knew he'd learn while being entertained. Minds were such a amusing little creatures - once you learned not to take them so seriously of course.

'Sure,' *Tara crossed her legs and leant back with her elbows supporting her.* 'Worrying is one of my favourite examples. You know, those mad, incredible, often entirely useless Thoughts that go round and round and tipsy-turvey?' Lee nodded. 'Let's assume the bus is late. Now, this is what the Mind does: "Oh no, the bus is late, what's going to happen now? When does the next bus come? The traffic seems to be getting worse, it's going to be ages till the next bus comes and then *that* bus will get stuck in the traffic. What will my boss think when I'm late? And my colleagues? And what repercussions will it have, could I get fired, bla, bla, bla". I can go on forever, right?' Lee nodded once again. 'So, besides the fact that these Thoughts stop us from being Now, they will not make the bus come any faster, will they?'

Lee looked up, met Tara's eyes and suddenly laughed, 'So, there's simply no point in thinking those Thoughts, is there?' Lee's eyes widened as he carefully repeated his last sentence. Something had clicked into place. **There's *no point* in thinking those Thoughts, because they *don't change* the situation. They are *figments of our imagination*. We're making them up! They are in our heads**. That's one for the books!' Lee said, grabbed his notebook and jotted down a couple of sentences.

'Yeah, but that doesn't make them any less real,' Tara warned. **'They might be figments of our imagination, but be aware that our Minds have a lot of practice in creating the most magnificently ridiculous scenarios and making us believe that they are real and true and that they surely must happen.'**

'And that they're really important,' Lee added with insight.

'Absolutely. Actually, I have a lovely story to demonstrate that.'

'Oh, stories are always good,' Lee laid back to listen.

Tara stretched her back, gathered up her long hair and threw it behind her shoulders, she drew in a deep breath and began, 'A long, long time ago, before the days of electricity and running water, there were four monks. They were to study their *perception of reality* by meditating in a cave. Their master gave them instructions and then send them off to practice. They were to meditate on their guardian deity, until they had manifested it physically. After a year the first monk came out of the cave, crying. He said to his master that he had tried, but hadn't succeeded in manifesting his deity. He was disappointed and left. The master let him go. After yet another year, the second and third monk came proudly out of the cave, each one of them with the manifestation of their deity walking behind them. The master was very impressed and asked them all to sit next to him and wait till the last student emerged. After another year the master became concerned about his last student who was still in the cave, but as only he knew how, he waited patiently. After a further 6 months the fourth monk came out of the cave on his own. No deity followed him. But to the other novice monks surprise he held himself upright and his spirit was strong. The master was curious and asked the monk to tell him what had occurred in the cave. The fourth monk told his story. He said that he had succeeded in manifesting the deity fairly quickly. It had been big, colourful, life like and quite impressive. He kept on meditating on it to make it stronger and more powerful. When he became sleepy and his meditation would slow down, his deity would begin to fade, he said. During the years in the cave, he spent a lot of effort in staying awake and to mediate continuously. He was about to leave the cave with the other monks, when a sudden realisation had struck him. He had suddenly understood something which until then had only been on the outer reaches of his Awareness: When he stopped giving the deity attention, it would fade! It suddenly hit him that he had *created* the deity with the power of his meditation, but that it wasn't real, it was an illusion! A very real one, but nonetheless an illusion, a creation of his Mind. The second he realised that, the deity disappeared and hadn't come back. At first he was shocked and wondered if he had failed his task. He stayed in the cave trying to understand what had happened. The monk bowed deeply to his master and said humbly, 'But I could see no use in trying to create the deity again, as my aim as a monk was to Let Go of all illusions. So please forgive me master if I have failed you.'

The master had listened carefully and finally said to the monk, "You have done well. You are the only one that succeeds. **You experienced that anybody can create anything with their Mind, and they will begin to perceive it as reality. To realise that it is an illusion, and be strong enough to Let Go of it,** *that* **takes true mastery**." At that moment, the master got up from his chair and offered the fourth monk his seat. "All these years I've been waiting for you to come and take my place.'"
Tara got up and directed an imaginary fourth monk to her seat, closed her eyes, folded her hands in front of her chest and bowed.

'Oh wow, what a fabulous story,' Lee clapped.

'It's one of my favourites,' Tara said quietly and sat down again.

They silently let the soft energies of the story sink in for a little while.

After a few minutes Tara picked up her train of Thoughts. 'So, back to the bus example.'

'Oh yes, from caves to busses,' Lee joked.

'We make great leaps here,' Tara drew a huge arch into the air with her index finger.

'As if hadn't noticed,' Lee grinned.

'So, back in the world of busses and electricity, not much has changed in the world of Thoughts. Thoughts are still not real. We make them up. They are scenarios of what *could* happen or *has* happened. **They are illusions, or as you said, figments of our imagination, but they can still cause us *Stress*, right? They can seem to be incredibly real.'**

Lee mulled over his ideas in his head and then said. 'Oh wow. **We *create* our own stress, by thinking stressful Thoughts! Just as the monk created the deity by meditating on it. The deities seemed so real that the two monks had been fooled,'** Lee said slowly and deliberately, trying to internalise and *feel* his new insight.

'Exactly. So, by realising that our Thoughts are useless, pointless, that they create stress, and that they simply aren't real, you can decide to Let Go of them or divert them to something different instead, maybe something less stressful. "No bus, flag, Nowness, a holiday in Spain, nice weather, oh the bus is late, oops, back to holiday in Spain, food, dinner, mum, must call Dan, the bus, oops, Dan, cinema, water plants, bus, television program until finally, the bus-Thought is gone. Oh and there is the bus and I won't be late after all. Phew, luckily I didn't just waste lots of energy worrying",' Tara laughed and pretended to wipe thinking sweat of her forehead.

'Or oops the bus is coming and I *will* be late,' Lee grinned, 'but at least I didn't just waste lots of energy worrying, *because* it wouldn't have made the bus come any faster either. And at least I stood there and waited all relaxed, rather than all freaked and stressed out,' **Lee made a mental note for next time when he was stuck in a traffic jam and was worried about being late or simply annoyed about being stuck. He would catch himself out and *become the fourth monk*.** After the mental note, he checked his physical notes to make sure that he had the most important points covered.

Persistent Thoughts:
* Let go with focus, concentration, determination and will power.
* If you don't have those skills, develop them.
* Be easy on yourself.
* Play with the Thought. *Dance* with it.
* Just gently, ever so gently withdraw your attention. Don't beat it or yourself up.

- Most Thoughts are figments of our imagination, they are not reality, they're in our head.
- Thoughts are *illusions*, no matter how real they seem. It's the monk and the deity example: Anybody can create anything they want to with their Mind, but to realise that it's an illusion, that takes true mastery.
- Be the fourth monk.
- There's no point in thinking Thoughts, if they don't change the situation.
- Some Thoughts cause us Stress.
- We create our own stress, by thinking stressful Thoughts.
- If we can Let Go of those Thoughts, we will not be stressed anymore.
- With more practice, this whole process becomes automatic, and the Thought just bounces off your Consciousness without even entering your Mind or it needing your active involvement anymore.

But Aren't Some Thoughts Important?

'In the end, all it comes down to is choice, right?' Tara said with emphasis. 'So, if I have a choice, why on earth would I choose to think of stuff that I don't like or that upsets me or stresses me out?' Tara shook her head, shrugged her shoulders and threw her hands into the air. 'Dooh?'

'Woha, hang on,' Lee held up his hand, **'Surely, some unpleasant things *have* to be Thought about. Some things *are* important.'**

'Yep, you would have thought so, wouldn't you?' Tara had that knowing look on her face again.

'But they turn out not to be?' Lee guessed.

'Some maybe, but certainly not *all* of them. How did you know?' Tara winked.

'Just a feeling,' Lee grinned back.

'You know, sometimes we fall into the trap of *allowing* Thoughts to keep coming back, because we *think* that they are important, but if we would actually examine them, they'd turn out not to be. The subject might be important, but not all the Thoughts you're thinking around it. Even if they'd be important, they would *not* be *all* day long!' Tara laughed.

'Ok?' Lee was still not a hundred percent convinced.

Tara continued unruffled, 'Well, let's play with that. Pick out four or five Thoughts out of your brain. The ones that you think are really important. Now check, how important they really are? Life and death? Would an employer pay you for an *entire* day to just think about those four to

223

five things? Continuously? Well? How long would you be able to talk to somebody about these things? And I mean continuously? Without them going nuts? For an hour? Two, Three? Try it and you'll see what I mean.'

Lee picked his hobbyhorse Thought since the break up with Kate. How would he pay the rent without Kate paying her share? Somehow he'd labelled this Thought as *really* important and *really* worth thinking about - *a lot*. It was constantly going round and round in his head. Now with Tara's instructions, he began to look at that Thought from a different angle. He look at the Thought itself, rather than the subject matter it was connected to. **As he was looking at *what* he was thinking, he realised that all he was doing, was telling himself how bad the situation was. How stupid, how unfortunate, how difficult. All of that, instead of actually dealing with the problem, instead of really trying to find a way out**. Well, now was the time to make a difference. Were the Thoughts he was having about the subject at hand essentially changing anything? No, *these* Thoughts certainly weren't. Were these Thoughts worth thinking about all day? No way! All they did was worry him, make him anxious and stressed.

But it was a problem and it had to be solved. So, what was it that he actually had to do? He had to come up with a solution. He had to stop worrying and literally sit down and figure out a way how to pay the rent! Those were *useful* Thoughts. He pictured his apartment and saw his office in the second bedroom. He could rent it out to somebody and make up for Kate's share of the rent, at least for a little while. Hey presto, problem solved. God, that had been so easy. The trick was to *consciously* think, to contemplate a solution, and to notice when your Thoughts strayed from a purposeful resolution. Interesting. Now, that the problem was solved, he didn't need to think about this subject any more. He grinned. Now he could class this Thought as one of the four or five Tara had talked about earlier, and attach a red flag to it to ensure he'd stop thinking it.

Thinking about other areas in his life that sometimes caused a little trouble, he assumed that not all Thoughts could be dealt with so easily, but he also understood that the simple mental roller-coaster didn't change anything either. Only action did, mentally and physically. Figuring out what it took, and then actually *doing* it. Initiative and guts. Or better: *focus, concentration, determination and will power* as Tara had said earlier. And physical action.

He looked up at Tara from his laid back position in the grass and summarised for her benefit, what he'd just realised for. When he was done he added, 'I see now what you mean. **Even if something *would* be**

incredibly important, like my rent obviously is, talking about it continuously would drive anybody, including myself, crazy and it won't pay the rent either! Only focussed and deliberate contemplations really sort the issues,' he laughed. Funny that he hadn't noticed all the useless stuff in his brain before, it was so obvious now.

'Yeah, that, or just stop thinking in the Now, or even asking the Guys for some help instead, but that's for another conversation,' Tara laughed and continued seamlessly, leaving her last words to bounce in the air in front of Lee's nose. 'But yeah, you're right. Funny how our Mind gets away with it, isn't it? It's just because all of these useless Thoughts are going on *in* our *head*, that we *can* think about them all day long. That's simply because nobody is pointing out to us that we're talking crap over and over again, and what for? But hey, we still always wonder, if the same Thought be somehow better the second time round? Or the third time?' Tara giggled.

'Man, it's so funny what we do in the privacy of our own heads.'

'I know. **So, the question is, *how long* is a Thought important for?** Does it really require all day long of continuous attention day after day? Those are the questions we need to ask. Those are the questions that really show us that a lot of the stuff in our head is useless,' Tara breathed deeply.

Lee slowly shook his head. 'Well, as I've just realised, sure, **some things are important to think about, but only maybe once or twice, not a million times! There's simply no need for it. Once - if done consciously - is enough. By then you should know the answer you were looking for, or you would know that you can't find the answer. You should have an action plan or know that you need more information to get one. In between those sessions or once you're done, you can stop thinking about it. All other Thoughts will just get you round in circles.'**

'Precisely. It's important to understand that **most of us *have to* do a certain amount of thinking throughout the day, be it for work or to plan our private life, but the trick is to *only think as much as necessary* and not to torture ourselves with unnecessary stress in our heads.** Be Now instead, where everything is calm, peaceful and stress free.'

'That's cool, only think as much as necessary,' Lee repeated. He opened another page and wrote.

Important Thoughts?
* A lot of Thoughts are *not* important, even if we think they are.
* If you decide that a Thought really is important, then think about it once or twice, not a million times! Come up with a solution or an action plan, but don't waste time or energy with more Thoughts.

- If it's not important, Let Go, Be Now instead.
- Only think as much as necessary.

Dots and Squiggles - Mental Loops

'**Be** Now is *The* answer,' Lee dropped his pen, sat back against the tree and closed his eyes. 'Man, so many problems we have in our lives, we cause ourselves simply by thinking,' he shook his head in awe. Tara knew how big a realisation this was, she had been there herself. 'It all sounds so enticing,' Lee said dreamily. Somehow the reality of Nowness didn't seem so far away anymore. He'd changed so much over the past 24 hours, he'd learned so much, applied so much of his new knowledge and most importantly, he'd noticed significant changes within himself already. Things were happening and they were becoming easier…

'Let me draw you a picture,' Tara offered. '**A picture** that a wonderful friend drew for me once **to explain what our Mind does all day long. It will help you to get a visual idea of what's going on up there**,' she tapped her skull. 'May I?'

'Sure, hang on, do it in here,' Lee opened his notebook on an empty page and handed it to Tara with his pen.

Tara spread the book out in front of her, drew a dot at the bottom of the page and pointed at it with the tip of the pen, 'This is Nowness, Emptiness. This is where no Thoughts exists. It's silence. It's peace. This is also where all Thoughts *begin*. First there's nothing, then suddenly, out of nowhere a Thought is born. That can be any Thought at all. A Thought about good stuff or bad stuff, how to Be, what to do, happy Thoughts, sad Thoughts, dinner, the movies, the fridge, the car, anything. Now watch, what that Thought does when it grows up,' Tara began to draw a squiggly line from the dot right to the top of the page, then to the left and right, and then madly all over. While she did that, she commented on every bend, every curve, every nook and cranny of that line with a squeaky little voice, 'Ok, I'm a Thought. I have been born and now what do I do?' she looked up and caught a bemused but attentive twinkle in Lee's eyes. 'Where do I go? I think I'll go up here, I think this is where all the answers are – oops, no, maybe not. Ok, so I try over there, yep, there we go, eh, nearly, but not quite. Maybe over there, or maybe back again? Oops, I missed it there too. Then again, maybe a bit further over to the left, oh no, nothing there either. Ah, I haven't been over *there* yet, oh, yes I have, oh well. What about over there, that looks interesting, oh, haven't I been here before? It all looks so familiar, but hey, whatever, I've got nothing better do.'

'Oh man, that's so funny. What a fabulous demonstration,' Lee burst out laughing. 'And yeah, that *is* the way it is,' he shook his head once again.

'Oh, and after an endless amount of going around in various, useless directions, your Thought ends up back at the starting point,' Tara picked up the pen, drew a line to join the end of the crazy squiggly line back into the dot at the bottom of the page. She looked up and said with a broadening smile on her lips, 'And you know the funniest thing? What do you think we do the millisecond we're back at the dot? In silence? In Nowness? Where we could be happily hang out in peace?' Tara pointed at the dot again, paused and looked at Lee with a meaningful look.

Lee was taken aback by the sudden realisation. 'Shit Tara, we start all over! That's what we do, we start all over again. Oh Tara, we never learn! We keep on doing it! We think about the same subject again, even though we've already thought about it a million times! And we keep on doing it!'

Tara threw her hands into the air in mock despair. 'Isn't it hilarious? I mean it's terrible, but it's so funny! And that's what we do all day long. And the worst thing is that most of us have no idea that this is happening. I could cry if it wouldn't be so comical.'

'Crazy. Instead of jumping off the train of Thought that drives us nuts, we stick with it and feed it and feed it. We go round and round in the roller-coaster of the Mind until our head explodes,' Lee made a dramatic exploding sound. 'Dots and Squiggles all day long. And you know what? Most of those Thoughts are made up, useless scenarios, which are not even real, just like the monks with the deities. **What if the bus won't come, what if I'll be late, what if this happens, what if, what if. It's What-if-s till we keel over,**' Lee was becoming more and more animated.

Every Thought is a Theory

'Yep, **the what-if-s are the part of our brain that make life so difficult**. We're complicating things by thinking too much, creating issues and problems out of nothing, without realising, that they're not real. If you really look at it?' Tara looked into Lee's eyes, '*Every Thought is a theory*! Worrying about the bus being late, will not make it come any faster. Worrying about the dark will not make it any lighter. Being scared will not help you to be safe. All these Thoughts are useless. They do *not* change anything. They are in *our* heads. They are stories. **Our Mind goes round and round, with all sorts of what if-s, could have-s and should-**

have-s. We prepare huge amounts of plans for possible situations and scenarios, which will never happen. But we think about them anyway, just in case. We think about vast numbers of answers to questions, despite the fact that at that moment in time the answer really cannot be known.'

'Oh man, I just remember the funniest example,' Lee said. 'I remember standing with my mum on a train platform once and there was an announcement that the train was going to be late. It was hilarious. For the entire 30 minutes waiting time, my mum told me about all the possible things that could have potentially happened to the train. "Maybe there was a problem with the tracks or somebody jumped in front of it or maybe a problem with the driver, maybe there was an accident." Let it be told that she had absolutely no idea what had in fact happened to the train, she was just making it up as she went along. She unknowingly did the talk-out-loud-all-your-Thoughts-thingy and she drove me absolutely insane. Then the train came.'

'And what was the reason for it's delay?' Tara was curious.

'Oh, I can't even remember,' Lee shrugged and laughed. 'The point is that my mum's Thoughts were unnecessary. Sure, if they would have made an announcement that the tracks were broken, she could have started to think about how to get to our destination, but otherwise? Her Thoughts were fictitious, they weren't reality. I remember realising that back then. So everything you've just said now, really hit a chord.'

'Excellent,' Tara said happily. '**I do have to point out though that it always depends on how far you want to take all of this. If you really want to be Now completely, you have to be quite radical and *always* catch yourself out when you're off on rubbish.** Sure, if you do want to think that stuff, maybe for entertainment purposes, that's cool, but that's *not* being Now. Besides that, **constant thinking wastes far too much energy, energy which our Body could use elsewhere.**'

'I know. I read somewhere that our brain uses between 30 and 70% of our Body's energy, depending on if it's active or not.'

'Right. Now, **can you imagine how *alive* and *energised* we'd be if we wouldn't use up so much power doing stupid stuff up there? If we'd be able to keep our Thoughts at bay? Coffee shops would go bankrupt. We'd always be full power without caffeine.**' Tara looked across the grass at a couple walking along with two huge extra-large paper cups of coffee - was that about three quarters of a litre each? The Thought flashed past her Minds eye. Crazy.

'Yeah, especially if we'd also do your special breathing technique!' Lee's Mind boggled at the Thought.

'Master student,' Tara said, praising Lee's quick ability to put all the pieces of the puzzle together.

'Cheers,' Lee grinned. 'So, **all in all, there's simply no point to most Thoughts, unless they're put into action.** I guess a large percentage of our Thoughts *never* make it into the world *outside* of our heads. They're just hanging out in there having a party,' he scratched his temples. 'Therefore, unless we actually do something about those Thoughts, there's no point in thinking about them, because they *are* and *will stay* a *theory*.' Tara nodded her head vigorously at Lee's wonderful spurt of inspiration. Confidently he went on, 'So, **to really *want* to be Now and to *want* to get into *that* space, we need to deeply understand and *consciously agree* that most Thoughts are useless**, right? **That we won't miss anything if we don't think those Thoughts. That we *can* Let Go of them. That Nowness is actually a useful and safe and good place to be.**'

Use Your Mind Like a Torch - Think Only As Much As Necessary, Consciously! - Be Aware, When You Are Thinking

'Brilliant. Yes, that's exactly it! **The point is to: *think only as much as necessary*. Think only as much as necessary to sort out the problem, *then go straight back to the dot*, by concentrating on your breathing**,' Tara tapped the Nowness-Silence-Dot on the drawing she'd made earlier. She looked up at Lee. 'The trick to get closer and closer to Nowness is to learn to catch yourself out when you *start* to think a Thought, to look at the Thought *immediately* after it leaves the dot. About here,' she marked the squiggly line with a cross very close to the Nowness-Silence-Dot. 'Then, we can decide *straight away* if that Thought is worth having in our heads or not. If not, it's just Dots and Squiggles again, and that means back to the dot,' Tara drew a hard line from the bar above the dot, straight back into the Nowness dot. 'No detours. Catch out. Decide. Back to the dot by breathing. Silence. Finished. Next. *Use your Mind like a torch*. **Use it when you *need* it and when you're done, *switch it off* and stick it back into the bag.** Hey presto, no more Mental Loops.' Lee smiled at Tara with amazement. Tara went on, '**The Mind is a tool, just like a torch. You don't always need it, but in certain situations it's really useful. It's dark and you need some light. So, switch it on. If it's light already, switch it off. Leaving it on won't shed any more light, so stop wasting energy.**'

'I like it,' Lee said. 'The Mind is a tool to be used when *we* need it, rather than the Mind using *us* 24/7, if we like it or not. When the torch is off, we're in the Now, or at least Mindful, and **when the torch is *on*, we need to make sure that it's on *consciously*, that we *think consciously***. That we're aware of what we're doing, *while* we're doing it.'

'Exactly. It's a little like contemplation. Let me give you an example. Let's say you need to plan to move house or organise a wedding or buy a car or pay your bills or plan food for a dinner party, or your children's ballet classes or birthday parties, or do your homework, or plan a project at work. The key while you're doing all of that, is to be aware, when and *while* you are thinking. To be focussed, Mindful, and to be aware when your Mind is going on a journey on this piece of paper,' Tara pointed at the Dots and Squiggles again. **'Always be Aware of your Thoughts!'**

'Like that we keep our Mind nice and tidy and sharp and hassle free - all the time.'

'Yep. So, what would you do now, if the bus isn't coming and it is actually important that you get to work on time?' Tara asked, trying to apply theory to practice straight away.

Lee thought for a second and then said, 'I'd catch myself worrying, then I'd decide that worrying won't make the bus come any faster. Then I'd decide, if the bus not coming actually matters or not. I mean, what's a couple of minutes, right? But if I decide that it really *is* important that I get to work in time, instead of Dot and Squiggling and getting lost in thousands of made up scenarios, I'd take a look at the situation *consciously*. I'd figure out if I could do anything about it or not. I'd only think the necessary practical Thoughts, Thoughts that I could put into action to remedy the situation: "Could I take a taxi? No, too expensive. Or yes, and I'd go and get one. Could I hitchhike? Fat chance. Maybe a friend passes by and could give me a lift? Well maybe, keep an eye out. Could I take the train?" I'd think, decide, do and stop thinking. Torch, on and off,' Lee flicked the switch on an imaginary torch in his left hand.

'That's it! Now let's assume that you've decided that you *can't* do anything to remedy the situation. You've worked through all the practical alternatives and none are workable options. Now what?' Tara asked, wanting to make sure all the angles are covered.

Lee was on the ball. 'I'd decide that to keep thinking about it, still won't change anything, it still won't make the bus come faster, it still won't give me a solution, so I'd stop thinking about it all together. **In that scenario, even if I'd be late to work, thinking wouldn't change that either,**' Lee felt unusually comfortable with the common sense aspect in everything he was discovering. 'And whenever the worrying Thought would come back, I'd remember that I've only just decided that it's useless, and I'd go straight back to the Now or Mindfulness,' he pointed at the straight line in the drawing. **'Oh wow,' he just noticed something, 'at that stage, I wouldn't even have to go through the decision making process anymore, I'd just have to remember the previous decision.** Wow, this is brilliant. **Letting go of Thoughts becomes automatic like this!'**

'Yes! You got it! And wait till you learn to Trust your Intuition.' Tara continued excitedly, **'the more you follow your Intuition rather than your Mind, the less of the thinking process you've just described is necessary in the first place. It's like our Intuition can bypass our Rational Mind. We don't need to think, we just ask our Intuition. But, that's something for a later chapter if you're interested.'**

'Tease,' Lee laughed.

'Well, everything in it's own time,' Tara winked light heartedly.

Lee knew by now that Tara had a logical order of how her explanations build up on one another, so he didn't press any further. Just to make sure though, he grabbed his notebook and made a little side note: "Remember to talk about following Intuition and thus bypassing the Rational Mind." He circled it, put a fat exclamation mark next to it, and begun to write a list summarising the last few minutes of conversation.

Use your Mind like a Torch:
- Think only as much as necessary.
- Think consciously – like during a Contemplation. Be aware *while* you're thinking.
- If you have to think, plan or sort out stuff, *be aware, while* you are thinking. Be Focussed and Mindful.
- *Always* be *Aware* of your Thoughts!
- When a Thought comes back, remember that you've only just decided that thinking it won't change anything and go straight back to the Now or Mindfulness. (Like that you don't have to go through the decision making process anymore, you just remember the decision. Thus, with time and practice, Letting Go of Thoughts becomes automatic.)
- Use your Mind like a Torch. On when you need it, off when you don't.

Good and Bad Days - *Feel* the Now

'I just remember something a friend of mine said to me once, he said that **if you want to be Now, your Mind feels as if one hundred policemen are running around in it in a frenzy, and they have one hundred industrial size torches with them. Now you try and tell them to switch them off.**'

'Okay?'

'What I'm trying to say is that the Mind *wants* to think and that different people experience the entire process of becoming Now in different ways. It's good to know, that **to get to a stage where we can really just take our attention of a Thought at will, takes practice**. It won't happen overnight. **You need to do it, do it and do it. You need to figure out how you can get those policemen first to calm down, and then to switch of their torches. All of them.**

If we'd be talking about puppies, as we already said, some days there are thousands of them fighting for attention, sometimes just a few. Some puppies are more determined than others and they'll hunt us down, wherever we are. They're lurking on the fringes or our Consciousness, just waiting to pounce on us whenever we're not looking. Indulging or wallowing in poor-little-old-me or why-does-this-happen-to-me-stuff or I-hate-this-stuff or this-really-pisses-me-off-stuff, are all Dots and Squiggles. Even good or overly excited Thoughts can rollercoaster. So, whatever Thoughts they are, just notice them and breathe. Finished,' Tara scrunched up her face, then breathed in deeply, her face slowly transforming to a peaceful and blessed expression - then she grinned, 'See?' Lee laughed. She sat up straight and looked back at him. 'And once you got the hang of it, you do it automatically. No big deal. **If you can't reach Nowness, cause it's just too mad up there,**' Tara tapped her forehead, '**concentrate on your breathing and** *feel* **your Body relax.** Breathe into your belly. Bring the balance point of your Body back into your centre. When your Mind goes crazy, find out where in your Body you breathe. You'll more than likely notice that you're breathing up in your chest again. As soon as you focus back on your belly, things will become clearer and easier again - puff - just like that. But you know, **if it gets really, really bad and nothing seems to help? There's one other thing that you can try.**'

'Oh yeah?'

'**If you can't still your Mind, try and remember what it** *FEELS* **like to be Now.** *Feel* **the peace. When your brain's going crazy, when your Thoughts feel edgy,** *be* **Now, by actively** *feeling* **the Feeling of it.**'

'More?' Lee prompted.

'Sure. **The way to know how Nowness feels like, is to get yourself a reference point *when* you *are* in Nowness,**' Tara paused. 'To do that, you need to set an active Intent to notice what it feels like when you are in Nowness. For the hair splitters out there,' she light heartedly winked at Lee, 'of course, as soon as you analyse it, you're not Now anymore, but you'll be able to get pretty close, even if only for a split second. And then, when you want to reach Nowness again, you'll just *recreate* that physical feeling.'

'Sounds great, but how do I recreate a feeling?' Lee wondered.

'Oh, that's easy. Let me give you an example. Can you remember a moment in your life when you were carefree? When you were wholly relaxed and peaceful. I'm not talking about a Nowness moment, just a generally blissful and chilled experience.' Lee nodded and closed his eyes. 'Now, remember that moment and how you felt. What kind of sensations did you have and what were they like? Were they soft, bright, gentle, warm? *Where* did you feel them in you Body?' Tara watched Lee's face for a few seconds and said softly, 'And now *feel* **that feeling. Be back in that moment**, and feel your skin, your Body, your insides, and most importantly, feel your brain. Feel what the insides of your brain feel like. Feel the slowness, the softness, the roundness, the gentleness, the lightness, the clarity, the wisdom and power. Feel how calm and balanced our breathing is in your stomach.'

Lee nodded slowly, still concentrating. After a few more minutes. Lee opened his eyes, 'That's amazing. I've really felt that!'

Tara grinned, '**There you go, you've just created a feeling. And what's best, you can do that *wherever* you are, *whenever* you like. You can feel that peace and depth anywhere, anytime. It just needs a couple of minutes of focus and remembering.**'

'Wow,' Lee looked at Tara. 'Now that's easy. Gosh, whenever my brain freaks out, I just *create* a peaceful feeling. That's cool.'

'Yep. It's magic, isn't it? What's more, **this usually works, even when things get seriously out of hand. It works because your Mind, your Body *and* your Emotions are engaged here.** But, and that's important to remember, it's *not* Nowness.'

'Right, because you're trying to recreate something.'

'Exactly, but it helps tremendously to keep your Mind at bay when nothing else helps.'

'Great. Thanks for that. But,' Lee said, 'If I recreate it and then actually Shift over into that state? When I stop trying to recreate, but when I actually become it? What then? Then it would be Nowness, wouldn't it?'

'So it would be.'

PART 6

12 Things that Distract Our Mind, Sneaky Negative Undercurrents

Sensory Overload - Good and Bad - A State Of Mind

Lee opened his bag, unpacked two bottles of Orange Juice and handed one to Tara.

'Oh thanks, just what the doctor ordered, some vitamins for our busy brain,' she opened her bottle and drank thirstily. 'Wohoo. Energy flooding through my Body! Nice!' They sat for a little while, talking about nothing in particular, enjoying the sun and each other's company. The sun was warm, the grass soft and eyes sparkly. When the Orange Juice was nearly emptied, the conversation slowly and naturally went back to the Cosmic stuff.

'You know, **we've talked about a bunch of hilarious things that stop us from being Now**, right? **We've began to identify the puppies so that you can notice them when they come. Well, there are more**,' Tara hinted.

'What, more little buggers that create Thoughts and distract our Minds?' Lee asked incredulously. 'Well, I guess, better the devil you know. Let's have'm.'

'Alright then, sneaky little devils they are too, because this?' Tara pointed around her, '*This* is the world of distractions. *All* of it! All around us are ridiculous amounts of sensory impressions that bombard us all the time. **Our senses work overtime all day long.** We see, hear, smell, taste and feel - constantly. **And each and every one of those senses triggers Thoughts, Emotions, reactions, even memories.** Now, our brain can't consciously cope with all the simultaneous sensory input, all the noises, smells, and things to see, so it filters out individual bits to concentrate on, and everything else becomes background noise. It's always there, but we don't consciously notice it,' Tara finished.

'I know what you mean,' Lee said, 'it's like having music in the background, but not really hearing it, until we put our attention to it and actually become *consciously aware* of it,' Lee said. 'I guess as our brain filters out the non-important stuff, it avoids madness through total sensory overload,' Lee held his head, imagining total sensory overload through sensing *everything*.

'Exactly. If we would be aware of *all* the Thoughts about *all* the impressions we're getting, all at the same time, we'd go mad,' Tara shook her head vigorously. 'Brrr! So, lucky for us, our brain can't have all our attention on Listening to music *while* one hundred percent *tasting* food, for example. It just doesn't work. Our attention can flick between the impressions at lightening speed, but it cannot do it perfectly at the same time.'

'Hang on,' Lee said and took a small sip of the rest of his juice. He paused a few seconds, then had another sip and then another one, finishing it off. When he put the bottle down again he had a surprised look on his face. 'Tara, this is another one of those totally obvious realisations that never occurred to me. I can't taste the drink *one hundred percent* with *all* of my attention, *while* also trying to listen one hundred percent to those two birds over there sing,' he pointed up at a couple of birds that were perched in the tree above them. 'It's one or the other.'

'I like the way you work,' Tara laughed, 'you try to turn theory into experience *straight away* to help you internalise new information. It's exactly what I do.'

'Yeah, it's *knowing* information *through experience*, rather than just believing somebody else's words,' Lee smiled. It felt good to be appreciated.

'Exactly! Now, all of that was just the beginning,' Tara announced in her usual there's-so-much-more tone of voice.

'Alright then, hit me with the *real* stuff,' Lee dared her with a big handsome smile.

'Nothing easier than that,' Tara smiled back at him vivaciously. 'Get your head around this one. **Everything that comes in contact with our *senses* creates a Thought, even if we're not consciously aware of it, it's there.'**

'Woohaoh, scary!' Lee was taken aback.

'Yeah, isn't it? That's why we've got so much shit going on up there!' Tara rubbed her temples. 'Some of those Thoughts only last a millisecond and go away, but others kick off lots and lots of chain reactions and Mind associations. **Usually most of the Thoughts stay in the background, but they still always create a certain amount of white noise in our brain.'**

'Ah, and **that background noise makes our brain feels edgy and buzzy,'** Lee deducted.

'Right. Without Nowness practice, as soon as we become *actively aware* of any of those little milliseconds of sensory crap, we invite them into the forefront of our Awareness. Then, as an immediate reaction, we quite happily start to think about them, and as soon as we think about something, there are immediate word associations that go off on instantaneous Dots and Squiggles. For now, **lets focus on the *very first* Thought that emerges *straight after* we managed to put our Awareness on just *one* of our Senses.**'

'Good plan,' Lee approved.

'Great. That *first* Thought is usually an immediate *judgement* if we like the impression or not, which in turn results in an entire chain reaction of more Thought associations, feelings and other Mental and Emotional reactions,' Tara drew Dots and Squiggles into the air to emphasize the point.

'Oh, that's so true,' Lee grinned in recognition. 'Ha, it's like: "nothing, nothing, hearing, sounds, nice. I judge that I like it. I remember that sound, la, la, la. More associations, I went with so and so to that festival and heard it there, oh and then we met that person and then we, bla, bla." Or on the other hand, I might hear the song and perceive it as horrible noise: "urgh, that's a bit too much, I wish they would stop that. Shall I go and ask them to turn it down, no that would be silly", or: "oh yes, let's go". Bla and more bla and off we go, once again on the Thought express, all initiated by simply hearing a song,' Lee remembered exactly such a situation from just a few weeks ago. 'And yeah, I can see how **we judge the sensory impression the split second we give it attention, and** also how we **tailor our word associations according to that judgement.**' Tara nodded as Lee continued, 'Man, you know what I just realised? That judging thing? It's automatic. I wonder if we have any influence on that.'

'We'll get to that,' Tara winked at Lee and swiftly continued, 'Now, if the judgement is *Positive*, it'll give us a Positive *sensation*, right?'

'Oh man. And **if the Thought is Negative, we get an immediate pang of Negativity,**' Lee said astounded.

'Exactly**, and all of that happens to us all day long, and mostly without us noticing it!**'

'But **that means that pangs of Negativity sneakily undermine our everyday existence.**' Lee's eyes widened dramatically, 'Gosh, **that means that we constantly have *an underlying vibe of Negativity* going on, without us even knowing about it,**' Lee was clogging on fast.

'Yeah, or Positivity. But yes. The little buggers creep in and set up home without us asking for it. But now comes the cool bit.'

Tara didn't get to finish her sentence, as Lee was making connections at lightening speed, 'So, **if we can nip the automatic judging reactions in the bud, we can stop the Negative undercurrents in our heads and lives. To do that, we need to stop the judgement of sensory input right at the core.** This is crazy,' Lee laughed out loud. 'I tell you, any Psychology degree is Mickey Mouse stuff compared to all of this.'

'It's not bad, is it?' Tara smiled broadly.

Lee noticed the sunshine as it sparkled through the branches of their tree, melting with the lusciousness of Tara's Being. How beautiful she was. He squeezed his eyes tightly shut for a moment and rummaged in his brain for his last sentence, 'So, *how* do we stop the judgement right at the core?' he wondered out loud.

'Well, **there are two ways really. First we can set an Intent to catch ourselves out** *every time* **we think something Negative or** *every time* **we judge something Negatively and then go back into the Now, and eventually, Negative Thoughts will be reduced and eventually disappear.**'

'Ok, and **what's the other way?'**

'You stop trying to figure out what's good or bad.'

'Eh, what?' Lee raised his eyebrows.

'Instead of trying to stop judging, it's much more effective to *understand that judging in itself is an utterly useless activity.*'

'Whoha, Hippy-Alert! Rational Mind is kicking in fast, I need more than that to be satisfied,' Lee cocked his head and looked at Tara alertly.

'More coming up,' Tara promised. 'Basically, the long and short of it is: who are we to know what is good or bad?' As Lee still looked blankly, Tara thought of an example, 'Take a thunderstorm. We're talking mad, copious amounts of rain, ok? You might be on summer holiday and all you want is sun and blue sky, therefore, for *you* the thunderstorm is a total nightmare, right?'

'So *I* judge it as bad.'

'Right. On the other hand, the farmer down the road, whose fields are dying of thirst, for him the thunderstorm is…'

'A gift from the Gods,' Lee finished Tara's sentence. '*He* thinks it's wonderful.'

'Right. So there you go, **it's the** *same* **event, but two different people have two different judgements. So, whose right. Is the storm good or bad?**'

'Well, yes, sure, but for *me*, the rainstorm is still *bad* or not?' Lee asked slightly confused.

'Well, **it depends on what you look at, if you look at the thunderstorms** *itself*, **or your** *judgment* **of it. The thunderstorm** *itself* **isn't Negative, is it? Your judgement is**. The thunderstorm is just a thunderstorm.' Lee nodded slowly, waiting for his brain to make the necessary connections as Tara continued. 'You see, **you might think that your judgements are a steady reflection of your environment,**

when actually, they are a steady reflection of *you*,' Tara paused once again. 'And in fact, your judgements are often not even as reliable or clear cut as you think. You see, **your judgement of *one and the same thing* can change depending on your mood.** One day you might judge something as beautiful or fabulous, and on another day you might judge the *very same thing* as really awful, maybe after a fight with somebody or because you didn't have your ten hours of beauty sleep,' Tara adjusted her hair, pretending to have just woken up slightly bedraggled. 'If you get down to it, our state of Mind, the environment, energies, all of it influences our judgements. It's not the thing or the event *itself* that's Negative, it's our Judgement.'

'Great,' Lee sat up, his face clear and open again. 'Connections made. Now I get it,' he butted in. '**Everything that happens to us, just is what *it is*. It's *not* good or bad. It's just an *event*.** Like rain. It's just rain. It's not good or bad. **If an event is good or bad to us, depends on how we *look at it*.** Wow. I mean, I've heard the phrase: it-all-depends-on-how-you-look-at-it a million times, but only now do I really understand what it means,' Lee said surprised.

'You've hit the nail on the head. ***We make* an event good or bad by the way we *judge* the event or our experience of it, but the event itself is and stays *neutral*. Therefore, good or bad is a *State of Mind*. A state of our mood, experiences, conditionings, our surroundings and our social circle. Nothing in this world is inherently good or bad**,' Tara shrugged her shoulders. '**It just IS, the way it IS.**'

Lee's jaw had dropped long ago. Another one of these animated insights and his heart would surely stop. A vastness of Mind-blowing facts was thrown at him, bang, bang, bang, one after another, each one of them ringing deeply true, and each flicking a new switch in his Consciousness. New parts in his brain lit up, opened and deepened. 'Give me a second, will you?' Lee closed his eyes and observed his Thoughts. He felt the grass under the blanked. "Nice". He heard the birds up in the tree again. "Nice". A motorbike. "Too loud".

'Gosh, judging really is instantaneous, *and* it happens all the time,' Lee said as he opened his eyes again. 'We really do judge *all* the time. It's constant,' he rubbed his eyes. 'And you know the wildest thing?' he looked back at Tara, 'I think that **everybody judges differently! I bet different countries, age groups, centuries, social classes all have *different* standards or ideas of good or bad.** At some stage it might have been perfectly fine to kill a human for food, whereas today that would be unheard of. Some think piercings and tattoos are fabulous, others detest them. Some love suits and ties, others hate them. Gosh, that's so interesting.

Different families, scenes, schools, they all have different standards of judging something good or bad. Your mates might think X is great, but Y is bad, whereas your workplace might think it's the other way 'round. To top that, all of these opinions change with the wind, depending on what mood everyone's in. Phew, when it comes down to figuring out what's *really* good or bad?' he hesitated, 'I guess, we really can't ever figure it out. There'll always be somebody that thinks differently.'

Tara grinned, a little light bulb seemed to flash above Lee's head as he paused for a second to catch his breath.

'**In the end judgements are just Thoughts!**' he continued, '**They are in our heads, right? They're just another figment of our Imagination.**'

'**Oh yes!**' **Tara said excitedly.** '**And once you realise** *that*, **you can** *choose* **again! You can choose what to do with the judgements!**'

'Sure, I get that. I can breathe and be Now, and the judgement would disappear, but, mmh, hang on, that's still allowing the judgement to affect me for a split second though, right? **That would just be Letting Go of it once it has occurred, right? But how can I not have the judgement in the first place? How can I see what IS rather what I judge it to be, if Judgements come automatically?**' Lee said slowly and deliberately, trying to cover all the angles.

Tara picked up his question without faltering, '**Judgements are our** *Opinions* **of a thing. They are our** *interpretation* **of it. They are our Mind's** *projections* **of our Opinion onto that thing.** To just see what IS instead, we first have to notice that we have those judging Thoughts in the first place.'

'Right. We've just done that.'

'Step one,' Tara ticked the air in front of her. '*Now,* **imagine a box.** **Anything in our lives, be it people, things, situations, Feelings, Emotions, things that we would normally judge one way or the other, put them into that box**,' Tara picked up some imaginary bits and bobs and stuck them in to an equally imaginary box. 'It's all in the box now right? Now look at it.' Lee looked. '**Our immediate reaction when we look into such a box is to start to describe the content, label it, name it, judge it or compare it in our Mind. The long and short of it is: we think! We interpret, we judge, we have opinions, we make stuff up**, right?' Lee nodded. 'Now, **instead, of doing that, don't think about it, just look at the. Just** *observe.*'

'Just observe?'

'Just observe rather than judge the sensory input that's coming in.' Lee looked into the box and back up at Tara. 'Let me give you another example. **See those two people walking over there?**' she pointed at a couple walking arm and arm across the lawn in front of them.

'Yep.'

'Tell me what just went on in your head,' Tara said with a cheeky smile.

'Oh great, here we go. This is embarrassing.'

'Go on, you know you want to,' Tara prodded his arm playfully.

'Well, I was judging him to be a bit wimpy and thinking how such a lovely girl could go out with a guy like that, then I was wondering where they're going and why. I judged their clothes, their hair, their movements, and I also asked the obligatory would-I-could-I-should-I-will-I question. Man, and I did all of that in a split second,' Lee was amazed.

'The what question?' Tara leant slightly forward.

'The would-I-could-I-should-I-will-I question.'

'What on earth does that mean?' Tara laughed.

'Well, whenever anybody of sexual age looks at *anybody* of the opposite sex, within the first nanosecond we ask and answer that question.'

'The would-I-could-I-should-I-will-I question,' Tara repeated slowly, until the penny finally dropped. 'That's hilarious, so we do. It's instantaneous, automatic. Oh god, that's so rude! I had no idea! Thanks for that, that will go down in my repertoire of hilarities,' she grinned broadly. 'Lee, you're impossible.'

She looked at him again, his big smile, his tousle hair, his strong hands. Would-I-could-I-should-I-will-I? There it was, loud and clear and so was the answer. She blushed slightly. When she looked back at Lee's eyes, she thought she saw a spark, a spark of recognition, of great-Minds-think-alike, just before she shyly averted her eyes to glance up into the tree to check out those two little birds again.

She took a couple of deep breaths to gather her wit and finally said to a boldly grinning Lee, 'Now, look at the couple again,' she pointed at the pair that was quickly disappearing out of sight. '**Instead of making up all sorts of stories about the sensory input you're getting, instead of asking yourself silly theoretical questions about them,**' she winked at Lee, '**just *look* at them. Just observe, just *see*, Be Now, where there are no words. Take them in, see just what *is*, not what you *think* is.**'

Lee tried to do that. He looked at the two people walking across the grass and tried to Let Go off the judgement before it even started, but the more he tried, the more edgy his brain became. He could literally feel it in his head. He felt dryness, hollowness, scratchiness, until something within him told him to *relax*, to *stop trying*. It wasn't about trying *not* to do something, it was about just *being* Now, where no judgements existed in the first place.

Ah. Lee concentrated on his breathing. **His Being calmed down as he felt his breath. His brain began to feel softer, rounder and juicier and suddenly he felt Present.** Now. Empty. Clear. And then it hit him. **Right now, he was just** *looking* **at the couple. He was not thinking them or about them. He was simply** *observing* **them. It was as if his focus, his attention and his Mind were on his breath and that he just happened to look at something else at the same time.**

'Wow, now I get it,' he splurted out spontaneously, 'If we're completely Present and Now, then Judgements don't even start. **It's not about stopping a judgement at the root, but about realising that when we're present, judgements don't even come up, so there's nothing to stop**. No Thoughts get created in the first place. So, all we need to do is to Be Now.'

'Easy, isn't it?' Tara smiled happily.

'It's fantastic. One solution fits all. But, then again,' Lee hesitated, 'wouldn't it be boring, if we stopped paying attention to our senses all together? It kind of sounds a little dreary to be honest.' Tara looked at him with an are-you-serious-?-? look. 'Ok, it's not boring?' Lee said with curious caution.

'Would I ever tell you anything that's boring?' her eyes twinkled. 'But seriously, it's not really that we stop paying attention to our senses, it's just that we observe what our senses receive in Nowness, rather than interpret the input with our Mind. We perceive what *is*, rather than what we *think* is.' Tara closed her eyes and said softly, 'As we've said before, the Here and Now is the space where everything *really* happens, not what we *think* is happening. **Being Now is like putting your attention onto** *everything*, **at the same time, but without interpreting any of it and thus without being frazzled by the vastness of all the input.** Do you remember when you played with focussing on *all* your Senses yesterday? All at the same time?'

'Oh, of course. I remember how difficult it was, that I couldn't really do it, but that I managed to get a little flash of what it could be like.'

'Wanna play again?'

'Sure.'

'Well, let's do the same thing again. Play once more with *feeling all* your senses at the same time, rather than *thinking* them. Don't try to create anything, just feel what's *already* there and see what happens.'

'With my eyes closed like yesterday?'

'Yep, just like before.'

Lee closed his eyes once more and fell silent. Right on cue, all sorts of stuff began to happen inside of him. Thoughts interpreted the feeling on his skin, the sound in his ears, his Mind judged good and bad incessantly and then - nothing, breath. Silence. Then back to: "Oh, what was that? Is something crawling on me? No it's not, yes it is, I can feel it!" Breathe. Breathe. Thoughts and little glimpses of Nowness bounced in and out of his Consciousness.

In amongst all of this he faintly heard Tara's voice, '**Now, slowly *open* your eyes and keep doing it.**'

'What, open my eyes?' Lee asked quietly, trying not to loose his connection. Keeping visual input at bay sounded much harder than doing it with his eyes closed.

'Yep. **Take that tree over there. Look at it, feel it, Be Now.**'

Lee opened his eyes, looked at the tree, and let his Being sync with his breath once more. **Slowly the tree turned from a *nice* tree and a *green* tree into - a tree. At the instant of that transition, there was an unexpected feeling of connection to the tree. His kept his attention focussed on his breath, in an effort not to judge that feeling, but to observe it instead. He tried not to dismiss or enjoy the feeling either, because neither one of them would be Being Now. He gently thought that even simply calling it a tree was somehow a judgement, so he Let Go of that too.**

Then when he stopped all his thinking, with his whole attention breathing, he was just there, in that moment. He felt clear, strong and connected. He felt One with everything and he and the tree were just a little part of a vast universe. And "no, it definitely wasn't boring", a little voice jumped at him from the depths of his Mind, it was just *different*. In fact, it felt alive. It felt free. He felt the experience, no, the *feeling* of the experience in every detail imaginable, to etch it solidly into his Awareness. This was the feeling he wanted to be able to recreate. This was as close to Nowness as he'd ever been, and he knew that he could get there again in a flash, all it took was a bit of concentration - and practice, of course.

'Now that's cool! I've never done *that* with a tree before. Man, it felt so peaceful,' Lee said and went on to describe what had just happened to him.

'So, is it boring?' Tara looked at him knowingly.

'Absolutely not, I vow to eat my words!' Lee made loud chewing noises.

'Are you sure?'

'After this experience? Oh yes, absolutely.'

'Fantabulous,' Tara said and smiled.

'That was a truly cool experience,' Lee glowed. 'Basically, if I'm not thinking, I'm in the space that *is*, rather than in the place I *think* is. The space that *is*, is the same space the trees are in, that's where I met this one over there for a little while,' he pointed over to the guinea-pig-tree. '**Without Thoughts, you become One. With everything**,' Lee was surprised to suddenly truly *know* the meaning of those Hippy words. He continued gently, 'It's Thoughts that separate us. In Nowness, we become One, we become aware of the world around us, in a way we never have before,' Lee paused and looked at his tree again. 'Actually, I remember us talking about something similar before. **We said that by focussing on our senses and *feeling* them, rather than thinking them, we slip into the Present. We said that that's where *everything* happens. *Everything*! So, yes, how on earth could that be boring? And anyway**,' Lee grinned broadly, '***boring* is just a Thought too, right?**'

He was on a roll. 'And the good thing is, I can always choose how far I want to take this. I can be entirely Now, where nothing is bad or boring anymore or I can play with learning about myself by catching out individual judgements as and when they occur. Or I could even be really clever and just filter out all the bad things and keep all the good things. But obviously that still requires judgements and opinions and most of all thinking,' Lee realised instantaneously, 'and I'd still have to deal with the split second of the possible Negative undercurrents, right? And I might not even catch all of them before they affect me.

Mmh, so, if I'd just Be Now, none of this would occur anymore. **Being Now would solve the whole judgement thingy altogether, without any Negativity undermining us**. Our Mind would be crystal clear. Phew, just the Thought of what we could use all that newly improved, un-distracted attention for,' he was astounded. "For example, if I had to concentrate really hard, but outside of my window is a chap with a pneumatic drill who creates total havoc, all I'd need to do is *notice* the: "Oh man, this guy is just too loud" - Thought, and the: "I wish he'd shut up and let me think, who does he think he is to make so much noise?" - Thought, and the: "No, I really can't concentrate with all of this going on around me" – Thought, catch myself out, breathe and study instead! The more I'd breathe and become Now, the drill just wouldn't bother me anymore. No Thoughts, no drill, no noise,' the words flowed out of Lee's mouth like a stream danced over the rocks in a waterfall. 'Oh man, I just realised something else,' he laughed out loudly, 'if I would give attention to the Thoughts about the noise, it would actually make it *more difficult to concentrate*, because I would not only have to battle with the noise from outside, but I'd also have to deal with the stupid *self-created* noise from the *inside*, the

Thoughts I'm making up myself! That's hilarious,' Lee plonked himself back against the tree.

'Funny isn't it?' Tara laughed with him.

'It's ridiculous.'

'Glad you think so too,' Tara looked at him warmly.

'Oh man, I've just realised something! **It's those Thoughts, that self created noise that distracts me, not the freaking pneumatic drill!**'

'Full points,' Tara held up her hand and stretched out ten fingers.

'Phew, so the gist of it is that nothing is inherently good or bad. Our judgements change due to our environment, our company and our own State of Mind. In the Now thinking and thus judgements disappear and sensory input won't even begin to create stupid Thoughts and associations anymore. Like this no sensory impressions can bother us or distract us anymore. Fabulous,' Lee grabbed his pen and started another list.

Nothing is Good or Bad:

* Instead of trying to stop judging, try to understand that judging in itself is an utterly useless activity.
* Everything that happens to us, just is what it *is*. It's not good or bad. Like rain.
* We make an event good or bad by the way we *judge* the event or experience it, but the event or the experience *itself* is and stays *neutral*.
* If an event is good or bad to us, depends on how we *look* at it.
* Good or bad is a *State of Mind*. Of *our* Mind.
* Judgements are Thoughts.
* Be Now, where no Thoughts, no judgement and no Negativity exist.
* All sensory input gets automatically judged, often subconsciously. If the Thought is Negative, we get an immediate pang of Negativity. Without us knowing, pangs of Negativity sneakily *undermine* our everyday existence with an *underlying* Negative vibe.
* Catch yourself out when you think something Negative, or just be Now.
* Don't interpret, judge, or have opinions, just *observe*.

When he was done, Lee looked over his list. 'That's a pretty good summary, I dare say, I'm getting good at this,' he chuckled.

'So you are darling, so you are. I'm truly in awe,' Tara said, bowing deeply.

Lee gentlemanly bowed even deeper, 'Noblesse oblige. We aim to please.'

'Pleased. Thank you,' Tara attempted to bow even deeper, somehow managed to lose her balance and fell over onto her side, squealing as she landed on the blanket so unexpectedly.

Lee grinned broadly, 'Could you do that again please? Please fall over like that again? That couldn't have looked any more comical if you'd have tried.'

Tara laughed and uselessly tried to get up. Lee reached over and pulled her back up to sit. They smiled at each other freely and comfortably. Lee was still holding on to Tara's hand. He gave it a little squeeze and gently placed it back on her lap. He grinned. Her hand had felt soft and warm - and like more.

Judging Others

> "We do not see things as They are,
> we see them as We are."
> - Talmud

Tara felt her hand tingle where Lee had touched her. Gosh, she was becoming seventeen again. "I'll never wash my hand again," she joked in her head. She smiled at Lee, leant back against the tree and said, 'Actually, there's more on the judgement thingy. Do you want more?'

'How come I'm not surprised?' Lee shook his head with laughter. 'Of course. Go on then,' he requested with a wave of his right hand.

'Righty ho, here we go. As we've just said, we judge things and people, all the time, constantly. It's what a lot of our subconscious Thought are all about, right? So we judge. And **we think that _we're_ judging others**. But if you think about it, **the way we judge others, in fact says more about us, about ourselves, than about the other person**.'

'Yeah, that sounds familiar. Somebody told me something like that before. Anything we don't like about another person, is actually part of ourselves.' Lee waited a second to think about that statement, then went on, 'I never really understood this properly before, but I think it's beginning to make more sense to me now. **In a nutshell it means that our judgments of others, reflects back to ourselves**, right? **Because _our_ judgements are _our_ Thoughts**.' Tara nodded and he went on, '**If we look at somebody and think they're too fat, that means _we_ have an issue with weight, or at least that weight is on our Mind, otherwise that Thought wouldn't have come up in the first place**.' Tara looked at him attentively as he continued, 'If we don't like somebody behaving a certain way, that means that _we_ have a problem with people

245

behaving that way for whatever reason. **We project our *own* standards, our *own* ideals onto *other* people. I guess that means that all the judgements and faults we find with others, in reality reflects on who *we* are. We feel that we should be a certain way, so others should be too.**'

Tara picked up where Lee had left off, '**We judge somebody to be a certain way and *we* think it's because of *them*.**'

'When actually it's because of *us*,' Lee finished her sentence.

'Precisely. It's *our* opinion. It's in *our* heads, it's what *we* think, it reflects who *we* are. When you really get down to it, it's as much *our* problems as it is the other person's. And anyway, why should everybody behave the way we want them to? **Who says we're so right**?' she looked at Lee, who nodded thoughtfully.

Tara continued, 'We can learn a lot about ourselves, if we actually tried to understand *why* we don't like somebody or somebody's Behaviour, and what it says about us. For example *why* do we think somebody is a show-off and *why* don't we like it? Why do we think that somebody's a twat? Because *he* gets all the attention and *we* don't? Because our friends are listening to *him* and not us? Because *we* don't get to say anything? Because *we'd* like to be like that, but we're too shy? Are we being intolerant? Why can we not see his point of view or understand why he's behaving like that? Why does it even cause us a problem?'

'Because he should comply to *our* conditionings and *our* ideas of the world. And if he doesn't, we don't like him,' Lee answered Tara's rhetorical question.

'Precisely. As a strange fact, I found that challenging individuals are often the greatest teachers. But then again,' she paused as a mischievous look spread over her face when she added deadpan, 'some people just are arseholes.'

Lee burst out laughing, 'I can't believe you just said that.'

'Well, we really *can* learn a lot from difficult people, but sometimes, you know? Sorry. Some people are just off! Sometimes I understand where they're coming from, and I learn, but still, if I have the choice, I rather do without them. I mean, I'm not a martyr, right? No big deal,' Tara said nonchalantly.

'Now there's a sensible person if I ever saw one. You see people for who they are, you learn from them about yourself, but you don't martyr yourself hanging out with idiots.'

'That's the ticket. And it's my own personal choice, you might choose to do differently,' Tara emphasized.

'Fair dos.'

'Fabulous. Oh, and I forgot. Besides how useful it is to *understand* all of this, *playing* with it is even more fun!' Tara wriggled her hands excitedly. 'When you begin to notice some of the judgements that hang out in your head? Man, you'll hardly be able to contain yourself. They're so funny, so ridiculous. Hilarious times a million, I tell you. The shit our Minds come up with is truly unsurpassed. So, if you do this, you'll be entertained *and* you'll have a fabulously clear Mind. Two for the price of one.'

'Clever entertainment, what more could I want? That gets the thumbs up from me,' Lee stuck out his thumbs, grabbed his notebook and wrote,

Judging others:
- Our judgments of others, reflects back to ourselves, because *our* judgements are *our* Thoughts, it's how *we* see the world.
- We project our *own* standards, our *own* ideals onto *other* people. All the judgements and faults we find with *others*, in reality reflects on who *we* are.
- We want everybody to comply to *our* conditionings and ideas of the world. Well, a lot of people don't. So if we expect that, we'll constantly get disappointed and as a result we'll be pretty miserable.

Self-Judgement

'**N**ow, there's more,' Tara said as soon as the list was finished.

'How could I have ever doubted that?' Lee smiled. 'Off you go.'

'Well, **we're not only judging *others*, we are also judging *ourselves***,' Tara said casually.

'Oh bugger,' Lee breathed out with a hiss.

'And we can be petty tough on ourselves.'

'Oh yes. I know about that,' he nodded. 'And Mr and Mrs Marketing help us nicely along with that,' his eyes gleamed. 'We always think that we should be different, that we should think different, behave different, be into different things, take more initiative, eat less or more expensively, exercise more, do different things, look different, our male appendage or our boobs should be different, bigger or smaller, our car is wrong or our watch or suit or house. We think that we should own different stuff, have more stylish accessories, another degree, a better job, different holidays or a more state of the art freaking coffee machine. We feel that we are not good enough, mentally, physically, socially and whatever else. Even if we feel that we *are* actually pretty cool, we still feel, even if subconsciously, that we could improve in some way or another. Very few people are really one hundred percent content with who and what they are.'

'Truth can be harsh,' Tara said wearily.

'It's startling to see how many Mental patterns are so deeply ingrained into our Subconscious. And what's more, we probably don't even know that they're there. Bugger! More sneaky Negative undercurrents!'

'Sadly so,' Tara nodded. 'Exactly *what* those self-judgements are, depends on our conditionings, how we grew up, where and who with, our past and current friends, family, work, schooling, physical and social environment, and so on and so on. All of it influences and thus shapes what we think of ourselves. From when we're little, even now still, we're being told all day long what we can and can't do, what to have and not to have, how we should or shouldn't behave or talk or look or feel. We're being told all day long by the Media, that we need to buy something to make us prettier, healthier, stronger, cleverer, richer and thus more likable. Our peers tell us the same thing, our family, the job, the school, advertising, marketing, all of them. And we believe it. Subconsciously or Consciously. And?'

'We comply.'

'Yep. Most of us do, some try not to, but still, in one way or another all of us comply, either by following those standards, or at last by judging ourselves and others against them. Some people do it more obviously, others more subtly.'

'Yeah, trying to fit in or complying with a certain ideal is really important for a lot of people, and they hate themselves if they can't quite make it. A lot of us feel insecure or worthless at some times, we put stress on ourselves to change or become something that we're not, to fit in or to try and have others approve of us,' Lee said with a slightly frustrated tone of voice. He had always experienced a great pressure to conform, especially in the City where he worked. To earn a certain amount of money, to wear the right suit, go to the right bars, network with the right people, have the big car, the newest phone, the right views.

Tara waved her index finger like a magic wand, 'But then, as if by magic, a trend changes and suddenly the outcasts become hip and the hip ones old-fashioned, and now it's them having to change *again*. Look at the punk generation. First they were rejects, then they became a fashion statement. First whole food was for silly Hippies and laughed at as extremism, now it's all the rage. You're nobody, unless you do Yoga, pretend to be healthy, don't smoke, try to look after your Body, blah, blah, blah. Fashion, Body shapes, jobs, hobbies, they're all trendy and some people are great at chasing every trend to the T, simply to stay cool and be accepted. **Appearances are everything. And because of that, self-judgement is obviously a big thing,**' Tara said glumly. 'By the way, **have you ever noticed how your personality changes when you**

are with different people? **Maybe only ever so slightly**? With the football lads you're all laddish, with the artsy guys you're all artsy and sophisticated, with the politics guy, you're all politic and world wise.'

'With your girlfriend's mum you're something all together,' Lee joked. 'It's like we put on masks or play roles to try to be somebody else or something else, to help us fit in. Our views and opinions change, depending on how comfortable we are with our social environment, if we feel the need to impress, if we can *be* ourselves or not.

It's funny really that for whatever reason, we never allow ourselves to just BE. Just Be who we are, without any masks and judgements, without trying to be somebody or something in particular. Just us. You know, I think most of us don't even know who we really are without all that stuff, we've *been* all that stuff for so long. Who *would* we be without it?' Lee said and looked at Tara with a sullen look on his face. 'This is terrible. We adapt who we are all day long. Sometimes for fun, but mostly because we think we *should*, even if it's not really us, but we do it anyway. Or, we simply do it because we don't know any better, because that's what we've always done. It's who we are.'

'Yep! Poor little us, we're hopping up and down all day long, trying to adjust what we are doing, thinking or feeling, to the people or the situation we currently find ourselves in. But you know what? Trends and ideals change constantly and so does society's judgement of us and thus our judgement of ourselves. **It's a game, *that's not designed to be won*!**' Tara said dramatically.

'Yeah, but we don't understand that! Instead, we feel that we simply can't fail to be a cool part of this society. We get pissed off, sad, frustrated or angry. We're hard on ourselves, because we just can't get it right.'

'You know the secret?' Tara suddenly asked.

'What?' Lee's ears perked up.

'**The secret is to stop trying to be somebody we're not. First, trying to be somebody else takes a lot of effort, but also, because we're not ourselves, we're not one hundred percent comfortable, and people notice that! It makes all sorts of situations awkward. That's why *trying* doesn't work!**'

'And I guess we stop trying by being Now?' Lee guessed expertly. 'By stopping to judge ourselves and just Be ourselves instead.'

'**How could it be anything else**?' Tara winked.

'Of course,' he grinned. 'So, the long and short of it is that *all* Judgements are Thoughts, even self-judgements,' Lee summarised.

'So they are.'

'And different people judge things differently and thus have *different* Thoughts.'

'Yep.'

'Oh wow, it's clicking into place. **Now there's no point having any of those judgements in the first place, because they can never be *right*, because everybody thinks differently, and anyway, they're in my head and they're not real and they're absolutely useless and they drive me nuts and now that I've realised that all of my judgements are rubbish, I can happily Let Go of them and just be now instead.** Wow, what a marathon sentence,' Lee drew breath and continued, 'Thinking, judging and the Now cannot go hand in hand, because in the Now all of that stops. And anyway, thinking so much is such hard work, so much effort, why bother when it could all be so much easier? In the Now, you just *are*. You can just *Be*. You. Now. It's effortless. And it's for free!

'What can I say?' Tara said excitedly.

'Be Now?' Lee smiled hugely and grabbed his pen to make a couple more notes.

Self-judgement:

- Trends and ideals change constantly and so does society's judgement of us and, in turn, our judgement of ourselves. It's a game, *that's not designed to be won*!
- In the Now, self-judgement doesn't exist and you can be happy just *being you*!

Lee looked thoughtfully at the list, 'come to think of it, only because we stop judging ourselves, won't stop other people judging us though, will it? What if people judge us and as a result they don't like us and we become Billy-no-mates? Well,' Lee began to answer his own question, 'My mother always used to say: "do you want to be friends with people who don't like who you really are?" It was difficult for me to understand as a child, but as I grew older, those words rang more and more true. Now, if people won't accept me the way I am, I'm not interested in them either. But I guess conformity is necessary to a certain extent, I mean you can't walk into work naked, can you?'

Tara laughed, confirming her own conditionings, 'Well, usually you can't, you're right, and **sometimes it can be hard if you *have* to conform even though you don't want to. But two things. First, do you really have to? Could you change your friends or your job or whatever, if it's really important to you to be who you are? Most of the time there's always an alternative if you only dare to search for it.**

But in the end, besides that, what we're talking about here is what's going on *inside* of you, *your* Thoughts. If everybody around you says that fat is ugly but you feel you're beautiful with your masses of flesh? Who cares what others think? If you have to wear a tie and you don't like it, do it and take it off when you get back home and sort out your head about it. As long as you stay happy inside, that's all that counts. If you can't avoid having to comply, do it, but *stop* judging it as a bad thing, stop hating it! Clear your head and be happy and content!'

We Think We Know What Others Think of Us

'**A**s we're on the subject...,' Tara sat upright, crossed her legs and looked at Lee, '**we judge ourselves and others all day long, and then of course, we think that *others* must surely do exactly the same! They must judge us too. So, of course, we think about *that* too.**'

'Oh bloody hell. **We're creating more useless Thoughts**.'

'Precisely, and **what's more, we're not only *thinking* those Thoughts, we are also *listening* to them. We buy into them. We *believe* them. It's who we think we are or should be!**'

'Where do we come up with all this crap?'

'Oh, that's easy. It happens all by itself,' Tara grinned, as Lee held his head in fake exhaustion. 'I have another funny example. Imagine you are in a pub or a restaurant and you're on your own, maybe waiting for somebody.'

'Ok?' Lee loved her little examples.

'Well, there you are, just hanging out and then it starts.'

'What?'

'Your Mind goes absolutely bonkers, thinking about what other people think of you. Do they think that you're sad because you're on your own? Billy-no-mates, as you said? A loner? That there is something wrong with you? Do you know what I'm talking about?'

Lee nodded, 'Of course. I might have to admit to have been guilty of that myself.'

Tara shrugged her shoulders, 'I guess all of us were at some stage. The funny thing is though, that actually, **in reality? We're being far less observed and thought about than we think we are. Most people are usually too busy thinking about what *you're* thinking about *them*, to be thinking about you!**' she laughed.

'That's so funny,' Lee shook his head in amused disbelief.

'My friends always used to ask me how I could go to a pub or club on my own, especially as a girl. They said they'd be far too self-conscious to do that. One of the little bits of wisdom which allowed me to do stuff like that, is something my grandmother told me. She said: "*Actually - Nobody is looking at you".* Even if you're in a pub on your own, hardly anybody actually notices, I mean, they are all doing their own thing, right? If you go to a club on your own, the likely-hood of anybody noticing that you're on your own is pretty much ziltsch anyway. Your friends could be half across the dance floor, right? But even if somebody does notice, so what? **Yes you're there on my own, and you're loving it. But no, we *like* feeling uncomfortable**?' Tara said sarcastically. '**So, let's keep doing it. Let's think about it – a lot**! Let's feed that puppy!' Tara first threw crumbs to some invisible puppies, then used both her arms to throw whole loafs. 'And then if we do a good job, we begin to feel even more uncomfortable.'

'That's so funny.'

'It might be now, but it's not when you're doing it. But that's what most people do. We judge ourselves and feel uncomfortable or unloved or unhappy or whatever, because we *think* that we know what other people *think* of us, then we make it worse by thinking *more* about it.'

Lee smiled and began to sing the old tune, 'You think that I think that you think that I think, but we'll never really know... - Well, something like that.'

Tara giggled, 'That's the one. I know we're laughing about it now, but it's heartbreaking how self-conscious we often are or how observed we often feel. **It starts when we walk down the road and wonder what people think of us.** Do they notice my new hair cut or the jacket or do they think I'm cool or fat or ugly or whatever. And that's just our appearance. **When we're done with that, we start wondering what people think of our Behaviour and our personality.** We might think: "she thinks I'm great. He is so impressed. They adore me or not," or one wonders: "If I say this, she must thinks I'm stupid," or: "he probably didn't think this was funny," or: "she probably doesn't agree. Does she notice my big nose or my problems? Can I mask them well enough?" Trying, trying,' Tara waggled her head.

'So true, and so sad. We come up with entire dialogues in our heads, without any real life person ever uttering a single word. Pathetic really,' Lee shook his head. **'We think we know what other people think about all sorts of things, including their opinion of us. But you know what? We haven't got a clue what anybody else thinks. We can't! We're *not* in their heads! It's what *we* think about *ourselves*, not what *they* think. It's our head making up stupid stories again. We're projecting *our Thoughts* once again, our *own* self-judgements onto *other* people. Gosh, the sheer stupidity of it!**

And anyway, even if they are thinking about us? Man, we're trying to comply with something that we can't even define, something we don't even know one hundred percent, because it's

not in *our* head, it's in *somebody else's* head! **We're causing ourselves heartache over something, which is doomed to failure. Gosh, and we're supposed to be the most intelligent beings on the planet**. This stuff really makes me doubt that,' Lee drew a deep breath.

'Oh yeah, and?' Tara looked at him expectantly.

'There's more?' Lee turned his head down and to the side, letting his fringe fall over his eyes. He looked at her through a few strands of hair.

'Of course. **Just in case that we're not busy enough with pointlessly imagining what the** *other* **person thinks, we also get pissed off, because** *we* **think that** *other* **person** *should* **know what** *we're* **thinking**,' Tara paused. '**In a relationship for example. The partner** *should* **know what** *we* **think, right**?'

'Oh, no way!' Lee nearly screamed. 'You're right. God, the shame.' Poor Kate. He had certainly been guilty of that. But then again, so had she.

'Yep, the shame and the hilarity.' Tara went on, 'Others should know that we don't like something, or: They *should* know that something's inconsiderate. But you know, that's rubbish too. **We can't know what** *they* **think and** *they* **can't know what** *we* **think. They can get to know us,** *learn* **us and our** *preferences*, **but they'll never know what we** *think*. **And anyway, even our preferences change. I for example like my coffee with sugar, but sometimes I prefer it without**.'

'Man, the amounts of relationships that could be saved if people would get that,' Lee marvelled. 'If they'd **just ask each other and tell each other what they** *really* **think, rather than second guessing all the time**,' Lee said and opened yet another page in his little book.

What do Others think of Us?
* We have no idea what other people think of us. We can't! Not about us or anything else for that matter! We're not in their heads! It's what *we* think about *ourselves*, not what *they* think.
* All we're doing is projecting *our* Thoughts, *our own* self-judgements onto *other* people.
* *We* can't know what *they* think and *they* can't know what *we* think.

Faster, Faster, Faster - What On Earth Are We Doing To Ourselves? - The Funniest Thing Ever! - Summary

'**Let me give you a little summary to show you what's going on up there**,' Tara tapped Lee's forehead. '**First we create a** whole load of Thoughts by judging other people against our own standards. At the same time we're working hard to have more Thoughts about judging ourselves. Then, because we have nothing else to do, we create a bunch of worry Thoughts about what other people think of us, and to top that, of course we have to think *a lot* about how to Be and how to behave, and we're thinking about how to fulfil all those imaginary standards other people place on us, how to change to *Be that* required person – and of course, how not to screw up while we're doing all of that. Then we're creating even more Thoughts when we *do* screw up. Then we get busy creating pissed off Thoughts, because we screwed up or because we think that other person *should* know what *we're* thinking, judging them why on earth *they* don't do what *we* think is so obvious.' Lee laughed out loud, Tara raised her left eyebrow enticingly and smiled, '**And as if that's not enough, by thinking about what other people are thinking of us, we don't only think *for ourselves*, we also think *for* other people. Lot's of other people!**'

'Bloody hell! That's ridiculous. **As if *our* Thoughts were not enough, we're also thinking other people's Thoughts**! Oh Man, that is *the* funniest thing ever!' Lee fell flat on his back and laughed and laughed.

'Isn't it crazy?' Tara smiled broadly. '**Oh and of course, all of that is *on top* of all the Thoughts we create by dealing with all the sensory impressions we talked about earlier. Five senses, simultaneously, continuously, all the time. Full on. And on top of all the other Thoughts in our heads that we've talked about earlier!**'

'God, **our brains are total workaholics.**'

'Yeah, **busy with completely unfounded, unreal, made up crap, which doesn't actually exist - but in our heads. We're talking Supreme Beings of Dots and Squiggles here!**'

'Man, how do we cope? This is pure craziness.'

'I know. On one side it's practice I guess, on the other hand, most of us simply don't know any better, don't know that there is a different way, so we just put up with it. And of course, lots of people obviously *don't* cope with it, or at least not very well. Those people are all around us.'

'God, how much stuff can we have in our heads? **That reminds me of a book. It's called: Faster. Not just Fast, but Fast-*er*. That's exactly what it's like. We think absolute rubbish at a million miles an hour, constantly speeding up,**' Lee screamed in mock desperation.

'And you know the worst thing?'

'Worse than complete and utter chaos in our heads?' Lee's eyes opened wide.

'Yep! **We're not only** *talking* **all those Thoughts in our Mind, we're also** *listening* **to them and** *acting* **on them and thus we're** *self-creating* **our reality**!'

They looked at each other in horror for a moment, then Lee took his notebook and wrote in large letters on a new page.

Fast-er:
* We're self-imposed, chosen Supreme Beings of Dots and Squiggles. We create our own crazy reality, simply by thinking it.

Look Into My Eyes Baby

They sat in silence for a while, letting the conversation sink in. Lee thought about the past few hours of conversation, when Tara interrupted his Thoughts, 'I just remembered a really bizarre experiment I did with a friend of mine. It relates really nicely to some of the things we've just talked about. I tell you, it was the weirdest and most wonderful thing at the same time.'

'Weird and wonderful? My favourite! Tell me more?' Lee said curiously.

'A while ago, a good friend and I decided to play. We sat opposite one another and looked into each others' eyes. The deal was not to look away,' Tara began. 'Man, it was unbelievable.'

'Really, why?' Lee couldn't quiet think why this would have been such a cool thing to do.

'It was surprising to us too. Despite the fact that we were really good friends, looking into each others eyes like that, made us squirm. We wanted to look away so bad, it hurt. I nearly gave up, I just couldn't bear it. It was so off the wall to observe what was going on in my Mind.'

'Go on,' Lee probed.

'At first, when we started out, I felt really uncomfortable. I felt my friend's eyes looking *at* me, probing, judging, examining. So I thought anyway. I was trying to keep up my walls, Conscious ones and Subconscious ones. My head was full of stories, wondering what *he* was thinking. Did he like my eyes, my face, did he notice the spot on my nose? Oh the shame. Did he remember all the things we experienced together? Did he like me? Out of no-where, all sorts of insecurities came up. It was kind of weird. I would've never believed how difficult it was going to be to look into his eyes for half an hour, if I hadn't I done it.'

'I can only begin to imagine,' Lee said intrigued.

'I noticed that my Mind never stops working, commenting, imagining and worrying. In that half an hour, I thought about myself, I thought about my friend, I compared the two of us, I imagined what my friend thought of me and what I thought about him,' Tara described her experience.

'And when you were finished, you started all over?' Lee stated with a grin.

Tara laughed, 'How did you know?'

'Because I learned today that that's the natural thing to do. That we never just observe what *is*. We just keep going round in circles, Dotting and Squiggling regardless.'

'That's exactly what I started to figure out at some stage during the staring match,' Tara said. 'I thought that my friend was probably not thinking about *me* at all. Maybe a bit, sure, but he was probably just as busy doing the same thing I was, wondering what *I* was thinking about *him*. He was probably thinking exactly the same self-conscious stupid Thoughts I was.'

'So funny.'

'I know. So there we were, us fools, both worried about what the other was thinking. Then **I suddenly realised that I had absolutely no idea what my friend was thinking. I didn't know if he was thinking about me or worrying about himself or if he was thinking about lunch for that matter. I couldn't know. They were *his* Thoughts. I realised that all the judgements were in *my* head, they were all *my* own Thoughts. They were judgements *I* was making about *myself*, *my* own insecurities, it was stuff *I* thought about *myself*. I realised that I was projecting my own Thoughts and judgements onto my friend, thinking they were *his* Thoughts, rather than my own. Gosh, and it had been so real. For a while there I really believed that they *were* his Thoughts. It so strange, I mean, my mate wasn't even saying anything, all he was doing was simply look at me.** I couldn't believe that all this stuff was going on in my head, without him even saying a single word. It was mad.'

'Isn't it bizarre, that once you've realised these things you always wonder how on earth you could not have noticed this before?' Lee marvelled.

'I know. But I tell you, this experience etched all of those insights into my Mind. Loud and clear. I don't think I will ever forget it again,' Tara said avidly.

'What happened next, did you run?' Lee asked.

'No. But I wanted to. I stuck it out though and it got even more interesting. **As soon as I realised what I was doing, I tried to stop thinking all together. I concentrated on my breathing and just** *looked*, **just** *observed*. **My Mind felt slowly more at peace, but I noticed that I was still looking** *at* **my friend's eyes, rather than** *into* **them. My Conscious walls had gone, but my Subconscious fears were still there.**

The second I realised that, I simultaneously felt a Shift in my friend's eyes. **And suddenly, without really trying, both of us Let Go.** We just opened up. **We didn't try to be anything in particular anymore, we stopped worrying what the other might think. We stopped the judgements and the comparing. Somehow it didn't matter anymore.** We had both realised at the same time how silly our worries had been. It was fabulous, it was as if we had rehearsed it, and suddenly we smiled at each other. A smile from deep within, a fabulously knowing smile. It was as if a blazing spark connected our eyes.'

'Wow.'

'Yeah, wow indeed. And the coolest thing was that we had these realisations together. Both of us knew, without talking, at the same time. **Both of us had stopped thinking and for a few minutes we saw right into each other's soul. He allowed me to look into his and I allowed him to look into mine. Suddenly I felt I had known him forever. I felt a closeness between us that we never had before.** It was mad.'

'Sounds like me and that tree earlier. In Nowness we became One.'

'That's exactly what it was like. There was no separation anymore. We had become part of each other. Now, when I see my friend, we look into each other's eyes and we look into each other's souls straight away. For us, that special connection that we gained from this half hour exercise stayed with us. It seems, that once the barriers have dropped, they stay away. It's a soul connection. A connection just a tiny notch higher than the usual everyday friendship thing.'

'Another fascinating little anecdote out of Tara's life,' Lee smiled genuinely.

Tara looked warmly into Lee's eyes for a moment, laid back and closed her eyes, when a Thought gently bounced up and down in her Mind: "Does Lee think I'm showing off?" Red Flag! She heard The Guys gently alert her to the silliness of her Thoughts. She laughed at herself. It was truly far out how these ideas still managed to sneak in from time to time. They had become so seldom by now, that she was hardly used to them anymore. But this time the voice persisted gently: "Don't think what he thinks, ask him!" "Aye, aye sir," Tara giggled and asked Lee, 'Do you ever feel that I'm showing off with my stories?'

'Don't be so silly,' Lee laughed in surprise and reassuringly touched Tara's arm. 'I love your stories. They're fun. *And* they're useful.'

'Good. Just making sure,' Tara smiled at herself, enjoying the warmth of Lee's touch. 'You know, some people are just naturally like that.'

'Like what?' Lee asked, keeping his hands softly on her Body.

'There are people, when you look into their eyes? It feels as if you look straight into their Soul. And that without practicing for half an hour, you might not even know them. **Those eyes don't look at you, probing, asking, judging, comparing. They just look. They don't give you the feeling that they're measuring you up or that they're hiding anything. There are no walls, no pretences, they are just open. What you see is what you get.'**

'Oh yes, I know them. Those are the people I feel really at ease with. I don't have to look away, because eye contact feels good and comfortable. Actually, come to think of it, I have felt that little spark you talked about earlier, connect my eyes with those of another person too. It felt as if we had really felt each other for a split second. As if we'd really seen each other for who we were. The coolest thing was that, I think, the other person noticed it as well,' Lee grinned at Tara.

For a few seconds, they looked into each others' eyes, experiencing that special moment again. They smiled openly at each other in recognition.

'Eyes truly are the mirror of our Soul,' Tara said warmly. **'Eye contact is so important to connect with another person! I think if everybody in the world would try the 30 minute Looking-into-each-other's-eyes with family and friends, they'd learn so much about each other, so much more than with many conversations. Allowing others to see our Souls is quite special. It says more than a thousand words.'**

'It sure does.'

'And what's more, **once you've experienced this connection with another, you'll also know how to *keep* your soul open! How to keep your own eyes clear and non-judging**. How *you* can Just Be who *you* are, without any masks, judgements, without trying to be somebody or something in particular. Just *you*,' Tara said with emphasis, repeating some of Lee's earlier words. 'And on top of that, once you've experienced that clarity and connection with someone, you can see the difference in other people's eyes too. You can see if they're open or not.'

Walls Of Thought

'It's not that people are bad if they they're not open, if they have their walls up,' Tara continued, 'It's just that they either don't know that there is a different way or that **they are scared to allow others to see their Souls. It can be an unsettling experience for some, as I've described, because you really have to Let Go of your pretences**. Whenever we interact with people, we consciously or subconsciously worry that they could see that we are not the ideal that we pretend to be. We build up walls and barriers around who we really are and how we really feel. And some people are not comfortable with dropping them.'

'And those barriers are what we usually see when we look at people's eyes and it's what they see when they look into ours,' Lee said.

'Exactly, unless you allow each other in.' Tara paused for a second, sighed and then said, 'That reminds me, for anybody that feels uncomfortable to try this with another person for the first time, there's an easy and 'safe' way to look at their own walls. They can just do it by themselves.'

Lee laughed out loud at the Thought, 'What, are they supposed do some crazy Yoga Posture and somehow try to look into their own eyes?' he said, pretending to try and stick his legs behind his head.

Tara giggled, 'When you master that, please call me, I wouldn't want to miss that for the world, but you can do it much easier than that, you just look into the mirror.'

'Now there's a Thought,' Lee laughed. 'Oh well, no bendy exercise routine for me today then. I do feel though that *my* option would have been much more energetically valuable. And - of much higher entertainment value,' he added as an afterthought, laughed and waved his hand at Tara to tell her to ignore him.

Tara giggled and took his advice, 'So, **you look into the mirror and you look into your own eyes. Forget the hair or pimples or whatever and just look into your eyes and stop thinking. Be Now. What you see then, *is all you are*. Nothing more! *Everything else is what your Thoughts made up.*'**

'Everything else is made up,' Lee repeated slowly and thoughtfully. 'Pretty deep, huh?'

'Guess so,' Tara said quietly. 'You'll learn some pretty important stuff about yourself if you do this.'

'I can imagine,' Lee said quietly and began to scribble.

<u>Check your Own Walls:</u>
- Look into the mirror. Be Now. Stop thinking. What you see then, is all you are. Nothing more. Everything else is what your Thoughts made up.
- Look at other people and drop your barriers by being Now.

Eyes Are the Mirror Of the Soul...

'Actually, now that I think of it,' Lee said, 'I can tell a whole bunch of things about people just by looking into their eyes. I know if I like a person or not, if I am on the same wavelength with them or not, actually, I can recognise like-minded Souls quite easily. I guess it's written all over in people's eyes,' Lee squinted which made Tara laugh. 'You know, I've never done the exercise you mentioned, but I always look into people's eyes anyway. My mum would be proud of me, it took her a long time to teach me that. I find it fascinating. Some eyes you look into, you see nothing. They are totally empty. No spark, no twinkle, no life. Others are truly radiant and happy. Others are sad or withdrawn or glare or even seem angry. Some seem impenetrable - now I know that they are full of walls and are holding back. Others seem to be scared and timid. Others feel devious or mischievous, interested, bored, absent Minded. Others are full of love and joy, they literally sparkle,' Lee said with a little sparkle of his own. 'I always felt that I could tell what kind of mood people are in, just by looking into their eyes. I had my mum, dad and sister pegged from a very early age and I still know exactly where the wind is blowing when I see their eyes,' he laughed. 'I can see how people's Behaviour changes depending on the circumstances, their mood or company, and with that their eyes also change,' he said. 'I think I can also tell if I can trust somebody or not. You know when somebody doesn't look at you and doesn't hold your gaze when they're talking to you? When their eyes kind of flicker a bit? Kind of shifty? It's really interesting too see how many people don't have any eye contact at all when they're talking to you. They look up and down and past you, but never actually into your eyes. Come to think of it, couldn't that also mean that somebody is just really shy, rather than shifty?' he said thoughtfully.

'Of course. It could also mean that they're feeling uncomfortable. Maybe it's even just be a habit. **That's why it's important not to _interpret_ what you see, but to listen to your Intuition. I don't interpret people's facial expression or them just not holding my gaze, but I listen to my Intuition. Like that I can literally _see_ or better _feel_ something in their eyes that tells me: stay away. It's not like a Thought or a judgement it's more a feeling and a knowing**.'

'Ah, I see what you mean. Yeah, I get that too. I get this pang of – no good,' Lee said. 'It is like an Intuition, I guess.'

'And exactly like Intuitions, those pang of 'no good', should *always* be followed, even if other people tell you differently.'

'Yeah, I know what you mean. It's like being in a situation, where everybody around you thinks that a particular person is amazing? But for you it just doesn't *feel* right? You feel uncomfortable with them?'

Tara nodded. 'Yes, that's your Intuition telling you to avoid that person, no matter what everybody else thinks. For *you* that's the right thing to do.'

'Which doesn't mean it's the right thing for everybody else, right?'

'Exactly. It's worth to consciously play around with the Intuitions that you get when you look into somebody's eyes, follow them, see what happens. Also, pay attention to different nuances of these Intuitions. The Intuition could be: "stay away!" Or it could also mean that you just *don't have* to talk to that person, or that you would simply *not* miss out if you don't talk to that person.'

'Oh, don't you just love double negatives?'

'Yeah, they're fabulous, they confuse people no end,' Tara grinned.

'So they do, but I just about followed it,' Lee winked, showing a smile with perfect teeth.

'I know you could. That's because you're a very clever man,' Tara smiled sweetly.

'Thanks,' Lee felt a little bit of extra blood collecting in his cheeks.

'With a bit of practice and the ever useful benefit of hindsight, one can figure out pretty quickly if and when people put up walls, if they do it deliberately or subconsciously and,' Tara looked up, 'with even more practice, we can even know what the wall is all about and what the appropriate reaction would be for us.'

'That's cool.'

'Yep. This kind of knowing might start like one of those pangs you've just talked about, **but with time they can develop to an intricate knowing of the other person just by looking into their eyes. Not a judging or thinking, but a knowing. You'll *know* if they have Integrity, if they are strong, if their personality is solid or not.**'

'Great, that's something for me to play with. I like the idea of analysing the pangs just like we did with the other Intuitions before. Gosh, there's so much to play with!'

'Once you get kicking, it's beyond anything you ever experienced. It's so much fun.' Tara hesitated, '**You know, I think that lots of people already know exactly who to trust, who is good for them and who** is not, but they ignore those feelings. That's where you really have to train yourself to always *act* on your Intuition. Otherwise Intuitions just become more useless Thoughts in your head.'

'Check and agreed.' Lee thought for a second, 'Actually, I don't think that people *always ignore* things, I think a lot simply don't *notice* what's going on.'

'Yeah, I agree. That's why it's so important to pay some active attention to what's going on in your head, to train your Intuition, to play with trial and error, learn, so that you *can* notice stuff,' she looked at him. 'Also, keep in Mind that it takes some practice to play with strangers that don't know what you're doing, without freaking them out, ok?' Tara hinted.

'But that could be fun too though, right?' Lee asked mischievously.

'Fun, but naughty. But besides your naughty enjoyment, it's not always a nice thing to do. Some people can find it really disconcerting if you stare into their eyes. They don't like it. **If somebody is insecure or feels uncomfortable, they put up walls, right? They might even just think that you're weird and put up walls because of that!**

Also if you stare into somebody's eyes trying to *get* something, an impression, or an Intuition, they might feel as if you're probing. So, always make sure to just *observe* people's eyes, never to stare or probe, but to just look and simply get any impressions that come naturally.'

Lee stared at Tara with wide open piercing eyes.

'Yeah, that'll be enough to make anybody run a mile,' she laughed. 'Actually, playing with eye contact has another really cool benefit,' Tara said. **'It's a constant measure of how present both of you are.** You see, it's difficult to zone-out when you're *really* looking into somebody's eyes, when you're *really* seeing the presence in *each other's* eyes. You can have heaps of fun pointing it out to each other. That'll of course be with a friend or so.'

'Oh great, could we try this for a second?'

'Sure.'

They looked into each other's eyes and kept looking and kept looking. Slowly a smile played around Lee's lips when he said, 'Yep, even if you know all about it in theory, the praxis is still not easy.'

'Never said it was, but it's just practice, as always,' Tara shrugged her shoulders, yet still keeping eye contact. 'Just Be Now. Remember the tree?'

And then there it was again, the twinkle, the sparkle, the connection of their Beings through their eyes - Oneness. Lee noticed it strongly this time. What had she said earlier? It's a soul connection, just a tiny notch higher than the usual everyday friendship thing. - "Good," he smiled to himself.

'You're thinking,' Tara whispered quietly, still looking into his eyes.

'Oh wow,' Lee was surprised that Tara could really feel it. He saw her grin. 'Ha, now *you're* thinking.'

'So I am,' Tara grinned, caught out.

'Ok, I think I get the point, that's enough,' he laughed.

'Oh, cop out!' Tara teased still holding his gaze.

'Let's call it a truce then,' Lee bargained.

'You start.'

'No, you start,' Lee leant over and started tickling Tara's sides. She squealed as she coiled her Body into a ball - breaking eye contact. 'Ha, *I* win!' Lee cried out triumphantly.

'By unfair means, you cheat!' Tara laughed with him.

'Excuse me?' Lee threatened to tickle her again.

'Ok, you won, fair and square.'

'That's better,' he patted her gently on the arm and laid back onto the blanket.

Tara looked at him. They smiled at each other, looking openly into each others eyes, noticing that the walls were still gone. They enjoyed the moment, feeling each other's Souls sitting on a blanket in a beautiful park, with the sun shining down on them.

Lee was the first to speak. 'Actually, that was interesting. **I noticed that I didn't only *see* in your eyes when you began to think, I also *felt* it. It was as if the roundness, the softness I felt from you was suddenly replaced with a slight edgy-ness, a slight fast-ness. It's like I could feel it resonate in my own brain**. Strange. I've never felt that before.'

'Yep. **When you're Now, anything else that's not, stands out a mile, even if it's another person's brain!**'

'Crazy stuff.'

Other People Distract the Mind - or Bits

'Eh, why were we talking about all of this again?' Lee suddenly wondered.

Tara thought for a second, 'It was all about how our interaction with the world through our senses and with other people distracts our Minds, creates Thoughts and keeps us from being Now.'

'Oh yeah, that was it. Let's continue with that,' Lee suggested.

'Sure. As you might have guessed, people can influence our Thoughts and disturb our Minds in many other ways then just the ones we've talked about so far,' Tara said. 'Let me give you a more general example. **Imagine that you are a magnet and everything in your surroundings, is made up of tiny metal bits**,' Tara flicked her fingers around Lee's Body. 'See?'

'Okay?' Lee looked around him, dutifully acknowledging the existence of imaginary metal bits.

'**With your magnetic force you automatically arrange the metal-bit-world around you in pretty little patterns, just the way you like it**. That's **nice and comfy**, right?' Lee nodded. 'Well, it is, **until other magnets come along, with their own magnetic force and start to disturb your bits**,' Tara energetically waved her hands around Lee's Body, disturbing his bits.

'Charming,' Lee somehow felt his comfort level changing. He suddenly felt a bit edgy. Why did Tara suddenly have to be so hectic?

'**Now, the automatic response to such a disturbance would be to blame the other person for it, right**?'

Oops, that's exactly what he had just done, Lee noticed. And yeah, that's the natural thing to do, or not? 'Well, sure, it's the other magnet's fault, it's affecting our bits,' Lee said, protectively holding his bits.

'**There's just one problem with that answer**,' Tara pointed out, tenderly averting her eyes from Lee's bits.

'I'm all ears,' Tara had finally stopped waving and he felt more settled again.

'**Well, there will *always* be other magnets out there,**' Tara paused for a minute to let the statement sink in.

Lee gasped, 'Oh, shit. Every single person, every situation is a magnet! Everybody and everything disturbs our bits, all day long,' Lee was dumbstruck by that realisation. '**If everything affects our bits, and we get pissed at everything, God we'd be so miserable**,' he stocked. '**Hang on, you are not telling me that we have to give up arranging stuff around us, because there's no point in doing that, do you?** Are you going to tell me to just let everybody around us disturb us and therefore live in a chaos of bits?'

Tara grinned at Lee's wild gesticulation of chaotic bits. 'No, no. Don't worry. **It's not about giving up arranging stuff**, it's more about becoming like a rubber-ball. Well, a rubber-ball-magnet more like it, if you can imagine something like that.'

'Eh, what?' Lee looked amused.

'**Imagine that all the metal bits around our magnet are attached to us with a rubber band.**'

'Ah, ok, **if somebody comes to disturbs our bits now, they just pop right back into place.**'

'Precisely.'

A sudden wave of clarity filled Lee's head, 'Oh man, **that rubber band, it's Nowness, isn't it? Our bits will only stay disturbed, if we keep *thinking* about the disturbance, right?'**

'That's exactly it.'

'No Thought, no disturbance. Peace. In Nowness,' Lee flopped back against the tree. 'It's like the pneumatic drill example from before. **In Nowness it doesn't affect us.'**

'Full points, young man,' Tara cheered.

Why are They Actually Causing Me A Problem? – Interpersonal Relationships

'**A**ctually, whenever you notice that your bits got disturbed and when you're blaming others, turn you're eyes inward. You can learn a lot about yourself when you do that, because if you really look at it…,' Tara's voice trailed off.

'It's not about the other person at all. It's all about the role our own Mind is playing in all of this.' This stuff was becoming second nature to him, he thought happily.

'Exactly. Instead of fantasising about what *other* people are thinking or *why* they are behaving a certain way, it's far more useful to understand what *we're* doing and *why*, how *we* think, act and behave and why.'

'It's the judgement thing again,' Lee picked up Tara's train of Thought. 'If we don't like the way *others* behave, it's *our* problem as much as much as theirs, because any problem or issue ultimately starts in *our* heads. And it's being kept there because we feed it with Thoughts, because we give it attention. It's the puppy thing again!' Lee pushed an imaginary puppy off his trouser leg. '**Problems other people cause us, the bits other people disturb in us, are what *our* Mind is doing to us.** It's our Mind indulging in Negative Thoughts, just like being sad or angry or miserable or feeling unappreciated or unloved, or wronged, or stepped on our toes, or somebody didn't do as we wanted them to, or everybody is out there to get us, blah, blah, blah. It's all feeding puppies.'

'That's right. *Anything* or *anybody* that *ever* distracts us or disturbs our bits, only does so because we let it, because we give it attention. By realising that, we can Let Go of those Thoughts and Be Now instead,' Tara said.

Lee cocked his head to one side once more, dishevelling his fringe in the way Tara loved so much, '**What if somebody is *relentlessly* in** your face though? You know, if a situation is *constantly* affecting you? If it's really intense? Couldn't that get a bit tricky?'

'Well, if you know how, it needn't be tricky. For situations like that, it helps to try and understand where the other person is coming from, in a clear and unadulterated way.'

'More?'

'**If you look at other people's Behaviour *without* your own judgements - and that's the fiddly bit - you might realise that other people's Behaviour or Thoughts might be as valid as yours.** Let me give you a classic example. A nice silly little one, the toilet seat. It might sound simple and trivial, but you can transfer any resulting insights onto bigger scenarios,' Tara smiled.

'Go on,' Lee could already see it coming.

'The man constantly leaves the toilet seat up and the woman has a fit about it, because she thinks it should be down. Nice and stereotypical.'

'Of course.'

'It's causing the woman a problem, she's upset. To maintain Nowness over this issue might be difficult for her, because every time she sees the seat, she gets pissed off again, right?'

'Right.'

'Ok, let's understand the situation. Let's ask ourselves why this is actually such a big deal? The man thinks it should be up, the woman thinks it should be down. Men and women are physically different, so both of their opinions are valid. I can already hear the Yes-But's, hygiene, aesthetics, blah, blah, but in the end, **only because *we* think something is right, doesn't mean that *other* person is necessarily wrong**.'

'That's true,' Lee could think of a million other examples without even trying.

'**Interpersonal problems usually arise, because we expect our partners or friends or everybody else for that matter to be exactly the same as us - to be the same magnet. To think the same, behave the same, want or like the same things. The fact is though, that we think they *should* be the same as us. They should *be* the same, because what *we* do is the right thing. They should *think* the same, because obviously, what *we* think is correct, or what *we* want is the only way to go, it's *our* right. Because, hey, the world revolves just around us.**'

'Ridiculousness,' was all Lee could say. It struck him time and time again how Tara could unknowingly point out some of his most ingrained Behaviour and ways of thinking.

'I know. **The funny thing is that obviously everybody thinks that *they* are right.**'

'Now that's a disaster waiting to happen,' Lee rolled his eyes.

'Exactly. Because as you're thinking that others disturb you, *they* all think that *you* are disturbing *them*. That's where the crux of the matter lies. Everybody feels disturbed by everybody, so everybody is having a go at everybody else, and like this? Nothing will get sorted, because everybody thinks that *they* are right. And of course nobody's going to budge. I mean, the dude with the pneumatic drill? What's the point in shouting at *him*? He's only doing his job. But in our little world, *everybody* imposes *their* feelings and expectations onto everybody else around them. Well, hello! It's a no win scenario. Born to conflict. So, the gist of it is, **that even if intense stuff causes *us* problems, it's still not the other people, but *our* projections onto them and our *expectations* of them,**' Lee deducted.

'Exactly. So, instead of getting pissed off at all the other magnets around us, look at them, understand *their* point of *view*, understand that *their* ideas are as valid as *yours* and Let Go. Be done with it. Be Now,' Tara cut with her flat hand through the air to emphasize the point.

'So, back to our example,' Lee stirred the conversation back to the previous example. 'The toilet seat being down is *not* the-ultimately-correct way for it to be, and on the same note, it being up isn't either. There are different points of view and they're both valid. **What one agrees on as a final mode of conduct in the end is a different story, but it's important to understand that nobody is ever ultimately right,**' Lee said. 'And I guess that's what you're trying to get at, right?' Tara nodded. **'Because if nobody can be *ultimately* right, it's like the Good or Bad story from before, there's simply no point trying to figure out whose right or wrong or to get upset about it! So we might as well stop asking the questions in the first place and just be Now instead,' Lee finished with the same breath.** 'Woha, somebody told me once that **you can't ever blame anybody else for your experience**. I'm beginning to understand what he meant. Man this is such Mind game. Funnily enough, I can really see how ridiculously simple all of this is, if we could just do this Nowness thing. All the stress, all the anguish, the paranoia, the problems with others would just fall away.'

But Sometimes We *Have* to Speak Up - Or Not?

'**B**ut then again,' Lee thought for a moment, 'realistically?' he stopped short, '**what if a situation is something that we *need* to do something about? I mean some situations really *do* have to be addressed, or not? I mean we can't just accept everything around us, can we? Sometimes we have to speak up.**'

To Lee's surprise Tara agreed, 'Unless you're Buddha sitting under a tree, I agree. **If we really can't help ourselves and something needs to be done, then, well, obviously, we need to get up and do something about it.** Let's say you observe a fight and somebody is beating the living daylight out of somebody right in front of you. You find this unacceptable and you feel that you need to act. That's cool. **Everybody has their own personal boundaries, but, whatever you end up doing, stay Conscious while you're doing it! Don't upset yourself, catch yourself out when your Mind goes nuts. You can act while your Mind stays clear. Make sure that you don't blame willy-nilly. See the other persons side, even if you don't agree with it, it might help you understand why they are acting the way they are. But act when you feel you need to.'**

'As long as you **don't get drawn into it with your Mind. See the situation for what it really *is*. Follow your Intuition without your judgement**,' Lee added.

'Right. Even if the situation would normally become stressful, no matter what the outcome, if it's to our liking or not, keep breathing throughout and stay Now.'

'Yeah, I can see that **we can still be addressing the situation, but without upsetting ourselves. We say calm and balanced throughout.** God, that would be so much kinder on ourselves. And by staying calmer, we'd get better results too. I know that only too well from work. Getting upset gets you nowhere. In Asia you 'loose face' if you get loud. I learned that it's much more productive if you stay calm and act appropriately when needed.'

'Right. That's if you *can* do something, but if you *can't* do anything, or if there really isn't any point? Shut up - at least up here!' Tara pointed to her head.

'**Get up or shut up,**' Lee said pleased with himself.

'Exactly. Either do something about it or stop moaning. *Mind Play* **is not about becoming a passive vegetable, being walked over and all that, but it's about looking at *ourselves* first, before we even get to the stage of confronting the outside world. A lot of problems can be fixed, simply by recognising that they might not actually be a problem in the first place, but that it is that sneaky little creature telling us another naughty story**,' Tara grinned. 'Do you want to go through another example, just to have something more practical to work with?'

'Good I idea. I think I've got one,' Lee remembered one of the silly little disagreements he used to have with Kate before they started to date. 'What about this one,' Lee recalled the details, 'your roommate has eaten all the Cornflakes and left the empty box in the cupboard. She didn't tell you and of course she didn't buy any new ones either. You flip out. Been there, done that. My Thought process used to be: she should know to throw the box away, why is she always doing that? Does she think that I'm stupid and won't notice that the box is empty? What am *I* to do about breakfast now?'

'Sorry to interrupt, do you mind if I point out something?' Tara asked politely.

'No of course not, go ahead.'

'Your *first* projection was to imagine that she did it *on purpose*.'

'Oops, that's true,' Lee said surprised. 'Ha, I didn't catch that. Thanks. Funny, now I'm not only pissed off because she finished the last of the cornflakes, but also because she did it on purpose - a fact that I have somehow made up. I'm making the problem worse by imagining reasons,' Lee smirked. 'Then again, what if she really did do it on purpose?'

'That might be so, but that's besides the point. **The point is that getting upset, is not going to make the cornflakes magically reappear, is it? So, there's no point in the act of getting upset, right**?'

Lee nodded. 'True. In the end it's still all just stories and fairytales going on in my head and those can be stopped right from the beginning. Mmh, but I'd still have to eat something different and I could be annoyed about that, especially if it's eight o'clock in the morning and all there is, is rice and pasta, but yeah,' he caught himself out, 'right. Annoyance. Thoughts. No point. My Thoughts are not going to change anything. Boy! God, it's always the same freaking answer, isn't it?'

'True. Let's go a little deeper though. Look at your Behavioural pattern. Think about it, how big a deal would it really be to eat something different? I know there are a million but-s, but *really*? In the end? We're pathetic! **We have such strong habits, we have our bits arranged in such rigid patterns. And the more rigid our patterns are, the more permanently they get disturbed, which will get us really upset. When the bits are rigid for a long time, they don't bounce back into place easily! They stay disturbed. If on the hand we can become more flexible? Stuff flows through us, or off us like water off a duck's back.** You'd just notice: she's done it again, oh well, you'll eat XYZ instead. There's only pasta? Oh well. End of story. There's no other stuff going on in your head. You stay peaceful and calm.'

'Stuff just bounces off us and we rearrange ourselves on the fly,' Lee said.

'That or, on the other hand, **you might even be interested in exploring the *new* position of your bits, maybe there's something there you could like about it?**'

'Oh I love it, there's always more to play with,' Lee grinned broadly. **'Is there a shortcut of how to uncover rigid patterns within us? We could play with them maybe to pre-empt problems,** couldn't we?'

'Yep. **All we need to do is ask ourselves the question:** *"Why* **is this causing me a problem?", and when we have** *that* **answer, we ask ourselves again: "and why is** *that* **causing me a problem?", and so on. Usually, in the end, the** *last* **reason we can come up with is a stubborn: "Because!"'**

'Oh man, that's so funny,' Lee said, '"Why is it causing me a problem that she ate the last cornflakes? Because *I* wanted to finish them?" Ha! Got ya!' Lee laughed loudly. '"Why is it causing me a problem that the toilet seat is up? Because *I* think it's prettier if it's down", "*Why* is *that* causing me a problem? Because *I* like it better", Got ya again. "*Why* is it causing me a problem that the other person has not told me that we don't have any toilet paper anymore? Because it's not fair", "Why is it not fair? Because *I* think it's common courtesy? Ah, and that's because I have different ideas of common courtesy than the other person", got ya again.'

'That's it. But you know, don't martyr yourself? By all means tell them, just don't upset yourself over it. Other people often think differently than we do. People don't always behave to our dislike on purpose. They might just have different standards, and that can often be talked about. Sit together with your flatmate and talk, calmly and nicely, sort it out, **come up with a solution**, you know, bulk-buy them, have spare boxes in the cupboard. If everybody has jobs in the house? Well, it can be *your* job to keep the cornflakes stocked up. Alternatively, **if the other person doesn't change or doesn't want to change, well, what can be done? Freaking out over it every time sounds like far too much hassle**! So, if you know that she *always* does this, and you simply can't re-educate her, and the extra boxes in the kitchen don't work either.'

'Yeah, let's say she gets mid-nightly cornflakes cravings and finishes all 5 boxes in one session?' Lee laughed and shrugged his shoulders as if to say, "Well, whatever, I'm just making this up as I go along."

'Ok, so she gets midnight cravings,' Tara giggled, 'if that happens, **you need to help yourself! Don't think that she's responsible for your happiness!** Have your own stash of cornflakes, anything!'

'What if she finds out about it and sneaks into your room at midnight....' Lee's eyes sparkled with enjoyment.

They burst out laughing.

Tara slapped his leg playfully, 'Well, if the situation *can't* be changed at all, then all there's left?'

'Is to change your head!' Lee said happily. 'We're loving it ma'am,' Lee lowered his head in appreciation.

'So is Ma'am,' Tara grinned, lowering her head in acknowledgement. 'I know it might sound extreme just now, but if people could just implement this stuff into only a few situations, it'll make a world of difference, believe me.'

'I don't just have to believe you, I can see it already,' Lee said appreciatively.

'Ok, maybe that's enough about stuff that disturbs the Mind, what do you think?'

'I think that I agree - if I'm allowed to think that is,' he added cheekily.

'Just this once,' Tara let him of easily.

Change Our Lives Big Time - Flick the Switches In Our Brains - Summary

"Be still and be quiet and allow yourself to look for beauty."
- Alan Ball, screen writer, American Beauty

'Tara, man, the sheer realisation of all the stuff that goes on in our heads, all the things we've talked about, regarding Mindfulness and Nowness, all the stuff that disturbs our Mind, all that can completely and utterly change people's way of living, you know? It can change our way of behaving, thinking and feeling and it can totally turn it upside down. Topsy-Turvy,' Lee said.

'Gosh,' Lee continued, 'it's so strange, even though we've been told a million times that happiness lies within, we still believe that we *can* be happy by looking outside of us. We seek entertainment, recognition, approval, love, status, *everything* from outside. **We try to get these things by manipulating people and situations to our advantage or by owning either things or persons, rather than by looking into our own head and flicking the appropriate switches.** Us humans are so focussed on material gain, that we have become so ridiculously attached to everything, it makes up who we are,' Lee said.

In the flow he went on, 'Then you come along and talk about Nowness and all that stuff, and man, it gives so many answers. You know, with that, **we can finally break out of our behavioural and mental vicious cycles - and low and behold, we can even have *fun* with it**. Now that's unheard of! We can become *self aware* rather than *self-conscious,* while laughing all the way. We can remember that everything we need to live and be happy is already within ourselves. **What's most important,**

271

we can *really* understand that, we can *experience* it, not just *believe* it because somebody told us. We actually *know*! Due to first hand *experience*. We know that we don't need any outside influences to make us a whole person. **In the Now, we are One, we are Whole, we are Beautiful, Strong, Secure, Balanced and Confident. And all our bits are just fine,**' he added with a grin. 'It's not make-believe, it's real! In the Now we don't tell ourselves, nor Listen to others anymore, that we're *not* these things. We are whole, just the way we are,' Lee drew breath. 'Man, **it really *is* all a State of Mind. And it's up to us *which* State of Mind we *choose*.**

I can see that most people would now say 'Yes but', the point is though, that there are no But-s - if you don't let them exist. In fact, in the Now, the But-s don't actually exist! **But-s are safety nets and comfort zones. If we *don't want to* break out of the vicious cycle, if we're too *scared* to do it, we will find But-s until the cows come home and nothing can make us drop them. But if we really want to be free, we drop the But-s and we *just do it*. It is our choice, it's as simple as that!**'

'Wow,' Tara's mouth hung open. 'Shit dude, you sound like me!' her smile broadened.

'Want some more?' Lee's eyes were shining brightly.

'Sure,' Tara laughed at the role reversal.

'Don't fret the little things. And then know that *everything* is a little thing,' Lee paraphrased and grinned. 'Man, the more we talk, the more I get it. It's amazing, us **humans are so distracted by all of these things, that we walk around this world with our heads deeply stuck in a cloud of Thoughts. They prevent us from fully appreciating or even noticing our surroundings and the sheer magnificence of it all**. Our heads don't process the beauty of the sky, a building, a poster, a person or a tree because our head-space is occupied with roller-coaster Thoughts, fretting about the past, what-if-s, should-have-s, planning the future, worrying, judging *everything* or just day dreaming. **We are far to busy thinking to be able to observe anything around us in any kind of detail or even to simply enjoy it.**

Our heads are never in the space where life *really* happens – NOW. We have forgotten that life is happening in the Now. Not yesterday, that's done with, over. Not tomorrow, that hasn't even happened yet,' he was still flowing. 'Yey, I just remembered a quote that fits this sentiment perfectly, Howard Marks wrote in one of his books: "Life is something that happens while you're planning other things." I think he knew about that Nowness thing too, what do you think?' Lee smirked.

Tara laughed. 'Wooha, what a clever man!'

'Yeah I know. I guess most of us just don't know any different. Most of us don't know that there *is* a different life out there. Some people might even assume that they *are* living Now. But I know that if we really look, that's often not true. Our head is *always* somewhere else. When I hear things like what James Dean said, you know: "living every day as if it'll be your last?" I get all fired up and I really try to live *that* day to the full. Like, *really* live it. I remember it during *that* day, make a real effort and usually have an amazing day, absolutely loving it. Gosh, those days are so fantastic, they really stick in my memory. But the problem is, that the next day it's all forgotten again. It's not a *permanent* thing! But now, with Mindfulness and Nowness, and of course with reminding myself by writing 'Be Now' on my hand, it's slowly coming into my reach! Jimmy Boy, here I cooooooommeeeee,' Lee howled. 'And now Ma'am, can I have some more?'

'What makes you think that there's more?' Tara innocently turned her nose up and sideways, playfully avoiding his eye contact.

'Because there always is,' Lee smiled broadly.

PART 7

13   Behaviour and Emotions

Strong Behaviour and Emotions Disturb the Mind

'**O**k, then, here it comes. More it is, just for you. If we look at what we've talked about so far, our Thoughts are created by a reaction to something, some kind of stimulus, right? Sensory impressions, people, our surroundings and so on. Now, we usually react in three different ways, with Thoughts (which we've already discussed in detail), with Behaviour or with Emotions - all of which create more Thoughts, and which are all interlinked, effecting one another. **As all of them create Thoughts in one way or another, they *all* need to be addressed if we want to be Now.**'

Lee nodded. His Emotions about Kate had certainly tried to keep him from Being Now, just as much as his Thoughts had.

'Let's begin with Behaviour. We'll talk about Emotions later if you want to,' Tara suggested.

'Sounds good,' Lee agreed happily.

14   Behaviour

'**R**ight then. Behaviour. For every Behavioural pattern, you have to address *two* areas. Each **_Behaviour_** has a *playing out* part, the *action*, and also a bunch of associated *Thoughts* linked to it.' Lee listened closely as Tara continued, '**To play with Behaviour, you have to address the Thoughts, that follow a Behaviour, and you also have to address the action, i.e. the Behavioural pattern, the habit.**'

'Hang on,' Lee said, and wrote a short list.

To play with Behaviour we have to address:
* Thoughts associated with it.
* The playing out part of that Behaviour, the action, the behavioural pattern, the habit.

274

Behavioural Thought Patterns

'So, throughout the day, we want to observe our Thoughts *and* our Behaviour. Just as with observing our Thoughts, the more we observe how we behave, act, react and what our habits are, we can begin to Let Go of the ones that disturb our Being, which helps us being Now. Besides that, of course, the more we observe ourselves, the more we get to know ourselves,' Tara began. 'Oh, and another cool thing, with practice we even notice the unconscious patterns.'

'What do you mean unconscious ones?' Lee asked.

'When Behaviour is *consciously* acted out, we know *that* we're doing it, and we know *what* we're doing. When it's un-consciously done, we do it automatically, without our knowledge, without being aware that we're doing it.'

'How could we *not* be aware that we're doing something?' Lee wondered out loud.

'Quite easily actually. Have you ever noticed that you have been doing something, behaving or reacting in certain ways for years, but had no idea that you were doing it until somebody pointed it out or until you just suddenly became aware of it? Maybe that you test people like your dad, patronise or mully-cuddle people like your mother, wipe your mouth like your sister? That you plan too much? That you worry too much? Have you ever notice that you've were reacting to particular people or situations in a certain way and you didn't even know? That you can be overly aggressive if the right buttons are pressed? That you get angry easily and shout at people, or that people take advantage of you? That you're shy and don't dare to initiate conversations? That you nag people all the time, that you're jealous and therefore really possessive? That you're insecure or cocky and that you're strongly behaving that way? That you always have to be in centre of attention? That you avoid attention? That you carry ridiculous amounts of resentment around with you? That you bear grudges very easily? That you let people off too easily? That you are edgy, mean, opinionated, petty, easily scared, dubious, whiny, complaining, overly confident, too self-conscious, and that you're acting those traits out in habits or behavioural patterns? The list goes on as long as you want it to.'

'Man, how do you come up with all these examples on the fly?' Lee shook his head with a grin.

'I'm a natural,' Tara laughed and continued unperturbed. 'Now, by becoming Aware of your Behaviour and the associated Thoughts, I don't mean that you just kind-of-know that the Behaviour and Thoughts are there in the background, but I meant the shit-that's-what-I-do,-that's-the-kind-of-person-I-am insight kind of Awareness.'

'It's the how-would-I-see-myself-from-the-outside kind off thing,' Lee said.

'Yeah, that's it. **Now, let's play with the Thought part of Behaviour first,**' Tara said. 'Now, as an example, **if you'd be behaving possessively, would your Mind Be Now?'**

'**More than likely not,**' Lee shook his head. '**If I'd be possessive, I'd bound to be thinking possessive Thoughts. I'd thinking, so I would not be Now,**' Lee concluded using simple common sense.

'What if you're nagging, you know, constantly complaining? Would you be Now then?'

'Same thing. You'd think about the things you're complaining about and thus you wouldn't be Now either,' Lee said.

'What about holding grudges?'

'No, Nowness there either,' Lee said.

'Exactly. Now, there's a double whammy, **on top of the Thoughts that naturally come with that Behaviour, you know, the Thoughts that *are* that Behaviour or that *describe* the Behaviour, you also have the *judging Thoughts* that tell you how much you hate being that way, or how much you love being that way, right? So those Thoughts have to be addressed too.**'

'Gosh, Thoughts are so sneaky,' Lee said surprised.

'Aren't they just. That one took me ages to notice,' Tara laughed. 'So, these are the Thoughts that come with every Behaviour and that stop you from Being Now.'

As Tara drew breath, Lee grabbed to pen and paper and jotted down a couple of reminders.

Behaviour Thoughts:
* Behaviour related Thoughts. Thoughts that *are* the Behaviour and or that *describe* it.
* Judging Thoughts of the Behaviour.

'Now, **the root of any Behaviour, is usually a Thought or an Emotion. You think jealous Thoughts or feel jealous, and as a result you're behaving in a jealous way**. As we're talking about Emotions later anyway, let's stick with the Thoughts for now.'

'Sure,' Lee said.

'So, you think angry or aggressive Thoughts and you behave angrily or aggressively as a result, right?'

'Right. Actually, hang on,' Lee's eyes suddenly widened, 'that would mean, that **if you can *Let Go* of angry Thoughts, you can't really be**

276

angry anymore. **Oh shit, does that mean that our Behaviour changes if we stop associated Thoughts?**' Tara smiled. **Lee took a second to think this over. Could he really not be angry if he didn't think angry Thoughts? Well, no. He wouldn't feel the *need* to be angry, because there wouldn't be anything in his head aggravating him.** He looked up at Tara again. 'Oh man, yes, it's possible. Wow. And you'd be Now too, because you'd stopped thinking. **Man, that's bizarre, in Nowness extreme Behavioural patterns disperse all by themselves,**' Lee added in amazement.

    'You've got it. That's exactly it,' Tara said happily. She loved how easily Lee put all the information into a coherent theory for himself.

The Pot

'Let me give you a metaphor of how the Just-be-Now thing works in this case. This approach might be too hardcore for some, but it works a treat for others. For me personally it changed my life.'

    'I'm all ears,' Lee said attentively.

    'Ok, imagine that you have a tendency to become quite angry, maybe even forceful or aggressive in conversations with certain people for example. You have recognised that your anger causes you lots of problems in your life. You're fed up and you want to do something about it.'

    'Right.'

    'Now, imagine all your anger is in a pressure cooker.'

    'One of those pots that cooks stuff by building up steam inside?' Lee clarified.

    'Yes, one of those. The longer they cook, the more steam they build up. When the steam gets too much, it has to be released, otherwise the cooker explodes.'

    'I get the picture,' Lee nodded.

    'Imagine that the pot signifies your *NEED* for being angry.'

    'Not the anger itself, but the *need*, check,' Lee repeated slowly. Something was beginning to dawn on him.

    'Now, there are different ways of dealing with **the anger,** which **is the steam inside the pot**. Some people might try to suppress the steam, the anger,' Tara said.

    'Suppressing it is never good. It's ignoring something and not letting it out,' Lee warned.

'Exactly. It causes lots of pain while it's happening and eventually the cooker will explode. You can't just ignore the steam. Even if you hope it'll go away, it's still building up, the pressure accumulates and eventually, the cooker *will* explode.

The other way of dealing with it, would be to find out where the anger comes from, you can confront the anger, experience the anger, embrace the anger, **feel the steam, understanding it, observe it, detach yourself from it, work with it, but it still won't get rid of it, will it? You'll know it really well, but in the end, if you don't** *actively* **do anything with it, it's still there.**' Lee nodded as Tara drew a deep breath. 'Another option would be to let all the steam gush out of the pot in one go, by opening up the lid. This would be equivalent to bursting out with all your Emotions.'

'But that's not good either, because that could hurt yourself or others.'

'Exactly. Or you could let out the steam bit by bit, pft, pft, pft. Doing this would give you temporary relief, but the steam would eventually built up again, and you'll have to start all over.'

'So what do you do?' Lee asked. Tara had pretty much exhausted all the options he could think of.

'You get rid of the pot.'

'You get rid of the pot!' Lee stayed silent for a second, then called out, 'Shit, Tara! You get rid of the pot! It's what I just said earlier. **You get rid of the NEED to be angry.** Bloody hell, this is mad, I literally just figured that out! Man!' Lee shook his head vigorously. '**In the Now, the** *need* **doesn't exist, the pot doesn't exist. The steam doesn't exist.** There is no flame under the pot that increases the steam and the anger. No Thoughts are feeding the fire. Shit, Tara, you just get rid of the pot. This is fantastic. **You don't suppress it, you don't try to change it, you don't need to do anything, you just don't feel the need to be angry anymore.** In the Now the freaking pot disappears and with that the anger. In the Now, the torch is truly off.'

Tara smiled. 'That's it! The Now gives you a new sense of calm and peace. Things that might have upset you before, are just not a big deal anymore. Your Being becomes quiet and balanced, which means that you'll begin to handle formerly big problems in a new calm and powerful manner. If you are Now all the time, anger, fear, jealousy, all the things we talked about earlier – whoops - gone. That is to be in the Moment! That is to be in the Now. **In the Now there is perfect balance, you don't think anymore, you don't label anything as good or bad anymore,** events just are. You see everything for what it *is*. You live *every* moment to the full. Life is out there and it's stupendously beautiful. Enjoy, be Now and balanced and it will be bountiful and beautiful.'

'Wow,' Lee just about managed to say, and after a good few seconds, 'Pfff, let me play with that for a minute. 'Let's assume that you get angry, that you rant and rave and scream and shout a lot. You have Thoughts in your head that are telling you that you are angry about something and that you should behave accordingly. I assume that to begin to play with this, just as before, I'd catch myself out when I'm having the I'm-angry-Thought or the I'm-really-angry-about-that-Thought and return to my breathing. **I've dealt with the Thoughts and thus the Behaviour will follow automatically, because I simply wouldn't feel the *need* for it anymore. Because in the Now, extreme Behaviour balances itself out. Then again,'** Lee interrupted his flow, **'what if the Thoughts come back.'**

'It's all puppy stuff.'

'So it's persistence.'

'You've got it!' Tara said excitedly.

Impatience

'Let me talk you through a practical example, so that you can get a better idea of how to do this in a real life situation. A friend of mine used to be incredibly impatient. He noticed that this was one of his main irritating Behavioural patterns in his life that really stopped him from being Now. He'd constantly be in his head, worrying, tapping his foot, changing lines he was waiting in to find the faster one, rushing around, making other people rush, becoming upset if others weren't rushing as much as he was. My friend really wanted to deal with this habit and he decided to deliberately create practice environments. Guess what he did,' Tara grinned at Lee.

'He started to go out of his way to find situations that he knew would *create* Impatience in him?'

'Exactly.'

'Really? Wow. Under normal circumstances, people would avoid these situations.'

'Well yeah, but **he wanted to *explore* this Behaviour pattern and you can do that best in the aggravating circumstances itself.'**

'Mad.'

'Yeah, but fun. It's a good way of doing it too, because **if you're doing this on purpose, your practice ground is under your control**. You can prepare yourself for it.'

'That's a good point,' Lee nodded.

'So, my friend had observed himself throughout the day and had made a note of the situations that caused him to be impatient. After a few practice runs, he found a pattern. He noticed that queues and standing in lines annoyed him most, so he began to seek out lines.

With practice and a lot of standing in line, he figured out two ways to deal with his impatience, depending on the circumstances. First, when he saw a queue, he would quickly assess the situation. If he had any prior commitments that he would be late for if he would wait in the queue, he would accept that he had to come back later and he would leave. Like that, he would actually avoid a situation that would cause him *unnecessary* grief. I mean, don't make your life more difficult than it has to be, right? So, if he would leave the line, he would make sure that he would not feel upset by the fact that he'd been unable to complete the job that day. He just accepted life the way it was and would breath any upset feelings away in the Now. In the Now, his impatience, upset and worry didn't exist.'

'Same old, catching out, bla, bla, bla,' Lee said.

'Right. Now, on the other hand, if my friend's mission was too urgent to be postponed and he had to wait in line and maybe even risk being late for something? Tough. No way out! He had to brave it. He knew that thinking like crazy or even worrying, wouldn't make the line go any faster either. So, while he was waiting, he would focus on his breathing and be Now.'

'And in the Now, his worries to be late or his general impatience would simply not exist either.'

'Yep. Of course it took some practice, but the funny thing was that instead of hating his impatient moments, he began to love them.'

'How come?'

'Well, first he didn't become impatient anymore and second, standing in line became the time in his day, which was solely *his* time. He *could* do nothing else but stand around, so instead of being upset, he began to enjoy it, he would either consciously relax and chill, or do Mind work. It had become a practice ground for him. Sometimes he would even just observe his Mind and have a little giggle about the silly stories it would come up with.'

'That's fantastic.'

'It is. He told me that standing in line became the time, when he would get some of his most amazing insights ever.'

'I can see why he's a friend of yours,' Lee grinned.

'Yeah, he's a darling.'

Un-learn Behavioural Action Patterns and Habits

'**B**y the way,' Tara said, 'did you notice that this example showed that my friend not only dealt with his Thoughts, but also with his Behavioural pattern, with his Actions?'

'I think so. **He analysed the situation, understood what his actions were and what triggered his Behaviour, then he had a look if he could avoid the situation and if not, he figured out a way of dealing with it that enabled him to be Now.** And in the Now, the remaining Behaviour balanced itself out,' Lee summarised.

'Correct. This shows you that by **becoming Aware of *how* you behave, you have a *choice*. You have the choice to stay in your ingrained Behavioural pattern, or to change it.**

That leads us to the second bit of playing with Behaviour**, addressing the Behavioural pattern itself. This is about un-learning existing patterns that are part of us, and about re-learning to do or be whatever we like instead.**

We behave a certain way, because that's who we grew up to be. Our conditionings and our environment made us into who we are. Now, I'm asking myself, why would I *have* to be what I became without my Conscious consent? Man, **it's your choice what you want to do or be. We can recreate ourselves to be just the way we want to be.**' Seeing Lee's uncertain look on his face, Tara asked, 'Have you ever excused anything you did with: "Oh, that's just the way I am?"' Lee nodded slowly. 'Well, rubbish, who says that that's the way you are? You can be who or whatever you want to be. If you don't want to be shy, don't be shy,' Tara let that sentence hang in the air for a moment. 'It's choice. **You can behave whichever way you like. If you become *aware* of your Behaviour and you don't like it? Hey, behave differently.**'

'That' reminds me of something,' Lee said, 'have you read "The Dice Man?"'

'I don't think so, but it sounds familiar. Tell me about it?'

'It's about a guy that starts to roll dice to decide for him what to do and how to behave. One time, the dice decided for him to have a 'Habit-Breaking-Month'.'

'That sounds fascinating.'

'It was. He was basically supposed to break every single habit he had, for an entire month.'

'Wow.'

'I know. Besides the fact how bizarre the whole book is, it was really interesting how he showed in such an interesting way how much a Human Being can be changed if he really wanted to. He showed that habits *can* be broken. That man *is* free. He really went totally off the wall with breaking his habits. He started by waking up. Usually he'd put on his slippers, habit number one. So he took off his slippers again and walked barefoot. He walked, habit number two, so instead he ran and crawled on another day. He was usually awake when he stood, so he tried to fall asleep. He usually slept in bed, so he crawled under the bed. He ate peanut butter with radish, because that certainly wasn't a habit, but it would have been if he'd done it again the next day.'

'Gosh, talking about extremes, and I Thought *I* was bad,' Tara laughed out loud.

'Well, this guy took it to the nth degree. What he tried to do, in your words Tara, was basically to catch himself out every single time he was doing something, deciding if it was a habit, which it usually was, and then trying to do something completely different. He called it The Random Man. The important thing was that he had *fully committed* himself one hundred percent to do this all month long, no matter if it compromised his sanity, his career, his marriage, his fatherhood or morality - which it did. Besides what the outcome of his extreme Behaviour was, the point is that he *could* do it, **he could change his *entire* Behavioural Pattern, just by *deciding* to do so and by *committing* himself to it.'**

'What a great example. Thanks for that. And yes, I agree, you can be who and whatever you want to be. I personally wouldn't just change my Behaviour randomly to the opposite of what I'm doing, but I'd just create whatever I'd want,' Tara picked up her previous string of Thoughts.

Lee scratched his chin. 'Come to think of it, how does that fit in with the school of Thought that tells you, that you don't ever need to change, that you are just perfect the way you are?' Lee asked.

'Well, sure you're perfect, but sometimes we'd *like* to be different,' Tara said. 'Not because we think we *should* or because somebody else tells us to, but maybe because we don't *want* it anymore. Over the years we might have been made into a person that we simply don't want to Be. There can be many reasons why you might like to Let Go of a Behavioural pattern. Maybe we don't want to beat people up, don't *want* to be so destructively possessive anymore, or maybe the consequences of us acting out a particular Behaviour, is simply eating us up, it might threaten us to loose our family or end us up in jail. A Behaviour might create a lot of Thoughts, cause worry, anxiety, agitation or just generally make us unhappy and upset us or badly affect the people around us. Vicious, violent or extreme Behaviour might create negative undercurrents in our lives, it might be destructive to ourselves and others, or it might simply stop us from being Now. An ingrained behavioural pattern might be opposed to our essential nature or to the new way we began to look at the world. We might not want to be hectic or loud or obnoxious or shy and reserved. It might not be who we really are or want to be, but we just can't help ourselves. It's who we've always been and we don't know how to change it. But we would jump at the chance if we could,' Tara said. 'I've talked about pretty extreme Behaviour so far, but the same applies to much more trivial ones. Maybe you like picking your nose in public or squeeze your spots on the train, maybe you love smoking, these are all Behavioural patterns and habits. Even *not* doing something you want to do is a habit, like *not* eating healthy food or *not* wanting to exercise.'

'So, you're not saying that a particular Behaviour per se is bad, but that you'll know for yourself when it's time to Let Go? That you can choose for yourself if and when you want to make changes?' Lee wanted to clarify.

'Precisely. Also keep in Mind that all Reactions and Behaviour are strongly interlinked with Thoughts, as Behaviour are *created* and *reinforced* by Thoughts, right? Therefore certain Behaviour will prevent you from entering Nowness. So, *that* could be an incentive to Let Go too,' Tara added.

'Now, let's say being shy excludes you from many situations, and that makes it difficult for you to make new friends, and because of that you're upset, ok? You don't want to have shy Thoughts that stop you from being Now anymore, and you don't want to behave shyly anymore either, right? How would you Let Go of shyness?' Tara asked Lee.

'I'd **identify the Behaviour that stops me from Being Now, i.e. the shyness, I'd put out the Intend that I would like to Let Go of it, then, I would catch myself out when that Behaviour turns up again and I would simply choose *not* to do it, and choose to do something else, just the same as with Thoughts.'**

'Master student once again. Yes, that's exactly it.'

'I can imagine that it'll take an enormous amount of will power and determination,' Lee scratched the back of his head.

'Absolutely,' Tara grinned. 'Now, **you can either just Let Go of it, or you could examine it and contemplate it, just like we did with any other Thought before. So, before you Let Go, you can observe yourself and learn about yourself if you want to.** *Why* does the Behaviour disturb you? Why would you like to Let Go of it? Contemplate it! Find out, ask yourself questions. What's the underlying cause? Which part of it upsets you and why? *What* creates the Thoughts, the Behaviour in the first place? All these questions will help you understand *why* you do stuff. It can also help you with setting up practice scenarios or avoid situations if need be,' she added as an afterthought.

'Like your friend did with his impatience? He analysed it, understood why and when he was doing it and then found a way to change it.'

'Exactly.'

'Man, this is going to be fascinating. I'll know everything about myself, my Thoughts and my Behaviour, this is great.'

'Glad you like it,' Tara smiled.

Re-learn Behavioural Action Patterns

'**N**ow,' Tara continued, 'you were right when you said that after you caught yourself out, you could either simply choose *not* to do it, or do something else, but there's also another option.'

'There is? What's that?' Lee asked curiously.

'You can then choose to learn a *new* Behaviour.'

'Oh, of course. If you are shy, you can learn to be confident, if you're angry, you can learn to be kind. If you hit people, you can learn to talk to them instead. That makes sense.'

'Exactly. And **you do that by directing your attention *away* from the Thought of what you *think you are* to a Thought of what you *could be* or what you'd *want* to be, right**? Then your Mind is telling you that you *are* confident. **Just *pretend* that you could be whoever or whatever you want to be, you could pretend for a moment that you're not shy, that you don't *have* to behave shyly.**'

'Uh, that could be tough,' Lee interjected.

'Sure, but it could also be fun to play with. I'm sure every shy person has once imagined what it would be like not be shy, right? **I mean, anybody can pretend in their heads that they're a super hero.** Just make it up, tell yourself a story. If you can't do it first time round, practice it. Sit on the bus and imagine, imagine and create, until you can come up with a half way reasonable story. **Then when you can do that well, then comes the time when you can begin to put that pretence into practice.** Imagine you're in a situation where you'd normally behave in a certain way. But you catch yourself out before you do. At that moment you can either disperse all the Thoughts that tell you to behave in that particular way by being Now **and as a result the need to behave that way will disperse too**, or, on the other hand, you can tell yourself to behave differently. You can ask yourself what a person with a different Behavioural pattern would do? Then get up and do it.'

'But that's exactly what people have problems with, the *doing something different*,' Lee butted in.

'True, but that's where the Mind thing and the pretending comes into it. **If you focus on something enough, you fool your brain into thinking that you really *are* different and as a consequence, after a while, you automatically act that way. Once the Behaviour is**

changed, you don't need to pretend anymore, as you already *are* the new person, and you can Let Go of the pretend-Thoughts as well.'

'And I can happily enter Nowness.'

'Yep. Obviously, this takes *constant* and *diligent* attention, catching-out and diverting until this process becomes automatic, and until eventually the Behaviour is changed for good,' Tara stressed.

'Understood. Let me just clarify something. Take the shy-example again. Let's say you've dealt with the being-shy Thoughts and you're theoretically not shy anymore.'

'Theoretically?'

'Well, you stopped thinking shy Thoughts, but you've behaved shyly all your life, and all your Behaviour patterns are those of a shy person. So, what are you now?'

'You are a Mentally not-shy person with an ex-shy Behaviour pattern.'

'So I'd have to address my Behaviour patterns to match my new personality,' Lee said.

'Exactly. **You can learn any *new* Behaviour that you want to!** You can be whatever you want to be! With the shy example, you might want to be confident. To do that, catch yourself out whenever you have the I'm-shy or any other related Thought and *actively* tell yourself, that you're *not* shy, or rather than using a negative, tell yourself something positive. **Tell yourself that you're confident, outgoing, accepted, open. Then you need to act on it. That's the beginning of learning a new Behaviour.'**

'Could you give me another example please? This somehow all sounds a bit too easy,' Lee said.

'Of course. Let me give you a real life example to make all of this a bit more practical.'

'That'll be great, but let me quickly write a few things down first,' Lee picked up his notebook and jotted down a few summary points.

Letting Go and changing Behavioural Action Patterns:
* If you want to be Now, you might have to address Behavioural patterns.
* If you want to be different, change yourself - but check your motives.
* If you don't want to change, be happy the way you are. Stop the any further self-judging Thoughts and Be Now instead!

Behaviour, Reactions
* We can actively observe, contemplate and change Thoughts, Reactions and Behaviour.

- We can choose what's in our head, how we think, how we behave and react.
- If you focus enough on *already being* a certain way, you'll fool your brain into thinking that you really *are* that way and as a consequence, after a while, you'll automatically act that way.

Shyness

When he was done, Tara continued with her example. 'Let me tell you how a student at my school played with this. The girl came to me because she was terribly shy. It affected her whole life and of course, it kept her from being Now.'

'That's so funny, I still can't believe that you teach this stuff to kids.'

'Well, they usually pick it up much quicker than adults, cause there's much less but-I-can't going on. They just do it. But this girl was actually a sixteen year old, and she'd done one semester of classes with me before.'

'What happened?'

'She asked me if I could help and I said, of course. First I told her that she already wasn't shy anymore. She was taken aback and asked me what I meant. I said it was because she had come to see me. She smiled and agreed shyly. It was very sweet. She told me that it had taken all of her guts in the whole wide world to come and see me. I asked her how could she be shy if she could muster up such guts? That was a nice foundation. She already knew that she could do it. Then I told her that playing with her shyness would be fun.'

'Fun? I can't believe that. This is something that I've struggled with so much all my life, how can this possibly be fun?' the girl asked.

'Playing with Behaviour is the most fun of all. Nearly as much fun as observing your Thoughts,' I said.

'Ok, that *was* funny. Tell me about having fun with it then,' she demanded.

'The first thing you do is to *consciously* decide that you want to be Now, that you don't want to be shy anymore, that you're taking *responsibility* and that you're making a *commitment* to yourself to make that happen.'

'I can do that,' she said resolutely. 'To do that properly, I have to part that curtain of fuzz in my head and *consciously* tell myself that, right? I remember that from class.'

'Exactly.' I was so proud of her, she really wanted to change. 'Then, next time you catch yourself out being shy in a situation, you *play* with it.'

'Play with being Shy?' her face looked uncertain.

'Sure. **Look at what your Mind is telling you. Remember that you don't *want* to be shy anymore. So what would not-shy-people do?**

'Go and talk?'

'Well, **go and talk** then.'

'Uooh. No way,' she recoiled. She was exactly as hesitant as you said people could be Lee, the *doing it* scared her - Tara added for Lee's benefit.

'Well, **if it's too scary right now, try next time. But make sure to begin the Thought process of *what it could be like to be different* and what you *would* do if you wouldn't be shy. Slowly inch your way forward, bit by bit, every time. Start with something non-scary. Start off with something simple, go and ask a stranger for the time or directions or something. You don't have to start by throwing yourself into full on conversations.**'

'That's still scary, but I can at least imagine that that would be possible,' the girl said.

Tara looked at Lee and said, 'You might notice how the girl talked to me. She was trying to take responsibility. **She was prepared to do whatever it took to Let Go of her shyness, even if it was scary.**

I said to the girl, 'That's fabulous. **Be sure to take it easy on yourself, but consistently play with this new personality that you want to acquire.** Do it nice and slowly. Play! Don't take it so seriously. Go and have some fun! **Sure, it might be weird or awkward at the beginning, but that's just practice, like anything else.**'

'Wow,' the girl said, feeling empowered.

'Yeah,' I said and hugged her.

'This is cool. You're telling me that it might be awkward. So, I don't have to change overnight?'

'Of course not. Some people can or want to, but if you prefer, **you can choose to be gentle, as long as you're still diligent and persistent.**'

'Sure, I have to make sure that I don't let myself be side tracked by too many excuses why I *can't* do it, right? And I have to keep thinking non-shy Thoughts,' the girl stressed, looking much more confident. She wanted to change and now she had a tool to help her and she was committed enough to do whatever it took.

'Right,' I said, 'remember, you *do* have *to do* it for your Behaviour to change, talking about it or postponing it *won't* change it.'

'I get it.'

'**Great. When a good practice situation comes up, breathe away all those Thoughts that tell you that people will laugh at you or that you'll make an idiot of yourself or whatever. Don't think of all the scenarios that** *could* **happen, don't prepare what you want to say over and over and over, just stop all that crap and just go and do it.**'

'Stop thinking, just do it. Go!'

'Exactly. **All you need to do is to persistently** *talk over* **those stupid I-can't-because-of-this-or-that Thoughts in your head.** *Drown them out* **with, yes-I-can,-I-am-confident, I-will-go-over-and-talk-to-that-person, or if you can, just stop talking to yourself all together, be Now and just do it. Dare yourself in the Now!** Once your shy and fearful Mind is switched off, then there's nothing to stop you from doing whatever you want. **Don't huddle up in a scared little ball, but stand up straight and confidently, look at your Thoughts and how silly they are. Notice that they're just Thoughts. It's the** *Thoughts* **that stop you from doing what you want to do.** It's your Thoughts that tell you that you can't or that you'll be laughed at or that you're shy. Notice that when those Thoughts are *not* in your head, you are not that shy person, and if you tell yourself something different for long enough, your Behaviour will eventually believe you! Before you know it, there you are, asking for the time, or talking to a guy. What an achievement! Immediate reassurance that it works! You've just created a new Behaviour. Yipeee! Off to bigger and better things next time.'

'That's nuts, I can actually imagine myself doing that. As long as I can be easy on myself,' the girl said astonished. It was so beautiful to see her open up. It was as if somebody told her that the chain around her neck wasn't actually locked, that she could take it off any time she wanted, she just had to dare.

'Well good, that's the point,' I said.

'And I can see myself giggling at myself too.'

'You'll get bonus points for that!'

'Yeah.'

'Now, **there's something very important to understand, when you play around with changing things about yourself, especially if it involves other people**,' I said to her.

'What's that?' the girl asked.

'Don't expect too much of other people.'

'What do you mean?'

'Well, only because that first ever person you dare yourself to be brave with is a grumpy bastard who growls at you, does *not* mean that you *had a reason* to be shy!'

'Oh,' she grinned at me. Lee laughed.

'It does *not* mean that you were *right* in thinking that all people are out there to get you.'

'Man, you know me so well,' the girl shook her head.

'Actually, it's common sense, normal human Behaviour, especially if we're still a bit self-conscious. **So, get into your head! Talk to yourself and realise the crap the you're telling yourself! Observe your Thoughts and how they're constantly trying to tell you stuff that you don't agree with! Don't let them or other people talk you into being something that you're not.**'

'I get it. Some people who I try my new skills out on, might have their own issues and might not be super nice, but who cares, it's about developing *my own* skills, right? It's what *I* do that counts. Playfully of course, I do want to have some fun on the way and not take it so seriously. So be it. I'll do it.'

'God, I was so proud of her,' Tara said to Lee and continued with her story.

'And now let's assume that you've played with all of this for a while,' I said to her. 'With time you'll realise that you *don't* have to actively tell yourself, that you're not shy anymore, you just aren't! Then, one day, you'll notice that you behaved or acted really confidently, *without* having gone through any of the process I've just described. You just did it. Without having to tell yourself that you're confident.'

'Automatically. God, it'll be so nice to be there now. I wouldn't think the I'm-shy-Thoughts anymore, and I also wouldn't have to think the I'm-confident-Thoughts anymore either. I'd just be acting as if I'm not shy, and instead of having lots of Thoughts in my head messing with me, I could just easily and comfortably be Now in situations that would normally have caused me anguish. Well, I'll get there! No more fighting with myself,' she smiled at me.

I looked at her warmly, **'Well said! It's not about fighting, it's not even about changing, but about understanding, Letting Go and learning new stuff.'**

'And of course having lots of fun,' she at me grinned broadly.

'Master student!' I hugged her once more and she hugged me back tightly.

Tara looked at Lee with a smile on her face, remembering the girl. 'After our conversation she was a changed person, she looked so much more confident already. She loved the approach, she felt empowered and stronger. She felt that she had the tools now to put the theory into action. She finally had something that she could use to *actively* change and sort out her life, rather than just talk about it. She could take responsibility for her own happiness and get on with it. She loved it. Well, that's it,' Tara concluded her story.

'What a fabulous story.'

'Want another one?'

'Sure,' Lee said without beating an eyelid.

Saying NO

'**A** woman I worked with, had problems saying 'no'. She was a total pushover and everybody used her. She could have just decided not to entertain the Behaviour associated Thoughts anymore which made her unhappy, but she decided to go further. She actually didn't want the unbalanced Behaviour anymore either, it upset her, unbalanced her and of course stopped her from being Now. She decided that it was time to take responsibility to Let Go of her habit. **She wanted to come up with a Blueprint, to help her with the next push-over-situation, a formula she could follow *every time* she felt pushed into a corner,**' Tara recounted the story.

'A formula, a Blueprint! What a great idea. **It's like a personally tailored reusable method for yourself.**'

'I know, brilliant isn't it? To create this Blueprint, she observed herself throughout the day and made a note of the situations that caused her to loose her power, situations where she gave in against her will. First she trained herself to stay relaxed in such situations by breathing, and calming her brain, so that she could rationally examine the situation without becoming upset. She would then consciously ask herself: "do you actually want to do what they asked you to do? Yes or no." She would try to stay firmly Mindful on that subject, making sure she would not worry about what others would say or think of her, but rather contemplate what *she* wanted or *needed* to do. If she wanted to say yes, she would, but she would *consciously decide* to say yes, she wouldn't be pushed-over. She also observed that now she couldn't moan about other people anymore, because she was taking the decisions herself now. If she decided that she didn't want to do it, not just for the sake of saying "no", but because she really *wanted* to say "no", then she would. She did it by staying Mindful and Present and making sure that her Rational Mind would not come up with any excuses. She would say: "I'm really sorry, but I really don't *want* to do it",' Tara stressed the word *want*.

'Ah, that's a good way to say it. People can argue with I-*can't*-do-it, but not with I-don't-*want*-to-do-it.'

'Exactly. It's these little things that make all the difference,' Tara smiled. 'It took her quite a bit of will power to overcome her habit though.'

'I can imagine,' Lee tried to put himself into the woman's shoes.

'The one thing that was initially holding her back the most, was that she was worried about what people would think of her if she didn't do what they wanted her to. "Wouldn't they think me selfish?", she asked me. I said to her: "well, you could turn the question around. What would it make *them* if they're just repeatedly using *you*? If they are trying to make *you* do something that you don't want to do? I would think that'll qualify *them* as selfish, don't you?"' Lee smiled. 'I told her that it was not about becoming selfish, but about learning to evaluate a situation. It was about learning to figure out if it was appropriate to help, and to learn about herself to be able to tell if she felt comfortable to help at any particular moment in time or not. At work, something might simply not be in her job description, and sorry, but she's busy with doing the things she's supposed to be doing. Sure, sometimes it's wonderful to go out of her way to help someone, but sometimes, it's just not good for her own well being, her own sanity or stress levels. Then she had to learn to say "no". **She basically had to play with, and ultimately adopt a new personality that *could* say "no".'**

'What a fabulous invention,' Lee looked across the park, realising how radically his life was changing every minute of their conversation.

Four Stages to Let Go Of Behaviour and Thoughts

'Isn't it marvellous?' Tara said enthusiastically. 'Can you see the different stages people go through to Let Go of Behaviour and Thoughts?' Lee looked blankly, so Tara elaborated, 'Once we have consciously decided that we want to Let Go of a persistent Thought, reaction, action or Behaviour, and once we have put the out Intent that we want to catch ourselves out, there usually follow four stages.

First, **we catch ourselves out *after* it happened.** *After* we had a Thought, *after* we felt, reacted or behaved in an old, ingrained manner. We might notice it *straight* afterwards or long afterwards, maybe only when we begin to analyse our Behaviour. **The point of the first step is too become *aware* that *we've just done it again*. The point is Awareness.**

We have to keep noticing it afterwards, until, after a while, we automatically proceed to the *second* stage.

During the second stage, we notice that we're at it again, *while* we're doing it - which gives us our first *choice* to do things differently,' Tara said.

'That's what the shy girl was supposed to do, right? She was supposed to notice her shyness *while* she was being shy. Only then could she go and play with approaching people instead.'

'That's it. **During the *third* stage we see the situation where we would usually do Dots and Squiggles or behave the old way coming *before* we do it, and that's the point where we can *choose* not to do it in the first place.** We can choose to *stay* in the dot instead.'

'I think I know what **the *fourth* stage** is,' Lee said. '**It's the stage where we don't even have to decide not to act out an old habit or think the old way anymore, because they don't come up anymore in the first place, they have stopped for good,** right? The torch is off. It's the pot example all over. The need is gone. **Getting rid of the pot is permanently being in the fourth stage**, right?'

'Yes, that's it. Some people go through all these stages really quickly, some take a few weeks or months, but as always, the trick is to be gentle with yourself and most of all, have fun on the way! It's not just about the end result, it's about enjoying the road towards it!

The most important thing to keep in Mind, is that we need to make sure that if we ever want to change anything about ourselves, that we do it because *we want* to, not because *somebody else* tells us to or wants us to,' Tara added.

'Spot on young lady,' Lee gave her the thumbs up and began to scribble.

Four stages to stop Thoughts, Reactions or Behaviour:
* We catch ourselves out *after* it happened
* We notice *while* we're doing it (which gives us a choice to do something different).
* We notice it *before* we do it (which gives us the choice not to do what we wanted to stop, we could play with something new, or we could just Be Now).
* It has gone and/or something new has been established.

Not Try-ing, But Do-ing - Taking Full Responsibility

'Now, underlying these four stages, is one inherent principle, one fundamental prerequisite without which none of this will work,' Tara said. **'If somebody is not ready or not willing to break through their**

self-imposed barriers, if they're not ready to make a commitment to themselves to be diligent and continue the practice, they'll have a hard time. They'll come up with so many But-s and I-can't-s, that they'll never actually let themselves do it. The gist of it is: "don't *try*, but *do!*" These semantics are really important,' Tara stressed. '**You don't *try* to Let Go, you don't *try* to change, you don't *try* to be Now, you *do* it. Saying that you'll *try*,** inherently implies the possibility of not doing it or not managing to do it. It's casting Doubt.'

'I can see that. **It's a very subtle way of saying that you're not wholly ready or committed to do what you're setting out to do,**' Lee said. ' Wow, little words like that make an enormous difference.'

'Exactly. It's all about being constantly, consciously aware of what's going on in your head! Be diligent and change the wording every time you say *try*. **Positively, confidently and playfully *do* it, rather than intensely *trying* to do it. It needs constant repetition to change an old Thought or Behaviour.** It takes constant catching out and diverting. **So, don't give up after the first go.** Stick with it and don't get upset or frustrated. And anyway, that would just be…?' Tara stopped mid-sentence.

'More habits!' Lee said as he bent forward over his notebook.

Be confident:
* Don't *try*, but *do!*

Tara had laid back onto the blanket, and dreamily looked up into sky, when she identified an urgent call of nature, 'I'm just going to nip to the bathroom,' she said.

'Yeah, sure, no problemo. Do you fancy continuing afterwards?'

'Of course, I'd love to. Do you mind waiting till I come back?'

'No problem, enjoy,' Lee smiled.

Tara slowly got up, stretched herself, waved at Lee and set out on her walk to the public toilets at the other end of the park.

15 Emotions and Lee

Lee got up too and stretched himself for a little while, when he suddenly saw Kate walk by - not too close, but also not too far - with her new boyfriend. As soon as he laid eyes on them, before his Mind could even think, he felt his heart contract in a pang, his breath speed up and his Thoughts fall over themselves in his brain, trying to get his attention, taking over his peaceful state from two minutes ago in an instant.

Lee was surprised about the intensity of the feelings that had so spontaneously arisen within him, that had jumped at him from out of nowhere. Jealousy, a hurtful feeling of betrayal, anger! He tried to breathe. Luckily they hadn't seen him and he didn't feel in the mood to talk to them right now. He hadn't talked to Kate since their break up and there were still a bunch of things left unsaid between them, that was for sure, but now didn't seem like the right moment to say them. A Thought flickered past his Consciousness, "These Emotions are causing you distress and they're keeping you from being Now. Do you remember your dream?" His brain was scrambling for the faint memories that were like thin clouds on the outermost hemispheres of his Consciousness. Slowly his dream took shape once more. He remembered, how **he had a golden line painted on his Body, which connected his head and his chest, his Mind and his Heart, and there'd been something about Emotions.** He also remembered the feeling that had remained with him after the dream - Mind and Emotions were somehow connected. But weren't they two separate things, Lee thought to himself. Mind and Emotions?

He stood back for a moment and observed what was going on in his head. He was amazed. He never used to think this way. Contemplating Thoughts and Emotions… now that was a new one.

He took a deep breath and threw himself into his new experience. Now, what was going on in there? He had caught himself out. He had noticed aggravated Emotions triggered by seeing Kate, and he noticed that those Emotions were stopping him from being Mindful. Great, now what? **After everything he'd talked about with Tara, he felt that he should somehow be able to play with this, to somehow get back to a nice calm and peaceful state.** The state before I've-just-seen-my-ex-girlfriend-with-her-new-boyfriend-and-it's-driving-me-nuts state.

"Now then, let's have a look what I can do," Lee thought to himself. "If my dream is right, and my Mind and Emotions are linked, then sorting out my Thoughts should have an effect on my Emotions," Lee began his contemplation. "So, let's have a look at the Thoughts first." He was upset that Kate and Mark were in the park. Could Kate have known that he was here? Not really. So thinking that she should have known and thus not come out of respect for him, was a silly puppy. He felt she should be more considerate than prancing around with her new boyfriend. Super silly puppy. She had a new man. What was she supposed to do, lock herself in at home with him? That Thought was just unreasonable, but he still felt such intense **hurt and pain**. He thought of his surprise about her leaving so abruptly, her moving in with Mark straight away, leaving him in their apartment with all it's memories. The strangeness about him being alone.

Then something hit Lee like a million bricks. **He had been through these very same Thoughts before!** Only this morning! Interesting! He had already done these very same Dot's and Squiggles. Craziness.

Now, instead of going round that very same roller-coaster once again, Lee decided to try and remember this morning's conclusions. Where had all the Dot's and Squiggles gotten him to? Ah yes. Kate was "the one". No she wasn't. He'd been over that. Kate wasn't The One and he'd established lots of reasons for that. Their views, interests, hobbies and what they wanted out of life had been too different. He remembered that he'd even decided earlier that it had been for the best that they'd split up, that it had even been inevitable and that it wasn't really that bad, because now they could go their own way and find somebody more compatible. And of course he'd eventually find somebody else. **So, with all of that, why was he feeling so betrayed?** Sure, *she* had done the breaking up, which meant that she had the advantage. The advantage? What a stupid thing to say. As if this was some kind of competition. He laughed at himself. Now that was better, instead of feeling miserable, he was at least laughing. He thought about Tara, she would have loved to be in his head right now. He wondered where she was. It'll be nice to have her back, but then again, he was enjoying sorting through all of this by himself. He didn't mind if she'd be a little while longer, to give him more time. Deciding that he might as well make himself more comfortable, he sat down again and peacefully went back to his contemplation.

So far he'd realised that all of his Thoughts regarding Kate were pretty stupid. He tried to push his Mind a step further. Even if his Thoughts would *not* be stupid, even if they would be as justified as could be, lets say Kate would have betrayed him, lied to him, taken all his stuff, behaved like a witch, whatever, even if all of that *would* have happened, his Thoughts about it would *still* be useless, because nothing that he thought would change the situation, because they were Thoughts - in his head. Now that was a powerful and empowering realisation. **Whatever was going on in his head about this situation was useless! Having understood that, he felt that he could happily Let Go of those Thoughts.**

He leant back against the tree, shut his eyes, breathed and redirected his Thoughts to his new little nephew, how sweet he was and what he could get him for his next Birthday. Suddenly Thoughts about Kate were back. Now, that was an interesting experiment. He had succeeded in redirecting his Thoughts away from his Emotional Thoughts about Kate. Even if it hadn't been for long, he had done it, and somehow, he felt a little better because of it. **He marvelled, "Does that mean that if I don't think about an Emotion, that it goes away? Could it be like The**

Dice Man again? Could I possible change my Emotions just like my Behaviour ?"

He opened his eyes and to his surprise saw Kate and Mark at the end of the park again. They had sat down by the far end of the pond and seemed to be feeding the ducks. Within a split second, all the good work he'd done over the past few minutes was balled over. He'd instantaneously gone back into the same Mental loop as before. The feelings were back and so were the hurtful Thoughts, but this time he watched right from the start. This time, **instead of being involved in his upset, he curiously observed himself.** He was surprised by what was happening to him. It was quite fascinating really. In a strange, new kind of way. All of a sudden he became consciously aware of a physical sensation in his Body. A sensation which he knew he'd felt before, not so long ago. A contraction of his heart, his breath speeding up and moving up into his chest, rather than his belly, his forehead wrinkled, his teeth clenched, all of that happened in an instant. It was an instantaneous whole Body reaction to seeing Kate and Mark. Lee was amazed. **His entire Body had gone from a relaxed state to tightly contracted in a split second.** It felt like a shock. Yes, a physical shock, wham into the middle of his chest and from there it had spread to the rest of his Body.

Tara had said earlier that he could be whoever he wanted to be, he could behave in whichever way he wanted to behave, Lee tried to spin those Thoughts further. **Well, what would a non-upset person do or be? They would *not* be contracted. He tried to actively relax his Body.** He unclenched his jaw, focused on slow and deep belly breathing, relaxed his forehead and his chest. Just in case he'd missed anywhere, he slowly scanned his Body from the top of his head down to his toes and up again, and actively relaxed any tightness, any contraction he felt on the way. **The more his Body relaxed, the more the shock feeling dispersed.** Not completely, but it was much lighter now.

He noticed that, as he put his attention on his Body, he wasn't thinking about Kate. Could he think about both he wondered? Kate *and* his Body? He tried, but he couldn't. It was the same as his little experiment yesterday, when he tried to drink orange juice and listen to music simultaneously. He couldn't think about Kate at the same time as he was relaxing his Body. **So, by relaxing his Body, his Mind automatically relaxed too.** What a nice trick. He had fooled his Mind.

This was getting better by the minute, Lee grinned. Man, all of this sure took an intense amount of focus and mental discipline, but it worked. He was amazed by the power of his Mind and his Intent. **He laughed out loud. Wow, he had just *actively* dispersed his Mental attachment** to his Emotion by *actively* thinking of something else, and better, **the Emotion itself had eased off too. When the Emotion had come back, he had identified a bunch of Physical Sensations, had actively relaxed them, and again, the Emotion had eased off again.** His Mind fell silent for a minute, then with a start he realised that he had **divided his Emotions into two elements, the Mind and Physical Sensations.** He remembered his dream again, the intense physical feeling he'd had. Maybe the dream was supposed to tell him that Emotions, the Mind *and* the Body were connected. Made sense. God, this was crazy, he'd dreamt the explanation. Nutty. **So, was he still feeling bad?** Not really, he surprised himself and then laughed. **He was far to busy being amazed by his new ability to analyse himself to be upset. His boldness and his new ability to play with such hurtful Emotions and laugh regardless startled him. It was all strangely surreal. It felt as if he had stepped out of the normal world, out of the normal way of thinking and feeling, into a new world, a new dimension, where all these things were curious and interesting rather than upsetting, shocking or debilitating.**

Still smiling, he remembered when he had created a reference point for himself earlier with Tara, the reference point of how Nowness felt like. He had felt the sensation of being utterly carefree and relaxed. Afterwards he'd analysed the feeling to such an extent that he was familiar enough with it to be able to recreate it - and he'd managed to do that. Tara had said that he could repeat the procedure whenever he liked. Another smile crossed his face, as an experiment came to his Mind, an experiment Tara would be proud of. He closed his eyes again and thought of Kate and Mark, in all sorts of hurtful scenarios, and right on cue, his Dots and Squiggles started again and the tightness in his Body returned. Lee opened his eyes and laughed. It was exactly what he had expected. **Just the Thought of Kate with her new boyfriend could recreate the Emotions!** Now, that was amazing! It was like the story of the Monks in the cave. By giving a deity attention, they gave it the power to exist, until it seemed utterly real. "**Man, I'm practicing just like Tara's friend did by deliberately standing in line, and I'm doing it all in my head,**" Lee praised himself. "I can practice playing with Emotions, just with the *Thought* of Kate. **And then, the easier that gets in my head, maybe then when I see her for real, it will be much less intense.** It's like the Blueprint Tara talked about earlier. I can create a Blueprint of how to deal with situations. What a fantastic idea," Lee patted himself on the back.

"**Hang on, if a Thought of Kate *creates* painful Emotions, and if I can recreate peaceful Nowness feelings...?**" he smiled broadly. **Could he think of something positive and happy and**

create a *happy* Emotion to replace the sad one? Could he actively create Emotions within himself?" Of course he could, he knew that, he'd already done it. This was crazy, this was a revolution in his little world. He couldn't wait to try.

He thought of a time when he was happy, when he felt strong and loved and appreciated by a woman, a time when he felt in his male power and the woman he was with was in her feminine power. When there was strength and appreciation and clarity and playfulness and love. While he was thinking those Thoughts, he felt his Body remembering the sensations he'd had, the Emotions he'd felt, even some of the Thoughts he'd thought back then came back. Just as he expected, he was beginning to feel that way again. He felt strong, powerful and full of love. **Then, as soon as he took his attention away from his happy memories and thought about Kate again, those happy Sensations collapsed.** Puff, gone. Edginess, dryness and staleness replaced wholeness, fullness and roundedness. **He put his focus back on the positive Thoughts and Sensations, and as he suspected, they returned. Ok, he gathered, it took *Continuous Conscious* attention**, that was good to know. So **wherever he put his attention, that was in his head.**

"Amazing." Lee slumped back against the tree in awe. Awe of himself, of this process and of his amazing ability to conjure up these ridiculous experiments, which were so incredibly effective. 'Oh, no way!' **he grinned broadly as he thought of something else. If he could recreate any Emotion he wanted, could he create fictional Emotions?** Could he just create whatever he wanted at all? He closed his eyes and let his imagination run wild. He actively thought up all sorts of different scenarios that would normally create intense Emotional Reactions. And just as he knew it would happen, he began to feel all sorts of interesting Emotions and their corresponding Physical Sensations. As he focussed on his made up Emotions, he concentrated on thinking the corresponding Thoughts and on actively feeling all the Sensations in his Body. He pretended to be in a war. He felt the fear, the anxiety, the loneliness. He pretended to have a baby, he felt the joy, the amazement of being a father - it was all made up, but the Emotions felt real.

He thought of Kate again and the sad, angry and frustrated Emotions returned once again. **This time he really went for it, he felt his Emotions and amplified them. He nearly made himself scream with their intensity. He felt his Body contract, his throat tie up, his breath becoming laboured, his eyes squeezing themselves shut. With an enormous summoning of willpower, he opened his eyes and looked at his Body. An understanding hit him. No matter how much it hurt, he was still alive. It was a**

Physical Sensation that could simply be relaxed with enough focus. It was a Sensation that he had actively created and reinforced and by Thoughts. There wasn't anything to be scared of or worried about. No matter how intense the Emotion got, he could un-create it and relax his Mind and his Body.

This was absolutely amazing, had he really found a way of dealing with his Emotions? Could it really be that easy? It was rational and clear and straightforward and it worked, he'd just done it. He had figured out that his Emotions were affecting him in two ways and he had worked out a way to deal with each one. "Would this apply to all Emotions?" he wondered. "Would this work for other people?" No matter how much he thought, he couldn't come up with a reason why it shouldn't.

He was getting more and more excited to tell Tara and see if his discoveries matched hers. Surely she must have played with this herself.

He flicked through his notebook and found one of the lists he'd written earlier about Behaviour and used it as an outline for his findings. His final scribbling looked something like this:

An Emotion has a
* Physical sensation and
* A Thought pattern associated with it

Emotions:
* Emotion equals Thought plus Physical Sensation: E-T+PS
* Each Emotion has two parts to it. Every *Emotion* has a *physical sensation* and a *Thought pattern* associated with it. To play with Emotions, to Be Now, it's not enough to just address the Thoughts patterns, you also have to address the Physical Sensation.

As he wondered what the difference was between Emotions and Feelings, he remembered his little electronic dictionary in his bag. In fact it was more than a memory, it was more an inexplicable urge to use it *right now*. Was it a Co-incidence that he had it with him? Well, he'd been told this morning to take it with him. Man, this was getting bizarre. "I think I'm slowly beginning to understand what Tara meant when she kept talking about this stuff being *Far Out!*" he thought. With curious and excited anticipation he took the dictionary out of his bag and typed in the word *Emotions*. He wrote the result into his notebook and he did the same with the word *Feelings*. This is an extract out of his notebook:

e‑mo‑tion n
- a strong feeling about somebody or something
- agitation or disturbance caused by strong feelings

feel‑ing n
- the sensation felt on touching something
- the ability to perceive physical sensation in a part of the Body
- a perceived physical or mental sensation (...)
- a perceived emotion

npl. feel‑ings
- somebody's emotional susceptibilities (...)

(Encarta® World English Dictionary © 1999 Microsoft Corporation)

A hazy cloud of knowing descended over Lee. As he reread the words, especially the parts he'd highlighted, slowly the meaning of the words he was looking at struck him. They read: Emotion - an agitation or disturbance caused by strong Feelings. Feelings are perceived Physical or Mental Sensation. He picked up his pen and made a note of the shortened version.

Emotions:
- are an agitation or disturbance, caused by strong perceived Physical or Mental Sensations.

Lee stared at what he'd just written. This was crazy. This was exactly what he had just figured out, by observing himself. He couldn't believe that the answer to his life long rollercoaster Emotions could be found in a freaking dictionary, of all places! Well, if you knew how to read the answers, that was, Lee laughed.

He reread the full definition once more and this time, the last sentence also struck him as significant. It read: *feel‑ings n - somebody's emotional susceptibilities (...)*

Now, what did *that* mean? He switched the Dictionary to it's Thesaurus function and typed in "susceptibility". The answer made his breath stock in his throat. The alternate words for susceptibility were: *Vulnerability, Receptiveness.*

Lee tried to stand back to see the whole picture to understand what this meant. **If different people had different *susceptibility* to Emotions, that meant that they had different vulnerability or receptiveness to Emotions - to the agitation or the disturbance that was caused by strong perceived Physical or Mental Sensations.** "Stay focussed!" he nearly screamed at himself. He couldn't loose the threat now! He scrambled his brain, so all of that meant that people reacted differently to the Physical and Mental Sensations that they receive, depending on their susceptibility, vulnerability or receptiveness. Gosh, this was huge! Oh man, **an Emotion is a reaction to perceived Physical or Mental Sensations**, he thought. Things clicked into place in Lee's brain. **It's a reaction, a Behaviour!** And Behaviour could be changed! Oh man, *he could change his Emotional Reaction to his Physical and Mental sensations,* which was exactly what he'd done earlier, and with that he could change his Emotions. Wow!

Another Thought hit him, was this varied susceptibility to Emotions, the reason why some people managed to deal well with intense emotional situations, whereas others didn't? Did people just react *differently* to the *same* external stimulus? Was that the reason why some people fell of a horse and never rode again, whereas others jumped straight back on? Was that the reason why one person after accident which confines him into a wheel chair starts to play basketball or partakes in the Para Olympics and gets on with his different, but new life, whereas another despairs and feels their life is at an end and becomes utterly miserable? Could that explain why one person that has been abused is never happy again, whereas another goes on to lead a happy and fulfilled life?

What was the real difference between these people? Paraphrased, the thesaurus said that **some people were more susceptible to feeling Emotions than others**. Would that be due to their genes or their conditionings or **was it maybe just down to the fact that some people knew how to deal with their Thoughts, Emotions and Feelings and others didn't? Could it all be down to knowledge and the ability to put that knowledge into practice**? He knew that if he concentrated on the root Thought of an Emotion, the Emotion got more intense. If he diverted his Thoughts, the intensity of the Emotion would ease off, and the same happened with the Physical Sensation. If somebody *didn't* know that, if somebody *didn't* know how to relax their Body and Mind, if they *didn't* know that they could do something about the way they felt and reacted? They would feel the Emotion to the full- however badly their Mind would care to make it. But if you knew how to play with it, it was a completely different story! Lee breathed deeply for a few minutes to let this realisation sink in. He stretched his neck, thought of Tara and still felt very happy on his own. He wasn't finished yet.

He felt that no matter how strong or intense his Emotions were, they were all a Reaction to some kind of stimulus, they could be separated into Thoughts and Physical Feelings every time, and according to what he'd just figured out, each one of those could be dealt with.

He tried to think how he would deal with having to sit in a wheel chair for the rest of his life. He had a friend who this had happened to. There were so many constant frustrations about such simple things, not being able to change the side of the street because the pavements were too high, not being able to get into shops, restaurants, cinemas, needing a special car, finding it difficult to shower, do sports, travel or live a normal life, feeling so dependent, maybe even getting a girlfriend. **None of his methods could stop those things from happening, but they *could* change the way he could *react to them!***

He could *choose* where to put his attention. He could put his attention on the past, or he could put it on the Present, on being Now, just as he'd done with Kate. **He figured that he could only do that though, if he *accepted* his fate, because otherwise the nagging Thoughts would keep coming back. If he wouldn't accept that he'd be in the wheel chair for the rest of his life, how could he move on? He would always stay in the past, being attached to the past and his Thoughts about how his Body used to be, rather than accepting how it was now. It was not about forgetting, but *accepting* that it was past. "And the past only exists in your Mind," - his brain added to his surprise.**

What could be in the way of acceptance? What could hinder him to accept? He thought that acceptance might be more difficult if he might not be able to withdraw himself from the triggering situation. If it was constantly recurring, constantly in his face, like the wheelchair example, where the frustrations are real every day. Well, no matter how terrible the situation was, one day he'd have to make a decision. Was he going to let it ruin his life? Did he want to give up or live? Accept and move on, or not? He felt he'd always have the choice to make those decisions. Was it *all* down to choice?

What did he have to do to *accept* a terrible situation? First he'd have to do the judgement thingy. He'd have to stop judging the situation as bad and see it for what it is. Nothing more and nothing less. He'd have to go into his head and *find every single* Thought that was linked to a judgement and Let Go of it, then every Thought that was linked the Past and deal with each single one of those too, including his Emotional reactions to them. He had to actively understand that each one of those parts made him unhappy, that they didn't change the current situation and that they were therefore utterly useless. Then he'd have to Let Go of them by being Mindful or moving into the Now. He'd have to *choose* to do so. It wouldn't happen by itself. It would take time, but he felt that it was possible.

Another Thought crystallised on the outer peripheries of his Consciousness. **The Thought, that besides *acceptance*, one needed *Objective Mental Clarity* to play with Emotions the way he did, because all of this was Mental work, based on *Mental analysis* and *understanding* of the situation.** That didn't mean intelligence, but it meant **ability, willingness, readiness and gameness to look at the whole Emotional thing in a different way. To stand back and observe and understand and dare to play. If he could not do that, he knew, he'd be far too involved to be able to divert his Mind and it would be near impossible to realise any of his ideas.**

Lee spun his train of Thought further. **If he'd be a very emotional person, if his susceptibility to Emotions would be very high, it might be difficult for him to follow a rational explanation. If he would be severely clinically depressed for example, where he'd have no access to Mental Reasoning anymore, this approach might not work.** If he'd received a terrible shock, maybe through a loved one dying in a horrific accident, it might need some time to gain that clarity again. Mother nature might have to initiate the healing process, such a person might have to go *through* the Emotions, live them, they might have to cry, rant and scream until they can't go on - and then, once their objectiveness is back, they could use this approach.

It was just like telling a woman on PMS to detach herself from her Emotions, to just look at things clearly. "You'd probably get your head ripped off," Lee grinned. Sometimes you've got to wait till it passes naturally.

Lee guessed that if he'd be in the midst of a strong Emotion, it might be difficult to distance himself from it, to pull himself out of it and look at it rationally. That's the nature of Emotions, they take over the Mind, bury you with Thoughts, confusions and associations and drown you in Physical Sensation. But, once the intensity was reduced far enough, his Mind could become clearer again, if he'd let it. If he let it? What did that mean? Well, he also knew that sometimes it was just *easier* to go with an Emotion, to moan and groan and feel sorry for himself. Sometimes he didn't want to be strong and clear, but he wanted to wallow in self-pity. When he was at home alone, he knew that he could do that sometimes, whereas when he went to work, he'd have to pull himself together. He simply couldn't allow himself to be that way. Very interesting. He could pull himself together when he had to. He knew that lots of people could actively pull themselves together and out of the muddle, they could stick their heads out of all the confusion and objectively look at and deal with what was *actually* happening, rather than what their head or Emotions wanted them to *believe* was happening. Some people's heads naturally cleared faster and they were able to *actively* pull themselves out of an emotional hole faster than others. Was it maybe not a question of *being able* to do it, but rather a question of *just doing it?*

Whatever the answer to this was, it would always be worth to at least try to pull himself out of it *straight away*, no matter how intense the Emotion was. Surely it couldn't make it any worse, he felt that it could only make it better. **He even thought that, if done with playfulness, no matter how serious the subject, he could even begin to laugh at himself at being so serious, so self-absorbed and self-pitying.** Gosh, he could choose to pull himself out every time!

Lee leant forward and began to write like a madman. He didn't want to forget even the slightest detail. When he was done, he fell flat on his back, totally exhausted. He relaxed his Body and his brain. He concentrated on his breathing, gently, softly. He had worked hard. He had lain there for about five minutes, when Tara's face flickered past his Minds eye. Yes, he was ready. He felt calm and relaxed again. He opened his eyes and there she was. Standing in front of him, a big smile on her lips, her hair moving gently in the wind.

'Hi, did they have to build the toilet for you?' Lee grinned up at her.

'Oh man, I bumped into an old friend I haven't seen in three years, we had so much catching up to do. But I checked in with my Intuition a bunch of times and it seemed that you needed some time to yourself, so I didn't hurry. So, what were you up to?' Tara asked curiously.

Lee looked at her in amazement, 'Your Intuition told you that I need time?'

'Yep.'

Lee remembered thinking of Tara a few times during his contemplation and deciding each time that he was happy to have more time to himself. He wondered for a moment if they had thought of each other at the same time, like a mental checking in, making sure that each one of them was ok? Bizarre. Lee took that notion in a stride, he had far more important stuff to share.

'Well, your Intuition was right, ma'am. You know what? I'm beginning to take everything we've talked about so much more serious than I ever thought I would. I believed that I had some kind of idea of the potential, but I could have never fathomed, how profoundly everything you've told me would affect my life. Tara, what do you think about Emotions?'

'Emotions? In what sense?'

'How do you deal with Emotions?' Lee clarified.

'They are puppies just like everything else. You deal and play with them the same way as you would with Thoughts. You can observe them, you can learn from them or you can just be Now, where the Emotions don't exist.'

'I knew it!' Lee jumped up and hugged the tree.

'That's great, but would you care to elaborate on what happened while I was away? I'm so intensely on tender hooks, it hurts!' Tara grabbed Lee's hand and pulled him down next to her. 'Get on with it, will you?' she laughed.

Something really significant seemed to have happened to Lee in the last hour, Tara thought. His entire energy had changed. He appeared to be much stronger, somehow wiser? What a strange idea. Lee looked at her. His hair even messier than it had been before, his eyes brighter. Eternally sexy. Tara noticed the Thought the same time she felt the heat rise in her cheeks. She grinned. Schoolgirl stuff was fun!

Lee sat himself opposite her, equally cross-legged and put his hands onto her knees. Then he told her everything. Kate and all. Well, he told Tara that he'd had a girlfriend and that it was over now. Then he told her every single little detail of what he'd discovered. While he was talking, Tara listened, her eyebrows raising from time to time, a smile creeping in here and there.

He finished off by saying, **'You know I sometimes wonder who started the thing about Emotions being so scary. Them being this big huge thing, when you can actually play with them. I mean, I laughed earlier! First I was all upset, then I started to change the Emotion the way I wanted to, I looked at it, turned it upside down a bit more, and suddenly it wasn't so intense anymore. To top all of that, I learned so much about myself by analysing the Thoughts that came with the Emotions,'** Lee **remembered his repetitive Mental loops about Kate being "the one".**

Tara gazed at him in silence. After a couple of minutes she recovered her wits, 'I can't believe that you just made all of that up in like, what, an hour?' she was well impressed.

'Yeah, I know, it all came straight into my head. It was so easy. So, what do you think?'

'Well, I'm stunned, you've perfectly summarised my own findings, but I took longer than an hour to even think of doing any of this, let alone actually doing it. Congratulations,' Tara was amazed. 'If you want me to, I can fill in a few holes here and there and give a few examples, but you've pretty much got it.'

'That'll be fabulous. Phew, it feels so good to have figured out my blueprint all by myself.'

'That's what makes it yours rather than somebody else's,' Tara said proudly.

'Yeah, agreed! And yeah, I'd love to hear your take on it.'

Extreme Emotions and Behaviour Keep You From Being Now - Puppies

'**As** you've already discovered, Emotions just as Thoughts, stop us from being Now, unless we can just be pure experience that is,' Tara threw in casually and continued before Lee could comment. 'By practicing Mindfulness and Nowness, we become Aware. **By becoming Aware, we get a choice about what to think, how to react, behave, feel physically and how to Emotionally respond. The most important thing to realise when we're dealing with all of these, is that they're all puppies.** Every single one of them. They might be different races, but in the end they're still puppies - and we can deal with all of them in the same way. Little nagging ones and big ones, soft ones and intense ones alike. Letting go of stuff that has been ingrained into our brain for a long time, takes more concentration, but it's done exactly the same way, as with any old random Thought that you might want to calm down.'

'Yeah agree. Now, I'm wondering though, how did *you* figure all of this out?' Lee asked.

'Well, I didn't use a dictionary, that's for sure,' she laughed. 'But I noticed that if I would think a lot about a break up or a problem or sadness or whatever, I'd have a pretty crap time. Whereas if I'd get distracted by a friend for example, I would *not* feel that Emotion. I played around with that for a while and noticed that if I didn't think about it, then I wouldn't think about it, full stop. If it's wasn't in my Awareness, it wasn't in my head, and at that moment in time, it wouldn't affect me. Ok, now psychologists of the world shoot me!' Tara held out her arms in theatrical readiness. 'Whenever I talk about this to anyone, this is usually where the yes-but's come running at me at a million miles an hour. But still, no matter what anybody else said, I found it to be true for me and by the sound of it, so have you,' she smiled at him warmly. '**The fact is that the more we think about an Emotion, the bigger it grows. By giving it attention, we give it the power to exist.**'

'Giving something attention gives it the power to exist,' Lee breathed deeply. He had used the same words just a few minutes ago. '**By thinking about something we make it alive!' he said.** 'No attention, no Thought, without Thoughts, it's not in our head. Without attention, without Thought it dies. Thoughts and Emotions are intricately linked, just like my dream told me.'

'Exactly,' Tara said. She had been amazed to hear about Lee's dream and how he had managed to figure out so much with it's help. 'I think once I realised that any Emotions I had, were just like a Thought puppy, everything else fell into place for me, just as it did for you. I realised that the Emotions puppy sits in front of you japing, wanting attention just like the Thought puppy. I also noticed that when you feed it, it also grows just like a Thought puppy. I figured out that if you feed the sadness puppy by giving it all of your attention, by going over my sad Thoughts again and again, that puppy will grow bigger and bigger. I realised that after a while it becomes so big that you wouldn't have a choice anymore to feed it or not, as it's taken over your life. I mean, if a ten foot puppy wants it's food, it's a little bit more tricky to refuse, right? By that time it has become pretty much impossible to ignore it,' Tara said sincerely. "I basically figured out that Emotions were just *really persistent* Thought puppies. **When I tried to take my attention away from them, they'd** stand there and jap at me, and I would turn around and look the other way.'

'Which means that we take our attention away from the Emotion.'

'Right. Now, when I played with Emotions, I found out pretty quickly that the doggies aren't stupid. They figure out in no time which way you turned and they begin to chase you. They run around you, until they're in your view again and start to jap all over,' she scrambled around him on all fours and looked at him all cute and attention worthy.

'The Emotions have just popped into your Mind and Body again,' Lee said, smiling at Tara's antics.

'Exactly. You turn around again and the game goes on for a bit, and you basically have to keep taking your attention away from the Emotions and keep putting it onto something else, such as your breathing or your little nephew, until the puppy finally gets bored and leaves you alone,' she sat there now, slowly moving away, looking like a very bored puppy, but also a very hurt puppy.

'Come here you poor little thing,' Lee said, wanting to pull Tara over.

'Ey, ey?'

'Oh man, of course, I can't give in, can I?' Lee laughed.

'Nope, as soon as you give in, you're feeding it again, and the more you feed it, the more it becomes attached. Have you ever fed a stray dog? Once you feed it? It's yours, even if you kick it or shout at it, which I never would, but you know what I mean.'

'I do, and thanks for the fantastic demonstration, I sure as hell won't ever forget that!' Lee grinned.

'My pleasure,' Tara smiled back at him. 'May I?' She motioned to the space next to him.

'In the form of Tara or a puppy?'

'Ah, you're on the ball now,' she laughed. 'As Tara this time.'

'Oh, absolutely. Come and sit,' he patted the blanked. Tara sat back down next to Lee, a little closer than before. They smiled at each other.

'And finally, just as you did, I also developed a Blueprint for myself,' Tara finished.

Lee loved all the little demonstrations Tara came up with. And oh boy, he'd been feeding puppies all of his life, ten foot ones, twenty foot ones, thirty foot ones. He could literally see himself sitting on his sofa again, feeling the sadness all over when his first ever serious teenage relationship had grown apart and finally ended. It had taken him six months to get over it. Looking back at similar experiences of his peers, six months had actually been pretty good going. Some of his friends were still at the getting-over-it-stage after years. Lee realised, that all he had done on that sofa was think about the break up - a lot - trying to figure out uncountable could-have-s, should-have-s, why-s and but-s, remembering all the good times and obviously blanking out the bad ones completely. He remembered slowly becoming more and more miserable, until he felt utterly rejected and sad and useless and unloved and without power and umpf and go and get. **He had fed that stupid puppy for six whole months and it had obviously not made a bit of difference to the fact that he was separated from the girl.** *That* undeniable fact had *not* gone away, but he had made himself utterly unhappy by simply thinking about it all the time. His friends had told him to get on with it, to stop his self-pity, his moping around. He had kept saying yeah, yeah, **but he hadn't really understood that it was possible to actually do so. He thought "pulling yourself together" was just a phrase. He hadn't known that he could actively do this. He hadn't known** *how*. **Now he understood.** He understood that puppies liked attention and liked to be fed, and of course, if he obliged, why shouldn't they stick around? Looking back on the situation, the separation from his girlfriend back then, had been the cause and trigger for his Thoughts. But only because he'd given the break-up-puppy so much attention, did it grow as out of control as it did. Only because he *allowed* all those miserable Thoughts in his head, did they get so amplified. Gosh, this Mind stuff would have helped him so much back then. Catch out. Relax. Breathe. Simple.

Tara watched Lee and thought how nice it was to meet such a like-Minded person. Somebody who really understood that us humans run around in a cloud of silly dots-and-squiggles and Emotions which make us upset, sad, angry and insecure. **It was so easy to be happy, blissful, calm and balanced instead, it all just depended on where we put our attention.**

'But sure, it's easier for some than others,' Tara thought out loud. **'On that note, you were talking about different people having different susceptibilities to Emotions?** I've also wondered why that is, if it's nature or nurture? Genetic or learned? Sure, there might be a certain extent of nature, but I feel that the environment people grow up in has a great impact on somebody's susceptibility to Emotions. Some people might have had a steady, stable emotional household, they might have learned from their role models not to fret-the-little-stuff-and-by-the-way-it's-all-little-stuff, as you said earlier,' she winked at Lee. 'Whereas others might have grown up in a pretty unstable household, drunken parents, beatings, suppressed Emotions, uncontrolled living out of Emotions, all of that. Well,' Tara raised her eyebrows, **'you learn by example and your own trial and error,'** she paused, **'you unlearn and re-learn with focus and tenacity, and of course a whole bunch of playfulness**. With that, you can do pretty much anything, if you really want it.'

'Yeah, I always knew that to be the case in the business world and in life, but this new Mental and Emotional aspect is beginning to bring a totally new dimension to everything I know. And man, it really does take some serious focus!' Lee recalled his previous efforts.

'I know, and I think that the required focus and tenacity is another reason for people's different susceptibilities. Some are able to focus for hours and days, others get fed up within seconds. It really takes persistence, to play with Emotions.'

'Yeah man, it takes *Continuous Conscious* attention!' Lee remembered.

'Right, at least until you've got the hang of it. **Once you get good, you can literally shush the puppies away in an instant, and they'll stay away, for good.** Then it'll only take concentration only for a moment.'

'And then? Stage four? It's become automatic?' Lee announced dramatically.

'Yep. You're well on your way,' Tara praised.

'Well, I've mastered the first few little stepping stones,' Lee bowed humbly.

'You know,' Lee said, 'the Physical Sensations that I talked about earlier, they're puppies too, right? Just that we deal with them by relaxing our Body, rather than our Mind.' Tara nodded and Lee went on, 'If you *can* relax and get into the Now immediately, then the Emotion and the Physical Sensation are gone like that,' he snapped his fingers. 'If you can't, Letting go of the Emotions will take as long as you need to learn to relax.

Man, with my little excursion earlier, I really noticed how much the relaxing thing depended on how well I could *focus on relaxing*, and on my discipline to keep turning around and not to give in to the little puppy that constantly tried to distract me.'

'At the beginning it might still feel all a bit clumsy, but with experience it gets better, faster, more familiar and finally stronger.' Tara said reassuringly. 'I can now switch off Thoughts *and* Emotions so quickly it sometimes still surprises me. Now it feels to me that most of the Emotions that used to really upset me, only barely touch the fringes of my Consciousness, most of the time they don't even enter my awareness anymore. I think the puppies have found different owners,' she laughed. 'Sometimes I only notice afterwards, that I would have usually reacted in a certain way but didn't.'

'That's noticing stage four through later analysis,' Lee said.

'You could put it that way, yes. In the end, the more Now I was, the less I reacted and as a result the Emotion got less intense, until in the end it didn't even come up anymore.'

'Yeah, **when you're Now all the time, you don't have any Thoughts anymore, there are no more interpretations, no more judging Thoughts of whatever you reacted to, no more associations, a sensation is just a sensation, and as a result there are no more extreme Emotions,**' Lee summarised.

'That's it. To get there you have to practice a little bit though.'

'Yep, and I've got enough incentive to last me a lifetime? One thing that will help me is that I already know that my focus and discipline can vary during different times of the day and even from one day to another. It varies as much as the amount and the intensity of the puppies that come at me.'

'Why does knowing that help you,' Tara wondered.

'Because it means that I don't have to stress. I can be easy on myself and not freak out when one day it's not going so well. I know that it's natural. So, I can go with the flow, be gentle, yet determined, focussed and disciplined!' Lee said.

'Good call. It's good to know that it's the same as with Thoughts, just as we discussed earlier. Some days there are Emotional puppies coming at you from all directions and they are so persistent that they won't leave you alone, and on other days it's fairly quiet. Some Emotions literally haunt you, whereas on other days, there are just a few little ones, and they're gone in a flux. But for all of them, just as you said, you need persistence, persistence, persistence,' Tara said.

'And for the really biiiig ones?' Lee lifted his hands, curled the fingers into claws and growled, 'Grrrrr.'

Tara showed her teeth and growled back at him, 'Huuge clarity, huuge focus, huuge determination!'

Lee laughed happily, this time he'd already known the answer.

'Be aware though, some Emotions can really take you by surprise,' Tara said turning back to face him directly.

'I know, the one earlier smacked me right in the face out of nowhere,' Lee said.

'Oh yeah, true. Then you'll also remember that **sometimes the Thoughts come first and the Physical Sensation follows, and sometimes it seems to be the other way round.** Sometimes a Physical Sensation comes at you seemingly without a Mental warning, - wham - straight from out of nowhere. That's what you were talking about earlier, when the Emotion hits you right into your chest like a sledge hammer and makes your whole Body contract? The ones that take over your Body before your Mind has had a chance to even notice?' Lee remembered only too clearly. 'Those physical sensations hit you spontaneously, seemingly out of nowhere, and the Mind only catches up afterwards, by noticing it, judging it or associating it.'

Lee nodded, that's exactly what happened when he'd seen Kate earlier. He thought for a moment and said, 'But whichever one comes first, the Thought or the Emotion, doesn't matter though, does it? I'd still deal with them the same way.'

'That's right,' Tara agreed. 'It just means that you have to make sure that you're prepared to catch both of them. For the ones that seem to come without a Mental warning, **you need to train yourself to instantly relax your *Body* first, whereas with the other one you need to relax your Mind first. You'll probably always have to address both anyway, but sometimes addressing the first one automatically looks after the follow up one too. Oh, and the four stage rule applies here too.** You notice after you had a Sensation or thought a certain way, then you notice it during,...'

'Which gives you a choice,' Lee remembered.

'Right. Then you notice it *before* and you can choose not to allow it to manifest within you, or not to act on it and then, with the next step, it's just gone. No more active involvement necessary. The pot's disappeared.'

'Cool. So I I'll train myself to catch both, Physical and Mental, just to have both angles covered.'

'That's my boy,' Tara twinkled. 'Well, I guess we're on the same wave-length, both of us actively played our way out of Emotions that kept us from Being Now.'

'We actively played your way out - what a great way of describing it. That's really what it felt like. Intense but fun, what a strange combination,' Lee held Tara's hand for a moment and squeezed it.

16 Playing With Emotions

Emotion Creatures On The Sofa

'So, now that we know that Emotions are puppies too, that we can relax the Physical Body and that we can divert the Mind or enter Nowness, one would assume that this would take care of the Emotion puppies, right? Well, maybe not. Emotions might need just a little more explanations than that,' Tara said.

'What it's not that easy?' Lee couldn't hold back his disappointment.

'Oh, it is, but some people might feel that it's more difficult than that.'

'I don't understand.'

'Well, most of us have never been taught how to *play* with Emotions. **Because nobody ever told us any different, we all think that Emotions are this big scary thing that takes over our lives from time to time and which we just have to bear or somehow get through, but nobody ever tells us how to do that. We've been told that Emotional Thoughts and Physical Sensations somehow seem to create this three dimensional hologram of a third entity within us. An entity that seems to take over the whole Being and strikes us down, an that's what people feel intimidated by. People will keep telling you, it's not *just* Thoughts, or *just* a sensation, it's *more* than that! People feel that Emotions need much *more* attention than Thoughts do, that they are *much* more important and *much* more difficult to deal with or Let Go of. They feel that even if they address the parts individually, they're still somehow missing something.'**

'Yeah, that's exactly how I used to look at Emotions, well, that's before I had the dream and before I had this crazy experience earlier,' Lee said. 'Certainly nobody has ever shown *me* how I can play with Emotions, how I can learn from them and even have some fun with them. Man, instead of believing everybody else, why not try and check out your Emotions for yourself? Why not *really* get to know them?' he was fascinated by the potential of his newly discovered ability.

'Exactly. **Why not make friends with the little Emotions creature that sits next to the Thought creature on that sofa.** Wouldn't you want to be able to sit there with *both* of them, have cups of tea and a giggle? **If we would only learn to see them for what they truly are, that would so quickly demystify the idea that Emotions are**

this big scary monster, when in fact they are fluffy and utterly snugly little things with beautiful light blue eyes.'

'Oh, little creatures! That's so cute,' Lee said charmed.

'They are cute, *once* they've been tamed. But until then, they are like little pixies. They are ever so mischievous, they test and try you and *the way you react to that* can make life really difficult for you. When they learn though that they won't get anywhere with you and that you are actually a really nice person and that it's in fact much more fun to just hang out with you, rather than making your life difficult, then they become cute. Then they're not scary anymore. Then they become fun,' Tara grinned. 'But it certainly takes some persistent convincing, that's for sure. Everybody else shouts at them and is scared of them, so why should you be any different? It takes a little while to gain their trust. But if you work on it? Watch out, you're about make one of your best friends yet!'

'Wow. This is like dangling a magic wand in front of my nose,' Lee crossed his eyes and looked at his nose.

'Oh, you've already got the magic, dude, you've already done it, remember?'

'Yeah, I rule!' Lee laughed. 'I'd be interested to her though how *you* would make friends with the little creatures?'

'Well, to inch your way forward to truly understand the third entity, the little creatures that run the show, you need to *get to know them* first. Keep in Mind though that they are pretty particular about their couch and they won't just invite anybody to come and stay,' Tara giggled. 'So, to get invited you need to get to know them and get to know what they're like. You need to find out what mood they're in, and how to approach them depending on that. Find out what amuses them, what calms them down, what distracts them. **Find out at what times they turn up in your Being and cause havoc, and when they sit on the couch and relax all by themselves. Then you can play with recreating an environment where you know they like to sit on the couch.'**

'Oh, that's cool. That's like creating a living-room of Nowness, knowing that the Thinking creature would love to chill in that.'

'Exactly. It's the same with Emotions,' Tara said. 'It's not about tricking them into anything, about ignoring them or about making them do something they don't want, but it's about establishing a mutual respect and in the end even a friendship. It's about creating an environment, where they simply don't feel the *need* to cause havoc anymore. Play with them, and begin to understand them, see them for the endearing, playful creatures they really are. Once you get the first glimpse of their true nature, which I feel you've already done,' she patted Lee's arm softly, '**you'll see that they really don't mean any harm, they just don't know how to express themselves, they just go crazy and create all those Thoughts and Sensations, in the hope that you'll Listen to them.**'

'It sounds as if they are like little children who with love, care and attention, can be guided to approach you in an equally loving, caring and respectful way,' Lee said enchanted.

'That's exactly it. Older children take a little longer to learn though,' Tara warned, 'so keep in Mind that this all sounds really sweet and cute, but as I said, it takes a little practice to really see the creatures to be like that.'

'And to *keep* seeing them like that, even when they have bad days from time to time and keep throwing Thoughts and Emotions at you regardless,' Lee pointed out knowingly.

'That's very true,' Tara laughed. Lee really hat gotten the hang of it fast. 'So, what about some more tips and tricks of how to help you make friends with the little creatures? Even in really intense Emotional situations?'

'That sounds like a fabulous idea.'

Objective Mental Clarity To Play

'**G**reat, here we go. If you're enmeshed in your Emotional Thoughts, or if your entire Being is taken over by the Physical Sensations you're having, you can't look at them *objectively*.'

'Makes sense,' Lee said. 'Like that you could never understand them wholly from the inside, because **to do that, you'd need to be able to look at it from the *outside*. And for that you have to be able to gain the distance and objectivity to do so.**'

'Exactly. The catch22 is that when an Emotion hits, people often find it impossible to keep their Objective Mental Clarity, as you called it earlier. **They find it impossible to distance themselves from the Emotion, to untangle themselves from the Emotional grasp and to look at it objectively. They feel that their Being was taken over by the third entity and they can't control it. Thoughts and Sensations pound in on them and they find themselves inside of an inescapable Emotional hologram. They fell that state is who they *are*, rather than what's *happening* to them!** In an instant, their Mind and Body contracts.'

'Sounds like fun,' Lee said sarcastically.

'Actually it is, once you can see what's rally going on! But for that, you need to be able to untangle yourself from the Emotional grasp first, you need to gain some clarity, you know, pop your had out of the clouds? And to do that, the first thing you have to do, is to *relax*. You have to relax your Mind enough to be able to use it to observe and to relax your Body enough to be able to function.'

'I think it might be tricky to relax your Mind and the Emotional Thoughts that are bombarding you when you're totally engulfed in the Emotion.'

'That's right, but you've already done it, remember? **And that's why we start with relaxing the Body.** As you've already figured out, by actively relaxing your Body, your Mind will automatically relax too, and the Emotional Sensations *will* disperse? **If you can learn to relax the Body straight away and as much as possible, that will *immediately* take the edge of the Emotion and reduce it's intensity.'**

'Ah, and because the Mind is focussed on relaxing the Body, rather than on other crazy Thoughts, that'll slow down the excess Mental Activity, right?' Lee recalled his own experiment.

'Exactly,' Tara smiled. **'And slowing down your Mental Activity, is a prerequisite to be able to gain the distance and the required Objective Mental Clarity you mentioned. So, when you feel an Emotion hitting you, don't worry about your Mind at first, just a*cknowledge* each physical tension and *actively relax* it.** Just as you did before, head to toe. Also make sure not to forget your brain. Feel the tension in your brain and relax it as the physical muscle that it is. Once your Body is more relaxed and your Mind has followed suit, simply because it had to be Mindful on relaxing your Body, that's when you can begin to play.'

'That's when we begin to get to know the little creatures,' Lee said with a little smile.

'It might take a little effort to stay Mindful, because the Physical Sensation will keep trying to butt in, but you just have to play around with that until you can maintain the relaxed state. Practice catching yourself out when the Physical Sensations return, and relax them straight away, with as little mental involvement as possible. With practice, you'll manage to stay present with whatever you're doing, even when the Sensations come back.'

'And, like that we can catch even the tiniest Negative Physical and Emotional undercurrent,' Lee butted in. 'That's fantastic. We talked about negative Mental Undercurrents earlier, now we've also got the Physical and the Emotional ones covered.'

'Yep,' Tara said as Lee already got hold of pen and paper.

- Slow down your Mental Activity.
- Relax your Mind enough to be able to use it to observe.
- Relax your Body enough to be able to function.
- Untangle *yourself* from your Emotion.
- Catch yourself out.
- When you feel an Emotion hitting you, don't worry about your Mind at first, just a*cknowledge* each physical tension and *actively relax* it, the Mind will follow suit.

Physical Sensations - Physical Emotional Undercurrents

'Can you tell me a bit more about the Physical Sensations? Better the devil you know, I'd say,' Lee asked.

'Sure. Most of it you can find out by yourself. Every time you get a Physical Sensation in your Body, which is in any way different to your normal everyday state of Being - and that is hopefully a grounded, calm, relaxed yet alert state - examine it. Ask yourself how the sensation feels like. Where in your Body it is? What texture it has? What colour it is,' Tara paused. 'Come to think of it, let me give you a few examples of specific feelings. That'll also give you the beginnings of a Physical-Sensation-Vocabulary.'

'That'll be a great 'hang-man' puzzle - 'Physical-Sensation-Vocabulary', wow, nobody would ever guess that,' Lee grinned, remembering one of his favourite childhood games.

'Yeah, I know, words can sometimes get a bit silly when you're making them up as you go a long,' she winked at Lee. 'So, a Physical Sensation can come in many different forms and in many different intensities. It might come as hyperventilating, breathing fast, restricted breathing, suffocating, a tightness in your chest, an inability to speak or move, excess energy, anger, typhoon like energy, a light tingling, a buzzing, vibrating, shaking, near explosion feeling, a tightness, a pulling, a feeling of being squashed or in a vice, feeling as if you're going to die, your whole Body churning and vibrating, bursting into tears, it can even just be a sneaky disposition, a slight out of sorts, a minute shift from your normal balanced, calm state of Being. It can be red or black, or murky, green or damp or wet or bright or hard or edgy, sharp or spongy, anything.'

'Wow, now I know what you mean with getting a Vocabulary. Man, I can so feel each one of those words,' Lee shivered.

'Oh I know, it's really interesting to describe how you feel with words. Sometimes you have this Sensation and the words just fail, there just aren't enough words invented to describe what it feels like. But once again,…'

'Practice makes perfect,' Lee finished Tara's sentence.

'Absolutely. Now, **whatever the Physical Sensations are, look at them, get to know them as the little creatures they are too. Feel them, notice all their little nuances, notice how they are moving around your Body or how they are stuck in one location. Are there any patterns? Are the Sensations always the same? Always different? Always in the same place? The same colour? Also play with actively changing the Intensity. Really feeeeeel it to intensify it, or take your attention off it to reduce it, just as you did earlier.'**

'It's great to hear you talk about it now. I had never looked at the colour of it. There's so much more to explore than what I came up with,' Lee said excitedly.

'And there's more. **Once you know the kind of Physical Sensations you get, you can start to associate them with particular triggers.** They can be situations, people, Thoughts and so on. Once you get the connections down, just the tiniest Physical Sensation can tell you a whole bunch about your entire Emotional state.'

'Oh, good point. Cross reference,' Lee's mathematical brain offered.

'Yep. Also remember, no matter how *intense* the Sensation is, you can *always* actively relax it. If the Sensation hits you really hard or seems to just take over, it might be tricky at first to concentrate on analysing it. If that happens, be sure to be gentle with yourself. **You don't want to fight. Instead welcome the feeling in, knowing that it can't harm you.** Feel the softness within the tightness, feel the roundness, and whenever you get distracted again, *gently* redirect your Mind back onto your Body, on feeling it and relaxing it. When your Mind has slowed down enough, then you can examine the Sensation in more detail.'

'That's a good idea. If it's too intense, tone it down a bit first.'

'Right. If you can though, try to play with observing and analysing the Sensation in it's original intensity. As always, that might require a bit of practice though, as the Sensation will always try to distract you and disturb your focus, but try it anyway, it's fun to look at all sides of everything.'

'I think that's a good idea,' Lee nodded. 'If we aim for knowing our Emotions inside and out, all intensities and all, there'll be no surprises.'

'Exactly. As you said, better the devil you know.'

'Yeah, or the little cuddly blue-eyed creature,' Lee opened his beautiful brown eyes and tried to look all cute.

'Yep or that,' Tara leant forward and stroked Lee under his chin like a cat. Lee flashed her a wide smile, his eyes sparkling, Tara only just managed to stay on the ball. 'So, **this was all about slowing down your Mind by concentrating on your Body, which establishes the initial Mental Clarity that is required to begin to *play* with your Emotional Thoughts.** This sequence is by no means set in stone, and you can obviously always decide if you want to change things round, but I find this way the most effective.'

'Right on, let's play!'

Untangle Yourself From Your Emotion - You Are Not The Emotion! - See Them For What They Are

'**A**s I've already mentioned, people see Emotions to be this intense third entity that grabs them and takes over. Therefore, for a start, we need to *untangle* ourselves from our **Emotions**. We have to learn to see them for what they really are, that they **are Thoughts and Physical Sensations that you are *having*! They are not *you*!** That might seem tricky, but it really isn't. This will be straight-forward for you as you've already done most of it.'

'Yeah, I know, it'll still be great to hear your take on it too.'

'Sure. Well, the first thing to do is to catch yourself out when Emotional Thoughts hit you.'

'Of course otherwise, how are you going to observe them?' Lee added cheekily.

'Exactly. Now, whenever we catch ourselves out to have an Emotion, we begin to play with it. **The point is to see it for what it is, *without* any Mental Associations or judgements. We don't hide from it, we don't brush it under the carpet, we don't battle with it, but we look it straight in the eyes, face it head on and we learn to see it for what it is. It's a Thought and a Sensation, it's *NOT* You! It's *Thoughts*, which are making you into a person that you don't want to be and Physical *Sensations* that you don't want or need. Neither are getting you anywhere and neither are changing the situation. They are Emotions that keep you from being Now. Once we understand *that*, once we can feel that to be true from the bottom of our Being, *then, and only then*, do we Let Go of it.**'

'And after that,' Lee said, 'if the same Emotion comes up again, all we need to do is remember that we've already decided to Let Go of it once before, so this time, we can Let Go of it straight away. There's no need to go through the whole Thought process again.'

'Exactly.'

'So if you do it once properly, you don't need to do it again,' Lee said happily.

'That's it. After that it's just Catch out, Let Go. Well, actually, you'll be making your way through the four stages we've discussed earlier.'

'Fabulous.'

'Oh yes! From my own experience, **to get to the point, where you recognise that it's perfectly fine to Let Go of an Emotion, might take a little more in depth understanding of** *how* **to get yourself there. Wanna hear some more?'**

'Of course.'

'**The question is, how do we get to see an Emotion for what it really is? To do that, you have to untangle yourself from it and gain objectivity. You have to** *catch* **yourself out and** *acknowledge* **to yourself that you're having an Emotion. Then you begin to** *analyse* **and** *contemplate* **it. You have to try to understand what the Emotion is all about, where it comes from, why it is there, what it's trying to tell you. With practice you'll be able to get to know your Emotions just as well as your Mind.'**

'Ok?' Lee said hesitantly.

'To Analyse and Contemplate and get to know your Emotions and all the little creatures up there, you can use exactly the same Mind exercises which we talked about yesterday. **You can** *observe* **Emotions, retrace them, talk out loud what you feel and so on.** You can take an **Inventory** of your Emotional warehouse, the Thoughts and the Physical Sensations alike, you can actively **spring clean** and *clear out anything existing and unnecessary*. You can actively put yourself into situations that aggravate you and come up with blueprints of how to react, emote and think.'

'Kind of like your friend did with his impatience,' Lee filled in.

'Just like that. You can either practice in real life situations or in your head, just as you please. **Once you are truly aware of the content of your Emotional Warehouse including Emotional Thoughts and Physical Sensations, any new ones will stand out a mile, just as we discussed earlier with all other kinds of Thoughts.** With practice, you can catch out a new Emotion, **one you've actively created, or one that came up on it's own accord,** the second it rolls into the warehouse, the second it occurs. *That* second is the exact moment, you *first* perceive it. **That's the core of the Creating Thought or the very initial Sensation, that's the** *cause* **of all the following associated Feelings and Thoughts.** Again, check, what the difference is between that initial one and all the follow-up ones, they will be different.

Now, **when you can catch yourself out at the core, you have the choice. The choice to divert your Mind and think of something else, to Be Now, or to learn. If you choose to learn, you'll be able to** understand what's going on in your Body and in your Mind, you'll **explore and play** and be amazed. You can **ride the wave of Thoughts, deliberately feed the Associations and observe them as they unfold. Watch and learn. Analyse, contemplate, just as we've discussed before.**

You can also learn to catch yourself out the very second an Emotional Physical Sensation occurs. When you do that, you have the same choices. You can divert, which means you can create a new Sensation instead, you can relax it and the Sensation will disperse by being Now, or you can *feel* it, **right there and then, right at the core, without** any **judgements** or Thought Associations or you can let it ride it's cause and observe it.'

'Wow. And all we need to do is keep our Mind clear and focused,' Lee said scratching his chin. 'To keep our Objective Mental Clarity rather than loosing ourselves in the distractions.'

'Yep,' Tara said cheerfully. 'Of course that takes practice. But believe you me, not matter how good you are at it when you start out, you'll come out laughing every time, just like you've done earlier.'

'I know, that was so funny,' Lee looked up into the sky and shook his head so hard his curls flew around his head. Two strong hands came up to bring them back in order.

'All in all,' Tara said, '**the closer to the origin or the core you manage to catch yourself out, the less time the Emotion will have to fully manifest itself. The longer you let it ride, the more you'll have to observe, and play with. It's a fine balance. The more present you are, the more Now, the emptier your Warehouse. The closer to Nowness you can stay, the less intense your Emotions will be, until they no longer occur.**'

'Where are you at with all of this, Tara?' Lee asked.

'Me? I hardly engage in the rollercoaster anymore. My choice not to get involved anymore has become pretty much automatic by now. Most of the stuff that used to upset me is gone. In fact, the more Now I am, the less any crazy Emotions come up anymore in the first place. Any new stuff that does come up, gets looked at, evaluated and Let Go of in milliseconds. I just look at it and laugh, or I don't even notice it to be anything that should even be noted anymore.'

'Cool. Give me a minute, it's notebook time,' Lee said and already flicking through the pages.

<u>See an Emotion for what it really is, Understand, Let Go:</u>

* Untangle yourself from your Emotions and gain objectivity.
* Catch yourself out and acknowledge to yourself that you're having an Emotion.
* Analyse and contemplate it.
* Understand what the Emotion is all about.
* Once you understood that, you can decide if you still need the Emotion.
* If not, Let Go. Relax Body and Mind. Be Now.
* If the Emotion comes back, remember that you don't need it, Let Go again and Be Now.
* Continue through the four stages, till the Emotion doesn't return.

<u>The Emotional Warehouse:</u>
* Inventory. See what's there.
* Get to know each Emotional box! *Analyse* and *contemplate* it. Understand what the Emotion is all about. Feel it, get to know it. Find out where it comes from, why it is there, what it's trying to tell you.
* Spring clean.
* Clean out anything unnecessary. Let Go.
* Now with a clean warehouse, any new Emotional boxes will stand out.
* Catch out as soon as new ones arrive.
* Let Go straight away.
* Make Blueprint for future situations.

Never Ignore the Little Creatures

'**A**ctually, I've just remembered something,' Tara said. 'There's something that's ever so important to keep in Mind if you decide to Let Go of an Emotion.'

'Uoh, you've got me on tender-hooks here, come out with it,' Lee laughed at Tara's ominous announcement.

'**We *never* ignore it**,' Tara said with emphasis. '**If you ignore something, it will never truly go away, but it will always come back one day and nip you in the butt.**'

'Makes perfect sense. We talked about that with regards to the pressure cooker too. **Ignoring it would just make the pot explode one day, but it won't make the steam go away.**'

'Exactly.'

'Also,' Lee grinned, 'I imagine that the blue eyed little creatures wouldn't like being ignored. If I'd have a job to do, the job of causing havoc, and I'm being ignored, I'd just find more and more ingenious ways of sneaking into your defences to turn things upside down,' Lee smiled even broader, he liked his little creatures. 'Actually, you said it's about establishing a mutual respect and in the end even a friendship with them, right? **You said it's about creating an environment, where they simply don't feel the *need* to cause havoc anymore, rather than just ignoring them.**'

'Exactly. So what you do is this: you notice that something is going on when you see the little creatures come down the road with their lunch boxes, ready for work. You begin to create a *friendship* by *acknowledging* their presence, you make them feel *liked* by *understanding* them, you *feel* them, by putting yourself into their shoes, you *accept* the situation that caused the little creatures to get upset in the first place.'

'Like the chap in the wheel chair. He needed to accept that this was the new way he was going to move around. Full stop. Or the relationship break up, that's the way it is now. Accept.'

'Right. Once you accepted the thing the little creatures tried to make you upset about and once you've Let Go of it, they won't have a job anymore, right?'

'Sure, but they won't mind, because they didn't really like that job anyway,' Lee giggled.

'Spot on. So now, that they're retired, you create a nice *relaxed* environment where they'll just hang out and chill and be happy forever after.'

'Ahh,' Lee said endeared. 'They're just hanging with you, having tea and the whole affair simply doesn't exist anymore. You got rid of the pot. And everybody is happy.'

'Right.'

'So, let me get this down. Before we ever Let Go of an Emotion, we always: Catch out, acknowledge, contemplate, understand, feel, accept, Let Go and *move on*,' Lee smiled a content smile. 'And then, as we said before, the second time the same Emotion comes up, we can just Let Go of it straight away, because we remember our previous decision making process. Its not ignoring, it's just carrying out a previous decision one more time. Oh, that's so funny,' an amusing picture flickered past Lee's Mind's eye, 'an Emotion coming back for more, would be like a big fat work-bell ringing. The little creatures jump of the couch, ready to work, simply because that's what they're used to, that's what they've been trained to do since they were little, well, even littler,' he grinned so hard by now, his cheeks hurt. 'All you'd need to do then, is to gently walk up to them, put your hand softly on their little shoulders, tell them to relax, remind them that they don't need to work anymore, fluff up the pillows on the sofa and watch them make themselves comfortable again. - Fabulous. Creature psychology, what can I say?' Lee finished as he already began another list.

Playing with Emotions:
- Never ignore!
- Catch out, acknowledge, contemplate, understand, feel, accept, Let Go, move on.
- You catch yourself out having an Emotion and play with it.
- Don't hide from them.
- Don't brush them under the carpet.
- Look them straight in the eye, face them head on but don't battle with them.
- See them for what they are, *without* any Mental Associations or judgements.
- They are Thoughts and Sensations, they are *NOT* You!
- They are Thoughts, which are making you into a person that you don't want to be, and they are Physical Sensations that you don't want or need.
- They are Sensations you're *having*, they are *NOT* You!
- They are Emotions that keep you from being Now.
- Once we understand that, once we know that an Emotion is useless, silly and doesn't do us any good, *then* we Let Go of it.
- Then every time it comes up again, we can just Let Go, as we've already decided to Let Go.

Tara glanced over the last few lists Lee had made, 'Well, you've had a great start getting to know your little creatures. You've looked at your Emotions, you picked your Thoughts apart and you realised that they were utterly silly, unjustified and useless, right?'

'Yeah, some of them even contradicted what I really thought. So weird.'

'I know, that's bizarre when that happens. Now, you've also figured out than you need to relax your Body and the effects it had on your Emotions, and you noticed that that's how it works with *all* Emotions, no matter how intense.

Let's go a little further though. **The more complicated or deep rooted an Emotion is, the more imperative it is to understand the *reason* for the Emotion occurring in the first place, because that would tell you what the issues are that you need to work on for the Emotions not to reoccur.** You see, sometimes stuff needs to get thoroughly sorted with the little creatures before they'll give up their job.'

'Ok?' Lee said tentatively, waiting for Tara to explain herself.

Tara got the hint in a flash, 'To show you what I mean, and to show you how this can work in all extremes, let me go through a few examples of some more intense Emotional situations.'

17 Emotions Try To Tell Us Something

'If you have an Emotion that really won't go away and which just won't let you be Now, try and understand what it's trying to tell you, you might find out that you might not have acted on it's message,' Tara began.

'What message?'

'Did you know that the ancient purpose for an Emotion was to tell us something?'

'I'm not sure, tell me more?' Lee was intrigued.

'The oldest part of our brain, is the reptilian brain. It's called that, because we share it in common with certain reptiles. This part of the brain has a singular focus: Survival. It's job is to kick into action by stimulating the Limbic System to abruptly move a creature to flee, fight, feed or procreate. The reptilian brain doesn't think in abstract terms and it doesn't feel complex Emotions, it just automatically reacts appropriately to a situation. As the human brain evolved, it began to fine tune Emotions to a great extent, and over time, Emotions became separated from the basic need to survive, and developed into a more abstracted response to maintain our way of perceiving the world and our desire to maintain our Ego.'

'Hang on, that's an interesting way of putting it: our desire to maintain our Ego. **That would mean that if the world does not correspond to the way we want it to be, we react with an Emotion!**' Lee deducted.

'That's exactly what we do! **The tiny pangs of injustice or jealousy, sadness, loneliness or mistrust, even of happiness and joy, they are all fine nuances of the most basic, most fundamental Emotions: fear or comfort and safety - or better, the way we want the world to be - or not.** So, if we look at the basic function of an Emotion,' Tara continued, 'we'll find that **Emotions try to tell us something. They are the messengers telling us to quickly respond to something and to initiate immediate change in one way or another.**'

'It's like a frog that perceives an immediate danger. There is a threat, the frog feels fear, it jumps away, end of story,' Lee said.

Tara nodded and added, 'Right. **Message understood and acted upon. Emotions are now *superfluous* and they stop. The**

frog goes back into resting position and chills. No more fear! A frog would do all of this automatically.'

'When acted upon, Emotions are *superfluous,*' Lee repeated thoughtfully.

'That's how it is. Unless we're human,' Tara shrugged her shoulders, 'Us humans? We make it all *much* more complicated that that. **When we feel fear, instead of using our deepest part of the brain to help us act on it appropriately within a split second, we begin to think. We begin to evaluate, to weigh up, to judge and to *create* Behavioural and Mental responses instead. We paint all sorts of future scenarios, mixed in with other experiences and memories from the past and like that, we pretty quickly further and further remove ourselves from the basic message**.'

'Yeah, the message of feeling fear is: "run, leave the situation", not: "live with worry, terror and anxiety." Pain is a basic message too: "don't do it again, or stop it,"' Lee said. 'The message is *not*: "live your life in fear of it or distrust everybody from now on".'

'Exactly. But our brain has become so complicated, and our processing of these simple ancient messages so overkill, that we can't see the wood for the trees anymore. **Instead of Letting Go of the Emotion once it has done it's job, just like the frog would do? We keep it**.'

'So, **one of the most important things to understand is that Emotions *don't have* to be kept**, right? Gosh, that's crazy. All these feelings, all these problems, and we don't have to have them! That's nuts,' Lee shook his head. 'As soon as the message has been received, it *can* be Let Go of,' Lee repeated once more. 'There is absolutely no reason or need to hold on to it.'

'No reason at all, just like for the frog. **Emotions that are just to upkeep our Ego, to judge and tell us that things aren't going the way we *want* them too, most of those Emotions we can Let Go of like that**,' Tara snapped her fingers, 'just like any other silly puppy. We play with the judging Thoughts, just like we did before and whoops, they're gone. **Now, any Emotion that persists, that seems to be about more than just Ego, anything that seems to be something bigger, anything that *really* keeps you from being Now, contemplate it.** See if there's a message that you haven't *heard* yet,' Tara said. 'Do you want to hear a bit more about what we can learn from Emotions and *how* to receive the messages.'

'Absolutely,' Lee nodded vigorously.

We Can Learn From Everything

'We can learn from Everything. *Every* Emotion, Thought, Sensation, Behaviour, Situation, everything. Always,' Tara began. 'No matter how bad our lives get, no matter how tough, we can learn from *everything* in our world,' Tara said. '**People always ask: "Why did my husband die and leave me alone?"**, or: "Why is my sister withering away from cancer?" But you know what? If you really look at those questions? *You're* not actually asking why that happened to *them*, but why it's happening to *you!*'

'Oh, clever,' Lee raised his eyebrows.

'I know. But besides that, **it's the wrong question to ask in the first place. It's useless and does not further our happiness. The question we should be asking is: "what can I learn from it for myself?"**' Tara sat straighter. 'Normally, when I say this, people get all defensive and say: "But what am I supposed to learn from my husband's death or from my sister's illness?" My answer would be that nobody can tell you what you're supposed to learn. Don't ask, but observe. Be Now. See what happens in your head and in your heart. Notice your Thoughts, your reactions, your Emotions, your Behaviour. You know, it might not always be obvious right away what the lesson is, sometimes it might take a while before the learning curve becomes obvious,' she shrugged her shoulders. '***While* it's happening we might regard it as a painful experience or as bad, but in *retrospect* we often realise that we've learned a valuable lessons, that we've had to experience the pain or the loss to learn or to grow, or maybe even to give us a reason to simply stop and reflect,' Tara paused. 'No matter what happens, we can always learn.'**

'I agree,' Lee said. 'We **often learn the most from the hard times in our lives. When we're at the point where we need to decide weather to go under or swim. That's when we get the most strength and power to survive**, and if we do it right, we grow through it. You know what a friend of mine told me once?' Lee looked at Tara more intently, 'He said that if you think about it, all the situations we've encountered, all the experiences we've had in our life, made us into the people we are now. All our mistakes, all the traumas, everything that went wrong in our life, is part of us. It made us who we are now and put us where we are right now,' Lee giggled. 'He said to me with a big smile on his that everything that *didn't* go right in his life, got him to where he is now. Guess where we were when he told me the story?'

'Don't know, where?'

'Under a palm tree on a beautiful beach. So I guess, he did all right in the end, ey?'

'That's a fabulous story!' Tara laughed. 'Thanks! And it's so true too. New doors that open all the time,' Tara looked up into the sky and pointed to all the doors. 'One thing not happening just makes way for something better to come, or to prepare us for something different or new.'

'You know what?' Lee shook his head at Tara's finger in the sky, 'Often we don't see the new door that has opened right in front of our nose, because we're far too busy looking at the closed one, waiting for *that* one to open again. So silly,' Lee shook his head once more.

'Exactly. **That's why its so important not to wallow in the bad stuff, in negative Thoughts and Emotions, but to keep a look out for new opportunities that come our way.**'

'Yeah, my mum always used to say that if you think you can't go on, there's always a little light that magically appears when you least expect it. There is always a light at the end of the tunnel. Even if it might seem very far away, it is there!'

'And additionally, **even if the shit really hits the fan, no matter how un-enjoyable the situation is, it will not last forever,**' Tara said. '*Accept* that shit happens. People get ill, people die, people loose businesses and property, people get mugged, hit etc. But life goes on. It's the cause of the world as it *is*. Use your strength to get through it and to help others to get through it,' Tara said.

'There's a lovely quote I read in a book once. It was about a very poor African family that even though they really didn't have anything, not even enough food, they were always happy. When asked why, they shared their motto. It said: *'That's your lot, now cope with it and be jolly!'* he recited. 'Now *that's* strength!

'Oh man, I absolutely love that!' Tara clapped her hands. 'That's brilliant. **That's it. I need to remember that.**'

While Tara repeated the quote a few times to herself to remember it, Lee made a quick note of a few things, that he didn't want to forget.

<u>We can learn from everything:</u>
- There's no point to despair in tough situation and get miserable because of it.
- It won't change the situation or make it less difficult.
- Instead of becoming angry or sad or whatever, become curious about what the lesson could be, what you could learn from it.
- Instead of judging it, just see it for what it is. A situation. Nothing more and nothing less.
- Deal with it, without wallowing in it, without 'keeping' it!
- Think only as much as necessary, then the torch goes back in the bag. Avoid mental loops, Dots and Squiggles and breathe calmly instead.
- No matter how un-enjoyable a situation is, it will not last forever.

- Deal with it - act consciously, rather than re-act automatically.
- There is always a light at the end of the tunnel, even if it might seem far away.
- That's your lot, now cope with it and be jolly!

Does Everything Happen For A Reason?

'You know, if we can learn from everything in our lives, does that mean that everything happens for a reason?' Lee asked.

'Well, **I trust that everything happens for us to** *learn* **something. Every event, if we judge it as good or bad, can help us to grow. Even if we don't like it, we can at least learn from it**.'

'Yeah, with that, I agree. So far,' Lee said.

'With regards to: "does everything happen for a reason?" Who knows? Nobody will ever be able to prove it, just as nobody will ever be able to prove conclusively that there is a God. But you know, I don't really care if it's true or not, because if you can just make yourself believe that it *is* true? **That everything really** *does* **happens for a reason?** That'll make your life so much easier, so much more fun, so much more enjoyable.'

'How so?' Lee was captivated.

'**Well, if you believe that, then every time the shit hits the fan, instead of being upset about it, instead of being sad or pissed off or angry, you'll be curious as to what's going to happen next, what's around the corner**.'

'Oh man, that's brilliant. Instead of looking at the closed door, you *actively* look for the *new* one to open.'

'Exactly. **So, even if you don't believe it, if you can** *make* **yourself believe it, it'll change your life**.'

'Tara, you're mad. You make yourself believe stuff. You're in your own little world, but it works for you,' Lee laughed.

'Oh yes, big time. And it works for many other people too. This simple make-belief can do wonders for your life, I can promise you that. Make-belief or not, I personally got so much evidence for myself that I trust now, that everything in fact *does* happen for a reason. **But if you can't make yourself believe that, ask a different question.** Don't ask if something **happened for a reason, but ask yourself what you can learn from it**,' Tara said.

'That's a good idea. That's a fair alternative,' Lee nodded, while his brain was already assembling evidence from his past experiences that seemed to confirm Tara's theory.

Maybe Yes, Maybe Not

'**D**o you want an example that shows that we *can* learn from *everything*, no matter what?' Tara asked. 'And some examples that show that some things might *really* have happened for a reason?'

'Absolutely. Hey, story time!' Lee said happily, loving the new headspace he was in. He felt clear, aware and confident.

Tara stretched herself for a second, 'The story begins with a friend of mine arriving in London intending to stay at her cousin's house. She'd been unable to get hold of him by phone, but hoped that he'd be there when she arrived, at the time which they'd arranged a couple of weeks earlier. A lot of things went wrong with my friend's train connections and she got delayed by several hours. She worried a lot and got terribly angry because she didn't want to arrive late. Needless to say that she did major Dots and Squiggles, up here,' Tara pointed at her head. 'All the poor-little-old-me stuff, the why-does-this-happen-to-me, and the I-hate-this Thoughts and Emotions were bouncing around unhappily in her brain. She diligently fed all her frustrated Emotions puppies and spent two hours angry and pissed off in the train station. When she finally arrived at her cousin's house, it turned out that he had been away for the weekend and had only just returned – literally minutes earlier. If my friend would not have been delayed, she would have stood homeless in front of a closed door, in a strange city, not knowing what to do, not knowing if he would come back or not.'

'Probably going bonkers about where on earth to stay for the night,' Lee said.

'Exactly. Now, if she would have believed that everything happens for a reason, she would have become curious on the train instead of pissed off. If she would have been in Nowness instead of doing Dots and Squiggles, she would not have spoiled her time with useless anger and worry that didn't change anything anyway, but she might have actually enjoyed the time she had to herself in the train station. She could have read or had some food, or gone for a walk, or people watched, or written a letter or maybe just observed or analysed her Thoughts,' Lee nodded. 'But, did it really happen for a reason? Who knows?' Tara said simply and continued without pause. 'If she would have contemplated the ancient message of her upset Emotion, she would have probably noticed that it was all Ego stuff, as there was no actual threat to her. It was just that she had to wait when she didn't want to. As simple as that. All the other stuff, she made up.'

'Ouch,' Lee said.

'I know, it can be pretty hard hitting. But you know what the funny thing was? With all her anger and upset, she didn't notice how *lucky* she had been until I pointed it out to her.'

'Oh, she didn't connect the delay with her luck?' Lee said. 'Oh wow,' Lee said, '*that's* why it's so important to analyse past Co-incidences, to make the connections!'

'Master student!' Tara nodded and grinned, 'More stories?'

'Absolutely,' Lee rubbed his hands.

'Another friend of mine got stung by a scorpion during her travels. She was in tremendous pain. She kept asking me, why this had happened, this was not perfect, this was not how it was supposed to be, this was bloody horrible, why is this happening to *her*? I just said, that she might not see the reason now, but that she surely would later.'

'And, did she?'

'Of course. It turned out that to control the pain she finally understood the concept of Mindfulness.'

'Really? How?'

'She dealt with the pain by concentrating one hundred percent on something different.'

'What?'

'It was quite funny really. She painted Henna Tattoos. All evening long. Until the pain had gone. In the end she had them all over her legs and arms. The comical thing was that she was right handed and that she'd been bitten on her *right* hand!'

'Oh no, she did Henna Tattoos with her *left* hand? All over her Body?'

'Yep,' Tara laughed remembering some of the rather distorted drawings. 'I tell you, *that* took some serious concentration. It turned out that this was the only way she could manage to take her Mind of the pain and thus not have it affect her too much. To this day, she still uses the term painting-henna-tattoos, when she talks about being Mindful.'

'That's so cool,' Lee grinned.

'Right. So did it happen for a reason? Who knows, but she learned something important. More?'

'Sure.'

'Another friend seriously hurt her foot and was unable to move for two weeks. She was upset, because she couldn't do all of the things that she had planned. At the end of the two weeks she finally realised that she had actually really needed the rest because she had put herself under far too much pressure at work. In retrospect, the damaged food had made her do something that was really good for her. Was it supposed to happen? No idea, but she saw a positive side in retrospect. One last story?'

'Ok, one last one,' Lee laughed.

'Cool. A guy I know, got delayed several hours in mad traffic, hating it, driving himself nuts with anger. Just to end up at the same place he started out. By that stage, his Mind had reached the near-flippancy-level on the anger scale, his Body was heaving, his face flushed, his heart threatened an attack. What happened in the end? Back where he started off and ended up again, he met a bunch of people he hooked up partying with for an entire weekend, enjoying himself like he hadn't done in ages. And boy he'd needed it.'

'And he would've never met those people without the traffic problems,' Lee grinned. 'I guess he could have saved himself a lot of mental trouble, had he believed that "everything happens for a reason, if only to learn". If he had only known how to stay calm, not freak out, and *play* with the situation instead. He could just have been curious about what was going to happen because he was so delayed. That's an interesting Mental switch you know? If you know how to flick it that is.'

'Exactly. And sure, maybe he might not have found out until a month later why he had to be delayed, but the reasons are usually pretty obvious if you actively wait and look for them.' Tara emphasised.

'Actively wait? Isn't that a bit of an Oxymoron?' Lee asked.

'Well, kind of. What I meant was that the point is to stay open to the new and not to close off, and also to try not to over analyse to find a reason, as it will become obvious eventually, sometimes even when you least expect it. There's a fine line.'

'Yeah, I can see that. Your friend in your first example missed the significance of her train delay, a Co-incidence that could have vastly amused her, *and* she missed a significant opportunity for her to learn something important. If she would have been open to learn from *everything*, rather than just be angry, she could have at least learned about her Emotions and her reactions. Everything else she could have learned beyond that, would have been a bonus,' Lee said.

'Yes sir. You're certainly getting the hang of this!' Tara said happy about Lee's quick understanding of the fine points.

'Actually, I think I have some examples of my own,' Lee remembered, 'When I didn't get a job I really wanted, I was terribly pissed off, but in the end I got a different job. The position was a little unexpected and kind of weird at the beginning, but I turned out to learn a lot from it. To my surprise, it transpired to be absolutely perfect for me - once I allowed it to teach me. Wow,' he said surprised. 'I didn't know that I was already thinking this way.'

'Nice ey? **A lot of this stuff just points out the obvious that you already know**.'

'Yeah. Oh,' a Thought jumped up in Lee's Mind, '**What if somebody gets seriously ill? With a fatal disease or something?** Is that's supposed to happen too? What's the message in that? What are they supposed to learn?'

'Good question,' Tara laid her index finger on her lips and paused, 'but remember**, the question is not *if* it was *supposed* to happen or not. *That* question is useless. That questions will just drive you needlessly nuts. You will never get an answer to the *if*. Either you trust that everything happens for a reason or you don't.** If you do trust, then just trust and instead of asking that question, look at the open doors, rather than fixating on the closed ones, be curious, look out and see the *reasons* in everything that follows. ***Get your confirmation because you're looking for it***. If you can prove it or not doesn't matter, if others believe it or not, doesn't matter either. If it works for you, what more do you want?'

'That's so funny. That would actually work,' Lee said gobsmacked, but sold.

'Oh yes, absolutely. **And if you don't believe it? If you don't trust? Well, the point is that the event *has* happened, so learn from it whatever you can.** All in all, I don't know what somebody with a terminal illness is supposed to learn. Everybody needs to figure that out for themselves on each individual basis. But what I can tell you is: learn from it what you can! Observe your Thoughts, your Emotions and your Behaviour. And remember that you have choices. **You can either let anything that happens to you which you don't like be *part* of your life, or you can let it *be your* life. It *is your* choice. Either you feed the puppy and wallow in self-pity, or you sort out your head.** You can either forget that you are actually still alive and be miserable from the day of diagnosis to the end of your life, or you can actively play to pull yourself out of it. You can realise that you are still alive and that you *can* have fun and enjoy life, even if it might be in a *different* way than you were used to before, but none the less, you still *can*.'

'Yeah, I can see that,' Lee nodded slowly. 'There's simply no point in wallowing in the past, in longing for your legs to grow back, or your sight to return, or your youth or whatever. There's no point. Finished. You're torturing yourself and it still won't change the situation.'

Tara agreed, but then said more gently, '**Of course some situations can be heartbreaking, Mind-numbing, horrendously sad and rip somebody's insides out and twist them. Circumstances can come with great uncertainty and can understandably cause a great deal of worry and pain, but in the**

end it's all the same. No matter how harsh it might sound, **what's the point driving yourself crazy with worry? It won't change anything either**!'

'Worry which will *not* prevent the event you're worrying about,' Lee added.

'Precisely. **What's the point wallowing in a past that is no more?** Speculating, going nuts with what-if Thoughts and why me-s about a future which is not yet to be? **There's no point to a what-if, if it's clearly *not*! There is no point to a why-me, if it *already is* you.** So, stop asking and begin to live Now instead. Remind yourself of how beautiful life can be if you let it. **Play with all the things that you *can* do, rather than all the things that you *cannot* do. Shift your focus from wallowing in the negative stuff and begin to enjoy life as it is, in a new and maybe *different* way. Sure, it might take some time to get used to, to change your point of view, but you *can* do it!** By looking for things that you *can* learn, you can develop a fascinating new dimension of looking at the world. And that?' Tara said with emphasis, 'That's what you could learn from a fatal disease!' Tara looked at Lee. 'But of course, **is it going to make the situation go away? Of course not, but understanding this deeply with all your Being, can decrease Emotional Intensity, and can thus assist the person to be Now, and maybe continue living a happy and fulfilled, yet *different* life**.'

'It's what you choose to make of it,' Lee puffed.

'Yep. As always,' Tara said simply. 'Do you want to hear another story?'

'Sure.'

'This is a lovely old tale which shows nicely how our judgement and what we think is good or bad, can be so wrong.'

'Let's have it,' Lee encouraged her.

'It's a story of a man who had a farm. One day a whole bunch of wild horses appeared on his farm, which by the local law, he was allowed to keep. All his neighbours said, how lucky he was. He just said: maybe, maybe not. Then, one of his sons rode one of the horse, fell off and broke his leg. All his neighbours said, how unlucky that was. The farmer said: maybe, maybe not. Then the Army came into town and recruited all the young boys, but they couldn't draft the farmer's son, because his leg was broken. All his neighbours said, how lucky that was. The farmer just said, maybe, maybe not,' Tara finished.

'That's a good story!' Lee raised his eyebrows.

'Maybe, maybe not,' Tara said cheekily. Lee laughed. '**The point is that life happens, and sometimes it might look lucky or** unlucky, but in the end you never know. So, don't get upset, just be curious! If something happens that you don't enjoy, stay in the Now. Stay relaxed. Figure out if you can change the situation, if not, stop thinking about it, stop feeding crazy Emotional puppies. Stay calm and go with the flow. **Stay open and observe, till the lessons, the answers or the reasons come. And when they do come, learn from them,**' she said. **'Is everything supposed to happen?** Who knows, but I can promise you one thing, the more you do your little Co-incidence analysis, the more you'll see some pretty interesting connections!'** Tara winked at Lee.

Look Emotions Straight In the Eye - Understand The Message! *Don't Ignore It*

'Now, back to Emotions,' Tara continued, 'if you want to contemplate an Emotion or if you want to find out if your Emotion has a significant message attached to it, *feel* the Emotion and analyse it.** Ask yourself questions. Find out what the most *basic* Emotion is. Is it anger? Neglect? Abandonment? Sadness? Loss, fear never to find another, feeling betrayed, hurt? What is it? Look at it. Where does it come from? What can you learn from it? Why do you have that Emotion? **Ask yourself, *why* the Emotion actually disturbs you?** *What* makes you feel that way and why? What *triggers* it? What makes it worse or better? **Find out, ask yourself questions!** Is it just one big Emotion or is it lots of little ones? Is it debilitatingly intense or is it just a little niggly one?

Let's say you often experience debilitating fear. Check, is there a serious message? Are you actually in **imminent danger, or are you re-living past fears? Is it reality *right now*, or is it a memory or a figment of your imagination creating this Emotion? Every time you find an answer, ask yourself what happened within you *before* that and what was *before* that? Get to the bottom of it. Play with different scenarios, observe yourself and learn.** If you can't get any answers, have a look if you can move on anyway, try and be Now instead, maybe the answers will reveal themselves later. And, of course,' Tara smiled at Lee, **'Wherever you want to, ask The Guys for guidance and clarity, you know**? Ask Them for help.'
'And what do I do until I'm able to do that?' Lee asked poignantly.
'Until then,' Tara laughed at Lee's attention to detail, 'play with the Emotions and learn by using good old contemplation. Learn what caused

the Emotion, learn from your reactions. Learn about yourself having *reacted* the way you did. Look at the situation *and* yourself.

A relationship breaks up, learn from it! Learn what's good for you and what's not. What you like and what you don't like. A person dies. Learn to live without that person. Remember them, enjoy the memory, but don't torture yourself with sadness or anger or loneliness. Be whole on your own.

You've been terribly hurt, physically or mentally or emotionally. What is the basic message? You know that humans can act in utterly unpredictable ways, evil ways, consciously or unconsciously. Well, they've done that for years and this time you were at the receiving end. *Don't* do it to others. Let Go, move on, live your life. *Actively* find a way. Play with your Emotions, find out what works for you, what you need to be happy again. *Actively* play with finding a *blueprint* for yourself!'

'You know what? It feels as if Emotions are like dreams,' Lee said thoughtfully. 'Some are profound messages, or teachers, others are utterly useless, fiction created by the babbling mind. Some come once, others reoccur, but as with dreams, there is no point to dream the dream over and over. If one reoccurs, it's best to stand back, examine it, understand it and try to learn from it. Once you've done that, most of the time the dream stops.'

'That's a great analogy. **Now, whatever answer you come up with during your contemplation of an Emotion, you can do two things. You can either Let Go straight away, or you act first and then Let Go.** If you've analysed the Associated Thoughts of an Emotion and have realised that they are utterly **silly**, you can **Let Go** of them. As you enter Nowness, the Emotion will disperse.

On the other hand, if you decide that there really *is* an issue, you need to *act* on it. If you cannot act on it, you need to *accept* the situation the way it is. You need to accept that what happened to you is what happened, and that you can't do anything about it. End of story.'

'Which then means that you can Let Go of it again,' Lee said.

'Yep,' Tara smiled at him.

'One of the main problems, why people have sometimes difficulties with Letting Go of an Emotion, is that they **hold or cling onto Emotional responses from *past* experiences and don't *want* to Let Go, be it Consciously or unconsciously,**' Tara pointed out.

'Ah, hang on, I can see what you're trying to get at. **The purpose of an Emotion is to alert us to deal with a situation *right now*! Once the situation is over, the Memory has become superfluous. Once the situation is over, it's just a *memory* of that Emotion. And sometimes, for whatever reason, we're still holding on to it.**

But man, *memories* of an Emotion serve no purpose. The *lessons* we learned from it serve a purpose, but we do not have to feel or relive the actual Emotion itself, to *remember* the lesson,' Lee was surprised by the clarity of his Thoughts.

'Exactly,' Tara nodded excitedly. 'If it's in the past, it's time to move on! Let the past be the past! As you said before, unless you Let Go, how can you move on? But for that, you need to *understand* and *accept* that it *is* past. **It's not about *forgetting* or ignoring, but about *accepting* that it's past, that's important.**

There is a lovely quote from *Gabriel Garcia Marques:*

"Our life is not what happened,
but what we remember. "

Basically Marques says that **the past only exists in our Mind.'**

'Wow. That's pretty deep,' Lee raised his eyebrows.

'Deep and true,' Tara said. 'If we would be *fully Now*, the past wouldn't exist. Would that be ignoring something? No, it just wouldn't be there.'

'Wow, and to spin that Thought further,' Lee's brain kicked a gear up, **'in the Now *everything* is a memory, and memories are Thoughts!** Oh man!' he reminded himself to breathe into his stomach to stay grounded.

'That's it! **No matter how strong our Emotions are, once we've been through all the analysing, at some stage in our life, we have to make a decision. Can we *accept* that they by now they are Emotions about a *past* reaction, or do we want the Thoughts to keep being part of our every day life?'**

'Some people might have a hard time to forget what happened to them though,' Lee interjected.

'Sure, but **it's not about forgetting your loved one that died** or about forgetting the injustice you've experienced, or the pain that has been inflicted upon you, Emotions can still be with you as a memory if you want that, but **it's about changing the your reaction to intense Emotional triggers.** It's about being able to move on, to have a new relationship after your husband died, about being able to love and be loved after horrific torture, about being able to be in a room with someone that really hurt you and be ok. **It's about trusting again, staying open and not closing up, no matter how many times you've been hurt. It's about knowing that you do *not* have to *relive* an Emotion every time you think of it, unless you choose to do so,' Tara emphasized, repeating some of Lee's words.**

'You know, that's what a friend of mine does!' Lee suddenly sat up, 'He *relives* his past! All the time! I never really thought about that. His biggest hang up is that he always wanted to have been loved as a child, to have had a happy childhood. After all these years, he still carries all his childhood resentment around with him and he won't Let Go of the past. **He constantly relives his Emotion of abandonment, insecurity and pain.** *It's who he is, who he has become.* **Those experiences defined his personality,'** Lee said.

'As they would and I hear you. Unfortunately, this is what many people do. If such a person like your friend would want to Be Now, he'd need to understand and accept a few things. Well, he didn't have a happy child hood! Now what? Does he want this to ruin the rest of his life? He needs to decide, gather his strength, find it within himself to battle up the courage to stop holding on to Emotional patterns from twenty years ago! He needs to accept and Let Go. He needs to learn new Behaviour to replace his old reactionary behavioural patterns, he needs to relearn how to react to his old Emotional triggers. **Whatever Behaviour or Emotional reaction mechanisms he was indoctrinated with, he can change!** He can decide to play with who he wants to be, who he could be!'

'Maybe he could even do a "Dice Man" for a day or so,' Lee giggled, **'just to show him that it *is* possible for him to do things differently.'**

'Sure, but be careful, you don't want him to go to the other extreme and get hung up on something new and different. The point is to *balance out* hang-ups, not create new ones,' Tara warned. 'The most important thing for somebody like that, is to understand that it's not about ignoring what happened, but about *consciously deciding* that he wants to *react differently to a certain stimulus.* Instead of cramping up, and doing Dots and Squiggles, every time he thinks of it or finds himself in a trigger situation, he needs to relax his Body and Mind, to stay calm and peaceful. He can still think about what happened, but it won't affect him anymore, it won't throw him off balance anymore! Like that he'll act, rather than automatically re-act.'

'Makes perfect sense to *me,* but you know, I did actually tell him something like that, and he responded: "are you telling me I'm not allowed to feel the way I do?" What would you answer to that?' Lee asked.

'I'd say that it's not about stopping to feel what you're feeling, or not being *allowed* to feel, but that it's about sorting necessary feelings from unnecessary ones, sorting the ones useful for your life from the ones that hinder you. It's not about fighting Emotions, because that would be feeding them with Thoughts of anger. It's not a fight, it's not *ignoring* or rejecting, all of that could cause you pain, instead, it is *Awareness.* Awareness that casts light on an Emotional shadow and through that, the shadow disappears.

Like that you can see the Emotions clearly, in full light. It's not this huge, great, big and scary thing anymore, but a Thought and a Physical Feeling that can be played with and learned from. It's about knowing that you *can choose* what you want *in* your life and what you want *out* of your life,' Tara paused for a second and looked up to the sky. 'Marques said: "*Our life is not what happened, but what we remember*". I add to that, that we can choose *what* we remember and what we want to be part of us!

Ask yourself a few questions. Do you want to burst into tears every time you think a certain Thought? Do you want to scream or rage or get depressed? If not, you need to do something about it. You need to make an active commitment that you do not want an Emotion to rule your life or keep you from being Now. And take notice that *every* Emotion keeps you from Being Now - little background ones and big persistent ones. You have to face them, look them straight into the eye and call them out. Sure, such a commitment can be scary at first, but it's no more scary, than having super scary Emotions take over your life - it's just that you're more used to that. Now at least you have the tools to take control!' Tara drew a long breath.

'Gosh, that's so true,' Lee scratched his chin. 'Then again, that's strange. We're more scared of Letting Go than of *experiencing* terror and fear and anger and pain. Why's that?'

'Well, some Emotions that are linked to past events can harbour *trapped memory of Intense Pain or fear*. **To uncover this pain or fear and to *actively* face them, is new, unknown territory and people are often more afraid of the unknown, than of what they know, even if what they already know is horrible.** I find that odd, but that's how most people reason. I think people just need to understand that they can play with all of this! Of course, it can be full-on at first, but you just need to head-butt your way through the first few times, until you notice that once you manage to stay present, it can be vast amounts of fun to put your attention on your Emotions and to begin to finally understand them. Most people laugh at themselves when they begin to analyse what's going on inside of them. Many had no idea about the ridiculous Feelings they'd been harbouring forever and ever, how stupid they were and how amazing it felt to be freed of them.'

'I happily second that. Accept, Let Go. It's an *active* process,' Lee said.

'Spot on! When you can say to yourself: "I'm ready to Let Go of this once and for all *right now*", then you're ready to accept. Watch out, for one of those possible tiny, little pangs inside of you though that says: "Actually, I'm not ready". That can happen, even if your Conscious Mind says you are ready. **For any of this to work, there really can't be any Doubt. You have to be with it one hundred percent. You have to be ready to jump! But once you do, you'll get your rewards quickly.'**

'**Right. Unless you jump, you won't know that you can** *fly*,' Lee said thoughtfully.

'Exactly**! People call the getting-over-it stage the Letting-Go-of or the coming-to-terms-with an Emotion. I would simply call it** *seeing-clearly*, **deciding to Let Go and** *actually doing it!*

It's being able to see and consciously distinguish three elements. First the trigger event itself, the way it really is, without your judgements and associations; second the *core basic* ancient Emotional Reaction you're having, be it fear, anger and so on; and then third, the way you developed, associated and bred this basic Emotion into a more complex Emotional pattern and response.'

'Like this we can distinguish the trigger and the initial core Emotional response from the new version which we created ourselves. Cool stuff,' Lee summarised.

'And once you see what's made up? What's created and what's not what it 'is'?' Tara grinned at her complicated sentence.

'You can safely Let it Go,' Lee said, having understood anyway.

'Exactly. And to hone it in just one more time, all of this is an *activity*. Accepting that you fed a puppy, the Letting Go of the little bugger, and the moving on,' Tara emphasised.

'Yeah, I get it. We were *actively* involved in *feeding* our Emotions and now we're getting *actively* involved in *playing* with them.'

'Precisely. It's about *actively*, *deliberately* and Consciously facing your Emotions, it's *never* about ignoring or just dismissing them. It's *never* about just stopping to think about them, *escaping* into Nowness or about just diverting your Mind away from them, but it's about getting to *know* your Emotions, contemplate them, *see* them. Learn how you tick, react, behave, feed them, associate and what triggers them off. Then with this new clarity you can see your Emotions for what they truly are, rather than what you made them into. With this new clarity you can see *yourself* for what *you* truly are, rather than what you *made yourself* into.'

'That's the moment when you can laugh about it,' Lee grinned, remembering his own Kate-scenario earlier. 'That's when you see how utterly ridiculous your Mind is. If you dig deep enough with your Emotions, you recognise the stupidity, the sheer and utter silliness and often the total uselessness of the Physical Sensations and Associated Thoughts. The stories your Mind and Body come up with to entertain themselves, can really be far out man,' Lee rolled his eyes.

Tara smiled, 'Far out and tremendously entertaining! Full points for laughing,' she gave him the thumbs up. 'You know,' she said quietly, '**I sometimes feel that we give far too much significance to simple**

chemical processes. Emotions are sensations passing *through* us, but they *are not us*. We really need to learn not to take the silly ones so seriously, but to learn to laugh at them.'

'Funny, that happened earlier all by itself. You know, when I did my contemplation about Kate,' Lee grinned in remembrance.

'I'm so glad you know what I'm talking about, because when you *really* get it, it really is just funny. It's funny to see what we do to ourselves,' she smiled broadly. 'Do you remember when we said that most Thoughts are silly and superfluous when we really look at them? Even when we initially believed them to be ever so important?' Lee nodded. 'It's the same with Emotions.'

'Yeah, and even if we can't find it within ourselves to laugh, if we just manage to accept and Let Go, then they're *still gone*, so nothing's lost! But hey, I *choose* to have some fun with it!' Lee finished.

'The best thing to keep in Mind is that once you've dealt with *one* Emotion, every consecutive one will be easier, especially as you begin to develop *blueprints* and *formula* of how to deal with your Emotions in general. Then all you need to do is look at your list and tick of the points as you address them.' Tara thought for a second and then said, **'A blueprint could be: Emotion hits. Try and be Now. If not possible, relax Body. Relax Mind. Try and be Now. If still not possible, contemplate Emotion, ask questions, understand where it's coming from, why it's there, if you want it or not. Can you act on it or not. Yes? Do it. No. Can you accept the situation? Yes, Let Go, if not, start from the beginning.'**

'Oh I love your realism,' Lee laughed, 'you really don't pfaff about, do you? **So funny, all of this sounds like deliberately blowing your Mind into lots of little pieces and putting it back together just the way you want to.** And you, my dear Tara, happen to have chosen the most beautiful, relaxed and fun way one could have ever imagined to do just that!'

'Works for me,' Tara grinned, leant back against the tree and wiggled her toes at him.

'And for me,' Lee stretched himself out next to Tara, touched her toes with his and smiled at her.

She laughed radiantly back at him, making his heart melt. He noticed the Physical Sensation in his Body with curiosity. It felt like melting. It felt soft, relaxed and wonderful. He wondered if such magnificent sensations also kept him from being Now. Well, that was worth a spot of contemplation. He gently closed his eyes. So, if he thought about those warm feelings, sure, he wasn't Now, but did he really have to Let Go of them? What if he could just observe them, feel them, without interpreting them, **if he could be pure experience, he'd be Now, he Thought.** That'll be something to play with later, he smiled to himself. He opened his eyes and looked at Tara.

'Welcome back,' she smiled.

There it was again, the Emotions returned, Lee smiled to himself. He already knew the trigger, it was sitting right in front of him. He tried to just feel, not think, not associate and still observe the Emotion. What an amazing experience this was. It was like feeling his core, without judgements. It felt strong, pure and eternal, yet detached from any particular outcome. It was intense, yet seemingly unlinked to any particular Thought. Interesting. He smiled as he noticed that he was still looking at Tara.

'Yep, nearly back, got myself lost there for a minute. Fabulously lost, I might add,' he laughed. 'Actually, I haven't done my list duties for while, let me just catch up with that.'

'Sure, take your time,' Tara said and handed Lee his notebook and favourite pen.

Accepting:
- You do *not* have to *relive* the Emotion every time you think of it, unless you choose to.
- It's not ignoring or suppressing, it's understanding, accepting and Letting Go.
- It's seeing it for what it is and understanding it.
- With this new clarity you can see your Emotions for what they truly are, rather than what you made them into.
- You can see who *you* are, rather then what you made yourself into.
- It's consciously deciding what you want in your life and what you don't.
- When you're ready to Let Go once and for all, without Doubt, then you're ready to accept.
- Analyse, contemplate, understand, accept, Let Go.
- Your life is not what happened, but what you remember.
- Unless you jump, you won't know if you can *fly*.
- Emotions about the past: It's over. Learn, accept, Let Go and move on.
- Emotions about the present: Learn, act, Let Go.
- Emotions about the future: It's not there yet. If appropriate act, come up with an action plan. If not, relax.

Seeing-Clearly - three elements:
- First: See the trigger event itself, the way it really is, without your judgements and associations.
- Second: See the most basic ancient Emotional Reaction - fear, anger and so on.
- Third: See the way you developed, associated and bred this basic Emotion into a more complex Emotional pattern and response (ERP - Emotion, Reaction pattern).

Lee looked up, absentmindedly bounced the pen on his leg a couple of times and added another list, this time a list of questions.

Emotions, Behaviour, Reactions, questions:
- How can we play with serious stuff like Abuse, Fear, Death, Anger?
- What about natural grieving periods?
- Does this stuff work for everybody?

When he was done, he reread the questions and asked Tara if she could talk about them.

18   Emotional Creatures

Abuse

'Could we go through a few examples together? I mean, what about abuse? An experience like that affects your whole life, it's huge. How do you play with that?' Lee asked.

'I'm glad you're asking. That's where everything we've discussed so far comes together. Thoughts, Behaviour and Emotions, everything that makes up our lives,' Tara said. 'To answer your question, of course **feeling dreadful about something like abuse is normal. Feeling terrified or shy or furious or hurt or degraded and helpless, all of these and more, are natural reactions, - but how you live your life afterwards, if you let the past rule your entire further existence or not, is choice for most of us.** Let me give you an example.

I once worked with a girl, who had been mentally and physically abused when she was little. It was a very sad story. To try and sort herself out, she'd been to a psychologist for the past 5 years, and there she'd talked about her abuse and all the details of what had happened to her, how it made her feel back then, how she felt now, and who she blamed. She talked and talked and re-lived every single aspect of her abuse a million times. After 5 years she was still talking about it and she was still not feeling any better. Having to re-live the abuse and talk about it constantly, meant that it was ever present in her life, twice a week for 5 years, for an hour at a time. She was never allowed to move on. The girl had heard of what I do and asked me for help. She was ready to Let Go of her past and she wanted what had happened to her and the associated pain out of her life. **She wanted to be able to be present and Now, and she knew that the trapped memory of her intense past Emotions would not let her do that.**

I told her that I would have an about thirty minute long conversation with her and that afterwards, it was going to be up to her to experiment with what I was about to tell her, and to implement what she learned into her life. I made it clear that she had to take full responsibility for sorting herself out, but that I would give her all the tools to do so. She said cool. I did and she did. A week later she came back to me, telling me that our conversation had changed her life. This is not about blowing my own trumpet or saying how fabulous I am, but to show you that this stuff is practically applicable and that it works. It's not just a fairytale, **there *is* an alternative to traditional methods and there is a practical alternative to Modern Psychology and Hippy-Shit.** Most people just don't know about it yet.'

'Yeah, yeah, I know. Now, are you going too tell me about the girl or what?' Lee was impatiently intrigued.

'Sure. I asked her how she felt. Not 20 years ago, but Now. That's what mattered, the past is past and the future is future. But Now is where her problem lies. **She said that she felt ugly and not worth anything and shy. She couldn't trust men or even relax with intimate partners and she felt angry because her abuse made her feel that way.**

I asked her how she felt when she thought about what happened. I could literally see the change in her as soon as I said that. She tensed up, her forehead furrowed, her mouth became tighter, her energies edgier. I asked her to feel that Emotion, to really give it her full attention and then to describe the Physical Sensations she was experiencing. I asked her where it was, how it felt like, what texture it had, what colour and smell. Then I asked her to look at *where* the tension was located. Was it in her chest, in her heart, in her lungs, head, back, neck, her whole Body?

Then I guided her attention to each part of her Body where she felt tension and asked her to actively relax it. Her back was all up tight and tense, her shoulders were hunched up. I asked her to drop her shoulders, move her neck around to loosen it up, relax each part of her back, bit by bit. I asked her to start from the top of her head and to go down to her feet, scanning for tightness and then to consciously and intentionally relax it,

343

exactly like you did earlier. When she was done, I asked her to do it again, and then again, till she could really feel her Body relax. Then, I checked in with her breathing, to make sure she breathed deeply and deliberately. All of that took maybe ten minutes. Afterwards **she was amazed by how much the intensity of the Emotion had reduced, just with this simple exercise.**

Then we started to play with the Physical Sensations. We **increased** them, **decreased** them and modified them, simply by changing our attention on them and by actively feeling or thinking of other things, just as you did earlier,' Tara said to Lee. 'And then, believe it or not, at some stage, while she was supposed to feel the Sensations super intensely, she burst out laughing. She realised that, what she had thought would destroy her.'

'Eh, and that was funny, why?' Lee asked confused.

'Well, **she realised that and something else. She spontaneously got that what she had thought would destroy her, was actually a Sensation that she could change willy-nilly. She could increase it, decrease it and change it, and just by understanding that, she felt liberated.**'

'Oh, ok,' Lee still needed more.

'But we weren't done yet,' Tara continued obligingly. 'I asked her to feel the Emotion again and make it as intense as she could. She did. Then I asked her to double it. Her face scrunched up, then triple it, her Body tightened, then quadruple it and then increase it to infinity. The look on her face is still etched in my Mind, I Thought she was going to explode.' Tara laughed. 'Then, I told her, **at the height of it, at the top, at the peak, when she thought she couldn't make it any more intense, to still drive it up a notch and then, then to look at it. I told her if she looked at the Sensation now, objectively, all it is, is a super intense Physical sensation. It was even too intense to call it anything in particular anymore, it was just really intense.** She could see that. **Then I asked her to flick a switch in her Mind and** *pretend* **that it was the most intense** *ecstasy* **she'd ever felt, that at the peak of Intensity, it could be any Sensation she chose it to be.** It took her about a second to open her eyes, scream her head of and fall around my neck. She nearly knocked me of my chair.'

'What happened?'

'Well, it had worked. She had switched her Emotion into the opposite, through pure attention and Intent.'

'Wow, that's powerful.'

'I know, it's great, isn't it? This experience helped to take the girl's fear away, the fear of the crippling Physical Sensations that came with her Emotions. Now she knew that she could make then into whatever she wanted to. **She understood that her Emotions did not have to rule**

what was going on in her Body, but that *she* had an *active* influence on it. I told her that she could play with her Emotions every time she wanted to, that this *ecstasy* was available to her whenever she wanted it - even just for fun - I added, which made her laugh. I said that she could either relax her Body or feel a different sensation, or really go into and learn from her Emotion, or for that matter, that she could do whatever she damn well pleased. **I told her that with practice she'd be able to flick the switches whichever way she wanted faster and faster and more and more effortlessly and efficiently.'**

'I love it,' Lee grinned. 'It's amazing too. It's so similar to what I discovered earlier.'

'I know, it's great, isn't it? Guess we're connected to the same thing,' Tara grinned back at him. 'But there's more. We hadn't played with her **Associated Thoughts** yet. I looked straight into the girl's eyes when I said:

'If you look at yourself, right now, do you really think that you're ugly? Like hideous? Horrible? An eyesore? Look at yourself in the mirror and compare yourself to the average person out there, do you really deep down belief that you're revolting?' I dragged her in front of the mirror that happened to be on the wall next to our table.

'Well, kind of. You know, I've always been told that I was ugly and repulsive, since I was little.'

'But right now, deep down, if you compare yourself to me, do you really think that? Do you really feel ugly and repulsive.'

'No.'

'So, it's bollox.'

'Ey?'

'Well, you said you don't really think that you're ugly.'

'Eh, yes.'

'So it's bollox that you're ugly.'

'I guess so.'

'You guess or you know.'

'Ehrm, I guess I know?' she said hesitantly, something was beginning to click. 'But there's still this feeling that keeps coming back when I remember what it was like to be told that I was hideous and worth nothing.'

'First, you know now what to do with any feeling, right? You can relax it. Second, is anybody still telling you that you're ugly?'

'No, that was my parents, when I was little.'

'So it's a memory, right?'

'Yes.'

'And what's a memory?'

'A Thought?'

'Precisely.'

'Oh shit! It's just a Thought!'

I ploughed on, 'Right. Now, pretend that you are able to be Now, you'll have to practice that to really be able to actually do that, but for now, just pretend. If you looked into the mirror and wouldn't think you're ugly, if you wouldn't *remember* that you thought you're ugly - because in the Now those Thoughts don't exist - what would you see in the mirror.'

'A face.'

'Would it be an ugly face?'

'No, just a face,' she stared at herself. 'It would just be me, without Thoughts or interpretations or judgements.'

'There you go. That's what's really there! JUST YOU! That's who you really are. Everything else is what our Mind makes up.'

Lee had listened carefully and slowly began to summarise, 'So, you gave her two ways of playing with her Emotions. First you helped her truly *understand* that she really wasn't ugly and that it was her Mind telling her a silly story. **You told her that her feelings were actually *memories* of feelings.** Memories are past judgements and Thoughts about something, which have been carried into the present,' Lee added his own ideas. 'But in the end they're just Thoughts. And then you told her that in the Now, none of those Thoughts exist anyway. Through all of that and some good old first hand experience, **she understood that her Mind was making up stupid stories which made her feel bad, and which were actually not true in the first place**. All of this helped her to feel comfortable with Letting Go of the Emotions by Being Now. Tara, that's brilliant.'

'Thanks,' Tara said humbly. 'Keep in Mind though that I had obviously explained a bunch of other stuff to her during our conversation, about the judgement thingy, Letting Go of Thoughts, Being Now and all that. But there's more.'

'Let's have it then,' Lee was hungry for more.

'I asked the girl: You said that you feel that you're not worth anything. Why is that?'

'Because I've always been told.'

'Ok, and do you think right now that you're worth less than I am?'

'Mmh, no.'

'Ok, so that's bollox too.'

'I guess so,' something else clicked in her brain.

'Good. And you feel shy? Why?'

'Because I don't really go up to people and talk to them.'

'Why?'

'Because I always think I'll make a fool of myself or that they laugh at me.'

'Ok, how many people have laughed at you over the past four weeks?'

'None.'

'So that's bollox too then?'

'Phew. Man, you're turning everything upside down,' she said defensively.

'That's the point. **I'm just showing you that *you* yourself, deep down, do *not* actually *agree* with any of the stuff that you *think* you are! It's *not* who you *are*, it's who you *think* you are.** And that's two very different kettle of fish. **It's that confusion that creates such strong Emotions. If you look into the mirror again and be in complete Nowness? That's all you are. Everything else, your head made up! Even Shyness. In the mirror you're not shy, you're just *you*.'**

'Bloody hell.'

'Exactly. And the only thing stopping you from being who you really are or who you want to be is your *Thoughts*.'

'Shit.'

'If you'd sit here right now and think you're wonderful, you wouldn't think that you're not, would you?'

'Right.'

'Good, so, think other Thoughts.'

'How?'

'First you decide that the negative Thoughts and Emotions don't do you any good, that they don't change the situation and that you don't want them in your head or Body anymore, because they stop you from being Now. Enough is enough.'

'I can do that.'

'Great. If you think Thoughts about being ugly, you feed the puppy and hey presto you're ugly. **If you think you're not worth anything, hey presto, that's what you are.** If you think you're shy, you will be shy. If on the other hand, you stop thinking that you're shy or ugly, if you catch yourself out *every time* you think that Thought or feel that Emotion, or if you feel yourself react in any way, go back to your breath instead or divert your Mind onto a different Thought. If you can do that, the negative Thoughts aren't in your head anymore, and hey presto, you're suddenly not ugly anymore, you're not shy anymore. **If you strip all related Thoughts away, there's no insecurity, no heaviness, no anger, no ugliness, no feeling dirty or used or disempowered, no *unnecessary* Thoughts, grieve, sorrow, shyness, resentment, blame, grudges, unfairness, embarrassment, sadness, jealousy, irritation,**

anxiety, guild, worry, impatience, frustration, - all those things don't exist anymore, - until you start *thinking* about them!'

'Man, that's crazy,' she hesitated. 'It sounds so possible, but it also sounds too easy.'

'I know, but hey, who ever said that it had to be difficult?'

'Everybody.'

'They just don't know any different. Try it for yourself. **Keep catching yourself out and divert your attention to something else, and do that until the puppy becomes bored,** and you know what? It *will* get bored eventually. *If it won't stay away, play with it. But don't feed it!* If you can bring yourself to play with it, that'll make the whole affair much more enjoyable!' The girl laughed. 'At the end of it, you might not think that you're a stunning self confident supermodel, but at least you don't think that you're ugly and shy anymore. You keep telling yourself that until your Mind is convinced. It might take a little time, but your Mind *will* give in.'

That's when she grinned widely, 'But if I practice to divert my attention and focus on all my good bits? Well, maybe I can make myself belief I'm fantastic, I won't allow anything else but that into my head anymore.'

'What do you mean - maybe?'

'Oh, sorry. I can!' she smiled.

'That's my girl! Semantics are important! Doubt breeds Doubt, right?'

'Yeah, I can see that.'

'If you can make yourself believe that you're fantastic? That's all that counts. If other people don't agree with that, quietly or openly? Well, sod them. They're not perfect either! So there. And who the hell are they to know better than you do?' Tara smiled.

Lee nodded his head slowly, thinking, 'So, she accepted to Let Go of the Sensations and the Thoughts, but her Behavioural reactions which she trained herself to have were still there, weren't they? Her Shyness for example? Did you address the left over Behaviour patterns too?'

'Yes I did,' Tara said. 'It was pretty much the same conversation we talked about earlier when we talked about the girl at school that was so shy.

When I went through went through those same concepts with this girl from work, she realised that she could actively change her shy Behaviour. After that we did the same thing with her inability to trust or relax with intimate partners. She played with pretending to be somebody else, with imagining what a trusting, open relaxed person would do. She practiced the situations in her head and later, after she got a bit more confident, she played in real life, just like we talked about before. This particular part was all about staying open, open, open and of course trusting her Intuition in finding a genuine, gently man to be with.'

'Fabulous. Now, what about her anger,' Lee asked. 'Remember? She felt angry because her abuse had made her feel that way.'

'Oh yes, well, first we played with accepting the situation. By the time I met her, she was already pretty far down the line with that. She knew that it was past and she had already decided that she wanted to Let Go of it. **She had accepted that it had happened and no matter how painful and destroying the experience had been, it was over. She wanted to move on and find a way of Letting Go and living a life, that was not overshadowed by her past experiences.**

By playing with her anger, she realised that *she* had *made herself* feel that way. The abuse had initiated it, but *she* was *holding* on to it. Once she learned to relax the angry Sensations and Thoughts, her reactions to trigger situations mellowed out. And once her Behaviour changed to being more relaxed and confident with men, there really wasn't anything to feel angry about anymore. '

'So, all in all, you picked her Emotions apart into all their little components and then addressed each one individually. It's like: how do you eat an elephant?' Lee cocked his head.

'How?'

'In lots of little pieces,' he grinned.

'Yeah,' Tara smiled broadly, 'or photocopy it and before you eat it, make some origami with it - I mean, Play and experiment! Don't just chomp your way through an elephant, try and make it fun!'

Lee laughed. 'Oh, I love how you can always find a way to play. You take the Emotions seriously, but at the same time, you can make a point to see them for what they are, rather than succumb to the associated stories. What a wonderful way to live,' Lee said and then added, 'oh, and the girl came back to you after a week and told you that it had worked?'

'Yep she did. It had worked a treat. She had begun to learn to Consciously and actively play with her Emotions, rather than to ignore or fight them. Her overall Awareness, Consciousness and understanding of her Mind, Body, her Emotions and her Behaviour had been raised quite drastically.

It took her a while to deal with all the puppies of her past, but she learned quickly to *actively* see the funny side of things, to laugh at *those stupid Thoughts telling her what she was or what she couldn't do, when she full well knew that she wasn't and that she could - she just had to do it.* Other people did it, so she could do it too.

She told me that it had been full-on, especially at the beginning, because she had to really face her fears and get out of her comfort zone to play with all those painful memories and

Emotions, but it had been worth it. She had *committed* to it and she had seen it through. In the end, she had really enjoyed to Let Go, she knew it was so good for her. She truly cherished Letting Go of the person that had never felt right to her, that she knew she never was, but was made to be. She did all of that by playing with new and different personalities, and then by actually becoming the person she had always wanted to be. *She had recreated herself*,' Tara finished.

Then, pre-empting any objections, Tara said, 'Sure you can nip-pik, "what if the girl would have been really ugly or if somebody would laugh at her or make fun of her and destroy her confidence again?" Sure the questions can go on, but I think you get the gist of how it can work even in such situations.' Lee nodded. As an afterthought Tara said seriously, 'And if she would have been really ugly, I'd have done her hair, put on make up, make her feel special. Also, if somebody would have laughed, she would have known that her lost confidence or renewed shyness would have just been another toy to play with.

That's what I mean with commitment. You have to stick with it, stay open and focussed, and not regress into the poor-little-me-persona. Like this you can make it work in all situations!'

'Fair enough,' Lee agreed.

'Oh,' Tara remembered. 'And you know what the greatest thing was? Once she was comfortable with her own memories and Emotions, she started to pass on her newly found skills to other people, first her friends, and after a couple of years, she started a phone helpline. She never forgot her abuse, but it had made her into a stronger person. Not through ignoring it or forgetting it, but because she had finally *faced* her fears head on and survived! And strangely,' a little smile curled Tara's lips, 'she even had some fun with it.'

'Wow, and she helped other people laugh again too. What a fabulous story,' Lee laid down and propped himself up on his elbow.

'I'd like to add something,' Tara said, looking at Lee, 'I know that in traditional Psychology, some of the questions which I asked the girl, could be regarded as 'leading questions' but hey, you know what? From time to time they're really useful, and they can really work. Sometimes people are ready and able and thus *need* to hear that their Minds are full of crap! Not to offend them obviously, but some of them really don't know. And unless you are aware of something, they can't change it.'

'I agree,' Lee said simply. Tara spoke right from his own heart, but nevertheless another question came up in his Mind, 'You just talked about the girl having to face her fears, having to step out of her comfort zone. I think that's the bit most people have problems with. Have you got some more examples for that?'

'I'm sure I do,' Tara said, thinking for a moment.

The Dark - Fear

'Let me give you one of my own examples,' Tara said. **'I always used to be scared of he dark and I wanted to play with a personality that was *not* scared.** Let's assume you're in a dark environment and you're scared. At first it's useful to make a reasonable evaluation of the situation. Is there actually anything to be scared of? If the answer is yes, then you should ask yourself: "what the hell are you doing there?" You really should know better than to put yourself into dangerous situations! Point One.' Lee laughed at Tara. 'Point two, sometimes you don't have the choice, so ok, it could be dangerous and you're scared. The second question is: "is being scared going to make that robber *not* jump out at you? Is being scared going to make that dog *not* attack you? **Will being scared make whatever you're scared of *not* happen?" Of course not. Being scared is in your head, it *doesn't change* the situation**. So, you can either drive yourself nuts and frantic with all those horrible Thoughts of what could potentially happen, or you could just stop thinking about them and have a much better time getting on with whatever you need to get on with.'

'Just be Now,' Lee picked up. 'Focus, breathe, focus, breathe, fear bounces of the fringes of your Consciousness, bounce, bounce, breathe, focus, flicker of fear, breathe, … oh, isn't it a nice day? Yep, it's still dark, but hey, I can breathe, uh a shadow, don't feed the fear of the shadow, divert your Mind, relax our Body, breathe.' He went through an imaginary scenario in his head.

'Right. It's about looking the fear straight in the eye, facing it and telling it head on - "you are not part of me! I don't need you! Get lost!" Then you stop feeding it, and you Let Go.'

'Gosh, doing that that sounds like such a liberating process, and what's more, it doesn't require re-living horrible scary moments if you don't want to,' Lee said.

'And on top of that,' Tara added, 'once the intensity of the Emotion has been reduced, you could have some fun with all the silly little stories your

Mind comes up with to scare you. You could be a child again, listening to your dad telling you stories, knowing that actually you're safe.'

'That's great. Listen to scary stories and enjoy the goose-bumps. *Enjoy* the ride!'

'Yep, as soon as you choose to look at it this way, it can be enjoyable - in a strange, new and different kind of way,' Tara said smiling. 'Do you want another example about fears? What about some full on debilitating fear?'

'What like a phobia or something?' Lee dared.

'Yes, that's the one.'

'Really? Oh, yes please,' Lee approved heartily. This was the stuff that *reality* was made out of. Real, concrete, hands on examples.

Phobias - Fear

'I had a girlfriend with a terrible phobia of heights. Through our conversations, and through practicing scenarios in her head, she learned to keep her Mind focussed on relaxing her Body, when she *imagined* looking down into fearful heights. It took a little while, and a bunch of determination and focus, but she had played well - in theory. Then, one day - and as Sod's law wanted it - she and I had to go over a very narrow bridge. We had to, we had no choice, and I tell you, it was a nasty little bridge. It was really flimsy and waves were crashing against it from all sides,' Tara remembered. 'To be honest, even I had my worries about it, and I don't have fear of heights. But I'd been over that bridge a million times, and I knew that it was safe. Still, facing this particular bridge as a first real life tester for my friend? The irony of it would have been quite funny, if it wouldn't have been such an intense moment. Poor thing,' Tara giggled. 'Under normal circumstances, you would increase the intensity of the trigger slowly, but hey, sometimes you have to eat the elephant in one go. Now, picture this, my friend stands in front of the bridge and I'm talking to her:

'I can't do it.'
'Of course you can.'
'No I can't.'
'Remember what we talked about?'
'Yeah.'
'You don't want to be scared of heights anymore, do you? You don't want those constricting physical feelings and those rollercoaster Thoughts in your head anymore, right?'
'No.'

'We've been over this bridge a million times. You *know* that there's nothing to be scared of, and that it's your Mind telling you a story of fear that is unfounded and that you don't want to listen to it anymore.'

'Yeah.'

'So do it. Relax your Body. Focus.'

'Ok, I'm relaxing. I'm relaxing my head, my shoulders, ...' She went through her whole Body, bit by bit, then started again from the beginning. She consciously slowed down her breathing and I could see her Body relax.

'Now, take your attention away from the fear and with all your Being, all your attention, your entire Consciousness, focus on breathing. Breathe, breathe, breathe and walk.'

'But I can't,' she tensed up again.

'Can you walk?'

'Of course.'

'Then walk.'

'But I'll fall.'

'Do you usually fall walking?'

'No.'

'So, you can do it. Stop thinking about it. Instead, breathe, breathe, breathe, with your whole Being, attention and focus breathe and walk.' I watched her follow my directions. 'Focus, concentration, breathe, feel your Body relax with each big breaths. Nobody can do this for you. Either you really want to change this or you don't. Breathe, relax, breathe, focus. The second your Mind is empty, let your Body move.' She breathed with me, her eyes closed. And then? She opened her eyes and walked. One step and another, and another. And then she screamed her head of. In amazement. She hadn't fallen. She'd done it, it had been easy. She had focussed so hard on her breath, that she literally forgot her fear for just a split second and her Body moved. Her fingernails had dug into her palms, and they were bleeding from four little half moon shapes, but hey, she'd done it.'

'Wow, that's amazing,' Lee said.

'I know, it was pretty cool. Obviously, some people take to this approach quicker than others, but it works if they are *determined* and have played with the scenario before in their heads to prepare themselves. To be honest, sometimes when I'm with somebody in a tight situation, I just talk so much about what they should be thinking of, that their whole head is so full of me jabbering on, that they can't think of their fears anymore, there's simply no space left in their heads. **When they're too busy listening to me, at some opportune moment, I redirect their attention away from their fear**, to thinking about something else, or their breathing or whatever I know works for them. **And then suddenly, even if only for a**

split second their head is empty of the fear. They literally forgot about it for an minute instant. That moment is enough for them to move. It's not a trick, it's just an automatic reaction. Sure, sometimes the rational Mind switches itself on again, usually at the most crucial moment, and says: "Oops, no, you're scared of that, remember? Don't do it!" Well if that happens, start again. And again. Relax, back to the breath. And with time, you can do it, just like surfing. You just have to want it badly enough! When you *really* want it? Then you muster up the tenacity and the courage!'

'Personal coaching by Tara,' Lee grinned.

'Yep. But if you don't have the privilege to work with me,' Tara winked at him playfully, 'you can do this by yourself, in your own head. You don't need me standing next to you.'

'But that would be much less fun.'

'That's a subjective judgement,' Tara laughed.

'Absolutely,' Lee flashed her a big, cheeky smile. 'But doing this on your own, probably takes even more focus, determination and discipline.'

'That's true, but it is possible. And if you need to, you can always ask a friend to help you.'

'But that wouldn't be you,' Lee pouted.

'Beggars can't be choosers,' Tara smiled. 'In the end you really don't need another person, all you *do* need, is to take *responsibility* for yourself and do it! Go into Nowness or occupy your Mind with something else. Think of a great holiday, a fabulous night out, your partner, kids, a gig of your favourite band, anything and just move your Body. Every time you think you can't, think of something else, till you just move. It might take a few tries, but in the end you will move. Actually,' Tara paused for a moment, 'there's something I want to stress with this example. The girl was mentally accessible when she had to cross the bridge.'

'Mentally accessible? Like, she was "with it"?'

'Yes. She was *able* to listen to me, and what I said actually *sunk in*.'

'You mean that she didn't freeze?'

'Exactly.'

'But that's what she practiced for, right? **The theoretical preparation had reduced the intensity so much, that when the real situation hit, she was able to stay open, rather than contract and close up, and she could actually listen to you. She could look at what was going on objectively, rather than being consumed by the situation. She had made a firm commitment that, even though she was still scared, she didn't want to be afraid of heights anymore and she was dedicated to actively work on it, even if it meant facing her greatest fears straight on. Without any** of this, the Conscious Mental Clarity I talked about earlier, would not have been there,' Lee finished, visibly impressed with himself.

'Exactly. **She had practice and trained herself to be Now, and when the fears came back, for real this time, she went back into Nowness and thus *remembered* and *regained* her clarity.** She never Thought that she'd be able to do that, but she did. **She practiced and played hard, and it paid off.'**

'Brilliant,' Lee applauded.

Mind Diversion

'**Y**ou know you just said earlier, that you redirected the girl's attention and focused her on something else, and at the opportune moment, when she forgot her fear, she just walked?' Lee asked, Tara nodded. 'I have a great example for that myself.'

Tara put her hands behind her ears, pushed them forward and laughed, 'I'm all ears.'

Lee gently took her hands, gave them a quick squeeze and replaced them back on her lap, 'You'll like this one. A chiro-practitioner I know used a nice little trick to adjust the head of a friend of mine. She had panicked with anticipation and her Body had frozen up. If somebody is as stiff as a board, it's kind of tricky to do an adjustment, right? He needed her to relax, but she couldn't. So, the chiro-practitioner told my friend that he was going to do something different and if she could just have both of her big toes touch each other. For a split second my friend forgot about her fear of her head being yanked, and diverted her attention to making her toes touch. Needles to say, in that split second where she relaxed, the chiro-practitioner adjusted. Childs play.'

'What a fabulous trick,' Tara raised her eyebrows jus like Lee usually did. 'That's what I call "Mind Diversion". The aim with Mind Diversion, is to get lost in other, nicer or more relaxing Thoughts, to distract you for a short period of time. To *replace* the intense Emotion or Thought with a positive, *nurturing*, or simply a different one, to just pick any subject and start to *actively* think about that instead. It could be dinner, a story, a dream, anything. **From my own experience, to get rid of hardcore Emotions, especially at the beginning, Mind Diversion often works better, than trying to simply focus on Nowness.** It just seems to be easier that way for a lot of people.

'Do you do that?' Lee probed.

'My personal focus is on being Now. **I breathe and focus on Emptiness, the space *between* my Thoughts.** I do pretty much everything with Nowness, I seldomly even need to analyse anymore. By now I've done so much analysis, and Letting Go, that my Mind is pretty clear all the time anyway. **You see, analysis leads to acceptance and acceptance leads to Letting Go, which leads to Nowness. I've just practiced it all so much, that I can cut out all the middle men.** Sometimes I still use them, sometimes I still do Mind Diversion, but the occasions are becoming less and less. I simply notice and am Now.'

'I can understand now that this can be a bit too hardcore for the beginning,' Lee said.

'True, but it never hurts to play with it anyway, for me this worked best right from the start!' Tara said. 'Let me give you a good Mind Diversion example. It also addresses your question from earlier about how to deal with Death,' Tara pointed at the list in Lee's notebook.

'Great, let me just make a quick note first,' Lee said and grabbed to pen and paper.

Associated Thoughts of an Emotion disappear through:
- Conscious Breathing.
- Focus on Relaxing the Body.
- Nowness.
- Mindfulness.
- Mind Diversion, by telling yourself stories, thinking of something else, just make up stuff, dream.

'Ok done, off you go,' Lee said ready for more.

Death

"I'm frightened by the total goal,
I'm drawn into the ragged hole...
I'm torn between the light and dark...
I'm sinking in the quicksand of my Thoughts,
And I ain't got the power anymore..."
- David Bowie

Tara began, 'I had a young man come to me for advice last year. Four of his best friends had died in a car accident and his girlfriend had left him shortly afterwards because she couldn't cope with his extreme mood swings anymore, which had started to manifest themselves after the accident. As a result he had become terribly depressed. He had spoken about it to a psychologist forever and after 2 years he still wanted to kill himself. He'd already had a bunch of suicide attempts behind him, he was still depressed and it wasn't getting any better. He didn't want to talk about it anymore, he wanted it to go away. The medical answer was tablets, which he didn't want. He still had enough sense to realise that becoming a vegetable was the epitome, the height of ignoring, postponing or numbing the problem, but not a way of healing himself. That's when he suddenly realised that this was what he needed. To heal himself. To find a way of living his life again.

That's when he came to see me. Before we started, I made sure that he *really* wanted to do something about this, that he *was* prepared to take responsibility and that he *was* prepared to look his pain straight in the eye. In one of his clearer moments, he told me that he was truly fed up. He knew that if he didn't do something to help himself, he would kill himself eventually. I knew that this wasn't an idle threat. I had seen the scars, where he'd cut his wrists before. He really wanted it to stop. **He wanted out of the depression, one way or another. In that statement was a hidden strength, a determination, a readiness that I could work with. That is essential. Without this strength, there's nobody 'in there',' Tara tapped her forehead, 'to go and take control."**

I hoped that I could appeal to his Mind, just for 10 minutes, without him loosing himself in Emotions. I made it clear, as kindly as possible, that I wasn't there to listen to his sad stories or whining, but that *he* had to *really listen* to *me* and play *with* me to sort this out. **I told him that *he* was the only person that could change his depression, he and he alone.** I also told him that my chat would be different to any chat he'd ever had before. **I told him that he wouldn't get humble sympathy, but clear and direct questions and instructions.** I asked if he was ready to accept that. He said he was prepared. He was ready. Good. We started:

'So, do you want to be depressed?' I asked.

'Of course not,' he said surprised.

'Then stop it.'

'How.'

'Well, you feed the depression puppies by constantly thinking about the accident and how sad it is that your friends are not in your life anymore.'

'But they were my friends and I miss them.'

'Yes, and that was two years ago. How much longer are you going to make your life a misery?'

'Grumble.'

'Do you understand that you're feeding the puppy by thinking those Thoughts?'

'Yes.'

'Do those Thoughts in anyway change the situation that your friends aren't around anymore?'

'No.' (quiet grumble)

'Do these Thoughts do you any good?'

'Of course not, I'm bloody depressed.'

'So, stop thinking those Thoughts.'

'Pfffffffff. Wow,... phew. How??'

'Same spiel, catch out, divert attention.'

'That's sounds like such hard work.'

'Well, who said it's easy?' Tara winked at Lee, different people, different methods.

'Brrr.'

'Well, **isn't your sanity worth a bit of focus and determination? Just pretend that it's a project at work and your livelihood depends on doing it well. Or pretend that it's a project for University or school, that takes focus and a bit of discipline. Pretend that instead of** *changing* **something, you're** *learning a new skill,* **and when you learned it, hey, your life will be new and fresh. It's not always easy at first, but it can be fun.** Try it, play with it! See it change your world so much! Don't dismiss it just because it's a teeny-weeny bit of effort at the beginning. It's *your* life and *your* happiness we're talking about here. And once you've done it, a whole new world of fun opens up to you.'

'I'm pathetic aren't I?' he asked.

'You said that.'

'Mmh.'

'I understand why you're weary, but either you actively decide that you want to pull yourself out of this one, and put in a bit of time, or you'll be in there for a good while longer or - till the end.'

That hit a note with him.

'Ok, agreed. Go on.'

'Give it a bit of time,' I said more gently. 'It takes a little while to get used to it, but after a while it gets more interesting, even fun. With practice you learn to see the depressed Thoughts and the Emotions coming a mile off. Knowing that you really don't need them anymore, can either go into Nowness - where these Emotions don't exist - or you can do Mind Diversions. Either way, after a little practice, all it takes is a quick flash and they're gone.'

'Sounds wonderful,' he said longingly.

'It is. And at the same time, as you're Letting Go of the old Thoughts, you can actively begin to fill your Mind with new Thoughts. Fill it with *nice* Thoughts, happy Thoughts, exciting Thoughts. Start thinking, about all the *other* stuff that you could do instead of sitting at home and moping! But, don't do it like this,' I said with a warning undertone, 'don't think: "maybe I should do something else, but: buuuuhuuuu, I miss my friends soooo much." No! Actively tell yourself *positive* stories in your head! Talk to yourself about all the wonderful things you want to do and how and when you could do them. Talk to yourself as if you'd be talking to another person in the same situation as you. Play with it! As soon as your mates come into your head again, catch out, aha, a misery Thought, and back to the other nicer story. **No dwelling in sad Thoughts or Emotions**.'

'Got it.'

'And gently, after a while, start thinking about *new* friends,' I suggested.

'But nobody can replace my old friends, they'll never be the same as my old friends,' he said defensively.

'Of course not,' I said soothingly. 'First, that's not the point anyway. The point is not to try and replace your old friends. People are unique, they can't be replaced. The point is to get *new* ones. With *different* qualities, different Minds, different ideas and different things they can bring to your life. And second, the story in your head, that nobody can replace your friends, what's that?' I paused.

'It's a Thought too. Oh, bugger. Right. Notice, Divert Mind.' As an afterthought he added, 'But I don't want to forget my friends.'

'You don't have to. **You can think about them, but choose the Thoughts you think well. Choose the happy ones, cherish the time you had together, without the sadness that they're gone. Think about your old friends, but learn to relax your intense Mental and Physical reactions, until you can be present, while you're thinking them!'**

'Ok.'

'There you go. Now go and play! See the world again. It's up to you. It works this way. It does take will power, focus and determination. But it works!' Tara said. 'It's such a great game if you play it. You get instant gratification, rewards and reassurance that it works, and you need nothing else but your own head. Anywhere,' Tara finished her story.

'You know Lee, **I appealed to his last bit of strength and his last bit of will that he had left, with simple common sense and I hit it home**. Hard. Something clicked within him. **He realised that his Behaviour was not only destructive, but also useless, it really didn't change anything.** So stopping something that was useless, made perfect sense. He tried what I suggested, and it worked. It was hard work at first, lots of *very* persistent puppies, but he learned not to be too hard on himself. When the Thoughts: "you're so stupid", "why can't you do this?", or: "why is that Thought still coming back", or: "why do I have to be strong?", or: "I miss my friends", or: "I can't cope", - came into his Mind, he recognised those as Thoughts too, as figments of his imagination, things that his Mind made up to tease him, and simply went back to his story about the mountains and the trekking he wanted to do. And when his friends suddenly turned up at the base camp of his mountain that he saw in his Mind, he said: "hi", and introduced them to his new friends that were trekking with him, and they all had a cup of tea. See? **You can make up** *whatever* **you want to. You can tell yourself whatever story you want to. If you want your old friends to become jealous and angry with you because you've got new friends? You can do that. Or you can have you all sit together happily drinking tea! It's your choice.**'

'You like your tea, don't you?'

'Yep,' Tara nodded, 'it's soothing and a lovely ritual to take your Mind of things,' she smiled at Lee. 'But back to the young man. So, all together I talked to him about the Physical relaxation thing and the practicing in his head, which helped to tone down the shock value of his strong Emotions whenever they surprised him and hit him hard. Once the intensity was toned down, he was able to look at his Emotions more and more objectively. After a while he understood that he really *could* Let them Go, that they absolutely didn't serve him.

Doing all of this, helped keeping the suicide Thoughts at bay, increased his happy and positive Thoughts, and over time, his depression lessened. Without a single pill.

After a few months he got over the deep end of his depression and a few months after that he was back to radiant health, mentally and physically. **I recently heard that he just enrolled for another degree and that he was using the same techniques I had shared with him to help him concentrate.**'

'How?'

'He would catch himself out when his Mind would wander away from his studies and focus back on his work. **Any feelings of boredom or fear of failure, were dealt with easily. In the end, his concentration was so sharp and his focus so strong, he told me, he could do the same amount of study in two hours, which would have previously taken him a whole day.** He also began to practice Nowness throughout the day to help him relax and calm down. He felt like a new person.'

'It sounds as if you changed his life Tara.'

'Thanks, but actually, no. *I* didn't do anything. That's the point. *He* did. That's the way it works - *has* to work. *I* just gave him a quick thirty minute pep talk, while he happened to *really* listen.'

'Yeah, the *sinking in* bit is important. I figured that earlier.'

'Yep, that's vital.'

Mental Objectivity - Or Not - The Will-Power Thing

"I must not fear.
Fear is the Mind Killer.
Fear is the little death that brings total obliteration.
I will face my fear.
I will permit it to pass over me and through me.
And when it has gone past,
I will turn the inner eye to see it's path.
Where fear has gone there will be nothing.
Only I will remain. "
- Frank Herbert, Dune

'Let me add something quickly about any Mental state that cuts you off from your Mental Objectivity,' Tara offered.

'Oh, yes please.'

'Such a state can be a serious illness such as depression, or it could be a Mind that's in a hole, not knowing how to escape. In such a state it can be difficult to focus, to detach yourself from your Emotions or even to just muster up enough willpower to face your Emotions head on. But that doesn't mean that you can't try!

One of the best ways is to practice as much as you can, *while* you *are* in your *clear* state. Learn, learn, learn. Learn about yourself and your Emotions *while* you're clear. I mean those minutes when you're *not* in the hole. In those moments learn when the Emotions come on, what triggers them, little situations where you're making them worse all by yourself, moments where they engulf you and you can't do anything about them, and identify the other moments where you *might* be able to influence them. **Practice, play and face scenarios so much in your *clear* state, that physical relaxation becomes automatic, that mental focus becomes an automatic response to an intense scenario on your Mind.** Slowly, slowly, your Being will get used to being that way, or at least to the process of *making* yourself to Be that way,' Tara pointed out. **'By the time the real physical situation comes along, your Mind and Body will automatically remember what you trained them to do.** It might take a couple of times to stick with it, but it will be a solid base. Just like the example with my friend that had to go over the bridge.'

'Use the moments of your clear state, where you have some Mental Objectivity, to learn to automatically reduce the intensity of your depressed state. That's a great idea!' Lee nodded appreciatively.

'Yeah, or overcome it! That's possible too. Don't limit yourself!' she winked at lee. **'The other thing with Non-Objective Mental states is that the unhappy person usually views *everything* as bad or unsatisfactory.** That could be their environment, their friends, themselves or their activities, and they react to all of that with upset, anger, despair and so on. **In a situation like that, a useful thing to play with is to check if your Mind is *looking* for those Emotions. Is your Mind interpreting actions and scenarios around you to *satisfy* this Emotion and the expectation of it?** If you see your girlfriend talk to another man, are you immediately thinking that she must like him more? Is your head spinning the picture out of control? **Are you *looking* for each movement of their Body, trying to find the hint, *the clue to justify* you being depressed, to *justify* you having those feelings? The unhappy person will find reasons to be unhappy, just as the jealous type will find a reason to be jealous, the not depressed type, the non-jealous type, the happy person, would only see a conversation between two people.'**

'It's the **same scenario, with a different response!'** Lee **said.**

'Right. So, analyse your responses and play with changing them, imagine, how a non-depressed person would behave and react? What would a person do that does *not* have *your* personality, behavioural or emotional state, a person who you would like to behave or emote like? Or maybe just, what would *you* rather do? **Play, pretend, imagine. You might even enjoy yourself,'** Tara smiled happily. 'Any situation that upsets you, try to see it the way it *really* is, *without your* judgements.

You lost a court case and lost lots of money. So unfair. Can you do anything about it. Yes. Then do it. No? Get over it! Let Go. Stop clinging on to it. Somebody hit you. You get angry. You like being angry? Fine. Enjoy. If you don't, play with it, change it! **Put some time and active effort behind sorting out your head! Practice anywhere, all day long, in *everyday* situations. You don't need to sit in a corner for that, you don't need a designated time of day**! You lost your favourite necklace. Tough. You lost it. Now, how long are you going to be upset about it? **Experience the joy of the moment, rather than being stuck in the longing and the hope for something that isn't.**'

'Sure, but doing that takes guts and that's what a lot of people can't muster when they're engulfed by their Emotions and Thoughts. They can't accept. **So, what is it that keeps us from accepting?'** Lee asked. 'Is it not being willing to face the Emotion? Not wanting to face the fact that we have lost our dream! Is our Mind going on forever saying: This can't have happened?'

'That could be it, but the point is: "Well, it *has* happened!" Sit with it, accept it. **Take however long you need, but *do* it. Actively,**' Tara stressed.

'**From what I understand, the duration of the pain is directly correlated to how much confusion there is and how willing or able we are to accept it,**' Lee said. '**I also feel though that we all have a certain predisposed capacity for pain and Emotions. With that I mean the ability to stay present while the Emotions are going on. Once this threshold is surpassed though, we shut off and our Mental Objectivity will be buried, until we're able to open again.**'

'That's true,' Tara nodded. 'That often happens with very painful experiences or shock. A friend of mine for example lost a loved one in an absolutely horrific manner. At the point I met her, about a year after the accident, she was in the process of coming to terms with her Emotions. She was beginning to gain the clarity she needed to see the past the murky clouds of her Emotions and to begin to rise out and above them. For the first time, she was able to see her Emotions clearly for what they were. Sensations and Thought patterns, still attached to a long gone incident, kept alive by her memories and by not coming to terms with it.

I talked to her and we discussed some of the things you and I have talked about so far. After a year of grief and not being able to hear any advice anybody had given her, during our conversations she noticed that she was finally able to *hear* my counsel. When she told me that a year before, she would not have been able to truly listen to me and have the messages sink in, I asked her why. She said that the pain had been too great and reason would not have eased it. **She described her Emotions as being locked in a room, in bed, hiding under the cover, sobbing. Sobbing until all her insides had died off, being incapable of doing anything, anything at all.** At that time, she simply would not have had access to the necessary Mental Objectivity that this approach required. But now she did. She felt ready to get on with her life. She talked about having needed time to heal, but now she was able to move on.'

Natural Grieving Periods or The Television Scenario

'**Y**ou know,' Lee said, 'after something really terrible happened to someone and the wounds are still pretty fresh? Do you think that there are *natural* grieving periods? You know, a natural amount of time to get over

363

something? Like a year to get over a death or 6 months to get over a relationship?'

'Well, it's difficult to say what's natural. Some people take 6 months, others take days, others never get over it, so which one is the natural period?'

'You've got a point there.'

'Some people need more time than others. Let me give you a simple analogy of how different people deal with the *same* situation. Let's say something really terrible happens, *you're in shock. You feel numb*. You hide in your bed under the covers with the television blaring and you're not even aware that it's even there. **The TV is your unconscious Emotions in the background, which is totally blacked out,'** Tara said.

'**You've shut yourself off from the world and from your Emotions,'** Lee said, 'you're in a state of shock.'

'Right. **Then one day, you hear the noise of the telly, but it's scary and frightening, so you keep hiding from it, you might react with Emotions under the covers, but you're not coming out,'** Tara said.

'At that stage you have become aware of your unconscious deep Emotions. The shock and the numbness has worn off, and you begin to feel the pain. Sometimes indescribable pain, physically, mentally or emotionally,' Lee added.

'Right,' Tara nodded. 'The TV, i.e. the Emotions, are driving you crazy, never allowing you to relax. It's constant white noise. You might just lie there and bear it, you might ignore it or you might scream and shout and rant and rave or cry and let it all out. Some stop, some never stop this phase.'

'**But if you never dare to move on from that stage, you will always be dominated by your Emotions,' Lee said puzzled.**

'**True. Some people live their entire lives that way,' Tara said with compassion. 'But maybe, one day, you become curious and you gather all your strength and power and decide to check out what on earth is making that noise.** You peek out from underneath the covers, just with one eye, and you see the TV, but you're too scared of it, you can't get out of bed. So, you stare at it, but you don't understand it, you can't really see anything, it remains to be static, just black and white dots and noise,' Tara said.

'If you kept doing that, you're *looking* at your Emotions, but you don't *do* anything with them.'

Tara nodded, 'Then maybe, one day you dare to get out of bed and *really* examine the TV, face it. Slowly pictures emerge. With practice, you can actually see and follow the program that's been going on in the background for all this time. You can finally understand what's going on. You sit in front of it, mesmerised.'

'You're observing your Emotions, but you're not acting on them,' Lee summed up, enjoying the ping pong quality of this conversation, as he was making an effort to put himself into the shoes of somebody looking at an Emotional TV, unable to act.

'You might simply not be able to do anything about it,' he continued, 'Your Mind and Body might be frozen, you might not have the *power* to get up and go, you might be too lazy or you might just not *dare* to get up and leave. Maybe you don't *want* to, or you *can't* or don't know *how*, maybe you're scared of what *could* happen if you *did* do something' Lee finished his train of Thoughts.

'That's it. Now, **some people get addicted to the TV programme and *keep* watching, that's when you are addicted to your Emotions.** Now, there can be different reasons for falling into that space. Maybe it's an escape from the real world, maybe it's a excuse not having to dare to go out, or having to explain or justify your unhappy state to others. **It might be any excuse not to do *something*, inside or outside of yourself.** The Emotions might define who you are, and it might even subconsciously serve you,' Tara threw out some random ideas.

'Interesting,' Lee said thoughtfully.

'If on the other hand, if you *don't* get addicted, you'll watch the TV for a while, and with time you get bored of it, cause it's always the same channel, right? You get fed up with it and wonder what's outside of the room.'

'You're beginning to accept, to move on,' Lee filled in.

'Exactly. Then one day, you might gather all your strength, get up and walk to the TV. You stand in front of it for a while and make a decision, you switch it off and walk out of the room!'

'Yeah. And that decision can happen sooner for some than for others.'

'That's true. If you're not quite that confident yet, you might leave the telly on, while you go outside to have a look, just in case - it is a good escape mechanism to be able to come back to after all - or you might switch it off for a while to save energy, knowing that you'll come back. But either way, for now, the most important thing is that you're out of the room!

Now, once outside, you might close the door firmly, or you might want to keep it open, to be able to look back at the telly from time to time, which can give you a certain safety level. You might stay outside forever or you might get frightened and run straight back in, back to the comfort of the Telly dinner, or even the bedcovers.'

'What a great description,' Lee raised his eyebrows. '**I can see how different people deal with extreme situations differently**. Man, some people might not even go into bed in the first place, whereas others might stay under the covers for ever or maybe just for a day, some might look at the TV and run out of the room, never needing to give the telly another glance, others need to keep coming back in for another show.'

Tara continued Lee's train of Thought, 'Some will find it easy to learn, develop a blue-print, and thus be able to tackle each new Emotion. They simply leave the room without having to go through the whole shebang, the whole process again. They know the telly, and they know it's more fun outside. End of story!

So, what's the natural grieving period?' Tara simply shrugged her shoulders.

'Ah, yes,' Lee loved Tara's knack to turn his questions up side down. 'I think we've answered that question - there is no answer.'

'Right. You know, my friend had decided after a year that her Emotional programming needed to change, that she had accepted that she was still wrapped up in it and that she couldn't be present because of it. She was *ready* for change. She had cried all the tears that she could cry under the bedcovers, and she needed to move on. Not to *forget* her loved one, but to keep him in her heart, and *continue* her life.

Now, she took a year to be able to even *consider* moving on, whereas other people would be keen and ready to move on as quickly as possible. Some would love to shorten the grieving period, to pull actively pull themselves out of it and to move on and they are able to do so. Other people like to take their time. From my experience it's all pretty subjective.

You know, if you get down to it? If you ask people *how* they get over Emotions? Most of them no idea *what* they're doing or *how*. They're just doing it. They are not *actively choosing* to stay in any one stage for any particular amount of time. It's just happens. They're not *actively* involved in any of the process. It's just happening to them!'

'And to some it happens sooner than later,' Lee added.

'Exactly. Well, I was curious, I wanted to know if I could actively influence that process. That's how I figured this all out.'

'Gosh, how do you come up with these ideas or even the guts to try? Some people would be scared shitless,' Lee looked at her with respect in his eyes.

'Well, **when I was miserable, I gathered it couldn't get any worse, right? So, I wanted to find a way to make things better, or easier or more fun, so I tried to find ways. Actively**. And guts? I personally find staying in those super scary Emotions much more in need of guts than to just go up to them *once*, switch them off and be done with them! Anyway, fear or the notion that it *has* to take guts, they're just Thoughts.'

'And well, we know what to do with puppies,' Lee grinned.

'Right,' Tara smiled at him. 'You did it yourself earlier, didn't you? How come *you* dared to do it?'

'I was just so *curious*. I wanted to see if I could come up with a solution, a blueprint for myself. **I wanted to see if I could get myself back to a nice peaceful state.**'

'There you go, and? Did it take guts?'

'I guess I was just so curious, that I didn't even think of guts or fear. Once I started to play with the Emotions, instead of scary, I found them absolutely fascinating. After a while I noticed that I wasn't even feeling bad anymore, I was far too busy being amazed by analysing myself. I was actually *enjoying* myself. **I remember how surreal it felt to enjoy Emotions that I would usually find so upsetting.**'

Lee smiled to himself. He loved Tara's clarity. It was nice to talk to somebody that looked at stuff from the same and from more angles than he did. It was good to learn, to fire his brain from different directions.

It's Not About Not Feeling

Tara looked up, 'You know, I personally feel that *natural* healing takes however long you want it to. A few years ago, I got over a 6 year relationship in 3 days.'

'Wow, that's a bit hardcore, isn't it?' Lee's old conditionings voiced their objections.'

'Sure, but in the end it's still down to personal choice,' Tara replied without batting an eyelid, 'and I wanted to find out how far I could take that choice.'

'Doesn't that sound a bit heartless? I mean, didn't you have any feelings?' Lee shook his head tentatively. **'It sounds kind of cold not to feel sad, to cut of Emotions like that.'**

'Ah, that's an important question! Let me clarify this. I'm *not* talking about *not* feeling anything, I'm talking about *not* wallowing and *making yourself unnecessarily miserable* – like *all* the time. I'm talking about becoming actively involved in the process. **Once you understand that you *can*? You *can* choose. An hour of misery a day? One and a half? A day? Maybe two?** Whatever makes you happy,' Lee grinned at the pun. 'If you need to, get your Emotional and energetic discharge out of the way, cry, scream, rant, and *then* look forward and move on. **I can understand that for a lot of people a method like this is might not be the first resort, not the first thing they would try when the wound is still fresh, but there comes a time,**

when most people feel that it's enough and that they want to stop. And then this blue-print works a treat.

All I can recommend, whichever state you're in? **Just give it a try anyway. Begin to play with the puppies just because it sounds interesting, just because it sounds better than being chased and bitten by them. I mean, what have you got to loose? How can it be worse than running all your life? Running away from your Emotions?'**

'I guess the smaller the puppies are when you catch them, the better,' Lee said. 'Don't even let them grow!'

'Well, yeah. **And the more you play, the more you realise that you really don't want to even begin to feel sorry for them, because you know, you don't want to be around when they've grown up!'**

'Gosh, that makes so much sense.'

'I know. Let me give you another example about choice or simply how we feel can change simply by being *aware* that a choice at least exists.'

'Sure, I'm listening.'

'I met a woman whose sister had died a few years back and the anniversary of her death was coming up. When I met her, I didn't know about that fact, I asked her how she was doing. She said she was sad and upset as the anniversary was coming up. She also said that she didn't like this time of year, because she always felt gloomy. I listened to my Intuition and got the thumbs up, so I said to her: **"You don't have to feel this way, you know?"** She looked at me all surprised. All her lights had suddenly gone on at the same time. She'd somehow understood that statement the second it had left my lips, but she needed more information for her Being to hang on to it, to internalize it. She asked: "I don't?", I told her: "No" and **I told her that I dealt with grief differently.** She was intrigued and asked me about it. **I told her about my grandmother dying and how I dealt with my Emotions shortly afterwards, and how on her anniversary, instead of thinking sad Thoughts, I actively thought happy Thoughts about her, remembering the good times, thanking her for having been in my life.** The woman was amazed hat this alternative had never occurred to her. She loved it. **She hadn't *known* that there was a choice, that she could simply think something different, rather than entertain the Thoughts that seemed to naturally *impose* themselves on her.**

Then she hesitated, what would people think, if she would just go about and enjoy herself on her sisters death anniversary? I said, first she shouldn't be concerned about what other people thought, and second, this was about *her* well-being, her happiness and not others. But if she did feel a need to explain, she could just tell them what she was doing and why. **She could tell them that she was remembering her sister in loving, happy memory, rather than holding onto the pain of her loss. It's not about *not* feeling, but about choosing *what* you feel.** I would call that setting a good example. To be honest, her sister would probably be happier 'up there',' Tara nodded upwards, 'to see the woman enjoying herself on her behalf, rather than to be miserable once a year.

The woman loved it. She left with a sparkle in her eyes and a spring in her step. She was still like that the next day and the day after. She didn't even need to do all the Emotions process, **just needed knowing that there *was* a choice, had lifted all the heaviness of her shoulders**.'

'Brilliant.'

Lee loved new refreshing ideas. They turned all his traditional and conditioned ideas up side down and blew a whole horde of new options in his face. Options that were already tried and tested - by him! ***Choose happiness. Actively.*** He wrote in big letters:

Always:
* Choose happiness. Actively.

Tara smiled at Lee's list. It looked so much like all the millions of little notes she had written throughout her own journey. 'Do you want another example about choice?' she asked. 'Choice about how long to let an Emotions affect you. It'll also cover the point about anger on your list,' Tara said.

'Sure, go ahead.'

Anger - Reactions - From 45 Days To 45 Seconds To Nil - It's Your Choice

'A friend of mine used to get incredibly angry, all sorts of little things made him fume. He'd done a bunch of Awareness work around that and had noticed some recurring Behavioural patterns. Those patterns stopped him from being Now, and greatly disturbed his Emotional and Mental balance, his work and his private life. He decided that he wanted to Let Go of this uncontrollable Emotion and the intense reactions that came with it. He had played with his anger for a while and had learned to observe his reactions and to identify the steps his anger moved through. By doing that, he figured out what triggered the anger and how much time he normally had from the first contact with the trigger until he exploded. He understood the

369

Emotional link between Thoughts, Physical Sensations and Behaviour and played with trying to change himself into the person he wanted to be.

When I met him, he told me about a few occasions, where he caught himself out getting angry, and then decided to actively play with it. Instead of holding on to his anger for days or even months on end, as he used to do, he consciously decided to find out if he could just be angry for forty-five minutes, just to let it out, and then to stop thinking about it. Needless to say, he did it. He ran around for a while, screaming and shouting, living out and discharging his Emotions, just because it made him feel better, then he sat down and focussed his energy on his breathing. He *deliberately* and *consciously* relaxed his Body and his Mind, and in Nowness, to his pleasure, his Anger dispersed.

The next time he got angry, he tried to stay *Mindful* and *observe* himself *while* he was having his forty-five minute reactionary tantrum. Suddenly, he told me, while being in total rage, he had to laugh. **By observing himself, he had seen himself pacing around the room, ranting and raving and it was just really funny to see himself run around and steam off as he did; scary too, but hilarious at the same time.** Some gone-crazy madman. He didn't want to be that way.

So, at the next opportunity, he tried to reduce that useless ranting and raving to ten minutes. When he reached ten minutes, he *consciously* and *actively* focussed on his breathing or for fun, played with behaving differently.'

'He played with a non-angry personality,' Lee recalled.

'Exactly. When that worked, he decided to really go for it and make it forty-five seconds! Something upsetting happened, he screamed a couple of times, then breathed. Then, when *that* became his new habit, he decided to reduce the anger to nothing at all, by catching himself out *before* he even reacted. He did it! He stayed peaceful. The anger was gone. It was due to his choice and his hardcore experimentation and determination!'

'That takes a lot of focus, will-power and discipline,' Lee said.

'Right. But it's also lots of fun. **My friend laughed at himself so much when he began to play with different personalities**. It takes a lot of discipline to make yourself do it, but once you start?'

'It's fun and enjoyable,' Lee finished Tara's sentence, also remembering his own experience.

'Exactly. Needless to say, my friend was pretty determined to deal with his anger. But it was not just determination that drove him, it was also an insatiable curiosity to see if he too could do this. He played with trying out what was possible, like the 'Dice Man'. Initially he just wanted to reduce the anger-time, but when he realised that this distant dream was finally a fact in his life, he change his goal. His ultimate goal became to switch the anger off, to wipe the slate clean,' Tara looked at Lee. 'Now, because I'm always interested in hearing about how other people switch themselves on, I asked him to tell me about the breakthrough moment. The one moment where everything changed for him. The crux, the turning point.'

'Oh, tell me!' Lee said curiously.

'My friend said that something happened to him one day, which would have usually made him freak out. An immensely important parcel hadn't arrived, and the people in charge of delivery, proved to be terribly incompetent. Normally he would have totally lost it, whereas this time, he noticed the feeling coming up and he consciously did two things. First he immediately decided that he didn't want to be angry and focussed on his breathing instead. So, the initial pang of anger rising in his Body disappeared as soon as it had threatened to arrive. To prevent the Emotion from growing and himself from feeding the puppy, he actively stopped thinking about the anger and the aggravating situation. Then he did exactly what makes all of this so much fun! He *played* with his new desired personality! **He deliberately behaved completely out of character.** He played a new role. **He suddenly became ever so polite, surprising everybody around him.** He even had smile while was doing it, because it was so funny to observe himself behaving like that, being a little unfamiliar and awkward with the new self. He felt as if he'd embarked on a mysterious adventure into somebody else's Body and Mind. At first it was new and strange, but then he noticed something significant. Because he'd stayed so calm, yet firm, people around him were suddenly much more open to help him. They actually made an effort to find his parcel, whereas usually, if he would have shouted at them, they would have more than likely just shut off.'

'That's powerful stuff. **By being *Mindful* of his actions and by observing himself during the goings on, he became more aware of people's reactions towards him, how other people responded to his different moods and personalities, and he figured out what worked for him and what didn't,**' Lee summarised. 'He became who he wanted to be. He *acted* the way he *wanted* to, rather than just *reacting* in his previously ingrained pattern. And to top that, he got an immediate reward from the people he was dealing with.'

'Precisely. And as an added bonus he learned that *not* being angry is much more useful, much more chilled and relaxed and of course much nicer to *himself* than flipping out and complaining and going nuts all the time,' Tara added. 'That's important. It was for *his* benefit!'

'True. Another useful thing to learn from that story, is that you don't have to become a pushover, but that there are better ways of dealing with situations than loosing control.'

'Agreed. My friend got four for the price of one. He felt a tremendous sensation of achievement, knowing that he could play with the little creature in his head, rather be dominated by it. He learned a lot, he had fun playing and he changed his Being to what he wanted it to be.'

'Good deal I'd say,' Lee grinned.

'Yep. **Oh, I just remember something, I also asked my friend to describe the feelings in his head a bit more, you know, what it *felt* like when he dealt with the anger.'**

'I really need to remember your questions, they're just too fabulous,' Lee loved the way Tara always probed deeper and deeper into all the most remote nooks and crannies of people's Minds.

'Don't worry,' Tara said reassuringly, 'the more you play, the more these questions start to come to you all by themselves. If you're curious that is,' she winked. 'Anyway, he said that initially he'd only become faintly aware of little nudges in his brain, of tiny little oncoming anger Emotions on the fringes of his Consciousness, quick glimpses of something coming towards him, which he couldn't quite interpret yet. When he began to become more aware of himself and he began to examine those little glimpses further, he noticed a slight tightening of his chest, he was actually holding his breath, his eyes would narrow, his forehead would crease, and his Body would tense. He realised that by the time he'd recognised those little signs as Anger, it was usually to late. But, the more he trained himself to notice the combination of these tiny Anger nudges, the more he got to know them and what *they* felt like, what his *Mind* and his *Body felt* like when they came up. With time he became more familiar with *exactly* how the anger manifested and affected his Being, until one day, he could see it a mile of. At the slightest tightening of his chest, he knew: time to breathe. That was when he began to play with Letting it Go right there and then, right at the source, at the core.'

'Oops puppy, yep, see ya. Gone,' Lee smiled.

'That's the one,' Tara nodded. '**My friend was amazed that by simply being *aware* and *Mindful* of his Thoughts, Emotions and reactions, he could *choose* which ones he wanted in his Being and which he didn't.** And what's more, he knew that if he'd done it once, he could do it *again*, and of course that it'll become easier every time he played with it. Needless to say, it did. He told me many a story about all the wonderful situations he got himself into and all the little things he changed about himself.'

'Man, you can gain such fascinating insights with this stuff,' Lee was still amazed.

'That's a bit of an understatement!' Tara sparkled.

19 Might Not Work For Everyone? Well, Let's Look At That

'Yeah, but,' Lee hesitated. Even though he realised and had even experienced the vast potential of everything Tara had explained and even though he knew that it would work miracles for himself in his life, he still wondered, 'This approach might not work for *everyone* though, or does it?' he asked.

'Well, *nothing* works for *everyone*, people are too different,' Tara said candidly. 'They are different with how fast they take to an approach and different in their preferences of which method to play with. Some people prefer to *talk* about their Emotions and problems, and they experience great relief from voicing their Thoughts, hoping that with time, the pain lessens and becomes easier to bear. Some people want to *feel* the problem to the full, to it's core, feel it as intense as they can, some people enjoy the pain, some people like to play with it, some need to have a strong wake-up call, whereas others want a more conservative approach to work with Emotions. You know,' Tara looked sad, 'the combination of the words *Playful* and *Emotions* often doesn't compute in people's brains.'

'I can see that. Personally though? I vote for your approach. It's fun light-hearted. Works for me,' Lee said.

'Same here,' Tara said, 'but other people might be different. Some people are like you, they want to move on, but some don't. Some people think: "why *bear* it if you can just get Let Go of it", or: "I've done this long enough, I want to stop it or change it". They are the people that like to speed up the healing and changing process, they take the *direct* route rather than the scenic route.'

'The scenic route would be seeing the sights of Emotions for a long, long trip?' Lee clarified.

'Precisely. For a lot of people, things can be sped up with what we've talked about. Sped up and made more exciting! Some people though might not want to be Now, they want to be the way they already are. And hey,' Tara shook her shoulders sincerely, 'who can argue with that? Everybody needs to know what's best for themselves. **Some people are cool with their extreme Behaviour and Emotions, whereas I feel that there are limits.** It might be ok to have a good cry or feel a little sorry for oneself, or to really let rip from time to time, but it might not be appropriate to live out your Emotions regardless. You can't beat people up to embrace your own aggression, you can't kill yourself to experience the height of your depression. **There is a limit as to what you can experience without affecting your environment or your own**

wellbeing. So, at some stage *something* has to be done, be it with my approach or any other. Which one it is to be, that's down to personal choice. And once you picked your way, you either do it, or you don't. All in all,' Tara said frankly, '**there is no right or wrong, there is no only-way**. Everybody needs to work out what works best for them by themselves. **I can't and I won't try to make anybody do anything, all I can do is fire up a little curiosity about a way of life, which is playful and entertaining, informative and fun and incredibly effective.** I'm sure many people will be inspired by it and will give it a go, and I'm sure many will be pleasantly surprised.'

Tara had that bright sparkle about her Being again, Lee noticed. She seemed to know something. Something big. Something that was going to change the world. "What a strange Thought," Lee observed the goings on in his Mind. Was this stuff really going to change the world? Somehow he had no Doubt in his Mind that somehow, somehow it would. And even stranger, he felt that in some way he was going to play a significant part in all of this.

He shook his head, his Subconscious just managed to register the content of his Thoughts and filed them away for future use, before his Rational Mind managed to quickly dispersed them.

'But hey,' Tara entered his Consciousness, 'if this approach doesn't work for people? I hope they find something else that does. As long as they're happy, that's all that counts,' she smiled openly. 'Everything we've talked about so far, is not supposed to be the one and only ultimate truth, the only one true way to play with Thoughts, Behaviour and Emotions, but rather, it's meant to be a practical, logical and highly valuable way – for certain people, when they're ready - to clear their Minds and Souls and help them to Be Now, to relax, chill and balance their lives,' Tara paused. 'Some people might say that this approach is far too clinical, far to Thought based, to cerebral, some might even Doubt that one can deal with Emotions or Thoughts like that. Well, it is, and people can. For some people this is the salvation, a new approach to an old problem, magic even, and others will hate it! And that's cool.'

Lee nodded. For him this was salvation. This was the way he worked, the way he thought. Even if some people might feel differently, how could they not be dying of curiosity to at least give it a little try? Just for the hell of it? Maybe it could work for them too? Wouldn't it be fantastic if it would? They might be surprised that it really *is* magic... Just planting seeds...

'You know, there's something I want to stress,' Tara's face suddenly became more serious. 'I don't ignore the fact, that

there are a lot of people out there in really bad situations and **this stuff will not make situations miraculously go away, but hey, you know what? So would nothing else!**' Tara said firmly and clearly. 'But what I am saying is that **you can then either let yourself get lost in mental stories, or you can see them for what they are**. You can at least start to Let Go of some of the roller-coaster Emotions and Thoughts that make situations even worse, and that might at least help you to make the every day survival easier. If it's tough at the beginning, start of with little things in your life, use it for whatever you think it might be useful, and slowly extend it. And you know what? If all the head stuff doesn't do the trick either? Well, maybe it's some time for action. Get up or shut up. In the end, nobody can your life for you. You do. You choose!'

Some People Don't Want To Or Can't Let Go

'**C**ome to think of it, I know from experience that there are some people for who this approach is straight off *not* going to work,' Tara said frankly. 'We've already discussed those people too. The people that would have difficulties with this approach are the ones that can't detach themselves from their Emotions enough to gain the necessary Mental Clarity. But even then there are exceptions. Some of those people try to use this approach anyway and manage to conquer their head-in-sand-ness, even though they thought they wouldn't be able to. To their surprise the lights got switched on along the way and they succeeded. But often, without Mental Clarity, this approach usually doesn't work, one would simply not be able to stay focussed enough.'

'That's what all the Nowness Play can help with tremendously though, or not.'

'Oh absolutely, if they have the willpower to stay focussed on *that*,' Tara responded sharply.

'Ah, good point.'

'**All in all, the most important thing for this approach to work for anyone, is that you need to *want* to give it a fair go. It takes time and practice, determination and commitment, guts and strength and will power. If you don't have that or you don't have, *can't* or don't *want* to try to learn develop those qualities, you'll have problems with it. If you can't or don't want to take *responsibility* for your own well-being, you'll have difficulties, because nobody else but you can do this**,' Tara took a breather.

'You know,' she continued, 'Actually, it goes even further than that. Lot's of people simply **can't imagine their current life without their intense Emotions, they don't** *want* **to Let Go of them. Those are the ones that are** *defined* **by their Emotions.**

'Ah, you used that term once before. Can you go into a bit more detail about what you mean by defined-by-Emotions?' Lee wanted to refine his understanding.

'If you are defined by your Emotion, you wouldn't know *who* **you would be if you wouldn't outlive that Emotion. Who would you be, if you wouldn't be a cancer victim or an abused person or a left housewife?** A person like that would have fed the puppy for such a long time, that it has grown and become stronger than they themselves, it has taken on a life of it's own and it has became an integral part of them. It has taken over their head, their life, sometimes even their every waking minute. **It's gone completely out off control, but they might not see it that way. It's just who they are.** In fact, it has *become* them, it has *become their personality.* **It has become so ingrained, so part of them, that they can't or maybe don't want to Let Go anymore.** Even though they might be unhappy, they simply can't or won't let themselves gain the Mental Objectivity from it. It's who they are, what they do, how they behave, how they interact. **Who would they be without it?** What would they do? Who would they be?' Tara repeated and shrugged her shoulders.

'Makes sense. So, to start playing, they'd have to see and then accept, if only for a split second, that it's their own Thoughts, Behaviour, Emotions and reactions that's making them unhappy and unbalanced. Then they could work their way forward from that,' Lee said.

'Exactly. **But they might come across their own denial in their warehouse.** It's a huge step for some people to say: "I'm an alcoholic" or: "I am defined by my Emotions and it's causing me problems" or: "Maybe I'm not right, maybe there is an alternative". Something has to click into place for people to see that, and they can actively start to play. But they have to *want* to Let Go.

Besides the people that unknowingly support and hold on to their Emotions, **there are people who consciously and** *deliberately* **maintain that state of dependence on their Emotions.** Those are the ones that *know* what they're doing and they *like* being that way. For them my approach obviously wouldn't work either, because they really don't *want* to be any different, they don't want to pull themselves out.'

'But how could you not want to?' Lee asked surprised. He couldn't fathom why anybody would rather me miserable than happy.

'Well, there can be many reasons. Some people might just be scared. I personally always find it terribly exciting to play with something new, to try and find new ways that make me happy, that enable me to be Now and at peace, to Let Go of the ingrained patterns, I mean, just imagine what it'll be like to be free of all that silly conditioning? To be who you'd want to be? To be able to choose? Well, that's my idea of happiness,' Tara said unassumingly, 'but other people might find it scary and intimidating to Let Go of the security blanket of who they have become, of who they've made themselves into. **Even if they're not happy, they'd rather stay with what they know, than jump and try something different.** Their excuse is often the sarcastic: "the grass is always greener on the other side". Well, you know what? Sometimes it is!' Tara said with emphasis. 'I know that from my own experience. **I've founds so many fantabulously amazing things by hopping over that freaking fence.** I'm always so curious, to see what else there is. **I see it as an adventure, an exciting journey of exploration, but you know, we're all different and others might see it as a scary trip into an unknown world.** They might find the uncertainty daunting. I thrive on it. **I look at things differently! I always try and find something positive**. When I wrote my first book, somebody asked me if I had written anything else before, to work my way up to that. I said no, I just started with the book. She said: "Wow, that takes guts!" I was surprised. Funny, it hadn't even *occurred* to me that it *should* take guts, it was just what I wanted to do and I did it. Doubt, fear and uncertainty disappear in the Now. And that's where I spend most of my time now.'

'You just cut through the bullshit,' Lee said simply.

'Well, it's what works for me. All that diddly-daddling never got me anywhere. But, that's personal preference. Anyhow, there are other reasons why people hold on to Emotions.'

'Let's have them,' Lee said incredulously, never failing to be amazed at Tara's bottomless well of examples.

'Some people *get something out of* holding on to them. I met a guy that actually *liked* having a huge puppy around. When I asked him about it, he said that he knew he had a pet.' Lee grinned at Tara's descriptions of people's intense Emotions. 'He said that it gave him a sense of security and strength. He regarded it as a part of his life. It had created his sense of identity, and he could not imagine life without it anymore. He liked being directed by it and told what to do by it. He *knowingly* kept it as an excuse to feel or behave a certain way, to have something to blame for his extreme Behaviour and his Moods, so that he didn't have to face them and take responsibility for his own actions. He was blaming his depression, the neighbours, the world, the puppy. He was the stereotypical little-poor-old-me, I-can't-do-anything-about-this, I'm-so-weak kind of person. He was like someone that pretends that their broken leg is much more painful and debilitates them much more than it actually does, just to get people run errands for them and serve on them hand and foot, and then goes and blames everybody else, including his foot for his misery. This guy *knew* that he'd chosen this state of Being, but he still kept whining that the world had made him into this person and that he just couldn't defend himself. **Being this way *served* him. He wasn't happy, Now or balanced, but he got lots of attention and help and he never had to take any responsibility for anything, because it was always everybody else's fault.**'

'Oh yes, I now people like that.'

'I think everybody does. Obviously, if somebody likes being that way? Our approach won't work.'

'Fair enough.'

'I have another example like that. **I knew a girl that was terribly afraid of the dark.** She told me that she had tried to deal with her fear of the dark for years, but that she was still scared of it.'

'And your way did work?'

'Actually, she didn't even Listen to it. She didn't even try.'

'Oh Tara, I can't believe you admit that,' Lee laughed.

'Well, there's no point in lying about it. The truth was, she wasn't *ready* to try, she didn't *want* to try. The plain reason was that she didn't want to Let Go of her fear, it had nothing to do with our approach. In fact she got so much out of being the scared little girl - she was thirty two -,' Tara added casually, 'she got so much attention talking about it and so much sympathy, why should she get rid of it? It fulfilled a fabulous function.'

'I can see that. If somebody isn't ready to change themselves, no approach in the world will help.'

'Right. Then, **there are people that are *addicted* to their Emotions for whatever reason**, they obviously don't really want to Let Go of them either,' Tara conjured another example.

'**I remember you mentioned that briefly earlier in the TV example. Addiction to Emotions could be an escape from the real world,** a substitute, an excuse and so on,' Lee recalled.

'Yeah, and there are other reasons too. **Some people like the *intensity* of their Emotions, to them it's like a drug.** I met a guy once who seriously, consciously revelled in his misery. Man, he literally indulged in his puppy's existence. He deliberately got himself into situations, where he knew he would be in trouble or get hurt. I was really surprised when he told me about that, because he seemed like a pretty switched on

378

guy. When I asked him why he did that, he said that he loved the intensity of it. **He enjoyed the emotional roller-coaster.** It was like a drug. He was seeking it out. On purpose. As far as I could tell he was truly conscious of his actions. Well, bless him. Whatever works for you dude. I do have to say though that he always looked pretty torn and never looked as if he enjoyed himself very much. But hey, each to their own. If that's what he wants to experience, who am I to argue? At least it was his *conscious* decision. Of course, **unless he would have decided to stop *wanting* to indulge in his misery, my approach would never work.'**

'**And so would nothing else,**' Lee said.

'Right. **But man, I really think that if you're choosing to be addicted to your Emotions? For heaven's sake, at least pick the fun ones! Silly twat!**' Tara said, looking all innocently.

'Yeah, silly twat indeed,' Lee laughed out loud. Tara's logic was hard hitting and ironically funny. 'What a bizarre story. The dude consciously chose to have intense experiences, which most people would rather not have, which in fact they would do anything to try and avoid. They'd rather be happy, content and blissful. Very strange,' Lee shook his head.

'Strange to us, I know, but there are more people like that out there than you think. And I'm not judging them, all I'm trying to describe, is that different people prefer different ways to live! As long as people take responsibility for their own Emotions, Thoughts, Behaviour and thus their own Happiness, I'm cool. But that's unfortunately where the problem often lies,' Tara shook her head sadly. **'A lot of people are either not prepared or used to accepting responsibility for themselves.** Why should I eat healthily? Why should I exercise? I know it's good for me, but… I can't be asked or I'm too lazy or I'm to weak. Moan, moan, moan, I'm too this, I'm too that. **People take the power out of their own sails, by coming up with excuses why they can't do the things they know are good for them.** I tell you ninety-nine out of a hundred people would rather have a part of their stomach removed, than fast for a day a week and for seven days four times a year. **"I can't because", it's one of the most favourite little phrases our Rational Mind has ever come up with, and - it's *all* in the Mind! People find excuses for their Mental, Physical and Emotional shortcomings.**

I know that life out there in the big wide world is not always easy, it can even be scary, boy I've had my fair share of it. I know that it's so much easier to revel in misery and non-action, than it is to get of your butt to stop the But-s and to begin to *actively* work on some Happiness,' Tara grinned at the But-ts.

'"Rewire your Brain". That was printed on a T-shirt of a friend of mine,' Lee said thoughtfully as his own brain rewired itself.

'Rewire, flick the switches and let there be light! Not freaking darkness,' Tara said with overplayed sarcasm, flicking a bunch of imaginary switches all around her.

They looked at each other for a long time. Kindred souls. Gently she took the pen out of Lee's hand and began to write into his little notebook:

> *"Happiness is not a natural state,*
> *It's a personal choice.*
> *If you want to be unhappy,*
> *Nothing in the world can make you happy,*
> *But if you want to be happy,*
> *Nothing in the world can make you unhappy."*

When she was done, Lee took the hand back and wrote underneath another little sentence one more time, just because he liked it so much:

> *"That's your lot,*
> *Now cope with it and be jolly."*

Puppies With Big Teeth or Gently Does It

'**We**'ve just discussed that a person has to be *willing* to move on, right? Well, there's more. For any of this to work, you *really* have to be *prepared face* your fears and your Emotions! **And I tell you, once you're starting to challenge your Mind and your Emotions? They won't like it. By opening yourself up and looking at things the way they *really are*, rather than how you've *thought* or *felt* them to be, maybe even for your whole life, you might discover some demons, and they'll want to fight!**'

'Yeah, but we said that it's only big if we make it, right?' Lee remembered his lessons well.

'That's right, but I just want to make sure that you are aware of what you're letting yourself in for when you begin to dig deeper. A friend of mine said once:

> *"The first thing you see,*
> *once you start to become Aware of what's in your Mind and Body,*
> *is the stuff you've neglected for years."'*

'**And that might not be pleasant,**' Lee said clenching his teeth.

'Nope. You might get surprised by what comes up, or by how intense or nasty some of the things you discover can be. **All those Thoughts and Feelings and Behaviour and Emotions, that were hidden, ignored or put into boxes so that you didn't have to deal with them, will come to the surface.** You have to be prepared for the fact that you might open a whole can of worms, and that you might have to deal with them.'

'Yeah, but that's the whole point,' Lee said simply. '**To spring-clean. To get rid of the cobwebs. It's only natural that doing that, one might find the occasional spider or rat.**' Lee went on unperturbed, '**And surely with the right attitude they can't be *that* scary**,' Lee said, feeling that he'd already had a pretty good taste of how a different Mind set can have a huge impact on the way he related to his Mind and Emotions.

'**Well, that depends if you're scared of spiders or rats,**' Tara joked.

'Sure, but one day you'll have to face that fear right?' Lee shrugged his shoulders. He had stared some pretty deep Emotions straight into the face earlier, maximised them to the hilt, and he was still alive. He even laughed about them in the end. He knew it was possible if he focussed on clarity and not getting lost in any scary or daunted feelings! It was not blind belief. His knowledge was based on first hand experience.

'I agree, but it's completely normal to be a little apprehensive. A lot of people are. Most people are surprised to see what's been stowed away in their Warehouse. But man, it's so worth it.'

'**I guess it's a bit like becoming environmentally aware,**' **Lee said.** '**First you see all the terrible, terrible things that are happening in this world, and it's completely overwhelming, and then, with time, when you begin to deal with them one by one, you manage to stay detached and approach them with clarity and strength.**'

'Exactly. Great example. And the most important thing to remember is that…'

'It's only Scary if you make it. It's only Big if you make it,' Lee finished Tara's sentence. 'Only if we feed that puppy will it have the power to exist. So, when it becomes scary, be Now. Relax. Play with it, and the big monster dog might just turn out to be a cuddly lapdog,' Lee grinned.

'That's it!' Tara clapped her hand excitedly. '**Keep in Mind though, if things come up that still ball you over, and if for whatever reason you can't deal with them yet, if Nowness is still**

far away, don't beat yourself up! If Nowness won't come yet. Well, sod it. Who cares? The point is not to freak out! Don't try and force it. Give yourself time. With time, you *will* be able to be Mindful. With time, you *will* be able to be Now. Until then, be gentle on yourself. If you can't deal with something, no matter what it is, try to just *observe* it instead. Be Mindful of it *while* it's going on. Don't judge it as good or bad, just observe it. No matter how crazy, no matter how hurtful or sad or intense or frightening it might be. Stay aware and open. Stay detached in the knowledge that it's just a Thought! Stay conscious and observe it *consciously*. Like that you won't become *involved* and you won't get *lost* in Dot's and Squiggles. And,' Tara added with a cheeky smile on her lips, 'just to entertain yourself, pay special attention observing yourself observing everything.'

'Ey?'

'Observe *yourself* observing. Observe how *you* play with all the ridiculousness that's going on within yourself.'

'Oh wow, that's like one step up.'

'Exactly! **That's when you start to laugh at yourself trying so hard to laugh at the Emotions! That's when it gets class!**' Tara smiled broadly.

'Always one extra,' Lee loved it.

'Of course, it can ever get boring, can it?' She winked at him happily. 'And, while you're doing all of the observing, the analysing, the Letting Go, start to piss yourself laughing at the silliness of all of it, at the shit your Mind and your Emotions come up with. Try to enjoy just sitting back and watching the film. It's a movie, a drama, you can be involved in or that you can just watch, it's your choice.'

'That's a fabulous way of putting it. It's a movie,' Lee nodded. 'Man, this is all such a, such a...,' Lee hesitated for words, 'I don't know, it's like taking your brain apart and putting it back again in a different way, in a way you want to, a way you choose for yourself. **It will be fascinating to just sit back and eat popcorn for a change, rather than being the main character in a really intense or scary film!**' Lee laughed happily, munching away on some imaginary little popped corn thingies. 'Beginning to look at your Mind, Emotions and Behaviour, is like going to the movies and not knowing what's on,' Lee grinned. 'You never know what you'll find, when you open up your Brain.'

'That's right. I can't describe or prepare anyone for all the possibilities, for all the eventualities, all I can say is that **you have to stay detached from your own stories and think out of the box, maybe even become a little creative with how to organise your warehouse and how to keep the puppies out.'**

'Any tips?' Lee asked.

'Sure,' the memories came back easily.

The Little Death Or Vacuum

'**A** guy I met had started to play with his Emotions in a similar way I had, but he'd hit a wall and couldn't go any further, so he came to me for advice. **He said, that Letting Go of his stuff had all worked fabulously, but that once he'd Let Go of the Emotion, he felt a hole, an emptiness inside.** It felt as if part of him had left. He said that it had felt like a little death and he felt a bit unhappy, even concerned about that. Having lost something made him feel uncomfortable.'

A smile crossed Lee's lips, 'Ah, I know what you mean with staying detached and getting creative. **You always have to look at *everything* from the *outside*. The guy was getting wrapped up in a *new* Emotion. The Emotion of feeling *loss*.**'

'Bang on,' Tara slapped Lee's leg with played vigour. 'He was stuck until I pointed exactly that out to him. So, when you start to play with this stuff, you need to be able to observe yourself observing to notice and to point these things out to yourself! Or you need to play with others and point things out to each other.'

'I shall remember,' Lee made a mental note. 'So, what happened with the guy?'

'Well, **I asked him to *redefine* the feeling of the little death**. Why did it have to be a *loss* or a *death*? What he'd Let Go had been a part of him, but it was a part of him that had made him unhappy, so Letting Go was something *positive*, right? He agreed. So, I asked him to call the *loss*, a *release* instead. It was so funny to see his face as soon as I'd said that. He suddenly smiled, his eyes sparkled. All of a sudden he felt relieved, free and light.'

'Wow, it was simply the *terminology* that made him uncomfortable,' Lee was amazed, 'mad how much difference a single *word* can make.'

'I know, it's so powerful. ***You are what you tell yourself you are. It is what you make it!*** And yes, it might sound trivial, but one word changed his world and his life!'

'It just depends on what we call it,' Lee repeated awed. '**Call it a *death* and we're unhappy, call it *release* or *shedding weight* and suddenly it becomes a full success.** And hey presto, we can call it whatever we want to and thus rewire our Minds. Hilarious.'

'Yeah. Actually, the guy said something else. He said that the hole which the released Emotion left, felt like a vacuum, wanting to suck the Emotion straight back in,' Tara said.

'Of course. That's the puppy coming straight back for his attention.'

'Exactly. I told him that that was normal, that it's a constant cycle. You Let Go of something, the puppy comes back, you Let Go again and you keep doing that, until it finally stays away. You settle down, and something *else* comes up! There'll always be something else. Your whole life long.'

'Till you're enlightened,' Lee grinned.

'Yep, I wonder if there are enlightened puppies that come to haunt you then too,' Tara replied dead-pan.

They both burst out laughing.

'Even though the word *release* made him feel so much better, he still felt that he should fill that hole with something. He'd released something and something needed to take it's place, right? He asked me what he should fill it with. I just said: **"Who says there's a hole? It's your Mind! If you don't think of your mum, is there a hole in your brain where the Thought of your mum would usually be**?" He had to laugh at that. All of those Thoughts about deaths and vacuums and holes are all stories, you're making them up. If you want there to be a hole, there *will* be one. At least you'll *convince yourself* that there is one. But that's making it complicated when it doesn't have to be! You released the Emotion. End of story.'

'We like it,' Lee said with a twinkle in his eye.

'Actually, the guy gets extra points,' Tara said waved her index finger.

'Oh yeah? Why's that?'

'Well, he, like me, had tried many different methods to play with his Emotions. He was one of the people that was actively seeking out a way to make his life more enjoyable,' Tara said with respect.

'Fair enough, full marks to him,' Lee replied appreciatively.

'Yeah, I was pretty impressed with that myself. Actually, one of my best bits of advice is to keep playing until you find something that *really* works for you. But even after that, keep open, you never know, there might be something better out there, even if it's just more interesting or fun. Sometimes the grass really is greener on the other side, and if it's not, you can always return to your side of the fence. Never get stuck in anyone way and never close yourself off to potentially fabulous insights, you could miss out on a lot of fun!' Tara ended enthusiastically.

20 Extremes vs. Balance and Detachment

'You know,' Tara let a lock of her hair flow through her fingers, 'a lot of what we've talked about so far, is about how to learn to become *aware* of ourselves. **Aware of how we feel, behave and think, and how we interact with our environment. If you look at it, what we're trying to maintain the whole time, is Balance. A balanced, calm and peaceful Being that can enjoy the moment to the full, be happy, strong and alive,** right? So, in a way everything we talked about so far is about Balance. **Only if we're balanced, can we be Now, and the more balanced we are, the easier it is to be Now.** So let me talk to you a bit more about Balance.

Once we begin to observe ourselves and our interactions with the outside world more Mindfully, we begin to notice, that we do everything in *extremes*. We either go up and down between extremes, or we just sit in one and enjoy it or wallow in it. We either store up all of our Emotions, or we're over-Emotional and blow up all the time. We might get terribly impatient or worry like crazy. We are a total party animal and never know when to stop, then we crash, trying to recover. We never pay attention to what we're being told, we might be overly particular or meticulous, lazy, shy. We are a gossip. We listen all the time but don't speak much. We talk all the time but don't listen much. We need to be the centre of attention or we might do anything in our power to avoid being noticed. We need to be mothered or we need to mother. We like to be in control or not. We're independent or we're not. We hate our looks or not. We think we're God's gift or not. We want to go around hitting everybody or hitting *on* everybody. The list goes on,' Tara drew a deep breath. **'How we feel and what goes on in our heads and Body, depends on the day, our mood, and outside influences. Who we are and how we feel, is a constant roller coaster and sometimes we feel good about it and sometimes we don't.** Sometimes we're happy, sometimes we're not,' Tara paused.

Lee thought for a second and then said, 'Well, don't the ups and downs make our lives interesting? You know, doesn't it spice things up a bit?' Lee paused. 'Then again, I guess it'll be pretty cool not to have such crazy extremes all the time. **In my experience highflying happiness usually gets eventually counteracted with total and utter misery, where everything just seems to go wrong**, right? Those days where you feel crap, unhappy, where you wallow in sadness, neglected-ness or whatever. And that's not so cool. Ok, tell me more about Balance then,' Lee said having won himself over.

'All I can say is Happy Healthy Balance.'

'Of course your balance has to be Happy,' Lee laughed.

'Sure, otherwise what's the point?' Tara grinned. **'The gist is that if you're not balanced, you're not Now. So everything that disturbs your balance keeps you from Being Now.** Can I draw a quick picture into your favourite book?' Tara asked playfully, wriggling her hands in front of Lee's face.

'Sure, hang on,' Lee grabbed the notebook from beside him, flicked through the pages, opened it on an empty one and passed it to Tara who took it and drew a few boxes. Her picture looked a little like this:

SAD	Involved, Indulged, Attached
	Detached - observe yourself in Sadness
BALANCED - NOW **Unconditional Bliss**	
HAPPY	Detached - observe yourself in Happiness
	Involved, Indulged, Attached

'If you want Balance for your Thoughts, Emotions and Behaviour? It's right there,' Tara pointed at Lee's belly. 'You're balanced when you're centred in the middle, in the Now. You are out of Balance and *not* Now, when all your Negative Mental Weight goes from your belly into your head,' she leant over and gently tapped Lee's forehead, 'when your Mind goes wild, when it does mad Dots and Squiggles or when it engages in Emotional roller-coasters, when you indulge in sad feelings and Thoughts.'

'Makes sense.' Lee looked at the table again and noticed something. **'Hang on,' Lee pointed at his notebook, 'looking at your drawing, it seems that if you indulge in happy feelings, you're not balanced either.'**

'That's right,' Tara began to answer his question, 'as soon as you indulge in *anything*, you're not on the ground, you're not rooted - you're diving or flying, right? Either way there's too much weight on one side of the scale.'

'I assume **by *indulging* in feelings you mean thinking about them too much**, yeah? **Have your brain filled with them to the rim? Feeding the puppy, making it artificially grow or even**

creating it artificially?' Lee wanted to make sure that they were on the same page.

'**That's right but indulging also means being *attached* to your Emotions. As long as you're attached, you can't Let Go, that's simple Physics,**' Tara laughed, '**and thus you can't be Now.**'

'Tell me more about attachment and detached observing?' Lee requested, looking at the drawing.

Impermanence and Detachment

'Sure,' Tara agreed easily. '**Everything in life is impermanent,**' Tara said simply.

'What's that got to do with it?' Lee didn't quite know what to make of that.

'Don't worry, you'll know in a minute, bear with me,' Tara said. 'So, *everything* in our lives is impermanent. People, events, situations, thinking, problems, good stuff, bad stuff, material things, immaterial things, *everything* we take for granted or not, *will* eventually end or change. And that's a fact,' Lee's mouth opened slightly in realisation. Tara continued, 'Think of anything in your life,...'

Lee thought out loud, 'My parents – impermanent. My apartment – impermanent. My job – impermanent. My friends – impermanent. That tree over there – impermanent. This city is impermanent. Shit, this moment, this world! It's all impermanent. Noise, anger, problems, issues, stress, arguments. Man, I had never thought about this before! My cells, my hair, my Thoughts. *Everything* is impermanent. Everything in my Mind *is* impermanent.' He closed his eyes and went on. He went through *everything* he could think of. It *was* all impermanent. He opened his eyes with a start, 'Shit, Tara. Myself! *I* am impermanent too. Of course I always knew that I will die one day, but I only just got it, I just *felt* it for a split second. I *will* actually *die* one day. It's a fact, it's inevitable. It *will* happen. *I* am impermanent. **There's no point to be scared of death. I can't avoid it. There's no point worrying about it. Being scared of loosing my life won't change the fact that I will loose it one day. Oh man, *in recognition I loose my fear. I go beyond fear.* Fear does not change anything, it's in my head,**' Lee looked at Tara slightly taken aback.

Tara nodded and smiled broadly. She loved his passion. Lee had absorbed everything so quickly and he was already using it to explain and answer his own questions. He was transforming his knowledge into wisdom - fast. He was getting it and he was into it as much as she was. What a wonderful Co-incidence to have walked into this fabulous fellow bare-footer.

She leant over, hugged him and giggled happily, 'You're brilliant.'

'Gee thanks, so are you,' Lee flashed her a loving smile, hugging her back. She felt warm and soft in his arms. He held her closely for a moment and let her go.

Tara looked up at him through her eyelashes, 'You know, what you just realised, is one of the most important things to understand. **You have understood and accepted, that every moment, every Being, every thing, every wonderful or terrible Sensation, every Thought or Emotion, *is* impermanent and *will* end eventually.** And of course that there's no point in being attached to anything that is impermanent.'

'Because if it ends and you're attached to it, you'll become sad or angry, you'll miss it, become unhappy, upset or miserable,' Lee finished her sentence. 'So basically, if I'm attached to something that is impermanent, then disappointment or sadness is *inevitable*, because the simple reality is that it *will* end. I get that. But,' he thought out loud, '**I do *care* though. I don't want to become *emotionless*.** I do care for my family, my friends, my apartment, my cat. **How can I not be attached**?' Lee asked with an uncertain undertone in his voice.

'**Oh, there's a big difference between *not caring* and not being attached!**' Tara said reassuringly. '**The way I use the term 'not being attached', is that it means to *be fully aware of impermanence*. Not being attached does not mean that you don't care or that you can't love or that you can't enjoy yourself. It just means understanding and accepting that one day everything *will* end, that it will be over.**'

'That sounds a bit pessimistic though. I mean, how can I enjoy myself if I think the whole time that it will end?' Lee wasn't so sure he liked that idea.

'Actually, it's not pessimistic, it's realistic. It's what *IS*, it's inevitable, and actually, it *increases* your joy.'

'Oh yeah? How does it do that?' Lee couldn't see it.

'*Because it frees you from worry!* You don't *have* to worry about anything ending anymore. You don't have to be sad anymore when something ends. What it comes down to is, that with practice, you can get to a stage, **where you can *observe yourself*, utterly enjoying the moment, without worrying that it'll end,** without being attached to any outcome, without having any expectations of it one way or another and without being thrown of balance when it finishes, or if it turns out differently than planned! You don't have to think about all of that anymore - *ever*! **You can just enjoy every moment, enjoy it to the full, without any Thoughts spoiling it - before, during or after!**'

Lee nodded slowly, 'That's cool. **And of course, with regards to any bad moments, you can** *observe* **the bad moments** *while* **they're happening, and stay detached and not be upset, because you know they will end too.**'

'Right. Not being attached, allows you to objectively observe yourself and your Emotions, *while* you're experiencing them. And in turn, **being able to** *objectively observe*, **helps you to stay** *detached*.'

'Ah, they reinforce each other, that's handy,' Lee pointed out with a smile.

'So it is,' Tara agreed easily.

Lee had listened carefully. 'Let me just summarize quickly to make sure that I got all of that. Basically, **indulging in happy or sad Thoughts or Emotions, removes you from being Now**, right? **A step closer to being Balanced and Now is to be** *Mindful* **and to** *observe* **yourself** *while* **those Emotions and Thoughts are going on, instead of mindlessly indulging in them and feeding them,**' he summed up eloquently. **'So, in plain English that means that we can enjoy as much as we can without being attached to the feeling,'** he paused. 'Ah, that's like Listening to music,' Things clicked into place amongst Lee's synapses. 'We know that every note is impermanent and we enjoy every single note to the full, knowing that it is the flow of notes that's important, that's what makes the music so beautiful for us to enjoy. You can't have music just playing one note. When a piece is over, we feel fulfilled, but we don't become angry or upset or pissed off because it's over. We're looking forward to the next one and we'll enjoy that one too. Ha, and if it's a terrible piece, well, you know it won't last forever. That's really is unconditional bliss,' he grinned at Tara. 'Fantastic!'

'That's a good example. Music,' Tara clapped her hands like a little girl.

'Yeah, music, that works for me. You care about the music, you enjoy it, you love every single note, but you don't get attached to each individual note. Every single note is necessary to make a composition. **The passing of one note is necessary for the next one to be created. It's wonderful, it's life. It's how it works!** The passing of music in itself is what makes life amazing. Life will always go on, and in the Now, you can cherish all the different experiences that are thrown your way.' Lee stayed silent for a few minutes, staring into the distance Tara gave him space to be. Lee looked up, 'What if the shit really hits the fan though? How can I not be affected by it, how can I not care?' he knew he used the same words as before, but somehow his Rational Mind was harping on about it.

'**Keep in Mind,**' Tara said with emphasis, '**it's not about not caring, or about not being affected, it's about *not* driving yourself nuts with sadness or worry or anger or despair or depression.** It's about learning how to play with strong Emotions and crazy never ending Thoughts, about **staying detached and just observing** them and eventually by just being balanced and **Now**. **It's not about becoming heartless or cold, it's *not* about not experiencing feelings. But it's about channelling destructive energies into something different, into balance, until one day, those destructive energies don't even arise anymore. It's about staying focused and clear and loving even if everything around you is going crazy.**'

Lee mulled over Tara's last few sentences in silence. 'I guess, if I look at it, it's common sense really,' he said. 'You can't play, have some real fun or be Now, when you're raged with self-pity or crazy Emotions. You play through balance and strength. And the way to gain those is through Objectiveness, curiosity and a bit of daring, but not through moaning, anger sadness or worry. Check.' Lee ticket of an imaginary list in the air.

Experience Without Attachment

'**To experience and play with Emotions by** staying completely objective and detached, **without becoming involved,** can be a challenge for some, but it is possible. *Experience* the Emotion as if it would be a wave on the surface of a great ocean, but you remain in the depths of the ocean, where the water is unaffected. From there you are free to observe what's going on at the surface. Or you could describe it as letting the Emotion flow through you without letting it consume your Being. **This way you get to experience it without losing your self into it.** One word of warning though,' Tara said carefully, '**always check, especially in the beginning, that you are *really* letting it flow *through* you, that you are really detached and that you're not just *pretending* - consciously or unconsciously.**'

'Got any tips on how to do that?' Lee asked.

'Sure. You do that by being Mindful of your Body and Mind, by Listening to it and by observing it. **When we're observing and not involved, we're peaceful and calm, when we're just an innocent bystander, our Body's natural state is relaxed.**'

'Ah, I see,' Lee continued Tara's train of Thought, 'and if we are Mindful of that state, we'll notice if our Body or Mind changes, even if only minutely.'

'Exactly. **When you are repressing Emotions, when you're loosing yourself to them, when you are getting involved, when you indulge, resist your living environment, your lifestyle, your job, or events in your life, you will notice your Body and your Mind tensing up.** Sometimes it's just a tiny, nearly imperceptible tension or dryness feeling - you'll figure out yourself what your 'symptoms' are-, sometimes you might feel numb all over, all throughout your Body, your eyes might glaze over, you might not have a great deal of energy or you might require a lot more sleep,' Tara twirled her fingers in the air to indicate: and so on and so on.

'Yeah, sleep is the Body's way of dealing with problems,' Lee nodded. 'It burns them off by shutting down the Mind.'

'Yep, it's the Body's very own defence mechanism,' Tara agreed. 'So, **be aware of those Sings, because if you're not, Emotions can manifest themselves physically, if you don't play with them properly.**'

'That sounds as if you're talking from personal experience,' Lee said softly.

'Oh yes.'

'Wanna tell me about it?'

From Indulged To Observe To Now

"It's not getting what you want,
But wanting what you've got."
- Sheril Crow

'Sure. A long time ago, *before* I knew any of this stuff, I was in a very challenging situation. I had rented out my lovely apartment for a little while and when I returned to it, it had been completely thrashed. I'm talking *completely* thrashed! Like the toilet being ripped of the wall, gaping holes in my floorboards, all my furniture and appliances broken or missing, doors broken, cockroaches, rats, the lot. It was really intense, and it was in my face all the time, all day long. I had to deal with the repairs of the place, the court case against the Property Management Agency, earning more money than I ever had imagined to be able to pay the costs of renovation and the lawyers, it was nuts. When my friends saw what had happened to me, they flipped out and became very angry, whereas I thought that I wasn't letting it affect

391

me. I had an initial rant and rave and then just got on with things. I thought I was observing my Thoughts and Emotions objectively.'

'That you were just observing them, rather than getting involved?' Lee clarified.

'Exactly. Well, I thought that I was dealing with my Emotions really well, I kept calm and composed, until I suddenly came down with five days worth of the worst diarrhoea I've ever had - and I've been to India!' Tara added meaningfully. 'I felt so ill and weak, I could hardly walk. I started to look at what was happening to me and found that even though the problem had not obviously affected me psychologically, it had found a way to affect me physically instead. **So it *was* affecting me! It wasn't flowing through me. It had found a spot where I *was resisting*, where I was still *attached*.** I had a look at myself to try and find out what was going on. **I have to stress that at that time, I really didn't know what I was doing and undertaking such an analysis of myself was fairly new to me,' Tara remembered.** 'I was pretty much making it up as I went along. Actually, that was one of the situations which helped me come up with many of my ideas of how to play with all this Emotional stuff.'

'Nothing better than first hand experience,' Lee said with empathy.

'I agree. In retrospect at least,' she winked at him, her eyes open and clear, without a trace of regret, pain or grudge. 'The theory I had come up with was to *experience* the Emotions, but to stay *detached* and not to get involved. When I observed my actions though, I realised that I was still doing Dots and Squiggles, Physically and Mentally. Even though I observed them most of the time, I found it difficult not to get involved occasionally and it was that, which ate away on my energy. I hadn't managed to stay detached, but I hadn't noticed, until the illness pointed it out to me,' Tara looked at Lee sincerely. 'No Doubt you'll make your own mistakes, but if I tell you about all of the ones I made, maybe at least you won't have to repeat mine.'

'And it's much appreciated, trust me. And anyway, I find it fascinating to hear how you developed your ideas, that'll help me with my own future theories. Please go on.'

'Cool,' Tara continued. '**I realised that this situation was too intense for me, I simply couldn't just observe it. I decided to *actively* look for the reason why.** I needed to find out what was going on with me and address it. So,' Tara shrugged her shoulders, 'I looked again. There was something that I wasn't accepting, something that I hadn't Let Go off and I was determined to find out what it was. The stomach, where I had gotten ill, is the centre of balance, so I looked at where I was out of balance, and **I tried to figure out where or what the resistance was. I asked many questions, analysed my feelings, the triggers, reactions, Associated Thoughts and so on.** After a while I finally figured it out. Even though I thought I was ok with the situation and that I was detached from it, I still felt hard done by, and I was still harbouring a lot of residue feelings of anger, betrayal and unfairness within me. ***The long and short of it was that I was resisting to accept the present situation as it was.* I realised that I had attached my Emotions to a *past* situation that was no more and that I had not yet Let Go of that.'**

'The past situation being that your apartment used to be wonderful and that your life was not consumed by having to sort out a mess which other people left for you,' Lee said compassionately.

'Right. And on top of that, oh sneaky Emotions**, I realised that I had also attached to a *future* situation.**'

'The situation of everything having been sorted out, the situation being over and your life finally being back to normal,' Lee guessed expertly.

'Exactly. **And the attachment to a better past and brighter future made me impatient and unhappy with living in the present. It made me wish that I wouldn't have to suffer the present circumstances, which I was resisting.'**

'And resistance can have consequences.'

'**Exactly. Resistance can manifest itself physically. I figured that's what might have happened to me and what had made me ill.** Of course,' Tara said realistically, 'I can't prove that it was the resistance that caused the illness, it could have also been the rats pee everywhere. But whenever I get ill, I look inside myself for reasons, and if I look hard enough, I usually find something Emotional or Mental, and when I work on it, suddenly I feel good again and I usually learn a good lesson about myself on the way. But hey, is this true? Do things really work that way? Well, I can't prove these things, they are too ethereal, and everybody has to get their own proof on this matter, but for myself? I got proof, and it worked a treat for me. Actually,' Tara winked cheekily and sincerely at the same time, 'you can also ask The Guys for some guidance if you need it.'

'Ah. Good point. When is it time to talk about that then?' Lee had totally forgotten about The Guys.

'Nearly there, promise. Let's just finish this bit first.'

'Sure,' Lee didn't mind, he was fascinated enough as it was..'

'Now, by following up on my realisations, by ***accepting* the situation and *actively* Letting Go of the resistance that I had identified, my energy came back, my mood cleared up and my diarrhoea stopped too.** So maybe it wasn't the rats pee after all,' she added with a little smile. 'So, if obstacles come into your way, teach yourself to see them as another adventure in your life, as a part of your new life. *Accept* that no fighting or freaking out or Dots and Squiggling will change that. **Realise that resisting just makes it even *more* difficult for you.** If you accept changes as part of your *new* life situation, then there is no resistance to these obstacles. **The more flexible you become in adapting to changing circumstances in life - and they will *never* stop changing** (!) - the easier it is to **move towards Nowness**. Be like water. It has the flexibility to flow around obstacles. It follows the path of least resistance and it can wear away the hardest stone over time.'

'With *soft persistence*,' Lee added.

'Exactly. Out there in the real world, we will always have goals, aims and hopes for the future, but the trick is to move towards those goals, without attachment, without it affecting our present wellbeing. **The secret is to let things *flow through you*. That's not just to *live* in the present, but also to *accept* the *present* the way it is, not just to see it as a preparation for the future or an intermediary between past and future!**'

'Because like that, we'd *really* miss out.'

'Exactly, and we wouldn't want that, would we?'

'Absolutely not,' Lee smiled. 'It's Jimmy Dean and Howard Marks all over.'

'Yep. So, **once I Let Go, I was able to observe without getting involved. That changed everything! My Emotions were just Sensations and Thoughts which I observed. I laughed at myself, at my silly Thoughts, how my Emotions were trying to drive me crazy. I stood back and observed and took the piss. I deliberately tried to see the funny side of everything that happened in my Mind, and of course I kept checking that I wasn't just pretending**. I sure as hell didn't fancy another bout of that diarrhoea.'

'I can imagine,' Lee grinned. 'Man what a story.'

'Well, that's only the beginning of it.'

'Oh, of course. I should have known,' Lee laughed. 'So, what happened next?'

'Well, just when I thought that that surely must be it, I had an idea. No Doubt, observing and not getting involved was great and it would change many people's lives - it certainly had changed mine - but why did I even to have these Emotions in the first place? Why did I have to put my Mind and Body through all of this? **I wondered if I could find a state where those Emotions, Sensations and Thoughts wouldn't even come up? A state where I didn't need to observe, because there wasn't anything to observe in the first place?**'

'Nowness?' Lee suggested knowingly.

'Right.'

'How on earth did you come up with that?'

'By coming up with theories and then trying them out.'

'More?' Lee prompted.

Moving Towards Nowness

'I gathered that to find a state where those Emotions, Sensations and Thoughts wouldn't even come up anymore, I could start by identifying the state where I had an Emotion, then Letting Go of it, and then identifying the state where I achieved that the Emotion didn't come back anymore. Then I could observe *that* state and play with *maintaining* it.

I wanted to find a state in which *no* old Emotions would return at all,' Tara said with emphasis.

'That's clever.'

'Well, at the time it seemed just like common sense, a natural deduction.'

'Yeah, special Tara common sense,' Lee grinned.

'Maybe, remember though, you've had your fair share of that yourself already,' Tara pointed out.

'Thanks, that's true. I like it when you keep reminding me of how clever I am,' he smiled, straightened up and stuck his chest out playfully.

'Pleasure,' she laughed and continued with her story. 'So, first I had to find a way to *truly* Let Go! I worked pretty much twenty-four hours a day for a year to prepare the court case, repair the apartment and to earn the money to pay for it all. Because I had to work and organise so much, I had to put my private life completely on hold for that entire time. The unfairness of the situation, the stress and the hassle was in my face every minute of every day. I had to constantly work on staying objective.

I was doing what I could with regards to my apartment, and I had accepted that any bad feelings wouldn't change the severity of the situation. I was comfortable to Let Go of any grudges and bad feelings, I just had to do it. I made a commitment to myself and put out an Intent. I caught myself out, whenever the Thought of injustice returned. I reminded myself that it was *ok* to Let Go of it and that I *could* Let Go of it. I constantly reminded myself to remember my well-being and diverted my attention to *that* whenever I remembered all throughout the day. I made an point to actively feel good feelings, to create happy and content Sensation. When any angry Thoughts came up, I diverted them to my Body or to Love or forgiveness or compassion. Sometimes I was able to actually feel those qualities, sometimes I would just say the words over and over in my head. I sincerely tried to remember that it's not about clenching your fists while going through the motions,' Tara laughed, 'Every time I had a bad Thought or feeling about the situation, I actively *played* with it or swapped it for a positive one. *Every single* time. It took tremendous focus, especially at the beginning, but with time it began to happen automatically. In the end, as soon as **I noticed a puppy, it was already gone. Eventually the aggravating pups got so bored, knowing that I wouldn't give them any attention, that they hardly came back at all anymore.'**

'And all throughout, you made sure that what you were doing was genuine, that you weren't resisting again, right?' Lee insisted.

'Right.'

'So, you had proven your theory. You had found a state where your Emotions, Sensations and Thoughts hardly came back,' Lee said with genuine respect.

'Yep,' Tara said simply. **'But I had only done it once, and I wanted to make sure that this wasn't just a fluke, so I waited for the next opportunity**, which sadly came only too quickly.'

'The eternal perfectionist,' Lee teased.

'Well, sure, I mean **what's the point having a blueprint if it's not tried and tested**?'

'Wholly agree,' Lee thought the same way, 'you needed to make sure it worked if you wanted to rely on it in the future.' He beckoned her to continue.

'The whole story got worse. When the court case approached, I thought that I would finally get justice. But, even though the Agency admitted negligence and took full responsibility for the damage, I still lost the case. I got no compensation for my huge expenses to put the apartment back into the condition it was in previously, or for my heart-ache or for loosing a year of my life.'

'What?' Lee asked in disbelief. 'How could you have lost? By the sounds of it the apartment was in need of a full refurbishment - brrr, and a pest control visit.' Lee got goose bumps just by thinking of cockroaches crawling over him at night.

'I have no idea why I lost, I couldn't understand it either. My lawyer, my friends, my family, nobody could, and as expected, my Mind went off on all the obligatory Dots and Squiggles once again. Was the case rigged? Had the judge been paid off? What about the money I lost? Bla, bla, bla. I remember leaving the court building, broke, upset and angry about having been failed by the so-called justice system. I looked across the street, saw a flower stand, went over, bought a huge bunch of beautiful flowers that I couldn't afford, took a taxi home that I could afford even less, called all my friends, screamed and shouted and ranted and cried, came up with all sorts of schemes of how to retaliate the Agency, which I knew I would never put into action, and generally let out as much steam as I could.

The next morning, I woke up and accepted the situation. It was a bummer, it was unfair, but it was done. It was past. I decided to move on *straight away*! I closed my eyes and went inside. I went through the scenario one more time, let out any more steam that had to be let out, cried, and decided that it truly *was* over, that I couldn't do anything about it and that any Emotions with regards to it wouldn't help me in any way whatsoever, that they would just make me unhappy. **When I said that, I made sure that there wasn't even the slightest pang of Doubt within me, but that I truly did mean it, that I really did accept.** If there would have been Doubt, I would have played once again with acceptance, and with trying to find out where the resistance was.'

'**I can see why there can't be any Doubt,**' Lee said, '**because if you're not *really* Letting Go through *absolute understanding*,** if you just take your attention away from it, **you are in fact *ignoring* it**.'

'Class A student,' Tara grinned. 'Once I was fully comfortable that I had genuinely accepted, I did the same things I'd done before. Intent, commitment, catch-out, divert, relax Body, smile, Love. **It took me about a month till the puppies became bored and came less and less frequently.**'

'That's cool. You knew what was good for you and what wasn't, and you simply decided to choose the stuff that *was* good for you,' Lee said.

'Yep. As I said, it's straight-forward.'

'Yeah, but man, experiences like that, really take some hardcore analysis and understanding, *and* a tonne of commitment.'

'**Yes they do. But only for a little while. Once you got it and you get used to the process, all sorts of situations suddenly become much easier to live with. Simply because you're able to just disperse even the most intense Emotions and keep them away. I tell you, a little effort can have a huge impact.**'

'I can see that, but man, that must have been an awful situation,' Lee said compassionately.

'It was, and I'm glad it's over, no matter how useful it was for my personal development in the end,' she said truthfully. 'But anyway, by the end of it all, I knew that my blue-print worked one hundred percent! **I knew that I could play my way towards Nowness, towards inner peace!**

But at this stage, there was still effort involved,' a smile flashed across Tara's cheeks, 'so, **I wondered, shouldn't doing nothing, which is what Nowness really was, be effortless?**'

'Oh, you're impossible,' Lee laughed out loud.

'Well, as I was at it, I thought, I might as well figure out the *easiest* and most effective way, right?'

'Yeah, I can see up. Thumbs up girl.'

Tara grinned, 'So, **I kept on playing, and the longer I did, the longer the puppies stayed away, and after a while I didn't even have to actively catch myself out anymore, the catching-out had kind of become *automatic*. The Thoughts and the Sensations of the whole affair just bounced right off the fringes of my Consciousness. Most of the time I hardly notice them anymore, but when I did, I noticed that I was always smiling. Well, I guess, I did initially replace the intense Emotional situation with a smile**,' Tara laughed.

'That's so sweet. I like how you don't just get rid of stuff, but how you really try to make it a nice and utterly pleasant experience.'

'Absolutely yes to the latter, but let me pick you up on the former straight away. **Please remember that it's not about *getting rid* of anything, but about *playing* with it, *changing* your *reaction* to it and it thus dispersing by itself, *allowing* you to be Now!**'

'Fair point,' Lee was glad that Tara was so meticulous. He only just noticed how important semantics were! Just the words 'getting rid of it' implied fighting. And it wasn't about fighting, it was about playing! He smiled.

'Also,' Tara added, '**it might be useful to know that the same blueprint works in reverse**. I could pick out any Emotion at any time, feed it, give it attention and make it grow and ultimately feel that Emotion with all it's attributes, Mental and Physical.'

'Then you can Let Go of it again, and start again...,' Lee laughed out loud.

'Well, yeah, if you have nothing else to do,' Tara laughed too. '**So, I figured out that in the end it's about choice**. Choice where you put your attention.'

'You'd be a great therapist.'

'Thanks, but this is not about therapy. I'm not trying to heal anybody, I'm just pointing out what stops people from being Now and where your attention has to be for that.'

'Now?' Lee smiled.

'Of course.'

Balanced - Now - Pure Existence

'Well, needless to say my experiment wasn't quite over yet.'

'Are you serious? What else could there be?'

'Well, even though the catching-out had become automatic, and the Emotions and Thoughts hardly came back, they still *did* come back from time to time. When they did, there was still the occasional bounce on my Consciousness, a minimal registering of them, which would prevent me from the *perfect* Now. An occasional undercurrent of tiny fragments of Emotions, Sensations and Thoughts. Most people wouldn't bother about that. Their lives would have already changed beyond belief, but I still wondered, could I Let Go of that too? Of that final bounce? That's what I had been after all along. The question was if I could find a state where the bounce wouldn't even occur in the first place? Where none of the Emotions would exist by default? None of the Thoughts? None of the Sensations? Then I thought of Nowness. I was wondering what would happen if I could just be Now *all the time*, without any extreme Emotions, Thoughts or Behaviour distracting me.

What really was Nowness? Instead of being a *goal*, could it also be a *facilitator*? Had I approached the problem from the wrong end? Now I asked myself how Nowness could facilitate everything I'd been playing with so far?

In the end, this is what I came up with,' Tara pointed at the middle box of the drawing, 'in the Now, Thoughts and Emotions don't exist. In the Now you don't have any Thoughts, a Physical Sensation is just a Physical Sensation, it's neither good or bad, there are no interpretations, no comparisons, no judgements of good or bad, no associations, you're just Now. Emotions are just chemical reactions. Your Emotions, Behaviour and Thoughts are perfectly balanced. **There's no indulgence but also no *need* for detachment or observing, as there's nothing to be detached from, or nothing to be observed.'**

Lee wondered how on earth that could be still be enjoyable, 'Can't we at least choose to keep the good ones?' Lee asked cheekily.

'You can do whatever you want to,' Tara said shrugging her shoulders.

'But then that wouldn't be Now.'

'Exactly.'

'Right,' Lee waited for Tara to elaborate, but Tara stayed silent.

He closed his eyes and as soon as he did so, a memory descended over the Hologram that was his brain. He remembered something that happened a little earlier. He remembered Tara smiling at him so radiantly, how his heart had melted within seconds and how wonderful it had felt. Looking back at it, this feeling had been loaded with expectations, with hopes of fulfilment, with desire. He knew that he had had the options to indulge in those Thoughts or to observe them, but without being consciously aware of it, he had moved his Awareness into the middle of the table in Tara's drawing, towards Nowness, towards Balance. What else had there been? Lee strained his Brain to be able to retrace his Thoughts *and* his Emotions. Ah, yes, he had tried to solely *feel* his heart melting. **He had tried not to *think* about the feeling, not to associate and feed the feeling-good puppy, but just to be Now instead. Doing that had changed the feeling, it had suddenly not been linked to any positive Thought or outcome anymore. It had just been a feeling, a *pure* feeling. It had felt eternal, and powerful. He had stopped indulging in the good feeling and had been left with an amazing sensation of connectedness, but without any kind of expectations. It had felt like *pure experience*.** He remembered that that's what he had wondered about before - **if he could be *pure* experience, where any outside influences would just flow through him, without disturbing him or getting stuck, in fact, without him noticing.**

It wasn't really about not feeling good feelings, or about choosing to feel good feelings, but about being permanently in this state of balanced bliss that Nowness provided! **It was a *different* feeling, not really describable in fact, but truly and absolutely amazing. In that state, he would be in true bliss and perfect balance, which nothing could rock any more.** Wow. Lee was amazed at his own reasoning, at his ability to make such easy connections in amongst such vast amounts of new information. Lee hadn't noticed that he had closed his eyes, when he opened them again, Tara laughed at him.

'Welcome back young man,' she smiled, 'where have you been? You had a huge great big smile on your face there!'

'Man, you won't believe what I just came up with,' Lee said and shared his little excursion into the depth of his Brain.

'Gosh, I can't believe you just did that. That's exactly it! **It's like Shifting, like slipping into this new dimension. You don't try anymore, you just *become* it, you just *are* it.**'

Let It Flow Through You

'**You know, it's exactly like you just said,**' Tara said delightedly, '**in the perfect Now, the outside world flows through you without any resistance from your Mind whatsoever.** There are no Thoughts at all. You are just blessed in the pure state of Being, which cannot be rocked anymore. **It's like a pipe with water gushing through it, without any obstructions, it's just a clear and powerful flow. Any Thought that is still in your Mind, is like a wire in that pipe, water can flow all around it, but there is still a slight resistance where the water touches the wire.**'

'**The wire is the last resistance,**' Lee scratched his chin.

'Exactly. That wire can be an obvious Thought or Emotion, or even one of the sneaky little buggers which we talked about before.'

'Like the last Thought? The one where we're congratulating ourselves with when all the other Thoughts are gone?' Lee suggested with a giggle, remembering at the sheer naughtiness of his Mind.

'Yeah, that one, but they can even go one sneakier!' Tara laughed. 'It can even be the Thought deciding to *Let Go* of the last Thought. The Thought to Let Go of any residue feelings.'

'Oh God, will it never stop?' Lee clasped his head in mock exaggeration.

'Well, **our brain is an intricate thinking machine, and believe me, it has managed to pervade every nook and cranny you care to look into and then some!** Even Thoughts that we assumed we dealt with, but hadn't, can still be unconscious wires. Even the tiniest cerebral attention to any of those things, even just the smallest *bounce* we talked about earlier, will still give the 'bouncer' ***existence*** and will still provoke a split second worth of a reaction.'

'Be it Mental, Emotional or Behavioural,' Lee added.

Nowness - No Resistance - Rooted Like A Tree

'**So, let me summarise,**' Lee said concentrating hard. 'Every Thought is resistance - it can push you over or attach itself to you, whereas in Nowness it disappears. **In Nowness there is no resistance, you're in perfect Balance where the wire doesn't exist.** You're not exploding, you're not over emotional, you're not ignoring. As Thoughts and Emotions don't exist in the Now in the first place, **the emphasis is**

Shifted from observing, analysing and laughing at Emotions, Thoughts and Behaviour, from thinking, assuming, judging and comparing, to just *observing* **the** *Now,* **the space between the Thoughts, Emptiness. In Nowness you take in everything** *as it happens.* You don't judge situations as good or bad anymore. You don't worry about the future or the past. It's not autopilot, it's not being in a trance. Nowness is clear, strong and powerful. **It's not bottling things up, it's not ignoring, it's being so sharp, clear and empty, that nothing can take a hold of you anymore in the first place, nothing can attach itself to you or affect you any longer.** The world flows straight through you. You see what IS, what *actually* IS, *not* what you *think* is, or what you *interpret* it to be, or what your Mind invented! In the Now, you see Emotions, Thoughts, reactions, Behaviour and people as they *really are,* right *Now.* In the Now, negative patterns of Thoughts, Emotions, Behaviour and judgement, will automatically dissolve, and with that the unpleasant extremes in our lives. In the Now *you* just *are* and *everything* just *is.*' Lee stopped talking, amazed by this sudden stream of coherent knowledge. It had flowed out of his mouth without his brain being involved. His lips had parted, he had breathed out and the words had come all by themselves.

'That's right,' Tara said, playing with one of her curls, feeling the softness of her hair. 'You know, **the longer you spend in this new state of Mind, the more you'll feel it's benefits.** A new balance and contentment comes into your lives. By ridding yourself of the constant judgement and measurement, you can attain a balanced, steady peace of Mind, you'll be solid as rock, deeply rooted like a tree. Nothing can disturb you or push you of balance anymore. You're naturally blissful.

Letting Go of issues, happens automatically when you *allow* **yourself to Be in the Now fully.** Being in the Now, is being Mindful, *is* fully Letting Go. **Letting go of all Thoughts that you have, the Thoughts that you think make up your personality, the judgement of your Self, the image you choose for yourself, the Emotions that rule your life, your Mind and your Body. Nowness allows you to just Be, to be yourself**, Now.' Tara smiled warmly, she knew that state well. It was truly as amazing as it sound. 'In Nowness we experience **Oneness**,' she continued. 'In amongst the storm of the outside and our inside world, Oneness gives us a tremendous amount of comfort, it gives us hugs and love. Not in the form of pity, but in the form of strength, clarity and peacefulness. We feel with every bone in our Body that we're strong, that we *can* cope and that we *will* cope.'

'And that we can bloody well have some fun with it!' Lee cheered with a massive smile.

'Absolutely!'

So..., What About A Shortcut...?

'You know when you said earlier that it's like *Shifting*, like slipping into a new dimension? Have you got any shortcuts for that?' Lee was getting the hang of Tara's way of thinking.

'Actually I do,' Tara said amused. '**Do you remember when you tried to find yourself a reference point for what it feels like to be in Nowness? That's how you do it.** You play with getting yourself to a state where Thoughts and Emotions don't come up so much anymore, a state, where you get a glimpse of Nowness. You keep on doing that, until can **get a really good feel for what Nowness feels like. Then**, once you've done that once, **for all future scenarios, all you need to do, is to recreate that feeling! Instead of going through the whole Letting Go malarkey, instead of dealing with Thoughts and Emotions individually, you just recreate that *feeling* of Nowness**!'

'Of course, man, and then the 'doing it' is not the difficult thing, the remembering to do it is! **You just need to remember to recreate the feeling, until it's just your default way of feeling**,' Lee was shocked by the simplicity. '**So why the hell did we do all of the analysis, all the examining**?' Lee blurted out.

'You needed to do it to know that being Now is ok, that it's not ignoring, that it's safe! And to be able to get a reference point!'

'But,' Lee paused in amazement, 'I already know how to do that!'

'Told you it's effortless! Now all you need to remember is the feeling. Nothing else is required.'

Tara got up and stretched her back. 'Wow man, that was a bit intense. Did you notice? We hardly even moved.'

'Yeah, it's what I call bubble-talk,' Lee grinned.

'Bubble-talk?' Tara giggled.

'It's when you're so enraptured with a conversation, it's like you're in a bubble. Everything else around you, sometimes even your Body seems to disappear.'

'That's certainly what it was! You'll be glad to hear though, that this was also pretty much the most serious bit of the Mind stuff. Now everything becomes much more light-hearted, because this?' Tara grinned broadly. '**This was only the *preparation* for what is still to come.**'

'What do you mean only the preparation? What else could there possibly be?'

'Well, **at last we've done all the necessary practice to Let Go of everything that could possibly disturb the Mind. We've played so much with everything up here,**' she tapped her forehead, '**we have become aware and clear and Now. We've even tuned in with our Intuition! And Now?**' Tara paused for effect and then announced dramatically, '**Now we're finally ready to go and really *play*! Now we get to play with the *Universe*!**'

'Play with what?' Lee was taken aback.

'Well,' Tara said mischievously and sat back down again, 'have another look at your '*What to do?*' list.'

PART 8

21 Talking To The Guys

Lee curiously shuffled backwards through the pages. He'd written a lot over the past couple of days and there were a lot of notes, but as he had earmarked the '*What to do?*' list, it was easy to find. He glanced over the page and ticked off the bullet points they had already discussed. When he got to the bottom of the list, he looked up in surprise, 'Oh man, I forgot about The Guys! That's why we started to talk about all this Mind stuff in the first place! Oh yeah! I'm really looking forward to *this*!'

'You've *forgotten* about The Guys?' Tara asked dramatically? She shook her head in mock disbelief. She took the notebook out of Lee's hands and began to read the remaining points out loud.

What to do?
14 - Listen to the Little Guys
15 - Talk to Them
16 - Now the world is an even bigger oyster
17 - Play with the Oyster and have some fun

'I remember now,' Lee said, once Tara was done reading, 'we had to get to know our Mind to be able to clear it and thus reach Nowness, which would then allow us to Listen to The Guys, right?'

'Yep, that's it. And now we're ready to talk about just that. Come to think of it, just to make sure we kick off on level ground, do you remember the benefits of talking to The Guys?'

'Of course.'

Why Do We Want To Talk and Listen To The Guys Again?

"(He) viewed the world as a web of
profoundly intertwined histories and events.
The connections may be invisible....
But they are always there, buried just beneath the surface. "
- Dan Brown

Lee found to his surprise that his memory was loud, clear and readily available. He began to recall, 'The Guys see the big picture. They know what the most effortless plan for us is. They can direct us to lucky Co-incidences and everything else we might need in our lives. They know how all Beings could be happy. They are the link to our True Self, the *real* Us, our gut feeling or the language of our heart – if you like the Hippy terminology,' Lee grinned cheekily at Tara, his eyes twinkling. 'Listening to The Guys, can lead us smoothly along the perfect path.

Now, all of this sounds great to me, but it's still a bunch of theory and I really need a bit of meat on this,' he said candidly.

'Nothing easier than that,' Tara promised as Lee quickly jotted down a few reminders.

Talking to Them:
* Increases the hit-rate of the Co-incidences in our life.
* They can be a huge source of information, help, assistance, support, advice and guidance.
* They can answer all sorts of questions (as they know everything, right?).
* They not only show us the Oyster, but they also show us a whole bunch of really cool cosmic games.

Tara read the list as Lee was writing and nodded along. When he put the pen down, first his eyes narrowed, then widened, 'Ha, *now* I'll make a list! The Guys can give me *all* the answers, right?' he said super excitedly. He picked up the pen again and pretended to write, 'So, what about the lottery numbers? The horses? Car racing? Golf? Phew, the Mind boggles. The potential! I'll be rich and famous in no time!'

Tara saw the smile in Lee's eyes, enough to tell her that he was joking - kind of. 'Shush boy,' she scolded him playfully, cuffing his side, 'you should ask questions related to personal growth. Questions about guidance and direction for your life, not about fortune telling games,' she said with exaggerated shock and horror.

'Uoh, spoil sport. And I thought I had finally struck Gold,' Lee made a deeply disappointed face.

'Actually, this is far better than all the Gold in the world,...' Tara flashed him a promising smile.

'That's quite a statement. So I guess I'll have to keep on listening then, won't I? Otherwise I'll never find the pot at the end of that Nowness rainbow,' Lee said beat.

'I guess so,' Tara said delightedly, nudging Lee's arm and winking at him slyly.

'Man, I have a million and one questions. How do I talk to Them and how do I listen, and...'

Tara gently interrupted, smiling at Lee's wonderful enthusiasm, 'One thing after another, let's start at the beginning.'

How Do They Talk To Us

'**T**o be able to listen well, first we need to understand how They *talk* to us,' Tara began.

'Why?'

'Because if we don't know what to look out for, The Guys might be talking to us already for all we know and we don't hear Them because we can't differentiate Their messages from our own babble up here, right?' she knocked her knuckles gently on her head.

'Makes sense,' Lee approved. 'Luckily, through all the exercises we did before, we got to know *our* own babble pretty well, so now, we only need to figure out how Their's sounds like.'

'Exactly.'

'Great, the Cosmic Babble, can't wait.'

Tara laughed at Lee's choice of words. This was going to be fun, she could feel it already. 'Are you ready for a list? Because there are a whole bunch of ways of how They can talk to us.'

'Ready,' Lee waved his writing utensil cheerfully.

The Guys can talk to us in:
- Words
- Pictures
- Physical Feelings
- Hunches and Intuitions
- Physical Signs
- Events such as Co-incidences

<u>All of those fall into three categories:</u>
- Physical Signs
- Mental Signs
- Intuitive Signs

'Plus maybe a whole bunch of other ways I haven't figured out yet,' Tara added humbly.

'Phew, there's a lot of points on these lists,' Lee sighed.

'Don't worry, it's easy once you've got the hang of it. It's all common sense, anyway,' Tara said reassuringly. 'The Guys have a whole bunch of different ways to get through to us. Basically if they *talk* to us in words and we don't get it, They can try to get the message through to us with a Co-incidence or a little Physical Sign such as a poster or something in a book for example, and so on. They might even guide us to a person that can communicate Their message to us, or to a place, where Their message would become clear to us.'

'Ah ok, that makes sense. Sounds pretty fool proof. **If we don't understand what The Guys are trying to say, or if we missed a hint, They can use another way to get through to us.** That's brilliant,' Lee was visibly impressed.

'It's great isn't it? They're so considerate,' Tara said lovingly.

'It's really is quite sweet,' Lee felt charmed by some Little Guys he hadn't even met yet.

'They really are endearing once you get to know Them.'

'I'm beginning to see that.' Lee smiled, then the smile turned into a frown, 'What happens if They talk to us and we don't get it, no matter how hard They try?'

'Then you're up there without a paddle,' Tara said looking all serious, but couldn't hold her stern look for long. Both of them burst out laughing. Lee loved how realistic and down to earth Tara was, there was no pretence or bull-shit, just straight down the line. **'That's why we need to learn how to Listen, so that we *don't* miss the messages,'** she smiled.

'Fair enough,' Lee still laughed.

'We can learn to cover all the angles quite easily, and then we just play with them, again, again and again, until we get a feel for Them, until we *know* how They talk to us and until we *don't* miss the messages anymore.'

'Sounds as if it might be worth the effort,' Lee said, his interest growing.

'It might just be,' Tara winked. 'Now, **the more we train our Listening skills, the easier it is for The Guys to talk to us. When you begin to play with Them, They might have to take a bunch of round about ways to talk to you, whereas later, once you've**

developed your listening skills, They can just simply talk to you with words. Eventually you'll be able to listen so well, that you automatically follow Their messages, that's when you don't have to think at all anymore.' Lee raised his eyebrows, but didn't interrupt. He knew Tara would elaborate on such sweeping statements sooner or later. She didn't disappoint, 'That's the state of Being where we are absolutely in tune with our environment and our own Mind, when we're Now. In that state, we don't miss hints anymore, because they stand out a mile in our crystal clear Warehouse. That's when we begin to wonder how we could have ever missed them before. At that time, Listening to our Intuition becomes second nature and following it becomes automatic and natural. That's when we live fully through our Intuition, that's when everything falls into place, when everything in our lives automatically follows the *perfect plan*. I mean how cool is that?'

'Off the scale. You're preaching to the converted, darling. Yippee, life is good,' Lee cheered, showing rows of strong teeth.

'Let's get to the nitty-gritty. The Guys usually start talking to us with short messages or individual words. They can talk to us in our own voice, or, depending on the messages given, the voices can change. Everybody experiences this differently, so don't expect anything in particular, just keep yourself open to whatever comes, and with a little practice you'll figure out exactly how *you* perceive them.

If something is really important The Guys can be quite firm in trying to get the messages across, but they also have a sweet and playful side. They can also be absolutely hilarious if They want to. Sometimes They crack jokes or are really silly and entertaining. **It's like having a guardian angel and your best playmate rolled all into one,**' Tara grinned. 'The more experienced you get, the weirder and more wonderful your conversations can become with Them, but of course, it's always up to you how far you want to take it – and how much fun you want too have with it.'

'As far and as much as I possibly dare,' Lee said and added with a huge grin, 'And then some!'

'That's my boy,' Tara grinned back at him, 'that's the way I look at it too. **With just a bit of practice, you'll learn to distinguish the real messages, the hunches and Intuitions that you are supposed to follow, from the random Thoughts and wishful thinking. Even this preliminary stage can be fun already!'**

'Yes, that's what I want to know about.'

'Yeah, everybody does, because the biggest problem most people have, is that even though we *hear* stuff, we're often not sure if it's a messages, or...'

'If our head is making stuff up,' Lee finished Tara's sentence.

'Precisely. But don't worry, I'll give you plenty of tips on how to tell the difference and how to begin to practice. You'll have to play around with it and experiment a little though, simply because different people have different natural abilities and strengths, and different techniques work for different people. Some people are very visual and visual images from The Guys work a treat, whereas other people are more verbal and Listen better to Their verbal messages and so on. The Listening thingy is pretty subjective and everybody needs to find their own way of how they talk and Listen to The Guys best.

Don't worry, I'll give you clear directions, so that you can play around with it, but still, in then end you'll learn by trial and error. There are no magical shortcuts. It *will* work, but you *will* have to work out for yourself how it works for *you*. As always, you have to take responsibility for your own development. You can get the guidance, but nobody can do the work for you.'

'I'd be happy to take that responsibility,' Lee said without missing a beat.

How We Listen

'In that case,' Tara said, 'let's talk about how to Listen. To begin to Listen, we have to become aware of our Physical, Mental and Intuitive environment. Let's talk about that *Awareness* first.'

'I remember that from *yesterday*,' Lee thought out loud. '**We Listen to Intuitions and see the Signs that lead us to Co-incidences by being *aware*, by *observing* and by being Mindful of our environment.** A trick we mentioned to help us become more observant, was to ask for things, right?' Tara nodded. 'And once we've asked, we watch out for Co-incidences, messages and Signs that are related to what we've asked for, which would then obviously be significant.'

'Wow, you have a great memory,' Tara was amazed by the amount of detail Lee had remembered from the previous day. 'Everything you've just described is what I call Listening to *Physical Signs*, which means we Listen to our *physical surroundings* by being *aware* of it and by recognising the significance of certain events. There you go, you already know about that.'

'Excellent. This is easier than I thought,' Lee said cocking his head to one side. He was glad that somehow, no matter how big Tara's lists were, it never felt like school, things never got boring or daunting.

Tara continued, 'The next category of Signs,' she pointed at the list, 'are *Mental Signs*. Here, instead of Mindfully observing our *environment*, we Mindfully Listen to our *Mind* and our *Thoughts*.'

'And I've already learned how to do *that* too,' Lee was impressed by the ground they'd already covered. 'We do that by getting to know our Mind, taking an inventory and spring cleaning it, so that The Guy's boxes stand out.'

'There you go, you don't need to learn that anymore either,' she smiled at Lee. 'The next lot are *Intuitive* Signs, such as *Hunches, Emotions and Physical Feelings*.'

'And we've done those before too, they are the kind of feelings, notions, knowing-s and physical pangs that we get, when we feel drawn to act even if we don't necessarily understand why. This is great,' Lee said happily. 'It's not all new!'

'I told you it isn't difficult. Not only do you already know how to be aware of all of the categories, but it gets even better, because, you'll be pleased to hear, you Listen to all of them in exactly the same way.'

'Tara, can I just tell you at this moment in time that I love you?'

'Sure.'

'I love you. Thanks for knowing my terrible tendency to be afraid of too much effort.'

'You're welcome,' Tara grinned, without pointing out the four fabulous steps of getting rid of that fear. He'll figure that out in his own time if he wanted to.

'So, we Listen to all of the categories in the same way. And?' Lee probed.

'For a start, **keep in Mind that *Listening* is not Listening with our *ears*, but it's *Awareness* of the entire world, the whole world, inside and outside of us, all at the same time.'**

Lee yelped. This did sound more complicated that he'd hoped.

Tara went on unperturbed, 'It's straight forward though. We Listen by simply having a still, calm, peaceful Mind - through Mindfulness or Nowness.'

'Ha, I love it. I can't believe I didn't see that coming! Doh,' Lee relaxed in an instant. 'Hang on, I'll just make a note.'

Listening:

* We don't Listen with our ears but with Awareness of everything inside and outside of us. We gain that awareness by having a still, calm, and peaceful Mind - through Mindfulness or Nowness.
* Yeah!

'Let me stress once more, the only way to Listen to *all* of this *at the same time*, is by being as much *Now* as much as we can.'

'The Now, the space where *everything* happens,' Lee remembered.

'Exactly. The space where our Mind is calm but highly alert and one hundred percent attentive,' Tara made a sweeping movement with her hand.

'So far,' she continued, 'we got to know our Mind really well, we've done an inventory, got to know our boxes and we spring cleaned too. With Mindfulness and Nowness we've also reduced the traffic going through the Warehouse. **Now, with not much going on in our Mind, it's easy to notice anything out of the ordinary in there. A new box, anything that we haven't seen before. And that's exactly how the messages from The Guys will feel like.'**

'So, we don't even have to go around *looking* for messages in the Mind or in our Stomach? **We just notice them naturally as they stand out unmistakably in our empty Mind?** That's great! Come to think of it, I don't even have to do anything. No-thing. Now that's true effortlessness! We like very big,' Lee grinned broadly.

'Yeah, it really is easy once you get your head around it.'

'I promise I'll believe you the next time you say things like that,' Lee said humbly.

Knowing what was still to come, Tara grinned at Lee's statement. The sheer far-out-ness of it all... Anyway... 'Actually, to reassure you even more,' Tara went on, 'if you think about it, you've been living your life without knowing any of this stuff for years, right? So if you can't do it straight away, nothing will be different from your current state, nothing will change, nothing will get worse. It's just that when you *do* get it, things get so *much better*. So there's no need to stress over any of this, it all comes in it's own good time. Don't worry, despair or be hard on yourself. Take it easy.' Lee breathed deeply as Tara continued, **'The best way to play with The Guys is to *Play*. Let it evolve naturally at it's own pace, be curious and playful, but don't push it fanatically. Like that it will stay interesting and fun, rather than fascinating but hard work.'**

'Sounds like my kind of Guy-s. And even if I'm really slow, I still don't have to worry, because if I stay open, The Guys will keep trying, each and every day, until I finally get it, right?' Lee said at ease.

'Full points. Let me quickly summarise for your list,' Tara prompted and Lee dutifully grabbed his pen.

Awareness to Listen to The Signs The Guys use:
- Physical Signs – be aware of events, Co-incidences and people – see and observe.

- Intuitive Signs – be aware of Emotions, feelings, hunches and Intuitions, Physical pangs in your Body.
- Mental Signs – be aware of words in your Mind, pictures and anything else that you see in your Mind's eye. It can be clear and obvious or just a picture flashing by.

When they finished the list and Tara had checked it again, she said, 'There is something else that you can do to help The Guys give you Signs.'

'Tuning the radio station maybe? Trying out different frequencies?' Lee ventured.

'Actually it's more like trying out different radios, different receivers.'

'Oh, I hadn't thought of that. Give me more?'

'You can give The Guys alternative ways of talking to you *directly*. You could use Tarot cards, Numerology, Symbols, Runes, I-Ching, all that can help.'

'Which brings us back to Hippy-shit,' Lee grinned.

'Well, they *were* onto *something*,' Tara smiled, her yellow dress moving softly in the wind.

Did he just spot a sunflower tattoo on her thigh? She was one, he smiled to himself. She was a Sunflower. A Hippy. A Hippy with a business degree. A smile crept up the corners of Lee's mouth. He shook his head, ah yes, Tarot.

'How would They talk to us through a Tarot card? I thought Tarot was just a Gypsy tool to tell fortunes. I never thought that they really worked.'

'Oh, the cards are real alright, it's just that some of the people that use them aren't.'

'Aha.'

'In fact it's easy, *everybody* can play with them. We simply ask a question and draw a card. Then all we need to do is look up the meaning in the book. Hey presto, done.'

'Cool, but how do The Guys get involved?'

'It's pretty straight forward. If you use the book, They know which card you need to draw to correspond to the right message in the book. They simply give you the right Intuition to pull the right card for that moment in time,' Tara said confidently. 'You always get exactly what you need to hear, believe it or not.'

'Yeah, a bunch of friends have been baffled by this before too, I've never tried it myself though,' Lee said thinking that he should maybe give it a try.

'Oh, do you remember that we talked about meditating on cards to interpret them?' Tara asked.

'Yes I remember. When we talked about Tarot and Psychometry and stuff. You said to ask a question, to go into the Now and wait what comes up.'

'Right. Tarot cards are a nice example, because they can combine Physical Signs with Mental and Intuitive Signs. To use them as pure Physical Signs, you use the book to interpret them, learn about the symbology in the cards etc. The more you get to know the meaning of the cards, the more detailed The Guys' messages can become. If on the other hand you're good with Mental Signs, sod the book, just ask The Guys for Their interpretation and Listen for the answers.'

'Well, but if I can do that I don't need the cards in the first place, do I?' Lee asked perceptively.

'You're right, but funnily enough, a Physical card sometimes makes it easier to believe that it's real. Especially once you play with asking The Guys first and then checking in with yourself if it really was just what you needed to hear. You can even double check with the book too.'

'Ah, no make belief here, we can double check!'

'Of course! If you do play with that though, keep in Mind that the books were written by people with different backgrounds, so the Intuitive meaning you might get for a card might be exactly the same than in the book or slightly different. But that doesn't matter, because The Guys know exactly how you would interpret the card or the text in the book, so They'll always give you the right card. So, with that in Mind, you can look at both interpretations and take what's useful. Give Tarot cards a try, they're surprisingly interesting.'

'I think I might just do that,' Lee said amazed at himself that he meant it. Tarot cards? Whatever next, he marvelled to himself.

Tara looked at Lee a little more seriously, 'It's important to understand, that *nothing* is set in stone with The Guys, nothing is the right way or the only way. People can give you lots of tips of how things work for them, what *they* think *the* way is, but in the end you need to try them and figure out what works for you. **Everything I'm talking about are all hints, tips, experiences and little pointers to show you a new world to go and play with by yourself and with your friends.** I can give you an idea, a starting point to kick off from, after that, it's up to you. There are no Right-s or wrong-s. Even if you figure out a way that nobody else uses, it's totally cool. To experiment like this by yourself and to find what works for you, requires a little courage, confidence and curiosity at first, but once you start, it's so much fun that any worry is quickly forgotten.'

'That's good to know. I can make up my own way, as long as I can take responsibility for my own progress. All in all, I can do whatever I want to! This rocks!'

'Couldn't have put it any better myself. Practice the basics a bit first though.'

'Yeah, yeah, walk first, then run, I know,' Lee said, overplaying his impatience.

I'd Go Nuts - or Conversation Guidelines

'So far we have talked about how to Listen to the Physical and the Intuitive Signs,' Lee said. 'I am aware of what to watch out for in my environment, and at this point I even have some kind of idea as to what my Intuition feels like, but now I'm becoming more and more curious to hear about the Mental Signs. You said that Mental Signs are messages, words, and pictures in our Minds eye, right? What kind of messages are we talking about here? Do The Guys actually *talk* to us? Like properly? With words and all that?'

'Yes, that's exactly it. Unless told otherwise, The Guys will talk to us in *our* own language. With me for example They pretty much talk exactly the way I do. They are light-hearted, They make jokes, are funny and pretty straight forward. So yes, They use words.'

'Great. Now I'll have voices in my head as well,' Lee rolled his eyes to the heavens.

'Well, yes,' Tara said casually.

'Man, I don't know if I actually want that. I mean, I've already got my own stuff up there,' Lee pointed at his head, '*and* other people's!' he added with a shake of his head, remembering their previous discussions. 'So, do I really want to invite The Guys' chatter into my head as well? I think I'd probably go nuts. Come to think of it, that's what they call schizophrenia, isn't it? Voices in your head?'

'Let me put your Mind at ease,' Tara patted Lee's arm soothingly. 'There are a few important things to understand. First, **They don't constantly talk to you, but only when you *need* it.** Sometimes more, sometimes less, sometimes every day, sometimes days pass with nothing. It's exactly the same as with Co-incidences. Your days aren't one big Co-incidence, are they? You get them when you need them. It's the same with talking to The Guys. **They talk to you when They feel that you need to know something, and you talk to Them when you need it. You Listen to Them and They Listen to you.** Easy.'

'Great, that's reassuring,' Lee said with a sarcastic undertone in his voice, 'that'll mean I'll have a schizophrenic *dialogue*, rather than a schizophrenic monologue going on up there,' he grinned. 'I don't think that puts my Mind at rest at all, sorry.' Inviting voices into his head? That was a bit below the belt line, or not? Was this really a good idea? I mean you never know what you'll get yourself into…

Tara smiled, she loved Lee's scepticism. It was healthy. Healthy because he was also always open to a good explanation, open to venture into the unknown. 'Actually, there is a big difference between The Guys talking to you and being schizophrenic. It's not like a mad array of crazy voices stumbling all over themselves trying to get your attention. It's *not* like *that*. The Guys don't just jabber at you for no reason. Well, they don't jabber, full stop. When They talk it's clear, precise and straight forward. No word is too much, what they tell you is useful and practical, it's not Mindless crap - and They don't tell you to do stuff that you know is really wrong, dangerous or bad, like schizophrenia often does.

What's more, schizophrenia doesn't stop when you ask it to, whereas if you're not comfortable with Mental messages from The Guys or anything else that They might do, you can ask Them to stop.'

'Really?' Lee was amazed.

'Oh yes. **If you want Them to stop temporarily, you know, give you a break for a little while, or if you want Them to change Their approach, even if you want Them to stop all together, you can just tell Them and They *will* Listen and they *will* stop.** It's as simple as that.'

'Just like that? You just tell Them?'

'Of course. Why make it anymore complicated than you have to?' Tara giggled.

'Now *that would* be silly,' Lee brushed his hair back. For a moment, until it fell forward again, Lee's mane reminded Tara of a tousley Elvis. Gosh, since when did she fancy Elvis? Well, he *was* sexy once, she thought with a smile. She looked at Lee again. His hair never stayed like that for long, it always fell back over his forehead and he'd look up at her through his hair. With those long lashes, …

She looked at him just a second longer than normal without saying anything, then the words came back to her, 'It's kind of logical that The Guys would stop if you'd ask them too. I mean, They don't want to freak you out, do They? That'll be missing the point. **You know, They are so glad that you are finally Listening, that the last thing They are going to do, is loose you again by annoying you or by scaring the living daylight out of you.** They *want* to work *with* you. In fact, that's the only way it works. You work on this stuff *together*. They want to be your mates, your friends. Not your nightmare.'

'Now that actually *does* make me feel better. If I should ever feel that I'm going nuts, I just tell Them to give it a break. I guess that's acceptable,' Lee mused. 'Anyway, taking into account what I know about The Guys up till now, it seems that They're far too considerate to let it even come that far, right?'

'Agreed, but as with everything, it's a learning process on both sides. It's team work. It's exactly like meeting a new person. In any new relationship you have to find a common wavelength, a way of communicating. **Different people respond to different approaches and sometimes it can take a little time to establish the rules of conversation. With some people you have to actively and consciously work on the rules, with others you seem to just kind of blend into one another. It's the same with The Guys.** Nothing more, nothing less.'

'The way you talk about this stuff, one would think that you were born like that,' Lee said flatteringly.

'Oh I wish,' Tara threw her hands into the air. 'It took me a while to figure all this out, but throughout my experimentation I realised one of the most important things. We can either make it all really complicated or we can make it easy and that choice is up to us. I personally like it easy and straightforward without any hocus-pocus and I would say that the approach I'm giving you, is pretty much as easy as it gets - and it works a treat,' Tara added nonchalantly.

'How did you figure it all out by yourself? I'm just amazed.' Lee probed gently.

'Well, if you really look at it, most of it is actually common sense. But how did I find out? Well, **I don't like things to be complicated, so I just try to cut everything down to the bare bones. I always asked myself, what would be the easiest thing to do? The most obvious thing that's staring you right in the face?** What would you do if The Guys would be people? What would you do if somebody annoys you or if you needed some space from somebody?'

'I'd tell them?'

'Well precisely, so I tried that with The Guys and it just happened to work.'

'You just tried it. That's brilliant.'

'Thanks.'

'Can I ask you a question?' Lee asked politely.

'Sure.'

'You said that "unless told otherwise, The Guys will talk to us in *our* own language", does that mean that you can tell them how you want them to talk to you in general?'

'Absolutely.'

'Cool,' Was all Lee managed to say.

Am I Nuts?

'Tara, I'm really curious. What was it like to find out how all of this stuff worked? What was it really like to play around with The Guys, not knowing what you were doing? Not being able to really talk to anyone about it? Were you never scared or worried that you were getting in over your head?' Lee asked.

'Not really. I was certainly a little distressed from time to time, but in fact, it's quite a fun story. I remember when I started to talk to The Guys. After a few weeks of chatting away, I had a sudden reality check. You know one of those when it suddenly hits you: oh man, I'm talking to stuff in my head *and* it's talking *back* to me. I've finally done it. I've lost it. I'm crazy, I'm bonkers, I've finally gone loopy. Congratulations.'

'Did you really think that?'

Tara shrugged her shoulders, 'Of course. I mean some of this is pretty weird to the average Rational Mind, right? When I started out, I didn't have anybody to tell me that it was all simple and normal and straightforward, and as you know, I didn't have anybody to exchange my experiences with either. So, at some stage I wasn't quite so sure anymore that I hadn't maybe lost it after all. So, just to be on the safe side, I decided that I needed to stop for a while, regain ground, check in, you know. Somehow, deep inside I knew that The Guys would Listen to my request for a bit of space. One night I sat down and told them: "ok Guys, I need a break. If you keep talking to me, I will go nuts, and then I'll be of no use to anybody anymore. So, please, give me some space for a bit. I'll let you know when I'm ready for more." And suddenly? There was dead silence. I didn't hear a word for days, actually I didn't hear a beep till I told Them that I was ready for more.'

'They really do Listen,' Lee was astounded.

'Oh yes.'

'Man, I can't believe you went through this stuff on your own. What did you do after you asked The Guys to stop?'

Tara thought for a few seconds, remembering her own trial and errors, how serious they had seemed back then and how comical they seemed to her now, 'I tried to figure out *what* had actually freaked me out when I was still talking to them, and then I looked at *what* They were actually saying to me. By doing that, I realised that it wasn't *what* They said to me that had spooked me, but that it was the sheer realisation *that* I was talking to *something* out there, and *that* it was talking back to me in the first place and to top that, that the messages were full with such wisdom and usefulness. It spooked me that I actually felt comfortable with something I could absolutely not explain,' Tara laughed. 'I realised that whatever I was talking to, had only ever helped and guided me, answered my questions, and was all in all really good to me. I noticed that my problem had nothing to do with Them, but with the fact that I Thought that this was not something *normal* people do. I didn't know anybody else who was doing it, so no matter how good it was for me, I started think that it must be weird.'

'I can understand that. Isn't it strange though, that even though something does us good, we still try to understand it with our Rational Mind, and if we can't, it must be bad? Phew, what a hurdle to overcome, and you didn't even find anybody to talk to. How did you get yourself out of that confusion?'

Tara smiled in memory, 'It was a funny natural progression and strangely, it wasn't anything I had thought of, or any conclusion I had come to on purpose, it ended up to be the simple fact, that after a few days, I started to I miss Them.'

'No way. That's so sweet.'

'Well yes. I missed them because They really *are* good fun when They're around, and Their little hints really *did* make my life a lot easier. Once you get to talk to Them, you realise how lovely They are. They really only have your best interest at heart. And,' she grinned, 'They're fabulous entertainment value too. So with them gone, there was something missing from my life.'

'Or out of your head,' Lee said with a smile.

'Yeah, and there,' Tara nodded. 'I ended up having a long think and finally decided that I didn't *care* if it was *normal* or not, that I didn't *care* that I couldn't explain it in a rational way. All I could say was that They had helped me and that They had given me really useful information and that I liked Them. I finally decided that it would be stupid to miss out on The Guys. And anyway, if I had to, I could always ask Them to take it easy again.'

'That very special build-in safety mechanism,' Lee grinned.

'Exactly. So what could I loose? I made up my Mind and lifted the ban. The question at that time was how to do that.'

'Did you just ask Them again?' Lee pre-empted.

'I did. I tried the easiest way first. I thought that since I had told them to stop and they did, that I could probably just tell Them that I'm cool now and ready to Listen again, so that's what I did. But knowing this time what I was comfortable with, I also told them my terms.'

'What your terms and conditions?' Lee joked.

'Yep.'

'Are you serious? This gets better by the minute, you told the Universe your terms and conditions under which it can talk to you.'

'Of course,' Tara said matter of factly. 'At first I told Them that They could talk to me again, but please only when I asked Them to. We did that for a while and it worked a treat and I slowly got used to Them again.

The Guys were very good about it,' she added sweetly. 'Then after a while, when I felt more confident, I said that They could talk to me again whenever they wanted to, i.e. without me having to ask them, but only whenever They felt that it was important. I asked Them to still take it easy on me, to start of gently and all that. And They did. It was so cute, it sometimes felt as if They were tiptoeing around me. Sometimes I could feel Them hesitating, as if contemplating if They should talk to me or not. They were really taking care. Once They even asked me quickly if I wanted to hear Their opinion, I nearly died laughing. I mean, how could I be freaked out by something so gentle?'

'Uh, that's adorable.'

'I know, They really are. Oh, this one you'll like,' Tara just remembered something. 'I tried something else, just to see if it worked. Do you want to know?'

'Of course.'

'Well, I just looked up one day, with a big fat grin and said: go on Guys, I dare you. It would be so great if it would work. So, please, from now on, only talk to me after 6pm. And hey presto, They did.'

'After 6pm? That's hilarious. Where the hell did you come up with that?' Lee burst out laughing.

'I know, isn't it funny? I couldn't stop grinning for ages! I was so pleased with myself,' Tara grinned broadly. 'But you know, besides the fact that it was a fun dare, it also gave me a time of day, every day, at which I could get direct proof that it worked, that it was real, because every day after 6 o'clock I got confirmation. It was really funny actually to observe the time around 6. Sometimes it felt as if The Guys were hanging around throughout the day, waiting for the dot 6 o'clock deadline. I even kept changing the times to see what would happen!' Tara grinned broadly at the memory.

'You didn't,' Lee's eyes widened comically.

'Sure. You got to make sure that it's not just any old Co-incidence, but a significant one, right?'

'Of course, got to make sure,' Lee mumbled flabbergasted.

'Anyway, after all that daily reassurance, besides getting confirmation that I wasn't nuts, I was also confident that anything I'd ask of Them would be Listened to. I knew that I could talk to Them in an easy and straight forward manner, just like I'd talk to a human person. There was no need for complicated wording or rituals. I had talked to them and they had understood and acted on it. Piece of cake. Tried and tested.' Lee beckoned Tara for a small break for notebook purposes. He scribbled:

Mutual learning:
- They learn how you Listen to Their Signs (Mental, Physical or Intuitive).

- You learn how They Listen to you.
- You learn how to talk to Them and They learn how you like to be talked to.
- They learn how not to freak you out and you learn not to freak out ;0)
- If you want Them to stop or change anything, tell Them. And they *will* Listen.

Lee couldn't believe Tara's cheek and inventiveness. Testing the Universe? *Daring* the Universe? Lee felt a familiar warmth spread around his heart, it took some special lady to even come up with stuff like that, let alone do it!

Help With the Nuts-ness

'I did something else too,' Tara added, playfully throwing her braids behind her back.

'What did you do?' Lee couldn't imagine what else Tara could have dreamt up.

'Well, back then I felt that I really needed a partner in crime, somebody to talk to about this stuff. Somebody that was doing the same thing. Even though by that time, I felt comfortable with Them talking to me, sometimes I still felt that I needed some Earthly reassurance that I'm not nuts.'

'So you asked for somebody?'

'How did you know?' Tara grinned.

'It's the most obvious thing to do,' Lee flashed Tara a smile. 'And? Did it work? Did someone come?'

'Of course.'

'Of course. I really should stop asking that question,' Lee shook his head laughing.

'Not really, I enjoy it,' grinned. 'I can understand that question well. I couldn't believe a lot of this for a very long time either. I tell you though, I had so much fun trying out the wackiest things, and I still always managed to get the proof that what I did worked, and with that I also got the necessary reassurance. After a while, and with a bit of trial and error, I managed to refine how it worked best,' Tara's voice trailed of reminiscing.

'So, who was your knight in shining armour?' Lee prodded Tara's arm curiously.

'Well, I was sitting on a bus and a young girl got really sick. When the bus stopped, this guy got up and asked me if I could help him get the girl out into the fresh air. I was on my way to a friends house, but this girl looked so ill, what could I do? There was also this feeling that I had to help this guy more than the girl, which was a little strange. Anyway, together we heaved her out and I'm already thinking what-an-interesting-Co-incidence, when I saw the guys eyes. Well, I just knew.'

'What, that you fancied him?' Lee teased.

'No, not that,' Tara laughed, 'Not that he wasn't nice, he was, but I felt Intuitively that we were going to help each other - somehow.'

'As you do.'

'Well yes, you do with...'

'Practice. I know,' Lee waved his hand in mock dismissal.

'You're learning fast,' Tara grinned.

'Ok, got knight of bus, what happened then?' Lee tapped his fingers on his legs.

'When our eyes met, I recognised in his eyes that he'd had the same feeling. A strong feeling of connected-ness, a feeling that we needed to talk. It was quite comical. It was one of those "Tom and Jerry" double-takes, when you notice something, look away, the significance of the moment hits you and you look back. That was what our first eye contact was like. After the girl had been looked after, him and I sat down at the side of the road, pretty much like you and I did, and started talking. It was completely out of the blue, but it somehow felt entirely natural. Even before I knew his name, we had already started to talk about cosmically far out stuff.'

'Does this kind of thing happen to you on a regular basis then?' Lee felt a tiny pang of jealousy. "Don't be so silly," he chided himself.

'Well, the more you deal with The Guys, the more stuff like this does happen, yes. But some are more significant than others,' Tara smiled openly at him.

"Did she wink? I think she winked. Thank you," Lee noticed himself thinking and laughed at himself. Hilarious. He straightened his back. It was funny to be able to observe himself in Tara's presence. It was obvious that they liked each other, but the subject at hand was so interesting that both of them seemed to be far to engrossed in it to act on their mutual attraction. Actually, Lee thought quietly, it was nice to be in a situation where things could develop naturally, slowly. And hey, no matter what happened, right now it was wonderful to be in the company of such an intelligent, lovely young woman. Lee only noticed vaguely that by thinking this Thought of *accepting* whatever happens, the feeling of jealousy slowly dispersed. He mentally slapped his back in approval. He was already applying everything he'd learned about Emotions. He was already doing it.

'You know,' Tara bounced in on his Thoughts, 'cool things start to happen more and more as soon as you become

Aware. You see, the perfect bits and pieces are _already always_ out there,' she waved her hands around her, **'The Guys just show you how to put them all together.** The Guys point them out to you and if you follow Their Signs, no matter how weird, well, it does get you into interesting situations to say the least.

Anyway, back too the story. It just so happened that the guy I met on the bus, had been dealing with spirits, haunted houses, hearing voices, playing with Intuitions, channelling and all sorts of freaky stuff for a long time, and believe it or not, he was able to give me fantastic advice. We had some great sharing sessions and learned a lot from each other. He was an incredibly aware human being and had played with similar things I had. It was nearly too good to be true that magically both of us got the reassurance that we had so desperately needed.

At some stage during our meeting, I was getting curious. I examined the Co-incidence, wanting to make sure that there really wasn't a Doubt that it was _just_-a-Co-incidence. It couldn't have been. It was significant all round. We got what we needed from each other and what's more convincing than that, was that the dude turned up _three hours_ after I specifically asked for him. In fact, the meeting was better than what I had asked for,' Tara added. That's a sequence of events which is a little to odd for anybody to dismiss it.'

'Definitely significant, I'd say,' Lee agreed.

'Yep. It really was amazing, we did _each other_ so much good. You know, a lot of The Guys Co-incidences that involve two people, are _mutual_ Co-incidences where both parties get something out of it. In this case both of us got reassurance, help and advice that we both desperately needed. It was ridiculous and simply unbelievable that it happened at all and to top that, that it happened only a few hours after I had asked for it. Both of us didn't know if we should laugh at the absurdity of the situation or be grateful or just be in total and utter disbelief. In the end we did all of it, while laughing all the way - of course.'

'Actually, that guy hadn't asked for a partner in crime as well by any chance, had he?' Lee asked jokingly.

'Well, funnily enough, yes, he had.'

'I knew it! That's ridiculous! You're not making this up, are you?' Lee asked just to make sure, but Tara shook her head. 'Ha, that kind of made it easy for The Guys, didn't it? You asked for _each other_. They just needed to hook you up. **Both of you were aware enough to Listen to get yourself onto that particular bus, and then open and able enough, to recognise the significance of your meeting, _and_ neither one of you felt too stupid to take advantage of it.** I am truly stunned.'

'So was I, I tell you,' Tara said unpretentiously. 'Not only did I get reassurance that I wasn't the only one out there doing weird shit, but on top of that, he was a sane, rational and intelligent person. A normal, everyday kind of person, *not* some kind of fruit-loop! It was exactly what I needed and for that matter, what he needed too. It just couldn't have been any more perfect if we would've tried. Thanks Guys!' Tara whispered briefly and looked up into the tree with gratitude in her eyes.

'Well, you did say that They have the perfect plan,' Lee said.

'And They do, and They do,' Tara squealed happily, laid back down, and to his surprise, rested her head in his lap as if it were a pillow. 'Is that ok?' she asked.

'Sure,' Lee said.

"Hang on," he thought, did he just ask for her closeness earlier? Well, not really, he'd said that it was cool either way - but now she put her head on his lap. Was *that* a Co-incidence? **He made a mental note: if you're cool with something either way and you really mean it, does something good happen?** It was a half-baked theory, but he began to see how the Universe worked.

"Lee is totally lovely," Tara thought. She had noticed her Thoughts straying to him more and more throughout their conversation, but she didn't want to expect too much. She went into her head, as she always did, and decided that she'd be happy either way. Right now, it was just lovely to be in the company of such a handsome and intelligent man. She knew that getting herself into that the *Mental space of acceptance,* took away any subconscious anxieties about a possible outcome of a situation and instead, let her relax and enjoy. Now, as there were no more ulterior motives, resting on Lee's lap, seemed like the most natural thing to do. She didn't feel the least bit self-conscious, she wasn't even flirting with him. It just felt right.

Equally as naturally, Lee began to play with a strand of Tara's hair that had come loose. - If Lee would have known Tara's Thoughts, he'd have known that his own theory wasn't so half baked after all...

Lying like this, they pondered their Thoughts for a while, when something suddenly asked for attention in Lee's Mind, 'You know you said that the guy was dealing with spirits and voices? I've heard that some people naturally have all sorts of voices in their heads. Some are born with them, for others the voices turn up one day out of nowhere. Some people see shapes or ghosts. Some people are happy with this, other's aren't and some know and some don't know how to handle it. Some love it, some get scared, some think they've gone nuts.'

'True,' Tara sat up again. 'A lot of people's life would be much easier if they'd know how to deal with the uninvited guests.'

'By talking to Them and by not being scared?' Lee felt the warmth Tara's head had left on his legs.

'Exactly. I have dealt with a lot of people that see and hear all sorts of things. When they asked for advice on how to stop it, I just tell them to ask the voices or the visions to stop, and They *do*. Additionally, the more aware people become in cases like that, the less uninvited stuff enters their head.

As you know, we've got lots of weird stuff up there already, it's just that we never notice it without awareness.'

'Yeah, it was our own stuff *and* other-people's-Thoughts,' Lee remembered. 'In both cases, once we are aware of the unwanted boxes, we can get rid of them,' Lee taped her forehead.

'Exactly. With spirits and voices it's the same thing. If we've invited something into our heads subconsciously, for example by saying: "Oh, it'll be interesting to see a ghost or a spirit", or: "I wonder what a ghost looks like or sounds like", by becoming aware, we can ask them to leave."

'Cool.'

'Oh, one more thing, before you ask any uninvited voices or visions to leave,' she added as an afterthought, 'it might be common courtesy to ask them what They want – just to be polite, you know, I mean, they might have something interesting to tell you.'

'You're absolutely impossible,' Lee burst out laughing.

'Oh, I try.' Tara grinned adorably and continued, 'And last but not least, the other lesson to be learned from this, is to be watchful of what you ask for,' she said, and gently snuggled her head back into his lap.

'Yeah, I'm beginning to understand that,' Lee said, as he twirled another one of Tara's curls around his fingers.

They Know When You're Ready For More... Go For It! – and How Tara Figured It All Out...

'**I** was just thinking about how you thought of asking The Guys to give you a break and yeah, I can see how with some far fetched common sense that could be figured out,' he winked at Tara, '**but how did you know how to Listen to Them and how to recognise Their messages**? Or even how to ask a freaking ghost what he wants? I know you said it was trial and error, but how did you know what to try?'

'**Well, I started exactly in the same order I shared things with you. I began to wonder about Co-incidences, through that I figured out my Intuition, then I started to Listen to my Intuition more and more, then I started to notice that I was getting useful tips in other ways too, through other Signs. Then when I heard**

425

the first message in my head, or what I thought could be one, I followed it, and observed what happened. And so on and so on. Step by step I figured it all out. Once I'd understood how to recreate the state I was in when I received an Intuition which had led me to a significant co-incidence, my Listening got better and better. The better my Listening became, the more The Guys could talk to me and finally I was Listening well enough for them to begin to tell me how to do stuff better.'

'That's cool. They tell you. Of course, that makes sense. But still, what was it like when They talked to you for the first time, like properly?'

Tara tried to remember, 'I think one day I just heard Them talk to me like a human person would. I wondered what it was and asked in my head: "What the hell was that?" – And They told me. The whole story. I just sat there and Listened to all that crazy stuff in my head, making complete sense, answering all the questions I'd had about all sorts of cosmic stuff. I knew it wasn't me or my own Thoughts, because I knew that I didn't know any of that stuff. At first I got a bit freaked out, but as always, They were gentle and non-threatening. Even though my bullshit-detector was on full alert the whole time, I never got anything that told me to be careful,' Tara laughed. Gosh, all of this seemed so long ago now. **From then on, The Guys gave me ideas of things to go and try out. They helped me to find some really cool books, introduced people to me that taught me stuff**. Most of the time they told me of something significant just before it happened so I could watch out for it. It was a wonderful mutual learning process.'

'Hang on, The Guys forewarned you to make sure that you wouldn't miss the Signs?' Lee scratched his chin. 'Are you saying that They don't only *respond* to your questions, but that They also make *proactive* suggestions?'

'Oh yes, very much so. You will see yourself, They can get pretty crafty at developing your abilities if you let Them.'

'How do I let Them?'

'Well, you tell Them that you let Them. You can tell Them to talk to you whenever They think it's useful. Like that, you'll get all of it.'

'Amazing.'

'Oh double yes. Once you are really in tune and you start to play *with* Them properly, They get to know how interested you are in experiencing more, and if you are, They give you more,' Tara said. 'With time, talking to Them and Them talking to you, becomes second nature. With time you won't worry about your sanity anymore, you'll trust Them one hundred percent, and you'll feel good about it. With time, your Rational Mind will become stable, strong, comfortable and at ease with all this whacked out stuff and it will finally stopped bothering you,' Tara smiled honestly.

Lee bent forward, and somehow managed to give Tara, whose head was still comfortably resting on his legs, a hug, 'You're great.'

She smiled up at him, 'Thank you.' Their eyes met and held contact for a little while before Tara spoke again, 'It really was cool. The Guys had learned what I could handle and what I couldn't, and after a little while longer, They and I knew when I was ready for more. It was a gradual process. First I got a bit more daring, asking for a little more, then, after a bit of mental preparation and finally fully trusting that They would take it easy on me, one evening, I lifted the final ban completely.'

'How did you know that you were ready for that?'

'I simply knew. I felt it.'

'What happened then?'

'I lifted my final limitations. I told Them to go-for-it, to give-me-what-They-had, to bring-it-on! If They had something for me, anything, They didn't need to worry anymore, They didn't need to take it easy on me anymore. They could just go for it in whichever way they felt fit. I told Them to give me what They had - and They did,' she giggled at her memories and her fabulous cockiness. 'Believe me, what I got was Mind blowing. They told me stuff I could have never dreamed off. They taught me about myself, about other people, about the world, about Co-incidences, about my Mind, about everything. You know what They taught me, we've talked about it for hours. It's so amazing, words sometimes still fail me.' Tara's voice trailed off and regained it's power, 'Actually, I think there was one thing especially that blew my Mind sideways.'

A Quick Bit About The Shift

'What was that?' Lee held his breath.

'A glimpse of The Shift and instructions of how to get there.'

'What's The Shift?'

'The Shift is the point that can be reached with all of this stuff if you take it to it's humanly possible limit.'

'Pftt, what?' Lee was stunned.

'Yep, I know,' Tara said remembering the moment. 'I can't even begin to tell you what *that* was like.'

'Uoh, no way! Cop out!' Lee shouted. 'Tell me. You can't get off that easily. Tell me about the Shift!' he demanded.

Tara grinned broadly, 'Ha, what do you think I've been doing here? Everything we've talked about is about The Shift.'

'It is?' Lee raised his eyebrows in realisation, 'Oh shit, I only just got that. **The stage in life where everything just works out, where you're so in tune that anything you need will be provided. The place in the Now where Time, Space and Consciousness meet. You call that The Shift**. I remember you using the word shifting before. Come to think of it, you've been using it lots of times,' he grabbed his notebook and did a shifting-brainstorm. The list seemed to grow of nowhere of it's own accord, once he was done they were both visibly impressed.

Shifting:
- Shifting our attention inside and outside.
- Shifting our attention to our environment and our senses.
- Shifting from not looking to looking.
- Shifting into a different dimension.
- Shifting our attention to the Now.
- Shifting from judging to observing.
- Shifting from not Listening to Listening.
- Shifting from being unaware to being aware.
- Shifting the emphasis from thinking, assuming, judging and comparing, to just observing the Now.
- Shifting our focus from wallowing in negative stuff and beginning to enjoy life as it is, in a new and different way.

'Wow, you Listen better to me than I do,' Tara was taken aback.

'Thanks. Looking at that list, everything on it makes our lives more balanced, easier and joyful. I think, I just understood what the Shift is,' Lee said whole-heartedly.

Tara sat up and clapped into her hands with exhilaration, 'That's it, that's it. And that's just the *beginning*,' a wicked smile crossed her face.

'Aah! I knew it! Yes, yes, yes. More, more and more. Fantastic!' Lee leapt up, pulled Tara to her feet and began to dance with her.

Tara laughed with Lee, dancing, her hair flying, her dress beautifully flowing around her Body. She was still laughing as she tried to get her words out in order.

'You know Lee, there's so much more to The Shift. *Knowing* of it is fascinating, but *experiencing* it is a whole new and mad Mind-bogglement altogether. It really *is* a different dimension.'

'Yeah?' Lee pricked up his ears.

Tara sat back down and pulled Lee back onto the blanket. They sat facing each other, their faces reddened with enjoyment.

Tara caught her breath, 'The Shift is like living in a different reality. You just can't believe how amazing it is. If you ever had any Psychedelics, you might have had a glimpse of what it's like to be in a different reality, in a

428

different dimension. If not, mmh, imagine a lucid dream. You know, a dream in which you wake up and become conscious, while you're still dreaming?'

'Oh, I know. When you wake up within a dream, everything is all strange and different and amazing and you can actively influence your dream environment. Everything you think and feel is so real, actually, it feels like real life - just that you can fly,' he added with a grin. 'It's different to those mad, crazy and uncoordinated dreams that we usually have,' Lee said.

'Exactly. Well, that's a bit like **The Shift. It really *feels* different. You *experience* the world differently. You don't just *think* it's different, it actually *is* different. After The Shift you're not dreaming though, you're fully awake and conscious!**'

'I'm gobsmacked.'

'So was I when I found out that it's as real as I'm sitting here.

Lets finish off with the talking-to-The-Guys thingy, shall we? I promise I'll tell you more about The Shift later.'

'Promise?'

'I promise. Scouts honour.'

'That's good enough for me,' Lee smiled widely. 'Man, I never thought that my Mind could boggle so much. I've been boggling for the world, I really have.'

Outrageous Stuff

'**W**ell, let's boggle you some more then, shall we?'

'Boggle ahead.'

'Boggle, boggle, steady, go, here we come,' Tara announced. 'Back to how The Guys talk to us. Before we got sidetracked, we said that we can actively ask The Guys for more once we feel ready. What's probably important to know, is that if we don't ever tell Them that we're ready for more, They probably get bored of us just peddling along when there is so much cool stuff to be played with, right? So after a while, when *They* think that we are ready, They might just try to give you more anyway. They just might give you a few little extra tit bits to check if you're interested. Sometimes They're really subtle with that, but sometimes They can really go for it.'

'Like how?'

'They might try to give you a few completely outrageous messages, which feel so ridiculous and so far fetched it's silly, and then just sit back and have a look if we bite.' Lee looked slightly worried and enchanted at the same time. Tara swiftly picked up on Lee's feelings, 'Don't worry, it's never a nasty kind of testing. It's more a quick check of if we are ready for new or different ways of communication, if we're ready to trust Them on bigger stuff - or even just to check if we really trust the whole experience to be real and true and good.

Once They know that we follow Their messages, no matter how strange or out of the blue or however unrelated to anything they are, then The Guys know for sure that They can begin to talk to us without having to pussyfoot around or having to wait for the right moment. They can just tell us whatever and whenever They want to. That's when They don't have to go through elaborate Co-incidence procedures anymore and it all suddenly becomes much more straight forward. That's when they just talk to you,' Tara finished.

A flicker of Doubt crossed Lee's eyes once more, 'I'm not quite sure about that, just doing what They say? I mean, what if it's totally nuts? I don't know.'

'I'm so glad you ask all of your questions you know? They're so important. In fact, I've asked all of these myself and I would never have gone as far as I did had I not asked them and gotten decent answers. **The important thing to keep in Mind is that you don't just blindly trust anything They say, you don't just willy-nilly trust in some mad voice that suddenly turns up in your head. The Trust I'm talking about builds up slowly over time.** By the time you'll begin to Listen to the really far out messages, you'll have played around with lots of *little* messages for a while. You will have Listened to Their more straight forward, the more obvious messages for a bit and you will have gotten constant reassurance that Listening to Them is good for you. **It's not because I tell you, it's because you've yourself had positive first hand experience, and because of that and only because of that do you begin to trust those voices, first tentatively and then fully and confidently.** You build yourself up to this. And of course, in the end, it's always your choice to follow a message or not. Nobody makes you. Also know that The Guys never tell you dangerous, nasty or threatening things to do, They just give you tips and guidance for your life. They're good to you. Even if They can get pretty outrageous, it's more like – give that guy a flower or talk to that person or sit over there, for example. Well, They do get more serious than that too, but you know what I mean. They're good and helpful, nothing else.'

'Could you give me an example of one of your most outrageous messages?' Lee wanted to know more.

'Oh man, where shall I start, which one to pick. I've got so many, I should start to index them. Ah, yes, I love this one,' Tara remembered an event from a couple of years back. 'The Guys gave me a spontaneous message once, which was absolutely wicked. It was so clear, so obvious, so in my face, that there was no Doubt in my Mind that it was a message. I knew that it was my choice to follow it or not, but I could feel deep down that I would be missing out *big time* if I wouldn't follow it. Therefore, despite the weirdness of the situation, I trusted it anyway and followed it. And boy, did I get amazing confirmation that I did the right thing. It was out of this world.'

'Are you going to tell me what it was or what? What was the message?' Lee demanded to know. This was like story-hour at kindergarten, he was loving it.

'Well, it was a few years ago, when I had planned to go to India. I had set the date, bought the ticket, got the visa, vaccinations, everything. I had been before and I was going to meet some friends there. I was really looking forward to it. A couple of weeks before I was supposed to leave, I went camping with some friends and on one evening I meditated in a field. As you do,' Tara shrugged her shoulders light-heartedly. 'The moon was nearly full and the stars where incredible. My Mind was crystal clear, no Thoughts whatsoever. There I sat, minding my own business, when I suddenly got a message. It was as if somebody had held a megaphone against my ear and screamed through it full power. My entire Mind was filled with just two words.'

'What did They say?'

"Cancel India."

'Ey? Why were you supposed to do that?'

'I had absolutely no idea.'

'Shit, and did you?'

'Yep.'

'Just like that? You followed a message that just came out of the blue like that?'

'Yep. I told you the messages come out of the blue.'

'Yeah, but *that* out of the blue?'

'Yeah, I know, I thought the same thing! Dumbstruck as I was at that moment, all I could think of was to shout: You must be kidding me! No freaking way! But all I kept getting was: "Cancel India". No matter how much I asked and argued, They didn't seem to want to elaborate. I kept asking why and why and why, but all I got was: "Cancel India", over and over again.

Until then it hadn't even crossed my Mind that India wasn't the place I wanted to be or needed to go to. I had no idea why I wasn't supposed to go. I tell you, this part of the message certainly wasn't obvious. It was just really bizarre.'

'But you followed it anyway?' Lee asked incredulously.

'Yep, I did. In all these years of Listening to Their messages, I had realised that no matter how obscure, following Them was always better than not to. So, believe it or not, I cancelled the flight.'

'That's amazing. You actually cancelled a perfectly organised trip because something in your head told you to? Without any rational reason for it whatsoever? That's what I call Trust!'

'You can say that again. I was truly surprised myself. It was funny really, when I first heard the message, even though I was one hundred percent sure in my heart, my Rational Mind was still playing havoc, it was literally screaming, but I didn't care. I *knew* that it was the right thing to do. So, whenever my Mind came up with another yes-But or no-But or any kind of But for that matter, all I could hear was my Intuition shouting: "No but! Cancel India!" - In the end I got so fed up that I just got up and screamed: "Ok, ok, I'm cancelling it, I'm doing it. I'm doing it. Leave me alone now, will you? I get the message. I'm cancelling it!" - So, there I was, sitting on my own, in a field, at night, with an imaginary megaphone next to my ear, shouting into the dark.'

'That's so funny, I can so picture you doing that.'

'Yeah, I'm sure you can. And guess what The Guys said?'

'No idea.'

'All they could say to my outrageous, Mind blowing, incredible decision was: "About time." Then, after a few seconds of me disbelieving Their total lack of appreciation, I heard Them laughing, then They said: "Actually, pretty excellent. That only took about six minutes. Well done. You're getting there". - Well, cheers, I thought.'

'Man, that's so funny. They are sarcastic?'

'Oh yes, They can *be* sarcastic, you better believe it. They're exactly like you. Remember? They *are* you. And well, I can be sarcastic in a fun kind of way. If you don't want Them to be like you though, They can be whatever you want Them to be. But if you want Them sarcastic? That's what they'll be.'

'I shall remember that. But man, what did you do instead of going to India?'

'Good question. I really didn't know what else to do at the time. I had a little project, which required me to be in a quiet, cheap place for a few months, preferably somewhere tropical. Because I had no idea what to do, I asked Them where I was supposed to go instead.'

'Now there's a Thought,' Lee grinned.

'They seemed to like that question and finally They seemed to be happy to elaborate. The answer came loud and clear: "Thailand". I had been there before too and as soon as They said the word Thailand, I got a little picture in my Mind of a bungalow by the sea with trees behind it, quiet, little wooden veranda, natural wood banister and I also got the name of an island where I had been to before as well. That was settled then. That's where I decided to go. To the island, to find *that* bungalow.'

'Phew. What happened then?' Lee wanted to know it all.

'I tell you, I have never been so curious, as I was in that moment. I still couldn't believe that I was actually following this whacked out message, but somehow it felt right. To cancel the India trip, I had to change my ticket, but it turned out that I couldn't, so I had to fly to India and from there I had to arrange an onwards flight to Thailand. It was a lot of hassle and I lost money on the flights too, but again, it felt the right thing to do. Without question.

On the way, lots of stuff went wrong, I got delayed pretty much everywhere, I was surprised because I thought that after following Their message, everything should have worked out smoothly. Doubt was creeping in, and The Guys were silent. Talking about testing!

After a while of wondering what was going on, I had a sudden and welcome feeling of certainty, another intuitive message from The Guys. They told me that I had to arrive on the island at a certain time, and that these delays were necessary to ensure that. I felt reassured. But I tell you, it wasn't easy to keep the Trust. The things that happened on the journey, were just too weird. The taxi driver got lost on a straight road, we ran over a dog, nearly ran over a woman, got stuck in a pothole. Missed a turning on a road that the driver must have driven a million times before, having to drive back. Could this really all have been part of the plan? But by that time I didn't care anymore. Instead of getting angry, my curiosity grew, this was all just too ridiculous. I started laughing. I thought if The Guys really went through so much effort to get the timing right, I should at least give Them a chance. I was beginning to enjoy the ride. Everybody in the taxi was ticking out and I sat there smiling and curious. I couldn't wait to find out, what could possibly be so fantastic at the other end, for all that effort to be justified.'

'Tara, Listening to you is better than telly. Go on,' Lee was fascinated.

'Gee thanks. I'm more entertaining than telly. I'll take that as a compliment, shall I?'

'Oh, very much so,' Lee took Tara's hand reassuringly and gave it a quick, gentle squeeze, before placing it back on her lap. 'Don't let me interrupt, go on with the story,' Lee looked attentive like a little school boy.

'When I finally arrived on the island, I went to the Reception of a hotel I knew from before, just to stay the night, chill out a bit and, as I was hoping, to receive some more instructions on how to find that bungalow. Before I entered the building, a Western girl walked towards me, our eyes met for a split-second, and just as with the guy on the bus before, something clicked. It felt like a strange recognition. I knew I had to talk to her, but I also knew intuitively that it wasn't the right time yet. I walked into the Reception, just to be told by an extremely unfriendly woman that all bungalows were full. When I turned around, the girl from outside stood next to me, tugged on my sleeve and pointed outside. I followed her. Outside she said: "I have the perfect place for you."

'No way,' Lee's jaw had dropped. 'I should just leave it open', he thought with a smirk, it would save a lot of energy.

'Yes way, and it gets better, just wait. The girl hadn't even been in the room when I had asked for the bungalow at reception. She could have had absolutely no idea of what I was looking for, what mod-cons, what price bracket, if I was alone or not, and so on. She didn't know me from Adam. How could she possibly know what the perfect place would be for me? It was such a surreal situation. It was too weird *not* to be significant.'

'Ok, and?'

'Fully trusting, I didn't even think about it, I asked: "Great, where is it?" She said that it was about half an hour walk away and that she could take me there and help me carry my stuff, if I'd like. She would only have to tell her work that she was going to take her lunch break now, rather than later.'

'With an in-build porter? This is getting freaky. She not only told you about the perfect place, but she also moved her lunch break just so that she could help you, *and* she carried your stuff, *and* she didn't even know you? This is unreal.'

'Wait, I haven't even started yet. I couldn't believe my luck. Well actually I could, but I'll never stop being surprised at just how perfect The Guys arrange these things. Anyway, ten minutes later I walked with her along the beach. I told her how unbelievably nice it was of her to help me and how much I appreciated it and so on.

Now comes the really cool bit. From our conversation it transpired that she was so relieved that I hadn't thought that she was a loony when she talked to me at reception. She said that she couldn't believe that she had talked to me like that, she never did anything like it before. It was funny, because when she approached me, she was everything else but shy.

She told me that somehow, when our eyes met earlier, she knew that she had to tell me about the place she was about to take me to. She knew, somehow, that it was the perfect place for me. And she was still surprised that she hadn't even questioned that fact. She had realised that it was an odd Thought, but somehow there hadn't been the slightest bit of doubt in her Mind. She knew that she had to talk to me, and before she knew it, she had already told me. She had been so relieved when I didn't get funny with her.'

'Why would you have done that?' Lee asked.

'I don't know. I wouldn't have, but I guess people nowadays can be very careful and not very trusting. If a stranger offers help, we usually suspect ulterior motives. Not many people go out of their way to help anybody they don't know, unless they're trying to get something out of it. I mean, when was the last time you tried to ask somebody for the time in a major city? Or directions? Very often people look at you slightly worried, clutch their handbags tighter and walk past you. Fast!'

'You've got a point. People are suspicious. Never-talk-to-strangers. We're impregnated with that sentence from the word go. Sad, sad world.'

'Yep. Anyway, when I told her about my own Intuition to talk to her, it was her turn to be amazed. It was all pretty nutty. Needles to say that both of us laughed at the strangeness of the situation, we laughed so hard that our sides ached. It had been good to clear the air and to establish that it had felt right for both of us. After half an hour wandering along beautiful beach side, we stopped in front of the bungalow I had seen in my Minds eye just a week before. I don't know who was more surprised my newly found friend or I.'

'That's outrageous.'

'That's what I keep telling you,' Tara giggled.

'What happened then?' Lee wanted to know.

'I won't bore you with all the mad details, but basically the bungalow was perfect. Previously I had asked The Guys for guidance on certain things, I had asked to learn more about certain topics, and just there by that little bungalow in Thailand, I meet all the right people. Some of them I could share some of my insights with and some who I could learn from as well. Staying there, I met a community absolutely perfect for everything I needed, for my own development at that time and for the progress of my project. Well, I got everything I'd asked for and more. All of it. There in that little bungalow!'

'Which was not in India! Wow.' Lee's amazement abruptly stopped with another little doubt creeping in, 'Yeah, cool story and sorry to be sceptical again, but couldn't this have happened to you in India as well?'

Tara didn't hesitate, 'Maybe yes, maybe no, I will never know, will I? But one thing I *do* know. Thailand was so stupidly perfect that I could not even begin to imagine that any other place could have even gotten close to it. It was beyond perfect, it was so good it was silly. The people I met were out of this world. I could have met lots of people in India, but the ones I met in Thailand and what I learned from them, was as perfect as I could have imagined for that moment in time. I could not have made it anymore perfect if I would have set it up myself. To be honest,' Tara shrugged her shoulders, 'I don't really care anymore if something similar *could* have *possibly* happened in India too. There's no point to even waste any energy on the what-if-s.'

'Fair enough, and anyway, something was definitely up, I mean you knew about all of this stuff beforehand, right?' Lee marvelled.

'Yep. You know, the more you follow Their messages, the more you'll realised that the result *will* be perfect, no matter what the alternative would have been. And to be honest, just that ridiculous trip in the taxi, and meeting the girl and having that far out conversation with her, was worth it all by itself. What an adventure! But of course, don't take my word for it, get your own proof.'

'Oh, I'm working on it, trust me. Man, you've got to be pretty flexible when you're playing with Them, ey? Changing your plans off the cuff like that.'

'It certainly helps, that's for sure. But They have messages and ways for all sorts of people, so that's never a worry. Actually, I just remembered something else. Besides how fabulous Thailand was, what I hadn't mentioned yet, was that a serious political coup happened only a week after I had left home, and travelling to India would not have been a good or safe time. So, by sending me to Thailand, The Guys also saved me from flying into an unsafe country.'

'I'm truly stunned.'

'I know how you feel. For me personally, during that Thailand trip and through so many other experiences, I got so much reconfirmation that this stuff is real, it's unbelievable, and by now, I trust Their messages one hundred percent.'

'And you also trust yourself to be able to tell Their messages one hundred percent from your Mind, right? That's an important factor as well.'

'Oh absolutely, but all of that's just practice. I've got hundreds of stories where I practiced that and of which I learned and gained my confidence in that.'

'I don't doubt that for a second. Do you have breath for another one? I love to hear one more.'

'Sure, if you want to.'

'I do,' Lee laid down on his stomach, playing with the grass.

Tara thought for a second. 'Ah, yes. That's a good one too. Through a really funny Co-incidence I had become the proud owner of a big yellow sunflower. I was in a shop and looked at it. The shop owner came over and gave it to me as a present. When I was given it, The Guys told me that it wasn't for me. I was surprised because I really like it, but hey, no problem, whatever. I wasn't meant to keep the flower, but I could feel another adventure coming on. I was on the train riding home, when I saw a Gothic guy, you know, dressed head to toe in black, with long black dyed hair, skull tattoos and piercings everywhere. All in all he was pretty fierce looking - and my Intuition told me to give him that stupid sunflower. I mean, just the Thought of it. Sheer ridiculousness.'

Lee burst out laughing, 'He would have eaten you for breakfast.'

'Right. I probably don't have to tell you what my Rational Mind thought of that!'

'Oh my God, that is so funny. What did you do?'

'I walked up to him, and as soon as I wanted to reach out to him, we arrived at a station, the doors opened and he got off.'

'No way. So you would have actually given it to him?'

'Wait, I'm not done yet,' Tara grinned. 'Anyway, as Co-incidence had it, I had to get off as well, but the dude was already speeding off in his huge army boots and I had a split second of – "shall I run after him?" But then I remembered that it's supposed to be effortless, so I told The Guys that if I am to give the flower to him They'd need to arrange for me to see him again, because I wasn't going to run after him up those escalators.'

'That's so funny. Bargaining with the Universe once again. What happened.'

'I saw him leap up the escalators like a mad man and out of my view. For a split second I doubted my Intuition again. It was strange, the message had been so clear, had I gotten it wrong? Anyway, I went up the same escalators, as it was on the way to the platform I had to go to, to catch my train home. I waited for only a few minutes on the platform, when guess who, walks in my direction?'

'Goth guy?'

'Absolutely. My Intuition virtually screamed at that point. I mustered up all my courage, and when he got close, I grinned at him and waved him over. He must have thought that I was some kind of nut, I grinned so wide. Anyway, I could see the 'click' in his Brain. At first he wanted too ignore me, but out of some reason, he came over anyway, still looking pretty fierce but also slightly baffled. I didn't say anything, but rummaged in my bag, got the sunflower out and handed it to him, with a little smile and a cute little shrug of my shoulders.'

'Would have melted anybody's heart, no doubt,' Lee looked at her lovingly, 'I can't believe you did that.'

'Wait man, it gets better. You should have seen the guys face. Big butch Goth guy suddenly melted. Literally, I thought he was going to cry. All of a sudden I had this little lad in front of me, dressed all scary, holding a huge plastic sunflower.'

'Oh, that's so sweet.'

'I know. When he'd gotten over it, he looked deeply into my eyes for a long time and then gave me a massive hug. In amongst all of that he whispered in a truly touched voice: "Thank you so much, I needed that real bad. I had such a crap day". At that moment his train arrived and he hopped on. He gave me a wave and a smile and he was gone.'

'What a story.'

'Mad, ey? It's one of my favourites. You know, you asked me earlier if I couldn't have had as good a time in India as in Thailand, and I said that I couldn't prove that? Well, I can't, but you know, there are so many fabulous situations, like this sunflower story, where you get reassurance galore along the way, and after a while you just know that it's real, and you somehow don't ask the but-couldn't-it-have-been-as-good-if-you-hadn't-followed-that-Intuition question anymore.'

'Yeah I can see that. To give a flower, in such a ridiculous way, by total chance, to somebody that truly needed it - and with that I don't mean just the flower, but also the kindness that came with it - that would have already been a pretty crazy Co-incidence in itself, but you actually having been told to do it beforehand, you missing him on the train *and* then meeting him again, *and* you getting the reaction you did? Fair enough. I can see now what you mean by getting-your-own-proof.'

'Yep. By the way, did you notice that the outcome of the "Cancel India" story was of direct benefit to me, whereas the other one?'

'Was of benefit to the guy,' Lee finished Tara's sentence. '**Ah, that's how The Guys work.** *For* **us and** *through* **us** *for others.*'

'Exactly. If we all follow *all* messages, everybody gets helped!'

'That's truly wonderful,' Lee loved the way The Guys worked.

They sat quietly for a little while, looking at each other, when Lee broke the silence. 'I would love to hear more stories, but would you Mind if we talked about the practical side of things, so that I can get started myself?'

'Of course, that'll be great. Once you've started to practice yourself, *you'll* probably be the one telling *me* stories.'

'I wish. Or should I say - I'll ask for it?' Lee grinned.

'Works for me,' Tara grinned back.

Lee sat up straight and said loud and firm, 'Ok Guys - or do you mind if I call you Dudes - well, Dudes, I would like to be able to do this stuff. Guide me please, help me.'

Hang on, Lee was taken aback, did he just feel something indicate agreement in his brain? Did he feel something promising to help? Woha, that was different. "It's only big if you make it", he tried to remind himself.

22 The Practical Listening ABC or How To Listen

Luckily Tara was already on the ball, 'Ok, as requested, here come more practical things. With the Practical-Listening-ABC, we'll get you Listening in no time.

As we said before, The Guys deliver Their Mental messages in a nice little box straight into our warehouses, and by having done our spring cleaning and our inventory, they'll stand out a mile. It's like always watching the same television program over and over again, and of course, if somebody switches the channel, we're gonna notice, right? And anything that differs from the initial channel,…' Tara's voice trailed off, waiting for Lee to fill in the gaps.

'Could be a message from The Guys,' Lee played along dutifully. 'So, does that mean that *every* time I want to Listen to The Guys, I have to observe and clear out my Thoughts and Emotions and boxes and stuff?'

'Well, that depends. At the beginning most people need Their Mind to be *completely* silent and ordered to be able to recognise new deliveries, and thus to Listen to The Guys. If they're not meditating, there's too much stuff going on in their heads for them to be able to pay proper attention. So, yes, those people will need to actively clear their Mind every time. But, once you have practised the Meditation steps for a while, your warehouse will be pretty clean and ordered and with practice it actually stays that way. **So, as long as you make sure that your warehouse stays tidy and our Mind is fairly calm throughout the day, you can pick up messages without meditating. On the other hand, even if some people have problems with clearing or calming their Mind, as long as they know their Mind really well, they might still be able to spot new boxes, simply because they're different to their normal everyday boxes.'**

'But unless I have lots of practice, the quieter your Mind the better?'

'Absolutely.'

How to Recognise Their Messages – How To Tell Thoughts From Intuitions

'I still wonder though how I can *really* tell if something is a message and not a Thought. The Warehouse thing sounds great, but it's still a little abstract,' Lee said truthfully. 'Then again,' he furrowed his forehead, 'I do remember The Guys telling me to take the dictionary this morning. All of that was pretty clear. Weird, but clear. Those messages were so random.'

Tara stood up, bowed humbly and began to recite one of her favourite quotes out of a book she'd just recently read,

'You're not remembering and you're not making things up,
you're just receiving.
Then, suddenly crouching forward in the bathwater,
I get a sense of urgency that's almost like an adrenaline rush.
Not quite heart-thumping, speedy panic
but very definitely an insane desire to do
- what?
Go to the mirror. Yup, that's it, go to the mirror.
Once again, I'm not thinking this,
I'm not generating it and I'm not hearing it.
Nobody is talking to me, there's no volume.
But it's like - what's is it like, this feeling?
It's like one word roaring at you.'
- Jessica Adams'

'Wow, ok,' lights had just gone on in the back of Lee's warehouse.

'See? You've already done this. You've recognised Their message this morning, just like in this quote, you *just knew* when you got it, right?' Lee nodded. 'And well, those are the things you have to keep Listening out for. **If you want to know, there are ways to refine your Listening skills, and there are some tips on how to tell your Thoughts from your Intuitions.**'

'Sure, tell me. I'd love to know what I'm doing, rather than leaving it to chance.'

'Cool. Do you remember when we talked about how to figure out if something was a Physical Sign or not?'

'Sure, we *asked* for something and then watched out for any Signs in our physical surroundings that were related to the questions we asked,' Lee remembered.

'Exactly. With Mental Messages we can do the same thing. You ask The Guys questions.'

'Ah, that's clever. **If you ask a question, you only have to watch out for the Mental message boxes in your Warehouse which are related to that question. Great, that would make it easier to recognise the messages, simply because I'd already**

have some kind of idea as to what kind of box I'm be expecting. That narrows it down nicely,' Lee nodded happily.

'Yep. **To** *initially* **train yourself, you can sit down, do the first three Meditation steps, clear your Mind, ask a question and wait for a related message.** It would be as simple as that. Sometimes you'd get the message straight away, sometimes it takes a little while. The more you practice, the easier and thus the quicker you can hear Their answers.'

'Great. Got that.'

'**And of course, once you've learned to keep your Mind undistracted throughout the day, you can ask questions and Listen to the answers all day long and you don't need to do the Meditation preparation every time anymore.**'

'Check,' Lee ticked of an imaginary list in the air. 'Actually, I just thought of something,' he said. 'If Mental messages are like Intuitions, then we could play with them the same way, couldn't we? I mean we said before, that we could figure out if something was an Intuition or not, even *after* we missed it, didn't we? When we talked about that, I was supposed to remember a lucky Co-incidence and then go back in time to see if I had some kind of notion, an Intuition, if I had seen a Sign, that told me that the lucky event was going to happen, right? I analysed the Tax example, and realised that I *did* have an Intuition. I remembered what the Intuition *felt* like and that it had really stood out in my brain. It's just that I had *ignored* it,' Lee remembered the details easily. 'Now, couldn't I do the same thing with Mental messages? I could pick another lucky Co-incidence, then go back in time and have a look if I got a Mental message, couldn't I? I could examine a bunch of situations like that, I could remember how the message felt like, what shape it had, what texture, what colour and so on, exactly as with an Intuition. Oh, and in the end, all I'd need to do is recreate the state of Mind I was in when it occurred, which should then allow me to pick up more messages really easily.'

'Well deducted Einstein. That is a really good way of playing with it. Now, let me tell you a bit more about the messages themselves, that might help too. **Sometimes messages are loud and clear, sometimes they're just a tiny little nudge, a knowing that flashes past your Consciousness.** Some people feel them like little voices in their heads, they actually *hear* them. Sometimes you *hear* words, sometimes you *see* or *feel* a flash of a picture in your Mind's eye. Those flashes are like the subliminal messages that used to be shown during the trailers at the cinema. You know, you're watching a trailer for a movie and an image of an ice cream is shown for a millisecond. Your Subconscious notices it, but your Conscious Mind might not have. Either way, you suddenly want to go and buy ice cream in the break. Do you remember those?'

'Yeah, I've heard of them.'

'Well, The Guy's messages can be just like that. It's a *Thought that's not your own* that suddenly hits your Being. If your subconscious already knows to Trust those messages, it follows them automatically, if not, you have to train yourself to catch yourself out the millisecond the message enters your Awareness, and then decide to trust and follow them.'

'A-Thought-that's-not-your-own. That's good, that's exactly what it feels like.'

'Yeah, once you know what you're looking out for, they really stand out. It's as if there's suddenly something in your head, a Thought, a voice, an image, out of nowhere, often completely unrelated to anything you've been thinking about before. You called it random earlier and that's exactly what it is. But all the messages, all the Intuition, always have a similar quality to them, a particular kind of feel that lets you recognise them.'

'That's a good tip, I shall watch out for that.'

'Fab. **Going back to what you said earlier, you're right, playing with Messages really is similar to the way we play with Intuitions, it's just that instead of it being a *feeling* which you can't explain or rationalise, it's an unexplainable *Thought* to do something, or a *Mental knowing*, or a Thought with an odd certainty to it. Another thing that makes Their Messages stand out, is that they are not wishy washy.** They're never like: "What about this?", "Maybe you could do this?", or: "Do really you want to do that?". But they are more like a *direct* statement, loud and clear, unambiguous and straightforward. The messages are more like: "Go and do this", or: "talk to that person, meditate on this, this is not a good idea, you spend too much time thinking about x, you worry too much", or: "that's the answer".

If you're not sure if something was a message or not, ask yourself what the wording was. If the possible message contained anything like: "I don't know if I should do XYZ", or **any sentence, that has an *if, should, could, maybe, try* or *hope* in it or any other fluffy stuff for that matter – then it did *not* come from The Guys. The Guys are gentle and lovely, but They tell you what's what, no But-s or complicated round about ways, no could-s or maybe-s. There's no vagueness, uncertainty or haziness. They just give it too you - wham. Their messages are so different from what usually goes on in your Mind, that you can't really help but notice it, and for a split second you will know that that's exactly the right thing to do.'**

'You know,' Lee scratched his head, 'that's exactly what the dictionary thing felt like. I'm pretty sure though, that if we wouldn't have talked about all of this stuff beforehand, I would have ignored the message. I know that my Rational Mind would have just argued it away. Like it did with the Tax example.'

'That's why we need to catch the messages *the second they come through*, *before* we have time to rationalise them away. When our brain is calm and empty, it should have slowed down enough to allow us to be *consciously aware of every split second in our heads*, which in turn enables us to easily receive messages as they stand out from our own Thoughts,' Tara said, trying to help Lee refine the knowledge and experience he already had in as many ways as she could think of.

Tara leant back, knowing that there was more, 'There's another way that helps you tell Their messages from your Mind.'

'Great, let's have them all,' Lee leant back against the tree next to her in his usual relaxed manner.

'Think about how you would normally get an answer to a question, or the solutions to a problem,' Tara suggested.

'I would mull it over for a while, weigh up pros and cons and make a decision based on that.' Lee thought for another second, 'Basically I would discuss the issue in my head and I'd prepare the answer in my Mind.'

'That's exactly what I was trying to get to. Well, The Guys *don't* do that! They just tell you what to do or what the answer is, finished. **They don't tell you endless stories or give you all the pros and cons, they just give you the end result.** Bang. **Their messages come from out of nowhere, it's a Thought that you have *not* prepared.** It's just there. Wham.'

'It sounds a bit like a Geistesblitz, a sudden flash of genius or a brainwave.'

'Good description. **As soon as you find yourself discussing *something* or *questioning* something in your Mind, it's your *own* Mind talking. It's not your Intuition and it's not a message either.'**

'Great.'

'So whenever you are wondering: "Oops, was that a message?"...'

'I can figure out weather I prepared that Thought or not,' Lee finished Tara's sentence. 'Ah, and I can do *that* by retracing Thoughts, which I learned earlier.' Tara just smiled. 'I can retrace my Thought process to the *initial* Thought on the subject, *before* I started to discuss it or think about it or rationalise it, the *core* of it. I can look if I prepared it, if it was wishy-washy or if the wording was straightforward,' Lee said excitedly.

'Precisely.'

'I guess it takes a bit of practice though to be able to trace Thoughts back that far.'

'Sure, but it's well worth it, and it's lots of fun to begin to notice all The Guy's useful stuff in your head for a change. **Oh, I just thought of something else, to hold on to a message long enough to actually look at it without it getting blocked out by your Rational Mind, you just need to learn to catch yourself out whenever your Rational Mind interferes.'**

'**Just like we did with Thoughts before.** Catch yourself out and back to the message. Just like contemplation,' Lee finished Tara's sentence once again.

'Exactly. **If you noticed a message but didn't manage to hold on to it, and it disappeared back into the vast abyss of your chattering Mind, retrace your Thoughts till you find it again.** If that doesn't work, go back into the Now and wait for it to come back there.' Tara stopped and then added, 'Actually, that's a really effective way to remember pretty much anything actually. You put out an Intent about what you want to remember, you go into the Now and wait.' Tara suddenly grinned, 'And if that doesn't work either, you ask The Guys to tell you again.'

'You just ask them again! That's brilliant. S'cuse me, I didn't quite get that, would you mind repeating that? That's so funny. Man, I wonder if They ever get fed up with our incompetent pestering,' Lee shook his head.

'Luckily they're pretty patient,' Tara said with that enigmatic smile she smiled when she talked about The Guys.

Lee looked at her, seeing the smile, the twinkle in her eyes, the sun in her hair.

'Last but not least,' he heard her say, '**I just remember one last vital point to tell your Mind from your Intuition. This one is really, really important! Especially for those people out there that have a kind of, lets say, more darker disposition, those people that suddenly want to justify their weird and inhumane actions with: "but my Intuition told me to...", well, no! The Guys would *never* tell you to do anything bad, to do anything dodgy. They would *never* tell you to do anything against the laws where you could get yourself into serious trouble, to hurt yourself or do harm to anybody else. An Intuition would *never* suggest anything immoral or unethical. The Guys are into helping you, doing *good* for you and into encouraging the goodness *inside* of people! So, if you get anything weird, anything nasty, anything you feel scared**

of or deeply uncomfortable with? Tell your Mind to *shut up!*'
Tara said with emphasis.

'If Thoughts like that come on a more frequent basis, maybe a little self-analysis might come in useful,' Lee said sensibly, 'cause *something* is trying to tell you something.'

'Agreed, but it sure as hell ain't The Guys. So yeah, **retrace the Thought, look at where it came from, what triggered it, learn about it and from that about yourself, and then breathe it away, you have no use for it!**

Obviously keep in Mind that what I just said doesn't mean that your Intuition always tells you nice and comfortable stuff, because it might give you a deserved kick up your backside from time to time, and that might challenge you, sure, but you will *always* know *deep down that it's good and right*. So, if in doubt, by all means, ignore the message, or whatever it was, until you've become more confident in discerning the difference between Mind and Intuition.'

'Good stuff,' Lee nodded.

'**Now, finally, whenever you feel that you've got an Intuition, you can check if it was a message or not by comparing it to a little list.**'

'A list?'

'Yeah, this one,' Tara quickly jotted down a bunch of bullet points, with Lee looking over her shoulder.

A message is:
- A Thought which is not your own.
- A Thought which you haven't prepared with other Thoughts.
- Suddenly there's something in your head, out of nowhere, often completely unrelated to anything you've been thinking about before.
- It's like Geistesblitz, a sudden flash of genius, a brainwave.
- It stands out in your Mind as clear as a bell (the more you practice, the clearer it becomes).
- An inexplicable Thought that tells you to do something, which might not make sense, but feels right.
- A bold statement, it's there - wham, loud and clear.
- Their messages contain no ambiguity, no vagueness, uncertainty or haziness, no wishy-washy stuff, no But-s or complicated stuff.
- Any Thoughts with should, could, maybe, try or hope, in it, or any other round about stuff, is not from The Guys.

- You can analyse messages just like your Intuitions and figure out what the message felt like when you got it. Like this you get to know the feel of a message.
- If you noticed a message, but started to discuss it in your head, and you are not sure anymore what the messages was, you can trace back our Thoughts to The initial message.
- Or wait in the Now, for it to come back.
- Or ask The Guys to tell you again.
- If think you missed one, or if you just want to make sure, you can always ask The Guys to tell you again.
- The Guys would never tell you to do anything unethical, anything that would hurt yourself or others or be destructive in anyway. They're The *good* Guys! If in Doubt, ignore the message, or whatever it was, until you get more confident in discerning the difference between Mind and Intuition.'
- Use this list!

'I'm amazed how you can just write a long list like that,' Lee grinned.

'I had a good teacher,' Tara laughed at Lee.

'Thanks,' he smiled. He held up his notebook triumphantly, 'Brilliant, this will really help.'

'You know,' Tara pointed at Lee's notebook, 'I'd love a copy of that little book at some stage. That's going to be a really useful document one day.'

'Two fifty,' Lee held his hand open.

'Bargain I'd say.'

'But for you? Just for the price of some more information.'

'Rip off!'

'Uoh, pretty please.'

'Well, if I have to,' Tara grinned.

'Great. I can't believe that there's always more. Will it ever end?'

'Nope. Infinity is the word,' Tara whispered devilishly, knowing that she wasn't even exaggerating.

'I'm Satisfied with your reply. Very satisfied. Go on then, earn your copy of this magic little book,' Lee waved the notebook teasingly in front of Tara's face.

'Sir, as you like Sir. Immediately Sir,' Tara bowed obediently.

Following Messages

'**I** think you have enough information now to be able to play with Messages and to practice telling them apart from your Mind.'

'Agreed.'

'Great. Now, *recognising* the Messages is only one part of the equation. **There are three things that we need to practice together for a message to have an actual positive effect on our lives.**'

'Three? Alright then, let's have them,' Lee waggled his pen in readiness. Tara dictated slowly.

Just like with Intuitions:
* First, you need to *notice* something out of the ordinary in your Mind.
* Second, you need to realise the significance of the message, i.e. that it actually *is* a message.
* Third, you need to trust it enough to actually *follow* it and put it into *action* (even if it doesn't necessarily make sense at the time – you'll get the reason sooner or later).

When he finished writing, Lee said, 'Your Cancel-India story is a good example for that. First you noticed something out of the ordinary in your Mind. A message, loud and clear, a Thought which wasn't your own. It was out of the blue and straight forward. You hadn't prepared it because you hadn't even Thought about not going before. It wasn't connected to any previous Thoughts you'd had and it really stood out in amongst all your other Thoughts. You said that it felt like somebody had just physically talked to you through a megaphone. It was an order, rather than a fleeting Thought. It was obvious that it wasn't your Mind talking to you.'

'Exactly. I don't talk to myself like that. I also knew from previous experience, that even though it didn't make any sense at all, I needed to follow the message, *and* I actually *did* follow it,' Tara ticked off the three points on the list.

'Great. I would have thought that playing with the Cosmos would be all mystical and vague, but your explanations are all straight-forward, logical and common sense. Ha, we even have lists to tick off,' he grinned, 'I really am surprised.'

'We aim to please,' Tara laughed.

'Pleased,' Lee said happily. 'Could you give me another example?' He didn't really need another one, but he loved to hear Tara's weird and wonderful stories. It was like being back with his Grandma. She always knew how to spin a good yarn.

'Sure. I can tell you as many as you want to, I had to build a whole building next to my warehouse up here to keep them all in,' Tara tapped her head grinning, as her memory truck brought out another story. 'One day, I was walking along a road and saw a small sign for a newly opened Gem shop. The sign was really colourful and happy looking. I would have loved to pop in for a browse, but I was already late for a meeting with a friend, so I decided not to. I had nearly walked past the shop, when I suddenly got a message, loud and clear: "You really *do* want to go into that shop - *now*". I recognised it as a message, but I wanted to ignore it because I was late. With me only being vaguely aware of it, somewhere on the fringes of my Consciousness an argument began. I said to The Guys in my Mind: "No I don't want to go into the shop, I'm already late." In response, They said: "Yes you do!", a bit louder and clearer. "No I don't." "Yes you do." That suddenly woke me up. "Oh, Guys, sorry, you're talking to me." "Yes, so we have been, stay with the programme, will you?" I heard a faint giggle,' Tara laughed at the memory.

'I see now what you meant when you said that They have a sense of humour,' Lee laughed with her.

'Yeah, I know. Now, there I was, really not wanting to go into that shop, but knowing that I had to. Not just because They told me, but because I *chose* to Listen. I knew from experience, that if I wouldn't follow their message, I'd somehow miss out, even if I didn't know *how* I'd miss out yet. So, to make a long story short, off I went into the shop. I didn't know why I was there, I didn't want to buy anything, I didn't even have any money on me. But whatever, there I was.

I had a little wander around, when the owner of the shop came up to me and started talking to me about the necklace I was wearing. It was a very unusual silver pendant with a quartz crystal, which was stuck into a carved out hole in the pendant. The owner asked me if she could hold it in her hands to have a closer look at it. I said of course and leant forward. The moment she touched the pendant, the crystal fell into her hand.'

'No way.'

'Yep that's what happened. The owner was horrified and apologised a thousand times for breaking my necklace, whereas I nearly died laughing, being grateful to The Guys for this very special Co-incidence. I would have been very sad to say the least, if I would have lost the crystal and I surely would have, maybe even just a few minutes later walking down the road, had I not Listened to The Guys' message.

Once I had calmed her down and even though I reassured her that it really wasn't a problem, she still offered to fix it for me. I told her that I didn't have any money on me, but she said it was no trouble at all. I was stunned. Not only did The Guys prevent me from loosing my crystal, They also arranged to have my necklace lovingly repaired for me.'

'For free.'

'Yep. And it only took a couple of minutes, so I wasn't even too late at my friends' house.'

'Unbelievable. And you had no idea beforehand that your necklace was going to break?' Lee asked.

'Nope.'

'That's just amazing. That *can't* have been just any old Co-incidence! I mean, you were actually *told* to go to the shop! '

'See what I mean? You get your own proof and reassurance all the time that this stuff is real, no matter how weird it is.'

'I do. So funny, that reminds me of your example with the girl that was going to show you to the bungalow in Thailand, you know, where you got the 'in-build porter' to carry your bags,' Lee laughed, 'with your necklace you got 'in-build repair service'! This is just crazy,' he shook his head. Mmh, let me just do the *Co-incidence analysis* on this story to practice a bit.'

'Sure, go ahead.'

Lee analysed Tara's story, 'First The Guys gave you a Physical Sign, the colourful poster. But even though you noticed it, it didn't sink in. You were late and you didn't know at the time that you had a problem with the necklace, so you ignored the message and kept on walking. The Guys had to try again. This time They sent you a Mental message instead and luckily, you didn't only notice this one, but you also trusted it enough to follow it - no matter how weird it was. Well, you did after a bit of arguing,' Lee grinned at Tara's cheekiness to argue with the Universe.

'Well analysed. You're definitely getting the hang of this. It still surprises me sometimes how well it works. Do you remember the story about the guy I met on the bus?'

'Sure, it's etched into my memory. Your knight. How could I forget.'

'Well, we were both at a stage where we were wondering if we were making these things up or if the messages were actually real, so we decided to test The Guys' messages together.'

'How did you do that?'

'**Whenever *I* got a message I told *him* straight away and *he* told me when *he* got one.** And you know what we found out?'

'What?'

'**We often got the same messages.**'

'You're kidding!' Lee was stunned.

'Dead serious. We couldn't believe it either. One day, we were supposed to meet a friend of ours. It was nearly time to meet him but both of us felt that he needed some more time.'

'How did that happen?'

'Well, we asked the Universe if we should go over now, but the answer that came loud and clear was: No, not yet!'

'First your question, then Their message answering.'

'Yes – and the fascinating thing was that both of us had that exact same message at the same time.'

'Because the message was for *both* of you.'

'Exactly. We looked at one another and asked each other: "Did you just hear that?" and both of us had.'

'Wow. Both of you Listened and you told each other what you heard. What a great idea. It sounds like it could be a lot of fun to play with someone else.'

'It is. It gives it all a whole new dimension. It's fun and you get a whole lot of confirmation that it's not just in your head, you get hard evidence, if you can call it that.

Anyway, after that message, my friend and I decided to wait and kept on talking. We had a very engaged conversation, when suddenly, all I could hear in my Mind was: "Matt." The person who we were supposed to meet. Somehow I couldn't concentrate on the conversation with my friend anymore, and he also seemed to have lost the threat of what he was saying. Both of us noticed the split second of confusion on each others' faces, then we burst out laughing and simultaneously said: "Matt!" The Guys had given both of us the *same* message at the *same* time again, and *both* of us had Listened.'

'And you were so surprised about the message that *both* of you lost the threat of your conversation. Talking about reassurance,' Lee's mouth gaped open just a tiny little bit, till he noticed and closed it again.

'It gets better,' Tara chirped.

'Why am I not surprised?' Lee grinned and looked up into the sky.

'When we arrived at Matt's house, he had only just come home and we found out later, that if we would've turned up at the earlier arranged time, we would have stood in front of a closed door. And, obviously, my friend and I would have missed out on our crazy mutual message experience,' Tara laughed.

'More reassurance.'

'Yep, as long we make sure to do the three things on the list!'

'Notice, recognise as significant *and* act. Unless we do that, The Guys can talk to us until They're blue in Their little faces without us getting any benefit from it,' Lee said.

'Precisely. Their job really isn't easy you know? The poor little sods have all this fabulous stuff lined up for us, but we keep missing out on the Signs or we just won't follow them. They have to start over and over and keep trying again and again relentlessly. All that re-trying also delays things, and if you don't get the message in time, you could miss out on really cool Co-incidences. Well, that's not quite true,' Tara corrected herself, 'actually, if They know that you don't Listen very well yet and that you typically *don't* get the messages the first time round, They often start telling you *earlier*. Like that they try to leave enough time to re-try again and again.'

'Gosh, Their cleverness never ceases to amaze me,' Lee said astonished.

'Yeah, but giving you the messages too early can backfire,' Tara pointed out.

'Ah, that makes sense, because if you manage to get a message really early, it could be far to abstract for you, because you can't see any relevance to a future event yet,' Lee said.

'Right, and that can be a dilemma. But that is usually not a huge problem, because the more you practice Listening, the more you manage to pick up the messages closer to the event anyway.'

'Yeah, but the message can still be abstract though, right?' Lee asked, remembering Tara's "Cancel India" story once again.

'That's true,' Tara grinned. So, all in all, the more we can improve our Listening skills, and the more we learn to trust and follow, even if the Messages don't make sense, the better. And don't worry, all of us make a few mistakes at the beginning.'

'Absolutely.'

23 The Asking and Question Malarkey

'**O**k, are you ready for some new stuff?' Tara asked.

'Do you really need to ask? I am so curious, my ears are burning.'

Tara opened her bag, got out her water bottle, carefully opened it and poured a tiny amount of water onto her fingers. She was just about to wipe it onto Lee's right ear to cool it down, when he second-guessed her intention and jerked sideways.

'I don't think they are that hot, thank you,' he grinned, carefully eying up the bottle in Tara's hands.

This time Tara guessed *his* intentions and, with a huge grin, hid the water bottle behind her back. Lee tried to grab it a few times but to no avail. Tara held the bottle in front of his nose a few times taunting him, but always hid it again just before Lee could get hold of it. Thinking of an alternative strategy, Lee, quick as a flash, leaned forward and madly tickled Tara's side. In surprise she dropped the bottle, giving Lee the chance he needed it to grab it and open it.

'Oh no, please, have mercy,' Tara crawled onto her knees and held Lee's foot over her head. 'I shall be a good servant from now on,' she tilted her head and grinned up at him.

'Ah, now we're talking,' Lee said in a mighty voice, looking down at her, 'I shall let you off this time. But do not dare to do this again *woman*.'

'Yes *man*!' Tara said with exaggerated obedience, as she watched him carefully, until he put the bottle down again.

For a second the sun reflected in one of the drops of water that had splashed onto his neck during the wrestle. It sparkled like a little gem. As she looked at him, for a second their eyes met. Soft and warm. She sat up again, brought her clothes and hair back in order, grinned at him and picked up her threat.

'Well, so far, we have talked about *why* asking for things helps to follow Co-incidences, Intuitions and Messages, but we haven't gone into much detail about the actual questioning *itself*, so that's what we can talk about now if you like.'

'Oh, great. Details of how to ask which horse will win.' Tara shot him a stern look, but the twinkle in her eyes betrayed her. 'Sorry,' he smiled at her naughtily.

'Of course, everything I say are just guidelines to help you start out and making your own rules. Within reason,' she added quickly, trying to make a point.

'Sure,' Lee nodded reassuringly.

'Let's write another list to help me get the order straight,' Tara said and began to dictate the next few bullet points.

The Asking and Question Malarkey:
- What you can ask for and how – what's possible.
- Asking for information, help and guidance – Intangible stuff.
- How to ask for physical things and events – Tangible stuff.
- What The Guys do with our questions once you've asked them.
- What you need to do once you've asked.
- Physical and Mental Involvement.
- How to ask questions.
- Question semantics. How to ask clear and precise questions.

'Got it,' Lee put the pen down and rubbed his wrists, fleetingly thinking that Stenography would be a fabulous skill to have.

'Don't stop just yet, there's a wee bit more to come. Now comes the: What-can-we-actually-ask-for bit.'

'Oh, I'd be happy to keep writing for that one. All I know is that it's *not* supposed to have anything to do with horses or car races.'

Tara smiled at Lee's tenacity, 'Well, let me elaborate on that indirectly. We can ask Them for pretty much anything we want to, the list is endless, but whatever we ask for, usually falls into a couple of distinct categories.'

We can ask:
* For and about Intangible things
* Tangible things

And within those two categories, we can ask for:
* Events
* Information
* Things
* Experiences

'Each question, be it Tangible or Intangible, has the *same* fundamental guidelines that underlies it. Guidelines of *how to ask for* something, and then guidelines for *how to Listen* to the answers. But each has slightly different nuances to it. Don't worry, even though all this might sound a bit complicated at the beginning, it's not really,' Tara promised.

'Because it's common sense?'

'How did you know?' she asked innocently.

Asking for Intangible Stuff

'As we briefly mentioned before, we can get heaps of information from The Guys just by asking for it. That's Intangible stuff. That'll be anything related to help, assistance, support, advice and guidance that we need or anything related to personal growth and direction for our lives. Well, that's the guideline, but in fact, They can pretty much answer *anything* you can think of. You can get pretty wacky with all this. I'd suggest that you give it some time before you jump in at the deep end and go too outrageous though.'

'Oh, spoilsport. Why can't I fly before I can walk?' Lee pouted. 'Hang on,' Lee thought suddenly, 'that doesn't sound like you, Mrs super-guts, what's the reason?'

'Because it prevents you from biting off too much than you can chew, and then blaming the process if it doesn't work. If you're asking for the solution to some highly specific mathematical question, but you have no idea of how to Listen to Their Mental messages or how read Their Physical Signs to get your answer, then it's going to be a bit tricky, right? And then you get fed up and might wrongly think that it's not working.'

'That sounds reasonable,' Lee grinned.

'Actually, I have a good example for that. When I went travelling, I tried to learn the local lingo. I learned a bunch of sentences to ask for directions to the hotel, the bus station, what time the bus leaves, where the market is, all that good stuff. One day I thought I'd try out my newly learned skills and walked up to a local to asked him where the post office was. I had an accent, but I dare say that I spoke pretty well. The local smiled at me, happy that a foreigner had made an effort to learn his tongue. I was delighted to see that he had understood what I had asked him, but then, he went off on one giving me directions, descriptions, hand gestures, the lot. I just stood there, dumbstruck and suddenly burst out laughing. I hadn't understood a single word.'

'Wonderful. You could ask the questions, but you hadn't learned to Listen enough to understand the replies. Nice example.'

'Yeah, it was pretty funny. It took me a while to explain to the poor local what happened though. He had made all that effort and I just laughed. When he finally did get it though, he was highly amused, patted me on my shoulder and went on his merry way.

Talking to The Guys is exactly the same as learning a language. You start out by asking easy questions, you learn to Listen to the answers, then you learn a bit more and slowly, slowly you can become more daring as your understanding grows. After a while you can confidently and comfortably ask and understand everything.'

'Yeah, but if I always bite off more than I can chew, I'd get so frustrated I'd probably go home,' Lee smiled.

'**I think a really important thing to always remember, is that if you don't get an answer or a message, that means very likely that you just can't listen to it yet.** The more you train yourself, the more answers you'll be able to get! To test that, you can start to ask the same outrageous question at intervals and see how long it takes you to learn to Listen.'

'Fabulous.'

'All in all, asking for Mental or Intangible things is simple. You ask, They answer. You can ask for…'

'Hang on,' Lee said, trying to find another blank page in his notebook. Together they wrote:

More about Intangibles:
- We can ask for messages to help us increase the Co-incidence hit-rate.

- We can ask Them, if a particular event is significant or not.
- We can ask for help and guidance (if we shall follow a certain direction our lives for example).
- We can ask them for answers for all sorts of stuff.

'If you can Listen really well,' Tara went on, 'The Guys can give you the answers straight through a Mental Message. Sometimes though, when the time is not yet right for you to get the answer, for whatever reason that might be, The Guys might tell you that you have to be *patient* and wait for the answer just a little while longer.'

'But we will always get some kind of reply, one way or another?'

'Always - if you can hear it. If you're not so good at Listening to Mental Messages, They will give you the Message through a Co-incidence or another person. If you can see the Signs, that can work really well too. Be patient at the beginning... Listening is a skill to *learn*.

Over time you'll probably notice that if you want to ask for Intangible stuff, it's best to learn how to receive Mental messages, because then you can just have a proper conversation with the Guys, just like you would have with another person, rather than having to interpret or watch out for Physical Signs, which would make things much, much easier,' Tara said, watching Lee make a quick note.

Cosmic conversations:
When you learn to Listen well to The Guys' Mental messages, you can have a proper conversation with them.

What Do They Do With Our Requests or Poor Little Guys...

'**B**efore we go onto talking about asking for *Tangible* stuff, there's something that's helpful to become familiar with,' Tara pointed out.

'What's that?'

'It's what actually happens when you ask for something. What happens on a Cosmic level.'

'The Cosmic cause and effect side of things?' Lee asked jokingly.

'You could call it that, yes,' Lee looked at her in surprise. 'It's about trying to put yourself into Their shoes.'

'What, They have feet?'

'You know what I mean,' Tara poked Lee playfully into his ribs. 'Picture what They would have to do if you asked for something Tangible?' Lee looked blank. Tara continued, 'The Guys would need to make the cosmic forces and thus the three layers of Time, Space and Consciousness work for you, right? They have to co-ordinate the Cosmic events and chain-reactions to give you what you asked for. The tricky bit is that you're not alone in this world and everybody else's requests also have an impact on the total TSC mesh, which as a result constantly changes. As you can imagine, these things can get awfully complicated and intricate.'

'Phew, The Guys really have Their work cut out for them.'

'Oh yes. With all of this going on, The Guys have to co-ordinate Co-incidences, hints and Signs for you to notice and follow. They have to do that for you and *everybody* else at the same time.'

'Man, The Guys really put a lot of work into this clamusel.'

'Oh yes. I mean can you even begin to imagine the effort it takes to organise *Everything*? And I mean Everything! At the *same time*?'

'I can't even fathom the Thought,' Lee wondered. 'CEOs of the world eat your heart out, you can learn something here.'

'You can say that again. Now, can you imagine what happens, if you don't Listening to *one* of Their messages?'

'Oh no!'

'Exactly. All Their lovely plans go down the toilet,' Tara held up her hand and pulled an imaginary chain. 'Flush, and They have to start all over.'

'I feel all sorry for Them,' Lee said tenderly.

'You can feel even more sorry for Them, sweetie, because most people don't Listen.'

'That's so sad. Poor Little Guys.'

'Yep, and that's what The little lads are dealing with every day. Can you imagine what it's like having to try to make all these fantastic plans work smoothly and nobody gives a damn? What it's like to try and make us see all the hints that would brighten up our life without being able to talk to us? Not because The Guys are not trying, but because *we're* not Listening? They go through all this effort to create the perfect Co-incidences and Intuitions and we just ignore them. And to make things worse, They then have to Listen to *us* complain that *They* are not working fast enough or that *They* are not doing *Their* job properly.'

'Poor dudes.'

'But it's Their job, it's what They do, so They keep ploughing away in the hope that one day we'll raise our Awareness and that day we'll Listen,' Tara hung her head, pushed her lower lip forward and sunk her shoulders, looking all little and vulnerable.

'Gosh, if The Guys look this cute,' Lee said, looking at Tara's pouting face, 'I'll do anything in the world to help Them,' he playfully pinched Tara's cheek. The surprise in her eyes made him laugh. 'I think it would be nice to give Them a bit of a hand in the endeavour, what do you think?'

'I think that would be nice,' Tara said rubbing her cheek, which had gained an extra bit of colour.

'Well, I'm learning as fast as I can,' Lee said.

'I know, you're doing incredibly well.'

Lee was surprised how great he felt with Tara praising him. Strange, when one had grown up to adulthood nobody seemed to praise anybody anymore. As a child there was praise from parents and teachers (if one was lucky), but as an adult? You just got a bigger pay-check. He liked to be praised. He looked at Tara smiling.

She returned his smile and said, 'But, you know, it's not all that bad. Luckily for us, The Guys *do* have infinite patience, They *are* unbelievably flexible and They *are* used to make infinite plans, They don't *Mind* doing it over and over again. They *never* get fed up or stop, They will always keep trying. But it would make things much *easier* for *Them* and thus so much *better* for *us,* if we would learn to Listen.' Tara's face took on a bright shine, 'Man, can you even begin to imagine what it would be like if *everybody* would Listen? The Guys could line up something really cool, something immensely useful for us or something ridiculously fun, and we'd all follow the *first* signal and the Co-incidence would already waiting for us and so on, all perfectly lined up. Events and people would fall nicely and communally into place,' Tara paused with a hint of longing in her eyes. 'You know, when *everybody* Listens, people can be part of each others' Co-incidences, get answers to each other, give each other what we need and most of all, we'd have so much fun together! People would cruise through Their lives, always having help at hand or *being* a helping hand. So perfect…'

'That sounds absolutely positively wonderful, but I guess Humankind still has some work to do,' Lee said with an equally longing look on his face. 'Or in your words, more *Play*!' Lee's face suddenly lit up.

'Agreed, until then, each one of us can help The Guys individually. Actually, do you want to know how you can give Them some more help than just by Listening?'

'Sure, what a question. What can we do?'

How To Help Them Help Us – Physical Signs and Physical Involvement - Tangible Stuff

> *"You are never given a wish*
> *without also being given the power to make it true.*
> *You may have to work for it however."*
> *- Richard Bach, Illusions*

'Let's talk about asking for *Tangible* stuff, because with Tangible stuff we can get properly involved, to make things even easier for The Guys.'

'Fabulous.'

'Ok, when asking for Tangible stuff, it's really important to understand that it's not rabbit-out-of-the-hat magic. It's not that our hat is empty and then suddenly out of nowhere there's a rabbit in it. It's not that kind of magic, but it's rather a matter of cause and effect. The Cosmic game plan requires that we get involved by following the Signs that The Guys put in place for us. If we Listen to and follow Their Physical, Intuitive and Mental Signs The Guys will lead us to the rabbit every time, without fail. But stuff will *not* magically appear,' Tara pointed at Lee's notebook for him to write the next sentence down.

Tangible stuff:
* By asking for something, we invite the *opportunity*, *not* the result.

'Most of the time, the fulfilment of our requests needs our input and our involvement. It needs us to grab an opportunity and go for it. We might have to physically go somewhere, do something, meet people or do whatever else The Guys suggest,' Tara elaborated.

'Oh yeah, like with your gem shop story, you were physically involved by going into the shop. You did what They told you to do.' Lee thought for a second and then asked, 'What do I do if I asked for something Tangible and I'm waiting for a Sign, but I *don't* get any Mental messages telling me what to do? How do I know what to do then? How do I know what to do or what to get involved in?'

'I'm so glad that you never let anything slide,' Tara said appreciatively.

'Well no. If I understand stuff I can make it my own and I can begin to play with it. If I don't get it, or have unanswered questions, then I'll never really be confident with it.'

'Full points for that kind of thinking. **Now, if you're not told what to do, you have to put yourself into as many different situations as you can, because The Guys would then have heaps more opportunities to give you messages, simply because you meet more people and go too more places.**'

'Sounds a bit too much like trial and error to me. I could be doing lots of stuff and still not get anywhere useful,' Lee groaned.

'Well, that's only if you wouldn't know what you're doing,' Tara said mysteriously. 'Let me give you an example to explain what I mean. Imagine you need to get your car fixed, but you don't have the money to pay a mechanic, so you ask The Guys for help. There's no point in sitting in the armchair and waiting for a mechanic to ring the door bell - well, sometimes that works too, but for that you really have to get in tune.'

'You're kidding.'

'Do I look as if I'm kidding?' Tara looked at him boldly, 'But until that happens, you have to get physically involved.'

'How?'

'It's all the obvious things. You go around and tell a bunch of people that you need your car fixed and that you're looking for help. If you don't have friends, you just put up some notes in a supermarket or on some lampposts or something. Nothing happens for a while, then out of the blue somebody comes to you or you bump into somebody and tells you a story about how a friend of a friend restores cars. First hint. You could now either not get the hint and go: "oh great. I love old cars, blah, blah," change of subject. Or you could get the hint and ask: "oh great, can he also fix cars?" Then, maybe he can, which would be great, you call him and it's sorted. Or maybe he can't. If he can't, again, you could miss out on a hint or an opportunity again and just say: "Oh bummer", and you'd be helpless again, wondering if it wasn't a Sign after all. On the other hand, if you'd really be working with The Guys, you could ask the restorer guy, if he maybe knows somebody that can fix cars?'

'I see what you're getting at. See everything as an opportunity, one door closes, another opens, if you can just see it. So always look for other doors, other possibilities,' Lee said.

'You got it. Let's say you eventually find a friend of a friend that does work very cheap. Maybe not for free, but cheap. But you don't have any money, well, ask The Guys to get help with paying for it. Get inventive. Maybe you can trade somebody something, fix a car for a painted wall or mow the lawn for somebody else to get money for the car, whatever. See how it can work? **The Co-incidences are all lined up for you, you just need to see the Signs.'**

'The Guys give you the *opportunities*, *not* the result,' Lee repeated the last bullet-point he'd written into his notebook.

'And there are shit loads of them out there,' Tara agreed, 'but you have to *notice* them and then *take advantage* of them. You have to *act* on them, even if your Rational Mind tells you that you could embarrass yourself, or even that you simply can't be bothered. With The Guys? You always have to be bothered, otherwise you might miss an opportunity.'

'Makes sense.'

'Do you want another example?' Tara asked.

'Sure.'

'Let's say The Guys know that I need to read a particular book to give me a bunch of answers to some of my questions and this book is waiting for me somewhere. I don't know about the book yet and therefore I'm obviously not looking for it either. The Guys now have the fabulous job of somehow getting me to the book or the book to me.'

Lee rolled his eyes, 'Phew, how on earth would They do that?'

'Did I mentioned that they're crafty?' Tara laughed. 'They might know that there happens to be a guy who has read that book, who sometimes takes the same train I usually take. Next time both of us are on the train, I feel intuitively drawn to sit next to the chap, still not knowing about the book of course. Then, as if by magic we start to talk about telly and then how the books are always better than the films and by the way, he's just read the best book, blah, blah and he strongly recommends it to me.'

'Now you know about the book.'

'I do. Now, I either get a huge Intuition that I really have to go out and get that book or I miss that Sign and don't follow up on that recommendation. Nothing special in that, it happens all the time. I mean, in a year alone I get a million and one book recommendations and not each one of them is a Sign. It's not about Listening to all recommendations, that'll be crazy, but about Listening to your Intuition and watching for the Signs. If they all scream yes, *get* the book.

Well, let's say I missed the Sign to get the book the dude recommended, I missed my Intuition telling me that it was significant. I forgot about the book and don't follow it up any further. Now it's time for the second hint. One morning I feel drawn to walk into that little second hand bookshop I've been wanting to check out for ages, and hey presto, there's a copy of the book. I remember the conversation, and now get a feeling of significance and pick it up. Somehow I want to open it…'

'And mysteriously you open it just at the right page with a profound message for you,' Lee finished Tara's sentence. 'This happens to me a lot - always *just* at the right time,' Lee was surprised how much of this stuff he'd already done, albeit unknowingly.

'There you go! You ask me how to do it, but you're already doing it!'

'Yeah, but now I know how to do it more consciously, rather than by accident and now I'll be able to increase my Co-incidence hit rate too. Man, the potential of this still blows my Mind,' both of his eyebrows danced up and down to the words he spoke.

'Oh, come to think of it, can you see the chain reactions in this example?' Tara asked.

'Of course. If that guy hadn't told you about the book, you might not have looked at the book twice when you saw it in the shop. But because he had mentioned it, you noticed it *and* you were curious enough to check it out. The guy telling you about the book somehow had an in-build back-up plan. Ingenious,' Lee said truly in awe.

'Isn't it amazing? It really is interesting to look at how The Guys work. To understand how things happen, helps us to know what to watch out for and which situations are prone to give us messages. You see, the most important thing for Them was that I got that one particular message and for that I could have bought the book and read the whole thing, or even just opened it and read that one sentence. So, The Guys left themselves and me a bit of room for manoeuvre.'

'I'm beginning the to see the extent of Their craftiness.'

'Pretty cool, uh? Ok, if you can see the chain reactions, you can also see where I could have missed the hints.'

'That's an easy one. First, you could have not followed the hunch that you should sit next to the guy on the bus, maybe thinking that he'd find it odd as there might be other spaces available or whatever. If that would have happened, your Rational Mind would have won. Then you could not have paid attention to what he said. The next one you *did* miss. You didn't notice the Intuition that you should get the book. Then you could not have followed the Intuition to go into the bookshop, which was particularly interesting that day. When you saw the book you could have forgotten that the guy told you about it. Then you could not have followed the hunch to look at it and open it. Even if you would have done all of those things, you could have been really stupid and not gotten the significance of the message on the page you happened to open. Even worse, you could have noticed some of the hints, felt the Intuitions, but for whatever reason just decided *not* to follow them, not to *act* on them,' Lee remembered the three steps on the list that had to be ticked off - Notice Intuition, realise significance, act! 'Phew Tara, it really seems impossible to *ever* get to the end of any of those chain-reaction, there are just too many pitfalls. So many Signs that can be missed.'

'Well, it can't be that bad, you just said that this has happened to you lots of times before,' Tara pointed out.

'I know you're right. I've done it before, many times, but subconsciously, it just happened, without me even trying,' Lee stocked. 'Crazy, I'm already doing it.'

Tara grinned, 'Yeah, I know. Now imagine what it could be like if you would be trying.'

Lee was getting more and more excited by the sheer potential,

'See? All you need to do is practice Listening, play with it and really do it. Only with practice will you get to know how They work and with time it will becomes easier and easier to pick up the Messages. It really isn't such a big deal. And by the sounds of it you already have plenty of past Co-incidences for you to analyse and learn from how you receive your Mental messages and Intuitions.'

'You're so encouraging.'

'Well, only because it's true.'

'I like it!'

'So do I. **The best thing is to keep on living your normal everyday life. Do what you normally do, but be more aware of your surroundings, your environment and the people in it. Follow the clues, and trust me they will come if you're Aware. There will be hints, no matter how subtle. Just keep your Mind open to receive.**
And, as I said before, even if you don't Listen at all, your life won't get any worse. You have been living your whole life without being actively Aware, but you still got the occasional a lucky dip, like when you found the right book at the right time. So now, it can only get better. That's why it's so cool. You can't do anything wrong. It's just that if you do it at all, just by the law of averages, you will hit the jackpot more frequently, right? And thus your life gets so much more fun and easy and cool and outrageous, it's crazy. If you like that kind of thing that is.'
'I think I do. Very much,' Lee nodded, still amazed.

The logic and practicality of Tara's words began to hit home more and more. He was glad to see that her explanations held up to his constant sceptical scrutiny. It really was common sense. Some strange, never thought of Cosmic common sense. He couldn't help himself, but he was surprised at how much he loved this stuff. He didn't have to stress about any of it. It was designed to be fun, not some kind of chore or drag. He could go on living his life and at the same time enjoy the added value that The Guys could bring to it.

When he shared his Thoughts with Tara, she agreed, 'I know, that's why it's so great. You can live your life, make decisions about every day matters and have your own opinions, and you can decide if you want to follow Their messages when they come. You also don't have to worry that it could get too much. They won't tell you when to go to the toilet or when to have a cup of tea or when to go and see your mates. They won't tell you things that are not important. But when stuff is important? Then They will try *really* hard to tell you, and if you're only half way awake, you'll begin to hear them.'
'Don't stress but Listen,' Lee summed up to make a quick note:

• Don't stress but Listen.

'And anyway,' Lee grinned knowingly, 'stress is an Emotion and I know now how to not let them stop me from being Now, right?'
'Master student, what can I say?'

'You can say more about the cool stuff,' Lee suggested helpfully.

Off-lines

'Nothing easier than that. Ah, I have an idea. Let me try and explain something to you with a drawing.' Tara picked up Lee's notebook drew a straight line, pointed at it and said, 'Imagine that this line is the ultimate path, yeah? The perfect route in your life, where everything is just perfect, where everything works out smoothly.'

'Like the Shift?'

'Yes, exactly, like the Shift,' Tara drew a line with the same starting point, as the first one, but branching off at a ninety degree angle. 'Ok, this is an off-line, a path where you really don't get anything at all. You know, those people for which everything goes wrong in life? The eternal pessimists, the black sheep, the painfully unlucky? They are on an off-line, a line that goes into an entirely different direction from the perfect line.'

'Oh yes, I know some of them,' Lee was glad that it wasn't him.

'So do I. On the other hand, some people Listen naturally. Those are the people that are eternally lucky. A lot of them are naturally very intuitive and aware of their environment. They were born that way and most of them don't even know that they're doing something different to other people. They naturally spend most of their time on the perfect line.

Then there are people who accidentally Listen to a Sign from time to time,' Tara drew a line from the off-line too the perfect line, and marked the point where the lines were connecting on the perfect line with a cross. 'These people touch the perfect line in a *lucky* Co-incidence. But as soon as they stop Listening, they go back to their off-line,' she drew a line back to the off-line.

'What a fabulous way of explaining this, what a great picture,' Lee was impressed.

'Yeah, I always find that I understand things better when I can see them. Now, people usually spend time on various degrees of off-lines. Some are miles away from the perfect line, others are closer,' Tara drew more lines into the sand, all going off at different angles from the perfect line.

'Do these lines symbolise the different Listening abilities people have?' Lee wanted too clarify.

'Exactly.'

'So,' Lee took the pen from Tara and began to draw zigzag connections between the perfect and the off-lines, 'do you just keep going back and forth like this for ever, or can you move over to the perfect line permanently?'

'Of course you can, if you keep Listening and acting on *all* the Messages that is. But till then, the more you practice, the more you touch the perfect line in lucky Co-incidences, the longer you stay there. And once you've Shifted, you stay on that line permanently.'

'Ah, I see,' Lee nodded slowly.

'The way you live your life and everything you do within it, can also have an affect on the position of the off-line you might be on. People who Listen, are active and easily make social contacts and are generally very involved in life, make it easiest for The Guys.'

'That's because The Guys can use a multitude of people, situations and Physical Signs to give them their messages.'

'Precisely. Whereas if we never put ourselves into an environment where we can get messages, well, that would make it kind of tough for Them, wouldn't it?' Tara shrugged her shoulders. 'As a result the angle of the off-line would be greater too.'

'But couldn't people that are not fabulously active, make up for it by being super Aware?'

'Absolutely. They might just get heaps of Mental messages instead.'

'And you can get those anywhere.'

'Sure, but limiting yourself to only one kind of Message, can really restrict you. Having access to a wide range of different Messages makes things easiest for The Guys. There's only so much They can get to you solely over the phone, other people, through the letterbox or the doorbell etc.'

'Makes perfect sense. Mmh, I'm wonder which off-line am I on?' Lee said thoughtfully.

'You know, in the end it doesn't really matter *which* one you're on, all that matters is that you know what to do to get *off* it. If that's what you want to do of course. **What you have to do to get off, is the same for everybody, no matter which line they're on.'**

'Uh, thanks, that's a nice reassuring thing to say. Don't worry, just do. Don't judge yourself. Just Listen.'

Tara nodded and touched Lee's hand to give him the pen back. When she touched him, he hesitated for a moment before taking the pen, feeling her hand on his. It was wonderful to be so comfortable, so familiar with someone again. What a strange but utterly fascinating new experience this was. He had not been close with anybody but Kate for a long time. Tara looked at him, her eyes warm and intelligent. She smiled at him. When she finally Let Go of his hand, Lee took the pen slowly, keeping eye contact for just a little while longer, then looked down to write another short list.

<u>To get to the perfect line:</u>
- Go out there, live your life and Listen!
- Follow Their Messages!
- Be active and aware!
- Be curious and play!
- It doesn't matter *which* off-line you're on, all that matters is that you know what to do to get *off* it.
- What you have to do to get off, is the same for everybody, no matter which line they're on.

When he was done he put the pen into the centre fold of the notebook and looked at Tara.

'By doing all of that consciously,' she pointed at the list, 'we actively and continuously zick-zack back to the perfect line, from which ever off-line we're on, rather than unconsciously hanging out on an off-line, feeling sorry for ourselves. The more we do that, the *longer* we get to hang out on the perfect line, until one day?'

'We Shift.'

Tara nodded. 'Let me give you one last example as to how we can get involved, that'll allow us to finish this bit off, is that ok?'

'Of course. Example ahead.'

'I apologise in advance, if I repeat myself a little bit, but it's important to get this point across. Let's say you need a job. If all you ever do is sit in your armchair, laze about and wait for magic to come to you, it would be a hell of a lot of work for The Guys to make Co-incidences happen to reach you back home, right?'

'Huge off-line,' Lee picked up the pen and drew another big fat line going off the perfect one at an extreme angle.

Tara nodded. 'It would also need a lot of *other* people to Listen *for* you, to guide them to your door. **I mean it's difficult enough to rely on ourselves to Listen properly, but to solely rely on others for *our* luck to such an extend?** Fat chance. **But if we can become involved ourselves? Then *everything* is possible.** We have to take *active responsibility* for following The Guys Signs as much as we can. Nobody can do this for us and we can't rely on the silver plate. In practical terms this means that if we're looking for a job, we have to go out, get papers and *actively* look for a job, do what we would normally do.'

'Or what we *should* do - if we wouldn't be so lazy,' Lee winked. 'People often know what they should do, but they just can't be bothered.'

'Important point well made. **We cannot just sit back all bored and lethargic and wait for the magic to happen. We have to put ourselves into situations where The Guys can help us.** Meet people, talk to them about jobs, keep our Mind open and follow the little hints. If somebody mentions an opportunity, we have to go and actually check it out, not just sit back and think about it. We can't just think: "Oh that job would be great, but I can't be bothered to follow up on it." Get of your backside! **We can't think: "I can't just go in there and ask for a job?"** Of course you can ask! Or: "What if I'm not good enough or what would they think?" Heeellooo! Do you want that job or what? **Just go and *do* it, check it out, just try it!'**

Lee nodded vigorously, 'Yeah, **what's the worst that could happen? It might not work out? People could say: no?'**

'Exactly. **Reboot your brain!'** Tara said animatedly. 'Maybe, just maybe it could all work out! Ever thought that they could even say: "yes, we'd love to give you a job." Ever thought of that? **We always think we'll fall, but we never imagine that we could *fly*.** It can be all so much easier, so much more fun, so much lighter! The Guys would never give us an opportunity unless we'd have the ability to follow it,' Tara said paraphrasing Richard Bach, 'but sometimes we have to jump over our shadow and jump in at the deep end, we have to dare, prepare, practice, learn, go for it, give our best, try it, put our Rational Mind aside, jump and fly!'

Tara opened out her arms, got up and ran across the lawn whooping and juchzing.

Lee shook his head at her, loving it. When she came back, he held his hands out to her and when she grabbed them, he pulled her down next to him, politely moving aside a bit, because she had landed much closer to him than he'd expected.

Tara loved the warmth of his hands, his spontaneity, the way he was so relaxed and mellow. He was just being himself, he wasn't trying to make anything happen. It was nice to just play and see where things went by themselves. **It did kind of feel as if they were going *somewhere*, she remarked to herself. Or at least that it could? Would she want to? She wondered to herself. Well, she knew exactly what her Intuition was screaming, but right now she really didn't want to go into that. There was far to much more to talk about to get distracted yet.**

Once she sat comfortably again she said, 'You know, not every hint gets us straight to the end result but each one will be a step on the way *towards* it.'

Even though Tara was talking about Messages from The Guys, both of them thought that this was also a nice way to describe what was going on between the two of them.

Lee got his Mind back to the example, **'This means that we might not necessarily get the *first* job we go for, right?'**

'Right. Sometimes we do, sometimes we don't. **If we don't, that's not necessarily bad, because not getting one, could just be another step towards the *other* job that we *are* supposed to get** – and you'll always realise later why that is,' Tara said. 'The long and short of it is that we need to stay open and not worry. We *will* get there in the end.'

Balanced Physical Involvement – The Fine Line Between Laziness and Craziness

'**P**hew, I can already see people going bananas with their social life and activities, just to make sure that they put themselves into enough situations,' Lee imagined people going nuts - as they always do.

'I'm so glad you said that. **It's important to understand that there's a fine line between laziness and trying too hard, between going mad and doing *everything*, and *not doing anything*. It's not about engaging yourself in a mad flurry of random situations for the sake of it, it's about working *with* The Guys and about Listening.'**

'Ah,' Lee had an idea, '**if you go mad, you become hectic, you speed up and you begin to worry about what to do next, you loose your Mindfulness and thus you can miss Signs!'** Lee said proudly. 'So, we definitely don't want hectic and uncoordinated-ness.'

'Exactly. All that madness really isn't necessary anyway. Our involvement can be much more intelligent than that, much more effortless. **The more *Aware* you are, the more Signs you *will* see, the *easier* you will get to the end result. Slowly and steadily, rather than mad and hectically. Be deliberate and tuned in.'**

'It's like the story of the race between the rabbit and the turtle,' Lee said, 'The rabbit runs around like mad, running in zik-zaks, missing the Signs and getting lost and going round about ways. Its Mind is mad and hectic, it can't think properly and it certainly doesn't enjoy itself. When it gets to the finish line, it's completely exhausted. The turtle on the other hand goes steadily and Mindfully, taking in all the Signs, seeing and observing. It's aware and actively takes in the environment. It gets to the goal in a straight line without distractions. It misses nothing and it learns a lot on his way. It takes the shortest and easiest path, with a lot less effort and it thoroughly enjoys itself while doing it. At the finish line it feels calm and relaxed.'

'Perfect example,' Tara cheered, 'The frenzied effort of the rabbit takes a lot of effort and doesn't get it to the winning line any faster than the turtle. And most of all,' Tara added, 'he won't have as much fun with all that rushing around!'

'So, the most important thing to keep in Mind is, that it's all about working *with* Them, *not* independently from Them and to always be aware of your surroundings,' Lee summed up.

'Exactly. Like that They *will* guide you along the way with new Thoughts and hints and tips. They will let you know what you need to know or do. **If at some stage you don't get a Sign, just go on doing what you would normally do to get you to your goal, be intelligent and not dull, lazy or crazy.** Do that until you get a Sign and if you still feel insecure, you can always ask for guidance, or some Mental messages, which They are always happy to give.'

Lee nodded, and quickly added a few points to his lists.

Balanced Physical Involvement:
* Be like the turtle, not the rabbit.
* There's a fine line between laziness and craziness, sitting back and trying too hard.
* Work with The Guys, not independently from Them.

How To Help Them Help Us – Mental Involvement vs. Mental Letting Go

'**O**k, so we're all turtles now,' Tara stuck her head out in turtle fashion and leant back comfortably against the tree. 'Nice and peaceful, yet strong, determined and clever, taking in all the Sings. That's the Physical side of the involvement done with. Let's move on, because now comes the Mental side.'

'The Mental side?'

'Well, after kicking things off by asking for something, we then have to Mentally hand the problem over to The Guys to let Them get on with it.'

'Right,' Lee stocked, this was getting a bit to abstract.

'There's really nothing to it,' Tara read Lee's face. '**All you need to do is hand your request over by not thinking about it all the time and by being Now instead. Only then can They really get to work. If it's *in* your head, They can't take it *away* to work on it, get it?**' Tara's hand motioned away from her into the space in front of her.

'Nearly,' Lee could feel the light bulb, but it wasn't yet turned on.

'Let me explain it with a lovely little story I read once. The story is about a guy that complained to God that even though God had said 'Thou shall ask and thou shall be given', whenever the man asked God for something, he never seemed to get it and even if he did, he never seemed to get exactly what he asked for or not fast enough. God patiently Listened to what the man had to say and then replied: Dear man, how could I take the burden away from you? You never Let Go of it.'

Lee gasped. He looked into the distance for a minute to let the story sink in. Tara gave him space. After a minute or so he said, 'So, basically, the man kept clinging to the task at hand, so God couldn't really do his thing.'

'Yep, and it's the same thing with The Guys.'

'I guess it's the same as if you would work for a company and you'd have too delegate work to someone,' Lee had thought of another practical example. 'Often you worry if the person is doing the job properly or fast enough or just the way you want it done, so you keep supervising, meddling, interfering, worrying. Any manager that does that, not only annoys everybody, but also holds people up and slows them down.' Tara nodded and Lee continued, 'I have been in situations like that myself, on both ends. It's unnerving. If people told me to do something, and then didn't let me do it in peace, I used to get really stroppy, I mean I knew what I was doing, I just wanted to get on with it. On the other hand, having to delegate, I always used to think that I could do it better, so I used check and check. But after getting some managing experience, I realised that I either had to really *do* it *myself* or I just had to let *them* get on with it. Otherwise, what's the point in delegating in the first place? If it doesn't take any work of me, but *does* make me anxious? Stupid. So I learned that little spot checks are great and necessary, but otherwise, I Let Go.'

'Absolutely right. That's a great everyday example and it's exactly the same with The Guys. You kindly delegate your work to Them, and luckily, working with Them, you don't have to worry about Them doing Their jobs properly. I mean, they are The Guys, right? They've done this kind of thing quadrillions of times before? They know what They're doing and you can happily Let Go. You don't have to think about it all the time. You can do little spot checks though as you just said, nobody ever minds you just asking: 'Have you got everything you need? Is there anything that I can do?'' Tara said.

'So, **we put out the question, and don't worry, don't drive ourselves crazy by thinking about it and letting it take over our Mind all the time, we just Let Go. We get Physically involved as much as necessary and simultaneously watch out for Signs and hints, right? All the while we make sure not to drive ourselves nuts over anything. Don't stress but Listen.**'

'You've got it.'

Lee silently recapped the last few hours. To his surprise he realised that he'd got used to the fact that he could in fact communicate with the Big Something out there. It struck him that his questions had shifted from asking *if* it works or not, to *how* it worked instead. He smiled to himself. His new knowledge felt good and strong. This short meeting with this extraordinary girl had started to change his life. It had uprooted part of his belief system and on the other hand, he'd had reconfirmed and explained things he had always suspected or hoped to be true. He was getting instructions for stuff he'd always wanted to know about and stuff he had never dreamed of. And as a wonderful bonus, the instructions were easy, intuitive, common sense and they sounded like a blast, a giggle and bloody good fun. Quietly in his Mind, but with a huge, great, big smile on his face, he said: 'Thank-you-Dudes' for the very first time.

24   What You Can Ask For and How – What's Possible

Would You Ask God to Make You A Cup of Tea?

'Tara, have you got any idea of the mad and crazy potential of everything we're talking about here?' Lee asked.

'Of course,' Tara said unpretentiously.

Lee laughed out loud, not even surprised at her confident answer.

'I do,' Tara repeated, 'but there is still a fine line between wishful thinking, magic, and what's physically possible. That's why it's important to learn *what* you can ask for.

So far we've talked about the categories of Tangible and Intangible stuff, but now we can talk about what's actually *possible* if you like.' Lee nodded and Tara continued, 'The easiest way of approaching the subject is once again with common sense.' She scribbled:

To know what's possible:
* Use common sense.
* Remember what is physically possible.
* No wishful thinking.
* No Magic.

'I think I can explain some of those myself,' Lee said looking at the list. 'The common sense bit? I guess some things are easy and fast to do yourself, right? For example it'll be silly to ask The Guys for a cup of tea when you're sitting in front of the telly and you can't be bothered to get up.'

Tara grinned, 'Exactly. Just get up and to it, don't bother The Guys with it.'

'I guess that would be wishful thinking too. If there's nobody home.'

'Right, a cup of tea in such a case could be magic or wishful thinking and also not really possible. That's what common sense would tell you, but it doesn't have to stop you from asking, just don't get upset if you have to wait for four hours until your partner comes home. If you ask silly questions like that, They might just send a friend round to you for a cuppa and *you* might have to make one for both of you. That'll be a nice little joke The Guys might play, ha, ha.'

'Seriously?' Lee laughed heartily at the audacity of it.

'Well, you didn't ask for somebody *else* to make you a cup of tea!'

'Aha, details!' Lee laughed.

'You're spot on with this example. Some things are just silly to ask for or even to bother Them with. I mean, the Guys are the Big Cosmic Forces, you wouldn't ask God for a cup of tea either, would you?'

'Two sugars please!' Lee burst out laughing again, 'Just the Thought of it. Imagine, you have your one chance to have a chat with the Big Guy and he gives you one question to ask. There you are with all those people, everybody has all these amazing questions and suggestions for the world, famines, hunger, wars, and you ask him to make you a cup of tea. Actually, you know what? If I'd be God, I'd die laughing,' Lee tried to catch his breath. 'In fact, I'd probably be so amused that somebody dared to ask me for a cuppa, that I'd probably give it to them. People always ask for health and protection, it's so repetitive. I think I'd see the tea request as entertainment, rather than as an impertinence. I guess if people would always stick to the rules, God's job would be rather boring, right?'

They both giggled at the Thought of God sitting on his cloud, bored, waiting for somebody to amuse him.

'You know, that's why it's so much fun to try out stuff, because sometimes? Just sometimes the weirdest stuff *does* work. Therefore the bullet-points that we just wrote down are good guidelines, but they are there to be played with right?' she winked at Lee. 'When I tested how far I could go, I had much more unlikely things than cups of tea materialise,' Tara reminisced.

'I bet the Guys love you, you must keep Them so entertained.'

'Well, it entertains me too, that's why I'm doing it,' Tara said light-heartedly. 'We have to keep in Mind though, that the occasional funny-one request might entertain The Guys and us for that matter, but when everybody and Their dog wants cups of tea, with two sugars,' she winked at Lee, 'and all the cosmic forces get employed making in tea, then we'd wonder over time why the hell nothing else ever gets done anymore.'

'Fair play. So we can have some fun, as long as we don't over do it.'

'That'll do. But of course if you would be desperate for a drink, and you really, really need a drink, not just want one, but *really need* one, ask for it, and look for the Signs. If you really *need* something they'll always Listen, even if it might seem impossible to you. If it's important and you're desperate, they *will* know and do their best to help. So ask!'

'Like, you walk down the street, you're parched, you need a drink, you ask for it and as if by magic somebody comes up to you and gives you a bottle of water?' Lee dared.

'I've seen weirder things.'

'I bet you have.'

'Believe it or not, but I have a story just like that. I was walking down the road and was so thirsty it hurt. I had forgotten my purse and had no money, so I asked for something against the thirst and believe it or not, but around the next street corner was a soft-drink-tasting-challenge and I got two nice cups of bubbly – for free.'

'No way,' Lee looked at Tara in disbelief.

'Yep, honest truth,' Tara suddenly grinned again. 'This stuff happens all the time, seriously. That's why I'm doing it!'

'I guess I better get cracking with my practice, every minute I'm not doing it I'm missing out. Well, not right now, of course,' he smiled at her, hardly able to fathom anything better than what was happening right now. 'You know, I sometimes imagine The Guys sitting somewhere, nice and comfy, looking at the human race, busying Themselves with organising and helping people. Working like crazy for all those millions of Listeningly-challenged persons out there. What would *I* do if *I'd* be in *Their* shoes? I'd do the important bits first,' Lee thought out loud, 'and whenever I'd have a break and I'd be in a good mood, I'd do some silly stuff, just to surprise people and see the looks on their faces,' Lee looked down from his imaginary cloud, waving at humanity, 'Ha, ha, you didn't think *that* was possible, did you?' he pointed mischievously at an imaginary sceptical human.

Tara laughed, 'You're getting to know Them pretty well, that's exactly what They do. It's not all hardcore messaging. Sometimes They get you involved in stuff or give you things, just because it's fun. It's supposed to make your life easier and more enjoyable, remember?'

'Yipee. So, as a little summary, What-shall-I-have-for-dinner questions are silly, whereas: please-help-me-with-a-new-job, or: my-life's-a-mess-I-need-guidance are more like it.'

'Right. But in the end, They're *your* Guys,' Tara emphasised, 'so, play with Them and find out what you can do for each other.'

'Great. Mmh, could you give me a few more practical examples, to help me get a better *feel* as to what to ask for and how? That'll be easier than trying to follow guidelines which are difficult to properly put into words anyway.'

'Absolutely, Here we go.'

You Can't Ask For Magic - But....

'**As** I explained before, The Guys don't do magic, but *how* close to magic it can be, depends on *how* you ask for things!'

'Check. More,' Lee beckoned Tara to go on.

'**You cannot ask for a tool to magically appear in your hand, but you can ask for something to help you with the *repairs* you need to do. You cannot ask for a road to be shorter, but you can ask for a ride. You can't wish people away, but you can ask for peace and quiet.**'

'I get it, you cannot ask for a rabbit in the hat, but you *can* ask for some cool tricks.'

'You got it.'

Don't Limit Them Or Yourself With What You Ask For Or With Expectations - How to Really Do The Asking Thingy

'**T**here is something which is really useful to watch out for if you're asking for something. You have to be careful that you don't *limit* Them,' Tara explained.

'What do you mean?'

'**If you ask for help with something and you specify *exactly what kind of* help you need, you limit Them *and* yourself. If you're dying of thirst and ask specifically for a Pepsi, but all there is, is water, They can't help you. The help would stare you right in the face, but you might not notice the hints towards the water.**'

''Cause my Mind is looking for Pepsi,' Lee concluded.

Tara nodded, 'The point is that we cannot even begin to imagine the infinite and fantastic, weird and wondrous ways The Guys can come up with to give us what we've asked for. They have *all* the options in the Universe!'

'I can see that. **In our little human Minds, we limit ourselves to the normal, traditional ways somebody could give us what we're looking for. We look for what we know, what we're used to, and in the process, we're missing out on the 'magic' They *could* be giving us,** which might be so much better, than what we could have ever asked for.' Lee added and set out to write another short list.

473

<u>Don't limit yourself:</u>
- Don't limit yourself by *asking* for messages or stuff to come to you in a *particular way*.
- Don't limit yourself by *expecting* messages or stuff to come to you in a *particular way*.

'If for example you ask specifically for water, you might miss the free drinks promotion or the bottle of juice in your friends bag or the grapefruits that are being offered,' Tara said.

'Or the front doorbell to my friend's house, who would only be too pleased to water me,' Lee laughed.

Tara giggled and went on, 'If you need money, don't ask to win the lottery.'

'That would be limiting, as I might miss the Signs that would lead me to other ways to make or get money.'

'If you want information about a place or a person, don't ask to meet somebody that has been to that place or knows that person.'

'Just ask for information *about* it. Then it's up to The Guys, *which* way They can use to give me the answer. I'm getting into this, you know?' Lee was on a roll and continued, 'You cannot ask for a specific person to love you, but you can ask for a partner. And maybe it turns out to be that specific person or maybe it'll turn out to be somebody else.'

'If you need information about something, ask for it, but don't *expect* a person to give it to you,' Tara said.

'Because I might miss the newspaper article or the billboard, or the film or whatever that has the info instead.'

'If you want magic, don't expect a rabbit in the hat.'

'As the magic might not come to us in the form of a rabbit,' Lee said.

'But if you really want a rabbit, ask for a rabbit! But not necessarily out of *that* hat!' They chuckled. 'If you need a lift, don't ask for a car, you might miss the bus or the donkey.' It was getting silly.

'Donkey?' Lee's eyebrows raised upwards as he smiled.

'Yeah, well, we're in Greece or something,' Tara said witty-ly.

'Oh, of course. A donkey it is,' Lee gave in easily.

'**The long and short of it is, be specific enough to help you get what you're looking for, but leave Them some space for Their own little tricks,**' Tara recommended and Lee nodded happily.

'Let's go back to the job example for a second. What you *can* exactly ask for, obviously depends on *what* you're looking for. If you want a very specific job, you obviously need to specify it, lets say a job in Sales or Retail or Film. Now, let me give you some tips. If you want a job to fulfil certain criteria, then ask for those criteria, rather than a specific job. Let's say, flexible, fun, car, mod-cons. Ask for that. The Guys might then get you a job you never even heard about before, which you didn't even knew existed, but which fulfils all of your criteria perfectly. If you just want a job in that particular industry, any job, then ask for that, but then don't moan if They offer you the dishwashing position in the kitchen of the Marketing company you were interested in.'

Lee concluded, 'Basically, the point is that **we *can* be specific, but the more specific we are, the more we limit ourselves.**'

'Right. So, experiment, play with The Guys and figure out how to phrase the questions so that you get what you want,' Tara said, took the pen once more and wrote:

Specifics:
* We *can* be specific, but the more specific we are, the more we limit ourselves.
* Ask for an *end result*, *not* the path (the how) unless absolutely necessary.
* Ask for the *opportunity* to get something, but don't tell Them what that opportunity has to look like.

Once finished, a cheeky grin flashed across Tara's face, 'But then again, it's always fun to play with going against these guidelines too, you know, just to see if it works and what you can get away with -or not.'

'Ha, I love you!' Lee laughed out loud. 'Nobody has ever given me so many rules and then constantly told me to break them.'

'Well, you have to test your and Their boundaries for yourself. Otherwise you will never see how far you can go. Some people are absolutely outrageous and they get away with it, others are more conservative and that works for them. Do whatever feels good for you. Oh,' a picture had popped into Tara's Mind, 'fancy a really funny story?' she asked with a big grin on her face.

'If you grin like that? How could I not?' Lee noticed a loving undertone in his voice. Tara smiled at him, had she noticed?

Tara went on unperturbed, 'A friend of mine wanted to try how far she could go with the asking thing,' Tara began her story, still looking at Lee. 'She knew from our conversations that being too specific was not really the recommended way of doing things, but what the hell, she wanted to try anyway. She got as specific as she could.'

'What did she do?'

'She wrote a list, asking for her perfect man.'

'I should have known,' Lee rolled his eyes.

475

Tara smiled at Lee's mockery, 'It's an obvious thing to do I guess. I'm sure everybody will try that at some stage. I mean you have to, right? Anyway, she wrote down everything from shoe-size to collar width, sense of humour, wine preference, bed stuff, everything.'

'And did she get him?' Lee asked cynically.

'Oh boy, did she. It was nearly scary, she exactly got the guy on her list, down to a T.' Lee looked sceptical and laughed out loud when Tara sheepishly added, 'And she got everything she had not put onto her list as well! He was the most annoying darling you could ever imagine. He was half fantastic and he other half, was exactly the opposite of what she liked.'

'That's so funny!' Lee's eyes teared with laughter.

'Isn't it? I nearly died when she told me that. She didn't quite see the funny side of it at that time yet though, that took her a little while longer.'

'Ha, talking about backfiring? I guess, if you get silly, They can get silly too,' Lee sniggered.

'Yeah, silly, but never nasty. If something silly comes in return to a request or a question and you realise that? Have a good laugh with them! Laugh at yourself! The stuff They come up with can be hilarious. Also, if you get something unexpected, learn from it, analyse it, how was it different to what you've asked for? Can you understand how your request could have been misinterpreted? Wherever possible, try and understand what's going on, like that you progress and develop your own way and your own understanding of The Guys and how They operate.'

'That's actually a useful thing to know, thanks. By the way, how do you ask for a partner that does fit you and makes you happy?' Lee asked casually.

'Ha, there you go! It's not that laughable after all, is it?' Lee grinned with a shamefaced twinkle in his eyes. He'd been caught out. 'But hey, you've just given your own answer,' Tara pointed out.

'Oh, I just ask for a person that fits to me and makes me happy?'

Tara nodded, 'It's safer that way, because we can never describe everything. Our Minds will always miss out something. So, if we leave the details to Them, it's easier. But remember, it might come in an unlikely person. Play around, experiment. Keep an open Mind. The person might not initially be your type, but you might get to love his long hair or his spindly legs, just because he's just utterly fabulous all way round.'

'His long hair or his spindly legs? Do I really have to keep such an open Mind?' Lee grinned.

'Well, you didn't determine the sex!' Tara said.

'What?'

'If your partner is supposed to be a man or a woman.'

'Isn't that obvious?'

'So you might think! I've asked for a soul mate once and got a girl!'

'That is hilarious.'

'Yeah it was. She was great, but unfortunately not my type,' Tara grinned again.

'Thanks, I will certainly keep that in Mind,' Lee shook his head amused.

'Oh, and if you are looking for your Soul mate, just make sure that you don't keep going out with the kind of person that you know is bad for you, ignoring all Their Signs, because if you do? What can They do?' Tara shrugged her shoulders.

'Check. Good point. I can see that it takes some practice to build up a rapport with The Guys and to get my questioning and my own actions up to scratch.'

'It does, but it *is* a hell of a lot of fun to figure this stuff out, because you suddenly realise that there's an entire new dimension to this little world. It really is amazing when you get a glimpse of it.'

'Yeah, I'm beginning to see that,' Lee nodded. **'So, all in all, don't limit yourself with specifics and expectations, because they shut your eyes to the world of possibilities. I get that, but how can I not *expect* anything? How do I do the actual act of not-having-an-expectation of an outcome?** That seems impossible somehow,' he wondered.

'Well, **first it's about what you're physically looking out for, it's *expecting* the bottle of water and missing the juice**, right? But then **on top of that, I'm talking also about the *Mental process* of having expectations. That means that after having put out the question to The Guys, don't clog up your warehouse with Thoughts of expectations.'**

'Ah, the Mental Letting Go thingy!'

'Exactly. Don't run around and expect everything and everybody to be the fulfiller of your needs. That makes you into the rabbit, rather than the turtle. Instead of doing that, put out your Intent, then Let Go of your expectations.'

'By not thinking about them! Catch out, blah, blah.'

'Right, and by replacing them with *Happy Curiosity* of what might come your way. Don't think, but Listen.'

'I like that! Happy curiosity. That's cool. Much more playful. Don't think, Listen. That's worthy a quick note,' Lee cheered and began to write.

Expectations:
- The Mental Processes of having Expectations are Thoughts which clog up your warehouse.

- Let Go of them and replace them with Happy Curiosity!
- Don't think, Listen.

'Oh, I've just thought of one of the funniest stories about expectations and entirely missing The Guys messages,' Tara said.

'Go on,' Lee said expectantly.

'There was a mad, mad flood and all houses got submerged in water, one man was lucky enough to save himself onto the roof of a skyscraper, but the water was raising, fast. The man asked God for a helicopter to save him. God had a look around, but couldn't find a helicopter, so he send a boat instead. The man told the boat to go away, because he was waiting for the helicopter,' Tara finished.

Lee slapped his forehead and rolled his eyes, 'Oh no! Man, us humans can be stupid!'

'Yep. Hopefully with becoming more Aware in general, we'll become more aware of *that* too,' Tara laughed. '**Oh, and besides the fact that expectations limit The Guys in helping you, it also means that you might get disappointed because of them. Not because you didn't *like* what you got, but because you didn't get what you *expected*.** India taught me that.'

'How?'

'Because no matter which restaurant I went to, I never got what I ordered. Seriously, I could go into a restaurant and order something and it would always *look* exactly like what I ordered, but it would always *be* something completely different. Some people used to really flip out over it.'

'Whereas you were Happily Curious at what the kitchen would come up with this time?' Lee used his newly learned favourite phrase.

'Exactly. I always tasted it, and sure, sometimes it was crap, but often it was oddly nice. I mean a chapatti with ketchup and vegetables might not be your idea of pizza, but it kind of tastes like a breakfast burrito. I just saw the funny side of it.'

'And ate burrito instead.'

'Precisely. Sure, you don't have to put up with everything, but all I'm saying is not to dismiss something only because it's not what you expected. At least *try* it, you might learn or experience something new. You might even like it. You might even like it more that what you *did* want.'

'**That's a real piece of wisdom: expectations affect everything in our lives! When we expect something and it's not being fulfilled, we get disappointed. If we *don't* expect things to be a particular way, but keep open to the world and enjoy *everything* that comes our way, we'll never get disappointed,**' Lee bent down to write again. He wrote fast to make sure he didn't loose his threat. This stuff was too good to miss. He knew that at some stage in the future, he would read through his notebook again and freak out over the wisdom in it.

Expectations:
* Expectations affect everything in our lives.
* If we don't expect, but keep open to the world, we enjoy everything that comes our way.
* Besides the fact that expectations limit The Guys in helping us, it also means that we might get disappointed because of them. Not because we didn't *like* what we got, but because we didn't get what we *expected*.

25 Question Semantics

The Divine Restaurant

'I guess, by now you have figured out how important the wording of the questions is, right? The Question Semantics?'

'Very,' Lee nodded affirmatively.

'It really is essential,' Tara corrected Lee lightly. 'If you just want to have a chat with The Guys, sure, simply chat away, but if you're asking for something important? Watch your words. Be clear! *No wishy-washy stuff.* **You need to formulate a question, which would enable another person to understand what you want *without* a doubt. So make sure that it's not ambiguous!** Obviously don't torture yourself trying to make it perfect, but aim to be as clear and precise as possible.'

'Like my dad always used to say: "Son, if you ask wishy-washy questions, you will get wishy-washy answers."'

'Yes, son, always agree with your dad,' Tara said in a deep, authoritative male voice.

'Yep, that's exactly how my dad sounds like,' Lee laughed. 'So, like with my dad, with the Guys wishy-washy questions also give us wishy-washy answers and Signs, and those are difficult to notice and understand.'

'Yes, son,' Tara padded Lee's shoulder just as a loving father would. 'If you're not sure if The Guys would understand what you ask of them, try to imagine what actually happens when you ask The Guys a question.' Tara smiled, 'imagine lots of the Little Guys around you, eager to help. If you simply ask Them: "Please help". They would think: "Great, we'd love too, but what with, dear? We can see a million and one thing that you need help with."' Lee shook his head grinning broadly. "If you don't tell them what you're talking about, The Guys might hang around for a little while to see if you're going to shed some more light on what you want, but if you don't,

They just do what *They* think is right. Which might be perfect in Their Eyes, and in the greater scheme of things, but it might not actually be what *you* were looking for.'

'So we need to make sure that our questions are *not too general*,' Lee deducted, 'because if we leave our questions out for interpretation or if they are *ambiguous*, it's really frustrating for The Guys and for us.'

'Exactly. Try to be pretty clear *what* you are actually asking for. Is it help? Guidance? An event? A thing? What?'

'Got it.'

'Also, **did you make up your Mind that you actually really want what you're asking for? That's important too, because it's confusing for Them if you keep changing your Mind.**'

'Aha?' Lee waited for more.

'Imagine, They've had your instructions and shuffled off to fulfil them. They get the messages lined up, the Co-incidence wheel cranking, the chain-reactions in gear to give you what you've asked for, and then you suddenly say: "oops, sorry, change of plan", or: "oops, sorry, I didn't actually want that, sorry to have cause you all that work, can I just have *this* instead?"'

'Would They get pissed of?' Lee grinned.

'No, not pissed off, but **constantly changing your Mind will have consequences. First, you'd probably never get what you've asked for, because you basically ask them to abandon each attempt before They get a chance to fulfil it for you. Second, you're obviously confused about what you really want, which would mean that you wouldn't really know which Messages to Listen to or which Signs to watch out for. So you'd probably miss out on most of Their messages anyway.**'

'Or not recognise their significance.'

'Exactly. And third, after a while, The Guys might stop running around like mad creatures, and organising stuff which doesn't get them anywhere, until you get sorted in your head what you really want.'

'Woha, does that mean that we have to get the question right first time, every time?'

'Oh, of course not. Don't worry. **Of course you can change your Mind from time to time, but just don't make a habit of it, especially not if you do actually want results.** It's common sense when you understand how The Guys work.'

'Fair enough.'

'**Also, make your question positive, without any negative undertones.** Starting a question with things like I-*wish* or I-*hope* or *try*, like:

I-wish-that-you-could-do-this, or: I-hope-you-could, or: could-you-try-to-do-that - is no use. **The words hope, try or wish imply Doubt.'**

'Come again?'

'These words imply that you don't really believe that They can do what you've asked for, because you're hoping for it, rather than knowing that it *will* happen. It gives the question a negative connotation rather than a positive one.'

'Oh wow,' Lee was impressed with Tara's attention to detail.

'Regard The Guys as the Divine Restaurant. You'll always get what you ordered! If you *order* Doubt, you get Doubt. If you order hope, They will leave you hoping for what you want, cause that's what you asked for − Hope. This applies to everything in life. I remember winning a huge deal at my previous job, simply because I change one single word.'

'What was that?' Lee was curious, that would be useful for his job too.

'I changed *if* to *when*. I kept saying in front of my colleagues and customers *when* we win this deal rather than *if* we win this deal. And I always used to correct them with a big smile on my face. After a while everybody, including the customer was talking about *when* my company was going to win the deal. Everybody's mindset changed because of it. It was amazing.'

'Wow. That's deep. Hoping leaves you hoping. Wishing leaves you wishing. *'If'* - keeps Doubt around.'

'Right. So, just tell The Guys what you want Them to do. Please do this, please help me with that. Simple.'

'I can do that. Ha, I love the idea of the Divine Restaurant, and man, you *do* get what you've ordered, I'm just thinking about the girl you mentioned earlier, the one that asked for the perfect boyfriend. **You really have to be quite careful don't you?'**

'Well, **I don't know if I'd say careful, I mean, are you careful in a restaurant? It's not really about being careful, it's just knowing what you want. Just treat Them like a *restaurant*. You wouldn't keep changing your Mind there either, would you? And you wouldn't order a lasagne, when you actually want potatoes. You wouldn't order food in general terms, if you wanted a sandwich.** It's the same with The Guys. It really is common sense. Ask for what you want. End of story.'

'I can do that,' Lee said reassured.

'I remember one day when I asked The Guys for some guidance on *how* to ask a particular question. Do you know what Their answer was?'

'What?'

'They said: 'Just ask it'.'

'That's funny.'

'I know. That's when I stopped worrying about how to ask stuff and just told Them what I wanted, without pussyfooting around. I observed what I got and slowly got to know how I had to phrase things to make sure they understood what I wanted.'

'Good plan. Be precise but don't kill yourself over it. Don't stress, just ask.'

'Let's have some more Question Semantics,' Tara suggested. **'When you ask for Mental messages, it's easiest to start with asking *closed* questions, questions that can be answered with yes or no.'**

'Because The Guys can answer those without complicated explanations, which makes it easy to Listen to.'

'Exactly. Ask for example: shall-I-stay-here, rather than giving them options such as: shall-I-stay-here-or-shall-I-go, or: what-shall-I-do? These are *open* question and for those open questions, you have to be much better at Listening to pick up the answers.'

'You know, I think it's going to be really exciting to learn how the asking thingy works, even if it doesn't flow perfectly from the start. There's so much fantastic stuff to discover.'

'Absolutely. That's what I always say. **Enjoy the *process* of doing it as much as *getting* to the end result.** If you can do that, you'll absolutely love it.'

'And that goes for everything in life,' Lee added.

'Amen.'

Right on cue Lee got stuck in with pen and paper to immortalise the past few minutes of conversation.

Question Semantics:
*   Before you formulate a request in your head or out loud, make up your Mind what you actually want.
*   Regard The Guys as the Divine Restaurant - you always get what you ordered.
*   Ask un-ambiguous questions, no wishy-washy stuff (like in a restaurant).
*   Be clear – don't order lasagne if you want potatoes (like in a restaurant).
*   Don't be too general - you don't just order 'food' if you want a sandwich (like in a restaurant).
*   Don't change your Mind all the time (like in a restaurant).
*   Don't expect to get something if you didn't ask for it (just like in a restaurant).
*   But enjoy if you get something 'on the house'.

- When asking questions, always keep in Mind how good you are at Listening to the answers, otherwise you might get frustrated (it's like learning to speak another language) - but of course, always try far out things from time to time, just for fun.
- Make clear positive statements, no I wish-s or I hope-s (you wouldn't use these words in a restaurant either - could you *try* to bring me a sandwich?).
- Words such as hope, try, if and wish imply Doubt.
- Begin with closed questions and slowly expand to open ones (like you'd do with learning a language).
- Don't stress, just ask Them for advice!
- Play with it, try things out and make up your own.

!! Effortlessly Please, Thank You !!

'Oh,' Tara's eyes sparkled extra brightly, '**there's one *ultimately* important thing to add to the end of *every* question. To *every* single question, *everything* you *ever* ask for**,' she said dramatically.

'Oh yeah? What's that?' Lee was intrigued.

'Always add the words: **Effortlessly please, thank you!**'

'Sweetheart, you're the best!' Lee leant forward and gave Tara a huge great big strong bear hug.

'I mean it! Dead straight. My asking life transformed when I started to do that! Things come to you *effortlessly*, rather than *just* come to you. It makes *all* the difference.'

'That is ridiculous! Only you could come up with that!'

'Actually, I can't take credit for this one, it was given to me by a friend. It was so funny when he told me, because I couldn't believe that I hadn't come up with that myself either! But there you go, ***that* is how you play with the Universe! You come up with stuff like *that* and then you share it for the enjoyment of others!** It's all a huge magic roundabout!'

'Brilliant,' Lee was deeply impressed and amused, all in one.

'Dude, I'm eternally grateful for this one, I really am,' Tara said, bowing gently in thanks to a vision of her friend. 'Actually, this comes with another funny story. I mentioned to another friend to always add those words to the end of every question. He repeated them a bunch of times: "Effortlessly please, thank you", nodded and went away happy. Then a while later we met again, and he said that he usually adds that sentence to all of his requests, but then he usually adds on top of that: "But, if it has to be *with* effort, give it to me anyway". - I was so surprised, I couldn't believe that he'd said that. It was the funniest thing. I had to laugh so much, so, I told him that he could really scrap that last sentence, I mean, The Guys are PROFESSIONALS! Hello! We're not dealing with some kind of amateurs here! The Guys are the Universe! They are IT! They can make it effortless if they want to! Don't belittle them, cheeky! I was so funny. When he realised what he'd done, he laughed like crazy and promised me not to do it again.'

'Hilarious.'

'Well, here you can see how people take some good advice and make it their own and unfortunately along the way, some of it gets really messed up, it's like freaking Chinese Whispers. Well, I guess it can go both ways, but this one certainly went onto an off line,' she giggled at the memory. **'Remember, make it your own, but don't make it any more *difficult*!** Doh!'

'Got it,' Lee grinned and added a few big fat letters to the list.

Always, always add to the end of _every_ question or request:

* ***EFFORTLESSLY PLEASE, THANK YOU***

He underlined it a few times and proudly showed it to Tara.
'That'll do,' she grinned broadly.

Their Name, Personalised and Useful

'Another thing to keep in Mind when formulating a question is, that it's nice to address Them with Their name.'

'Why?' Lee wondered.

'Using Their name, adds Consciousness to your request. If you have to think of using Their name, you have to, if only for a split second, jump out of the muddle in your head, part the curtains in your Mind and pay some attention to what you're doing.'

'That's clever.'

'Very much so. It's therefore important to find a way of addressing Them which is comfortable for you _personally_. I call them My Little Guys and that's great for me. You seem to have decided on 'The Dudes',' she giggled. 'A friend of mine calls Them Bluey – don't ask me why. Another one calls Them My Friends, I've also heard Dave, Peanut, Big Guy, Bro, Superstar. You get my drift?' Tara smiled.

'Dave? That's the best one!' Lee could hardly hold himself upright he was laughing so hard, 'Can you imagine? If somebody told you that you could name the Universe anything you'd wanted to and you'd call it Dave! That's hilarious. No offence to any Dave-s out there, but that's hysterical!'

'Well, you know, whatever works for you,' Tara said with a big grin. 'In the end, *what* kind of a name it is doesn't matter. And yes,' Tara laughed pre-empting Lee's question, 'You can change Their name if you want to at some stage, and if you should forget it for whatever reason —well, They won't exterminate you.'

'That'll be so funny, can you imagine, if one day be my question to Them would be: Ah, sorry, what's your name again?'

'I think They're going to like you,' Tara chuckled.

'I think it'll be very mutual,' Lee said comfortably. 'It's funny actually, the name 'The Dudes' just came to me, I didn't even consciously make it up.'

'There you go, you're already Listening better than you thought,' Tara winked.

Try Stuff and Fly

'Here comes some more: **Never do what you've always done, or expect what you always expected, or see what you've always seen, think the way you've always thought, or even follow idiotic rules,'** she winked at Lee. **'If we do that, we miss out so much. Always keep your Mind open and *actively* invite in and try out some *new* stuff from time to time.** Obviously, don't go around and kill people or steal stuff, but go and try *new* things, wild things, *go* and have some *adventures*. Get your own experiences! Don't just Listen to other people's stories! The Universe is so huge and we see so little of it.** A friend of mine used to live by the rule to-at-least-try-one-new-thing-every-day. Now that's the spirit to adopt with The Guys,' Tara said passionately.

Lee nodded, 'It seems that playing with The Guys makes sure that we see more of the world by default, because man, if we *do* follow all those whacky messages, we'd get ourselves into all sorts of weird and wonderful situations. I think as soon as we hang out with *Them*, we'd begin to do things we'd never normally do, or give people a chance that we normally never would, or go somewhere we'd never go to, or talk to someone even though we'd normally be far to shy. Yep, I can see how this would be adventurous,' he said. "What an understatement," he thought to himself.

Tara continued happily, 'Even if you can't listen to The Guys yet at all yet, you can still begin to do things differently in your life just for the hell of it, you know? Play with your Mind, Emotions and Behaviour, play with it, make them into what you want them to be. Play with the world. **Give a stranger a flower of** *your own accord***, just because it's nice.** Play! **Become old and wise, but never grow up!**'

'You know, I always wondered about that. Why on earth would I want to be a grown up, when I can finally do all those things I always wanted to do as a kid, without anybody telling me off?' Lee shared some of his life philosophy.

'Well exactly. Somehow when we grow up, we forget how to dream, how to jump up and down barefoot in a puddle, climb trees, run down a street just because it feels good! So, go for it and play! There's nothing too be scared of! If you don't like it, well, you can always go back home, stop doing it, go powder your nose, whatever, but at least try it once! Maybe you even get to like it, maybe you'll even have some fun, maybe it's really weird, but even that'll make a fabulous story for your friends. Accept strange invitations, go to odd parties. You might not like them, but experience them anyway! Don't expect that everybody does things the way you do, because they don't. Experience and see what *other* people do! It's soooo entertaining and soooo much better than TV. Real life freaks and fairies, even bores. Watch people, observe people, go to a weird concert and just observe the people there, how different they are from you, be a fly on the wall in situations you would have never dreamt yourself to be in. It's not about judging, but it's about opening your horizons. It's not about laughing at people and their ways – well, at least not all the time,' Tara giggled, but then added seriously, 'but it's about learning. Even the biggest freak might have something that might be useful to you, even if it just shows you how definitely *not* to be.'

'You know what Tara? I'm coming over to your way of thinking more and more. Gosh, the world really is one huge playground, isn't it? We just don't see it. We judge and take things far too seriously, rather than just seeing then for what they really are - or could be,' he added with a smile.

'Exactly, and hey, if something doesn't work out? So what? At least you've tried! Don't fret about it forever, go and do something else. *Play!* That's the word! **The world is a huge great big toy, so go enjoy! Ask for the impossible, but don't expect anything. Don't be afraid, don't be scared, but go for it! Dreams are important.** And if you Listen really well, they might just get fulfilled. We can do *whatever* we want to, we can do *everything* we want to, it might take a bit of time and practice, and lots of open 'ears', but if you really want it? Do it. But remember,' Tara said with a warning wave of her index finger, 'you have to help Them, you can't just sit on your butt and wait for it, you have to give them a hand.'

'Yes ma'am,' Lee saluted happily.

'Oh, and never let anybody else tell you that you can't do something. Imagine that your dream is to get a job in Marketing. You have no education and no contacts to help you on your way, so right now an immediate fulfilment of this wish is pure fantasy right? A dream.'

'Keeping in Mind everything we've talked about so far, a job like that could be still be physically possible though, right?' Lee said.

'Right. But still, common sense also tells you that you can't expect somebody coming up to you and ask you to become the Chief Executive of MarketingInc, can you?' Lee shook his head in amusement as Tara continued, 'But, if you really want to be in Marketing, put out that request! Begin to put yourself into appropriate situations and look out for Signs to lead you towards that goal. Signs could range from the obvious to something entirely unrelated. If your Intuition tells you to follow something unrelated, Trust, it could be a means to *prepare* you for what you're looking for. You could find a space at a college or a secretarial job at a marketing company or a job at a newspaper writing about Marketing stuff or you could even just have a conversation with somebody in a completely unrelated field of business, who happens to know somebody and so on and so on.'

'Makes sense, it's the car repair story from before. And as you said earlier, we have to get involved. We might have to get more education or change our lives or do something pretty drastic to get that job, but the Guys will help us and guide us all along the way. It's not magic, but They do have all the worldly and all the other-worldly ways to help us. Some paths might seem round-about and there can be pitfalls, but we learn from everything and we'll get there in the end,' Lee concluded.

Tara sat up straighter, 'You just said something really important,' she pointed out, 'You said that **sometimes we might have to do something pretty drastic to get that job**? That's true. **You know, sometimes, if you ask for *big* things, you might have to implement *big* changes in your life.** If you want a job in travel writing, but you're not prepared to be away from home for weeks on end? Don't ask for such silly things! It's pointless. You'd only get disappointed if you get the chance and then decide not to take it. **To get what you want you might have to leave what you know or your home comforts behind, and exchanging it for uncertainty, new experience and adventure. You might have to leave people or possessions behind, your ingrained routines might change, but well? So what? If it means putting up with all of that to get what you always wanted? It might just be worth it. It might be drastically different, but also absolutely fantastic! However you have to dare!** No more of the: I'd-love-to-but-the-job and yes-I-wish-I-could-but-the-house and yes, but blah,

blah. Well no! Stop the But-s and do it. Either you want it really badly or you don't. And if you do?'

'Jump and flyyy!' Lee shouted.

He got up, opened out his arms and ran across the grass whooping and juchzing just like Tara did before. Tara jumped up and joint him running around with her arms wide open like an airplane. They zoomed around till they were gasping for breath and fell into a laughing heap on the grass. Gathering their last strength they crawled back onto the blanket, lying there sprawled out like two copies of DaVinci's Vitruvian Man. This time it was Lee's turn to put his head on Tara's lap. He nestled himself contently into the soft bit between her Hip and Thigh. Perfect height he thought, relaxing his neck comfortably.

Tara had her eyes closed, when she felt the warm of Lee's Body. She opened her eyes and saw him lying happily at an angle next to her, using her as a pillow. Absentmindedly she touched his hair, remembering how much she'd wanted to touch it all day - and yesterday for that matter, all that tousleyness, she grinned.

They enjoyed the sun like this for a little while, feeling utterly comfortable with each other's closeness, when they heard a little voice, 'Excuse me, could I have my ball back please?'

They looked up, to see a small blond girl stand next to the blanket, pointing at a ball, which must have landed in between them without them noticing. A happy smiley face had been painted on it with finger paints, and grinned up at them adorably.

'Sure,' Lee said, picked up the ball and gently threw it back to her.

The little girl caught it expertly, said a shy "thanks", and ran back to her dad who was visibly proud of his courageous daughter.

'Now, where were we?' Lee grinned and made himself comfy again. He looked up at Tara briefly, just to make sure the pillow thing was still approved. Looking at her face he could see that it was. He closed his eyes again and said softly, 'Let's continue.'

In A Rut? - They Really Care

Tara dreamily tried to remember where they had left of. Ah yes. That was it. **She continued with a quiet voice, 'You know people often say: "yes, it's great to be carefree and adventurous and excited, but sometimes we find ourselves in situations where we know, that something in our life is not right, and that we should** be doing something else, but we just don't know exactly what we're supposed to do, or we simply don't know how to change our existing situation. We might feel stuck or in a rut, without seeing a way out. We might be unable to see a solution to a problem that's affecting our life, or we might just not know what to do with our lives in general. We might need help, guidance, inspiration, options, possibilities, ideas.'

'Yep, that used to be the story of my life, until I began to take my life into my own hands!' Lee said confidently.

'Yeah, same here. But you know what?'

'What?' Lee asked with his eyes still closed.

'In case you ever find yourself in another one of those situations, The Guys can be a great help! All you need to do is ask Them for assistance and guidance and then,' Tara held her index fingers against her forehead like little antennae and wriggled them around, 'be open to receive. Once you tune in you'll see that The Guys are full of wondrous ways, choices, opportunities, alternatives, little tips and tricks and suggestions, which are all there for your support and entertainment. And if you're feeling really miserable,' Tara grinned, 'They're amazing at cheering you up too. They really care.'

Lee moved his head a little to be able to look up at Tara, 'I like that idea.'

Tara wriggled a bit and Lee was about to lift up his head of Tara's lap, when she reassuringly padded it down again, 'Sorry, I just needed to readjust a bit, my leg's falling asleep. Ah, yes, that's better.' Calmly she continued.

If We're Desperate

'Please note that I'm not saying all of these words lightly. Seriously, even if you are in an absolutely terrible situation, no matter how desperate you are, *always* ask Them for help. They will *always* do whatever they can to help you. Even if it might seem impossible, ask Them for help, a way out, guidance, a friend, whatever. In desperate situations especially, *don't limit* yourself! The fewer expectations you have, the more open you are, the easier it will be for The Guys to show you a way out or a solution! Just be aware. There *will* be Signs. Be as aware as you can and *really* Mindfully observe everything around you. There is *always* a way out, it's just that it's not always the most obvious – then again, sometimes it is, but either way, you can't see it.' Tara said.

Lee sat up reluctantly, leaving a warm spot on Tara's thigh. 'Sorry, gotta make some notes,' he said apologetically, catching himself saying that and wondering why he had apologised. When he felt the warm blood rising to his cheeks, a reason dawned on him. He smiled, softly let the Thought go and started writing.

When we're desperate:
- In desperate situations especially, don't limit yourself!
- *Always* ask for help, even if help might seem impossible.
- The fewer expectations you have, the more open you are, the easier it will be for The Guys to show you a way out!
- There is *always* a way out, it's just that it's not always the most obvious - then again, sometimes it is.

Ask The Guys For Presents

'**O**h man, with all the serious stuff, I nearly forgot one of the most fun things to ask The Guys for,' Tara said with a little sparkle in her eyes. She sat up, crossed her legs and grinned widely. '**It's stupefyingly amazing to ask The Guys for a *Present*.**'

'A present?' Lee repeated simply.

'Yes, ask Them for a Present! You know, a *surprise*. When I'm bored or when I want some spice in my life or I just need a bit of cheering up, I ask Them to surprise me. I ask Them for something that would make me laugh.'

'Ha, that's brilliant!' Lee grinned but then Thought the better of it and said, 'Woha, giving Them free range like that though? Imagine all the stuff They could come up with!'

'Exactly! That's the point!' Tara said cheerfully. '**They come up with the weirdest stuff, it's so comical, so fabulous, so entertaining.**'

'I can imagine,' Lee envisioned Cosmic Free Range bouncing in on him.

'And besides entertaining you, it also helps you get a hang of how the Universe works,' Tara mentioned sweetly.

'How's that?'

'Well, whenever something really cool happens, like when you got a fabulous present or an amazing Co-incidence for example, look at *how* you got it! Look at all the little bits and bobs the Universe had to arrange for you to receive it, all the little Co-incidences, all the little connections! It's truly Mind blowing to become aware of that.'

Lee nodded slowly and said with intent, 'One day I'll ask Them to give-me-what-They've-got, dare Them just like you did a few years ago.'

'No time like the present!' Tara poked him playfully.

'Oh, you're naughty,' Lee turned his head and looked at her out of the corner of his brown eyes. 'Let me find my feet first, will you? But when I'm ready?' he grinned mischievously, 'I'll ask Them to: "give me what They've got in the most fun way possible!"'

'Ha, I never even thought about that. **Effortlessly please thank you and in the most fun way possible!** Wow. You are a superstar. Yes! Thanks. Man, I promise you, if you would do that? That'll really make the cosmic wheels shake, rattle and roll,' Tara grinned. 'May I tear a page out of your notebook?'

'Sure, why?'

'I need to write something down.'

Obligingly Lee tore out a page and handed it to Tara together with his pen. She wrote:

Effortlessly PLUS:
* EFFORTLESSLY PLEASE THANK YOU *AND* IN THE MOST FUN WAY POSSIBLE!

She folded the piece of paper and put it into her bag. Inspired, Lee wrote the same underneath his last list.

'Ha, I forgot, **do you know what the nicest thing is about asking for presents?**' Tara suddenly remembered.

'No?'

'It's that whenever you get it, you will *always* know that that's what it is, you will always know that that's the present you asked for.'

'Tell me more,' Lee was intrigued.

'Nope, you'll have to find *that* out for yourself,' Tara laughed. 'But I will tell you that They have a wicked sense of humour.'

'Uoh! Tease.'

'Their presents are amazing. They can be ridiculous, outrageous, bizarre, absurd, hilarious, comical, unbelievably entertaining and sometimes extraordinarily useful. And often you will absolutely not be able to believe how on earth They managed to arrange it for you.'

'Cosmic Presents,' Lee grinned. 'They will be on the top of my list,' he said as he wrote down a quick reminder.

Presents:
* Ask The Guys for Presents and surprises.

Forgotten Secrets - It's Too Simple, There Has To Be A Catch - or Not?

'You know, the principle of Asking for stuff, has been known for ages,' Tara ventured.

Lee hesitated a second, then a strange realisation hit him, 'Shiiiit, I think I know what you are getting at. You said in one of your stories earlier that God said: "ask and thou shall receive"? **Man, we were *always* told to *ask*!'**

'Forgotten Secret number one,' Tara threw in casually.

'But we don't believe anymore that it works. There are too many Religious, Hippy or Lunatic connotations attached to it. Disbelief and scepticism prevent people from even trying. It's old fashioned, it's make-belief, it's blind faith and most of all - it's not cool!'

They both giggled at the image of a skater-boy trying to look cool by flicking a rosary through his fingers, telling his mates: "Yeah, sorted, dude, I prayed for that yesterday."

'There are lots of people though that *do* ask for stuff, with or without the religious undercurrent,' Tara said, 'although unfortunately most of them have no idea of how to actively Listen to the answers or watch for the Signs. **It's more an accident than an art.'**

'And if they don't know how to Listen, they won't get the *solid* proof they need to trust that asking works in the first place. It will always remain faith and hit and miss rather than fact.'

'That's right. Forgotten secret number two is that **Listening works and that you can learn how to do it,**' Tara threw in casually.

'Duly noted,' Lee said. **'Actually, another reason why people are sceptical is, that 'Listening' is just too simple for most people to believe that it can be so powerful, so they don't even try it. Today, things have to be complicated to be of value, otherwise they don't count.'**

'That's Forgotten Secret number three, I believe,' Tara counted her fingers. 'Isn't it strange that us humans somehow seem to *like* things complicated. If it's easy it can't be right, it's too good to be true. If it's free, it certainly can't be worth anything. Could it really be as easy as: "ask and thou' shall receive?" People always ask me: if it really is that easy, why isn't everybody doing it? Because it's simple and straight-forward, people think that there has to be a catch,' Tara said. 'Strangely though, if you could do a university degree in it, with lots of rituals, rules, regulations and exams, then they might feel it's worth looking into. People never believe that anything so fundamental, anything so life changing, anything so important for our very

Beings could actually be easy and fun and for free! Who'd have thought?' Tara shook her head sadly, still baffled by these simple facts.

'Agreed. In our society everything worth its money requires years of training and taking exams. Actually, sometimes even years of practice and experience don't count anymore, unless we have a bit of paper to prove it. It's paper over good old hands on skill. Somebody leaving University often gets paid more for a job they just entered, despite the green behind their ears, than somebody that has worked in the same job for a number of years, somebody that really has some experience and skill. To do anything nowadays requires certificates, and diplomas. If something is easy and everybody can do it, we Doubt it's validity and it's effectiveness. Maybe it's just because nobody can make any money on it,' Lee added quietly as he began to write down the Forgotten Secrets.

Forgotten Secrets:
* You *can* Ask – yes it really works!
* You *can* Listen and you can learn how to do it.
* Yes it *is* simple! No it doesn't have to be complicated. Why make it complicated if it doesn't need to be?

Why Make It More Complicated? - Use Your Language

'It's funny really what we invent because we just can't trust that things truly *can* be easy, yet highly effective,' Tara said poignantly. 'We come up with all sorts of rituals to talk to the Universe. We use dances, songs, incense, special signs, big and complex ceremonies, strange words, prayers, fancy or formal language, Japanese signs or Indian Sanskrit and much more to communicate with The Guys. We seem to think that the more complicated our communication is, the more ceremonial and formal the better. I mean we *are* talking to the Universe, right? That qualifies as *Big* Stuff, and Big Stuff has to be done with reverence and worship.'

'Yeah, it has to be done by the book. A *Biiig* book,' Lee stretched his arms out to either side, grinned and waved Tara to go on.

'Exactly. But man, we don't have to live by a book or any piece of paper for that matter,' Tara went on unperturbed. 'We were just made to believe that. You wouldn't talk to yourself with all those complicated rituals, would you? The Little Guys are *part* of us. Why on earth would I talk to myself with all that stuff?' Tara was lost for words.

'Can't argue with that,' Lee nodded wisely.

'I think an easy and straightforward way is important for the people of today.'

Lee looked at her earnestly, 'I second that. People simply don't have the time to spend hours chanting or dancing before every question they want to ask and then dance and chant again to get the answer.'

'Right. Of course rituals are useful and they can be very powerful, and sometimes it might feel right to take some extra time for The Guys alone or make things nice to say thanks, but the long and short of it is that you *don't have* to. The important thing is the *Intent* you put out, not the ritual - and the Intent can be put out in a few seconds. Joanne Harris summarises those Thoughts in a lovely way in her book "Chocolate":

> *"People always think that real magic*
> *Has to be a flamboyant process.*
> *But actually, the real business is very un-dramatic.*
> *It's simply the focusing of the Mind towards a desired objective.*
> *There are no miracles."*
> *- Joanne Harris*

'I like that. No rituals or special effects needed,' Lee said satisfied and made himself a little more comfortable.

'Right. The point is that They are *your* Guys and you can talk to Them in whichever way *you* want to. If you want to be all: "I, your humble servant, beg for your bountiful universal gifts, blah, blah", you can do that. On the other hand if it works better for you to go like this: "Yo man, what's up? Could you Guys get your butt down here and get this going? Pretty please, effortlessly and fun, thank you," - then that's cool too. Whatever works for you.'

Lee burst out laughing, 'You have a wonderful gift to clarify a big cosmic issues with a bad, bad Bronx accent.'

'Thanks,' Tara grinned. 'Why on earth would I use an alien language for the problems that are closest to my heart? That just doesn't make sense. Just speak the way you'd normally speak and feel comfortable with. Talk to Them as you would like to be talked to yourself. You know? With a bit of common courtesy, not demanding or threatening, just be friendly, They're your mates. They will understand whatever way you choose to talk to Them. If all you can do is grunt, that's fine. If you can't use language at all, they'll read your Thoughts and Emotions. They don't care *how* you talk to them, as long as you *do* talk to them.'

'Wholly agree. Common-sensually and personally,' Lee laughed at his made up word. He stared into the distance, breathed in the early afternoon air, when he heard his stomach rumbling. Food. Yes. Refuelling needed. 'Fancy some nosh?' he asked Tara.

'Yeah, I do, I'm pretty hungry,' she nodded and watched him unpack his bag slowly and deliberately. She laughed at all the goodies he had stashed in his bag visibly impressed, 'Wow, and I thought you were well prepared with your blanket.'

'I just thought that we might need a little nibble before you go off to meet your mum,' Lee smiled warmly at her.

'Fabulous idea,' Tara said and heartily bit into one of the apples Lee had produced. 'Uh, they are good.'

'Yeah, I love these ones,' Lee said, biting into his own.

They sat in silence, munching away, both lost in their own Thoughts. It was good to have a few minutes of not-talking.

Tara thought about the last few hours' conversation. She knew that she had more practical experience with The Shift than Lee did, but she tried to make sure to share her knowledge and not to preach or show off. She was the last person to try and shove her ways down anybody's throat. Lee seemed genuinely interested, and well she loved talking about The Guys, that was pretty obvious. She knew that she could get a little excited when she talked about this stuff, but it was just too good not to want to share it. She loved talking to people who had their own points of view, who were asking questions (Lee was particularly good at asking excellent questions) and her having to explain things in different ways, it constantly gave her new ideas and inspiration. There was always something new around the corner. It never failed to amaze her that it never got boring. She loved the fact that she never stopped learning herself. What a life, she thought.

Tara was grateful that she kept meeting like-minded people to have heaps of fun with and of course to share her playful experimenting sessions with. People who also appreciated the Cosmic Toys, and who were as keen to share their experiences as she was. **Phew, she sighed to herself, if everybody shared everything as soon as they discovered something new, man, that would really speed up everybody's growth.** The Shift's iceberg was huge and they were still only looking at the tip of it sticking out of the water. As Lee had said, the sheer potential was unbelievable. She smiled broadly, she had already discovered so much more. So much more. She hoped that Lee would play with her to the end. Gosh, they would have so much fun.

When Tara suddenly laughed, Lee looked at her. 'Phew, I could go on for ages. Please, please tell me if you ever get bored or if you've had enough of me going on, ok?' she said half apologetically.

Lee shook his head vigorously, his mouth full of Cashew Nuts. He swallowed, considering the potential that had crossed his path barefooted, Tara's worry was probably one of the most ridiculous things he'd ever heard.

'Don't worry Tara, I will. But I don't think there'll be a chance in hell that that will happen. I mean, this is the stuff I have wanted to know about for ages and I've never met anybody that I could talk about any of this coherently in any way shape of form. So no, I'm just fine. Thanks for asking though. In fact,' Lee cupped his hands and held them up in front of him like little Oliver out of the Dickens' novel, 'Sir, can I have some more?'

Tara grinned, 'My answer might be historically and Dickensically incorrect, but oh boy, you can have as much as you want to.'

'Thank you sir,' Lee smiled and busied himself with summarising the last few points.

Complications? No thank you!

- The important thing is the *Intent* you put out, not the ritual. In fact, the Intent can be put out in just a few seconds.
- There is no need to use alien language, just talk to Them the way you'd speak normally and feel comfortable with.
- Talk to Them as you would like to be talked to yourself. Use a bit of common courtesy, don't be demanding or threatening, just be friendly.
- Of course rituals are useful and they can be very powerful, but they're not always necessary.
- Treat Them like your mates, cause that's what They are.

PART 9

26 Universal Laws

'**N**ow what's next?' Tara's eyes flew over the '*What to do?*' list. 'We've covered "Listening to The Guys" and "Talking to Them" and we've begun to talk about why "the world's your Oyster".'

'It's an Oyster to play with and have some fun with,' Lee pointed out.

'That's it! Before we talk more about that, let's talk about some Universal Laws.'

'Universal Laws? That sounds intriguing.'

'They are, and tremendously enjoyable.'

'Enjoyable Laws? Now there's an oxymoron if I ever heard of one,' Lee raised his right eyebrow.

'Agreed, but hang on I'll explain,' Tara promised.

'Can't wait.'

'So far everything we've talked about were guidelines, right? And I said, that you *can* play around with most of them, till your heart's content. **But the Universal Laws should *not* be challenged, they should be abided by. They are Laws or better Universal Agreements, that have been made for the greater good of the whole Universe and all it's inhabitants.**'

'Sounds ominous.'

'Not really. Remember earlier when we talked about the fact that The Guys would never tell you to do anything that would harm you or others? Well, that's because everything The Guys do or advise you to do, complies with the Universal Laws. They are the kind of Laws, that everybody deep down knows are just and right, no matter where they're from, who or what they are. If you don't usually follow them, play with Shifting your Behaviour, as we discussed before, to act accordingly. Try it and have a look how your life magically transforms once you comply with them. Following these laws makes us all good little pixies,' Tara giggled.

'So, tell me about the Laws,' Lee was curious to hear what would make him - how had she put it - a good little pixie? He smiled to himself. That'll be something for his friends in the pub. Maybe they'd all like to be little pixies too? His insides screamed with laughter. He loved it, but they'd think him to have totally lost it!

The Universal Law of Basic Goodness

'The First Universal Law is: Never ask for anything that can hurt another Being, directly or indirectly,' Tara said.

'Ah, ok, I get what the Laws are about. Good stuff. You've got all the angles covered, don't you?' Lee said with appreciation.

'I try to. It's important. Otherwise people get themselves and others into all sorts of troubles.'

'Just out of interest,' Lee asked, 'does that mean that asking for something that is *against* the law, wouldn't work or just that it wouldn't be nice?'

'Ha, I love how you always manage to distil the core of any statement I make. Well, besides the fact that it would obviously not be a very nice thing to do, questions and requests like that always seem to back-fire in some way or another. As soon as you don't adhere to the *Universal Law of Basic Goodness*, it seems to come back at you to bite you. Cause and effect usually catch up, sometimes in the oddest, most unexpected ways. But you know, nobody tells you to take my words for granted. Test them. Play with them and see. Ultimately you have to find out for yourself what that means for you,' Tara said sincerely.

'Fair enough,' Lee understood what Tara was trying to get at. 'Now, why is it called The Universal Law of Basic Goodness?'

'Exercising *Basic Goodness* suggests that you shall allow *every* Being to Live and to Be Happy. So any requests to The Guys should respect others needs and shouldn't hurt or harm anyone. Basically, **don't do to somebody else what you don't want them to do to you.**'

'Get it. **Respect other Beings and their rights.**'

'That's it. You can ask for money and jobs and cars and stuff, but the Universal Law of Goodness suggests not to steal, to take what's not yours, or to do anything to set yourself above anybody or try to be better than anybody. All of these things either take away from others, limit or belittle others or put others down,' Tara finished, then thought she needed to clarify just one more little thing. **'That doesn't mean that you can't go out and get that job that pays a lot of money or increase your social status, but it means, don't go out and belittle the cleaning lady because you're think you're something better.'**

'So if you ask for anything with a pure heart and good intentions, and if you behave the same way, it's cool,' Lee clarified.

'That's pretty much it.'

The Universal Law of No Greed or Ego

'The second law is the Universal Law of No Greed or Ego. This law says that you should only ask for what you *need*, not just what you *want*. **None of your questions should be motivated by *greed*, self-indulgence, insatiability, gluttony, decadence or a need to satisfy the Ego.** Want-to-know and want-to-have-just-because-you-can, even though you don't really want it, is different from need-to-know or need-to-have. Tell The Guys what you really need, but don't just make ridiculous demands. This Universal Law obviously goes hand in hand with the Universal Law of Basic Goodness.'

'Sure. **If you're greedy, you take more than you need. And sometimes that means taking away from others,**' Lee said.

'Right. Of course you can ask for things that you want to have or that *would be nice* to have, but the point is just not to be greedy or to deliberately take away from others.'

Universal Law of We're All In This Together – The Guys' Little Family

'The third Universal Law covers the fact that we're never alone and that we're all in this together. The Guys are there for us and so are many other people. **Other people are incredibly important in the fulfilment of The Guys' plans for us.**'

'As they can be part of *our* Co-incidences,' Lee remembered.

'**Right, and obviously, if *others* are part of *ours*, *we* can be part of *theirs* too. Consequently *we* can help The Guys by helping others.**'   'So everybody needs to help each other, because if nobody would ever help anybody, we'd never get helped either. It's only fair,' Lee nodded.

'Right, but besides it being fair, it speeds up the process for *everyone*, including yourself. Remember the example of somebody coming to your door and giving you an answer that you need? We said that this would be tricky, because it would need a lot of other people to Listen to *and* act on their Intuitions. Well, this is where the acting bit is as important as the Listening. **Sometimes people hear the Messages, but just can't be *bothered* to go and do something for a complete stranger, or even a friend, just because it's nice or because it might help that person.** We can be so lazy.'

'Maybe we're just scared or shy,' Lee threw in.

'True, but if we'd all get over that and just help anyway? Think about what would happen if more and more people would clog onto this stuff and would begin to Listen *and act* on their Intuitions? If everybody could *always* be bothered?' Tara asked provocatively.

Lee hesitated for a second while the sheer magnitude sank in. **'The potential is unfathomable,'** Lee's eyes got bigger.

'I really can't wait for that to happen,' Tara grinned. 'I do have to say though that so far, I've been incredibly lucky, or let's say, looked after. I've been in a bunch of small communities and groups of people, where everybody was really switched on and in tune. I tell you, it's amazing how people can work together. If others Listen, it really becomes possible for somebody to turn up at your door out of the blue, and give you what you need. If those people were told, X needs some help, they actually went to see what they could do. They didn't need a big explanation, they just did it.

When stuff begins to happen on a big scale? Co-incidences roller-coaster and snowball, bang, bang, bang,' Tara, snapped her fingers. 'The more people Listen, the more people work together, the better and the more fun we can have. Oh, and it gets even better when people begin to follow The Guy's messages automatically, because then they *automatically* do stuff for each other. They don't even need to know anymore that it's part of the Universal Perfect Plan. There's no debating anymore if they can be bothered or not. They just do it because that's what they do.'

'That sounds truly wonderful.'

'I've lived in communities where this happens Lee. It's real! It really is! The Guys know that we're all part of each other's plans and that it's a lot easier when we all help each other, so *They* help *us* help each other.'

'That sounds really cool. It sounds like a proper family, all working with each other and for each other. It sounds as if this could be the way that the balance of the human Body, which we compared the Universe to, could be restored,' Lee said dreamily.

'Exactly. But for that we have to start to work together!' Tara said with emphasis. 'A friend of mine told me about something his grandmother had said to him once, something that had changed his life drastically.'

'More secrets, yippee! What was it?'

'He told me that his grandmother "could always be asked".'

'What do you mean?' Lee didn't quite understand.

'Well, his grandmother would always help. She was always there for him and other people. She could "always be asked" and she would always help wherever she could. So, he loved her, because she could-always-be-asked.'

'That's so sweet.'

'Yeah, sweet and incredibly wise. This little sentence changed my life too,' Tara said quietly. 'It became my mantra for a while. I remember being on holiday and a guy, who'd cut his foot pretty badly, came into the restaurant I was in and asked for band-aids. Suddenly everybody looked intensely into their books or at their food or whatever.'

'Ah, the don't-look-at-me mentality we have so expertly developed in our world,' Lee pointed out.

'Unfortunately so. Ha, and guess what, I caught myself out doing the same thing, even though I knew I had band-aids in my room across the road. I was shocked by my Thoughts! What a terrible way to be. I felt dreadful, I had just caught myself out, that I was not prepared to help somebody, simply because I couldn't be bothered to go to my room and get a freaking band-aid. Pathetic! I laughed. I got up, told him to sit down, got him a bottle of water, went to my room, came back and looked after his foot. It really wasn't a big deal. I got a huge smile, and a very surprised thank you. It took nothing, but meant everything.'

And that became the next bullet-point.

Grandmother's advice:
* Can always be asked!

The Universal Law of Unconditional Giving and Receiving

'The next Universal Law, is The *Law of Unconditional Giving and Receiving*,' Tara announced.

'That sounds cool.'

'Yep, it's one of my favourites. **It suggests that you *give without expecting* anything in return and that you *can receive* without feeling that you have to give something in return.'**

'Sounds beautiful, but in our day and age? Fat chance. We're in the age of everybody-fend-for-themselves. Frankly, I don't think that's ever going to happen. I don't think we can make people do that,' Lee said sceptically.

'I agree, but even if we could, *that* would be against the Universal Laws anyway. It's not our job to *make* anybody *do* anything. The only way a Law like this can begin to work, is when people start doing it out of their own accord, no matter what other people do. *Somebody* needs to start. **There are already many people who happily apply these Laws in their lives.** They stopped saying: "Uh, but we're just going to be a drop of water on a hot stone, there's no point, *we're* not going to change anything", and did it anyway. For themselves, and their immediate environment.'

'That's beautiful.' Lee was touched.

'A lot of us are still scattered all over the world, but we're slowly growing in numbers. If you would get all these people together? You'd already have a significant mass. But hey, even if you have not found people like that yet? Nothing stops you from kicking it off yourself. Start to behave unconditionally at home. Invite somebody for dinner, because you want to, without *expecting* them to invite you back. Give something that is dear to you away, because you want to make another person happy, not because you expect something in return, or just because it's a special event or because you know somebody is watching and they'll think you're cool when you do that. Don't look for approval or appreciation in return. If you look for that, it's not unconditional.'

'Wow. That's hardcore.'

'Not really, it's just a frame of Mind. ***Do** and **give** because you **want** to, not because you think you should or because **you** want something.** It's beautiful to observe how surprised people are if we do something nice for them out of the blue, without them expecting it, if we react nicely for example when somebody expects anger**. Treat a check-out person at the supermarket nicely, say a friendly hi to the guy packing your bag, thank the bus driver, whatever. It's incredibly rewarding and so much fun to go out and do *Random Acts of Kindness*.'**

'What a great term, Random Acts of Kindness,' Lee grinned.

'Yeah, I know, I read that title in a book one day and love it, and that's exactly what this Universal Law is all about. **Do stuff for people, just because it's nice.** Watch peoples faces, their surprise, their disbelief that somebody should have just gone out of their way to do something nice for them. The entertainment value you get out of this is better than telly, and it takes so little effort.'

Ever wondering, Lee asked, **'Sounds great, but won't people take advantage if they pick up on to the fact that you always give unconditionally?'**

'Sure, some people might try to take advantage, but people like that? **You can see them coming a mile off.'**

'How?' Lee wasn't so sure.

'People that take advantage are people that don't *ask*. They *demand*. They are people that try to *shame* you into giving them something, people that try to make you feel guilty if you don't do something. People that constantly ask for things they could do or get themselves, but they're too lazy or think that it's just easier to ask you. People that think that you *owe* them something. People that feel for whatever reason, that they have the *right* to demand something of you.'

'Yeah, we've talked about that before, when we discussed learning to say "No",' Lee remembered.

'Ah yes, it's the same way here. So, when we talk about *Unconditional Giving*, we're talking abut *you* giving because *you* want to, because it would make somebody *happy* or because it would really *help* someone. You do it because you *feel* like it, not because you're being *told* to do so or because it's *demanded* of you.'

'Mmh, if you would have reservations about giving something, because you feel uncomfortable with somebody's demands, your giving wouldn't be unconditional anymore anyway, wouldn't it?' Lee deducted.

'Precisely. So if it really doesn't feel right, say "No". I know it's often not easy, but it's the only way. And if in Doubt, follow your Intuition,' Tara said simply. **'Oh yeah, and there is another way that prevents people from demanding to much off you.'**

'Oh?' Lee was surprised. *Preventing* people from doing something? That wasn't really Tara's way. 'How do you do that?' he asked with curious anticipation.

'You give *before* you're being asked,' she smiled cheekily.

'Tara you're impossible!' Lee laughed. *That was* like her.

'You can either work *with* The Guys guidance on that, or you can just see for yourself what you think people need. **What do *you* think could make somebody happy - and then just do it for them. You know, just because it's nice.** Give a beggar a flower and say with a nice smile that you thought they could do with a bit of colour. You see that somebody needs a light? Offer one! Don't wait for them to ask. If somebody is struggling with something and you can help? Ask if they need a hand! No matter what their age or sex is. If somebody could really do with some help carrying a suitcase up the stairs, or a pushchair? For heavens sake, don't wait to be asked and then breathe a deep sigh of relief when they *didn't* ask you for help! Just get of your backside and help! And yes, woman can help men carry stuff too!' They giggled. 'If it's a nice gesture? Do it. Be nice!

Do stuff just for fun! You don't need Intuitions for that. You can do that *now*, with or without Listening capabilities. Pick a flower and give it to a random person, just because it might make them smile. Pick up some rubbish, pad a dog, smile at someone, hold a door open, do somebody a favour, make somebody happy, buy their favourite donut, put a coin wrapped in a piece of paper with little love hearts and similes in a beggars or street performers hat, just because it's really cute, hide a present for somebody and *don't* leave a note saying who it's from, do that for a stranger, leave a funny note on a train just for anybody to find and have a giggle. Is all of this silly? Of course it is, that's the point! It's silly, it's fun and you'll make somebody laugh! You don't even need to *see* them laugh! Just imagine. I remember taking a photo of a stranger at a party once. He had the time of his life and asked me to immortalise the moment and send the picture to him. I took his address and actually did it. I didn't put a return address or anything, just a lovely note. Just imagining his face when he opened the letter was more than I could have ever wanted,' Tara smiled at the memory. **'You know, people are not used to Random Acts of Kindness!'**

'Or strangers sticking to their words,' Lee said how amazing it was that Tara cared enough to go through the trouble of developing a photo and sending it to a stranger, just because she'd promised.

'Right. Let's change that! Lets go out there and do silly stuff! Make people smile. Even if it's just a little bit! Yippeee! **You can even do all of this wearing a suit, you don't even need bellbottoms for that!'**

'Unconditional,' Lee tried to think of less drastic ways to comply with that law. 'We could offer our seat to a nice lady on the bus, not because she's old and frail, but just because she looks tired and it might be nice for her to sit.'

'That'll do. For now!' Tara cuffed Lee playfully. 'If you start playing with this Law you'll get yourself into all sorts of interesting situations. You could make a new friend, learn something, or even just get another story for the freak-book,' she laughed.

'The freak book. Yeah, I can imagine a few entries that could go in there,' Lee winked. 'Anyway, I get the gist of it. It's to **be aware of other people's needs, to be nice and help.** And if somebody doesn't get it,' he added, 'well, at least we tried. No harm done,' he smiled.

'Right. And you know what? **Once you follow the Universal Law of Unconditional Giving and Receiving, you'll suddenly notice that there are lots of other people around, that adhere to it already.** Once you get into the swing of things, those are the people that you attract to yourself more and more. So there's even an incentive of getting involved with this. **You'll get more people around you that will give to *you* unconditionally too.'**

'Incentives are always good,' Lee said truthfully. He knew how Human Kind worked.

'True, but you know the strange thing?'

'A strange thing? Let me think, no, I don't think I know anything strange at all!' Lee grinned sarcastically, considering the weird, far out and superbly strange things they'd been discussing for hours.

Tara giggled, **'Well, it's obvious why people have difficulties *giving* unconditionally, right? They just can't be asked, they can't be bother, right?'**

'Right.'

'But what's strange is, that many people are completely and utterly unable to *receive* unconditionally. The bus example is a good one. If *somebody* gets up for *us* and says that "we look tired and if we'd like to sit", most of us would go all Dots and Squiggles in our head: "why, do I look that bad?", or: "do I look that old?", or even: "What does he want?", so instead of just accepting, we say: "no, I'm ok, thanks. We don't want to put the other person out, or we feel silly, or we feel that somebody wants to take advantage if we accept an offer of help, like: what does he want in return when he comes to my house to fix the car, - or we wonder what's wrong with us, if somebody offers us help. I nearly got whacked with a handbag once when I offered help to a lady that had obviously trouble crossing the street.'

Lee laughed out loud, imagining Tara being whacked with a handbag by some old feeble lady, but then he saw the sadness in her words, 'God, is that really what the world is coming to? Are we really always suspecting ulterior motives?'

'Very often we do, simply because we're not used to anything else. I mean, *we* always expect something when *we* give, so why should anybody else be different?'

'Scary.'

'I know. Well, let's start to change things and not do that. Chill out! Smile, say: "thanks that's very kind" - and accept help. And then *tell* them that it was a lovely gesture. That's Unconditional Giving and Receiving.'

'I love it,' he really did.

'If one of our friends comes up to us and says: "you look as if you could do with a hug", - and gives you one? I'd just say: "oh great, thanks. Hug." Don't think: "oh my God, do I look that sad or bad or what? Why on earth do I look as if I need a hug?" - I tell you, we have so much crap going on up there,' Tara tapped her forehead. 'We find it incredibly difficult to accept things from strangers, even from friends sometimes.'

'Because it has been bred into us from a very early age, remember? Don't accept anything from strangers? Don't talk to strangers?'

'Well, sure, but let's learn a bit about positive discrimination, ey? Well, yes, there are obviously loonies out there, but man, don't just dismiss all offers per se. *Trust your Intuition*. If the offer is genuine, accept it.'

'We can also always look-into-their-eyes-baby,' Lee stared at Tara with twinkly, open eyes.

'Good point. That'll also help you to know if you can trust somebody. **And of course, if you have Doubt? Well, *don't* do it. But if it's safe? What the hell! Go for it!** Accept it. You can mention that you're accepting unconditionally. That you can't give or do anything in return and ask if that's ok. Again, if the offer is genuine, it'll be fine. If not, well done for asking! You've just wisely followed an Intuition.'

'Intuition really is a one saves all, isn't it?'

'Absolutely. That's why it's so important to play with all the exercises we've talked about. **Once you have your Intuition straight?** Man, life becomes so straight forward. **You don't need to worry about the pros and cons anymore, your Intuition will just tell you what's what.** Once you've developed it of course.'

'So, **for the Universal Law of Unconditional Giving and Receiving to work, we have to make sure that we don't only learn to help others, but that we also learn to allow others to help us, to do us good,**' Lee summarised.

'Exactly. Accept offers, allow people to show you things or give you stuff. Don't walk by when somebody stops you in the street. Stop and Listen, and if the person turns out to be a nut case, you can always politely make your apologies and walk away, but if the person is sane, maybe you just got yourself a message or maybe *you* could just genuinely help someone.'

'I think the sheer experience level, the sheer adventure in our lives will shoot through the roof with your ideas,' Lee made a loud soaring sound, imitating a plane with his right hand.

'I dare to agree with that. Enjoy.'

'Thanks.'

'Do you want to know how the Universal Law of Unconditional Giving and Receiving works in the big Cosmic sense.'

'Sure,' Lee gestured Tara to elaborate.

'**Imagine the Universal Law of Unconditional Giving and Receiving is like throwing an apple, what goes up, has to come down, but not necessarily at the same place.**'

'Eh? Does that means that the person I give an apple too, could give that apple onward to another person?'

'Exactly,' Tara gave Lee one of his apples and beckoned to put it behind him, pretending he'd just given it to another person. Then Tara turned around and pretended to get an apple from somebody behind her. 'Basically, if everybody passes the apples on, you will get another one eventually, but not necessarily from the same person that you gave one to.'

'Exactly. It means, don't waste your time and energy chasing that one particular apple or waiting for it to come back or get all upset if it actually gets eaten on the way. You see, there are lots of people out there, passing apples around and when you really need one, one will fall into your lap. Effortlessly. And if you're really in tune, you'll have apples around you all day anyway. That's how the Universal Law works. It's like a circular chain reaction,' she drew a circle into Lee's notebook. 'You give in one direction of the circle and you get something back from behind you. What goes around, comes around – it always does,' she retraced the line of the circle. **'So don't limit yourself by focussing on that one person to give the apple back to you, but rather open your eyes and notice that you're standing in an orchard!'** Tara expanded her arms to point at the world around her.

'Nice.'

'In fact, don't even necessarily expect an apple.'

'Because I might get a pear instead.'

'Or a lift in a car when the bus came late.'

'Oh, I see, it doesn't have to be a fruit? Lee laughed.

'Exactly. **What you get, doesn't matter. What *does* matters is that you get what you *need*, when you need it. Believe me, there are surprising ways in which The Guys can return things to you.** Be amazed! Notice it and giggle. That *is* compulsory!'

Tara prodded Lee with her index finger to emphasize the point, 'And you know, when you have abundance? Give. If you *have* nothing, *do* something. Never compare material value. You might give something monetary or something valuable and get a hug in return when you really need it, sometimes when you least expect it. It's not about like-for-like, it's about happiness and warmth and consideration.'

'Tara, this is so beautiful I could cry,' Lee sniffled.

'Thanks. It really is one of my favourites,' Tara said sincerely.

'I can see that in your eyes. You really believe all this stuff don't you?'

'From the bottom of my heart, I *know* this stuff to be true. I'm doing it and it works. Big time. I learned these things by observing what's going on around me, by observing the Cosmic game and by getting involved.'

'I can see that. You know, I wonder how we could make the whole world do this?' Lee thought out loud. 'Gosh, it would be so wonderful.'

'We can't make anybody do anything. **We can just do it ourselves. But you know what?'** Tara grinned, 'It rubs off! We can kick off a chain-reaction by inspiring others.** But do things because *you* believe in the concept of Un-conditionality, because *you* believe that it is the right way, not because you want others to learn from you. If you're trying to *make* people do stuff, or if you wait until everybody else is doing it, it will never happen, not even in a million years. **We have to start with *ourselves* by looking after our own happiness, and have that happiness extend to other people.** That's what this last Law suggests. That concludes the Universal Laws.'

'Thanks, that was great,' Lee slowly opened his notebook and wrote down the Laws to remember:

Universal Laws:
- The Universal Law of Basic Goodness.
- The Universal law of No Greed or Ego.
- The Universal Law of We're all in this Together – The Guys' Little Family.
- The Universal Law of Unconditional Giving and Receiving - Random Acts of Kindness.

'Tara, how did you find out about these Laws?'
'The Guys told me.'
'Of course, silly me,' Lee laughed.

Thank The Guys From Time to Time

'The Guys are quite something, aren't They?' Lee mused. 'They go through so much effort to help us. They never get fed up, They keep talking to us, even though most of us are as deaf as a slice of bread, and They're always there for us with advice and guidance and help. Is there any way to say "thanks"?'

'Oh yes, of course! How could I forget? Yes, there are a few ways. **The first one is to just say: "Thanks".** You know, acknowledge Their efforts. I do it all the time. Even though They've become an inherent part of my everyday life I still get blown away, I still notice Their efforts, I still appreciate what They do for me. I just look up and say: "Nice one Guys, that was a good one, cheers", - or: "Yipee, you're the best", - maybe even just a quick: "Thanks Guys", - or looking upwards and giving them the thumbs up.'

'That's easy enough. What's is **the other way of saying thanks**?'

'Well, obviously by helping to make Their job easier, just as we discussed before.'

'By Listening, acting, by being physically involved, by handing our requests over to Them and let them get on with it, by helping other people, and by following the Universal Laws,' Lee summarised expertly.

'Exactly. If we do all that, or at least some of it, They don't have to organise so much. They'll be thrilled, and so will you.'

Lee grinned at the Thought of a bunch of, well, Guys, sitting 'up there' being thrilled.

27 The Guys

'Tara, can I just ask you a question?' Lee asked hesitantly.

'Sure, why are you asking?'

'Well, we have spoken about The Guys for ages and they seem to be all-knowing and all pervading, they know what's best for the world and everyone in it, They can answer all our questions and make stuff happen for us. Tara, are The Guys... are they God?'

Tara laughed, 'Oh I love you Lee. I love how you always ask all the questions everyone else thinks, but never dares to ask.'

'Well, what's the answer?' Lee persisted.

'There could be many different answers:

If you believe in God my answer would be:

The Guys are *part* of God, just like we are. God is the totality of everything. God is Infinity, Oneness. We are part of it and so are the Guys. You could regard The Guys as God's little helpers.

If you don't believe in God my answer would be:

Well, we could never prove God was real either, so how the hell am I supposed to prove to you that The Guys are real?

If you like the "Hitchhikers guide to the Galaxy" my answer would be:

They Guys are a bit like the Robin Hood of the Universe. They help wherever They're needed. And they are currently assigned to Earth.

And to all of you I'd say:

You know what? It really doesn't matter who or what The Guys are, if they're real or not, if They make events around us happen or if the events happen by themselves or whatever. In the end that's all irrelevant because we will never get one hundred percent proof either way. We'll never know if God exists, we'll never know if The Little Guys are real or not. But The Guys are a convenient explanation that seems to work surprisingly well for the matter at hand. We'll never know how The Guys *really* do things. But to be honest, it doesn't really matter *why* it works or *what* is behind it all. What matters is, that Listening works and that Talking to Them works and that being aware and that being Now works like a treat, and that it's all heaps of fun! So get out there and do it and stop asking stupid questions!' Tara finished.

Lee nearly collapsed in shock and horror, then with sheer surprise and then with laughter. Tara spoke so true, so ridiculously spot on. Ruthless but sweet and funny, while still being sincere.

'Before I forget, I need to point something out,' Tara interrupted his amusement. 'You just said that The Guys make-stuff-happen-for-us. That's not quite right like that. Let me clarify this to make sure there are no misunderstandings. The Guys are not physical, They are not made of matter as you and I are. They are of a different dimension, and They *cannot directly* interfere with the world on a physical level. They don't *physically* do anything. They are not magic wonder helpers, but teachers, friends, confidants and guides to *help us help ourselves*. They give us access to the Collective Consciousness, the Knowledge of all the Worlds, the Awareness of all events in TSC, to our Intuition, and thus to all the wonderful Co-incidences around us, but the action itself is still down to us,' she said and quickly wrote down a few points before she forgot.

The Guys *and* Us:
* They help us *notice* the Signs around us and guide us to where we need to get to, but it's still up to *us* to follow those Signs.
* They can answer all our questions, give advice on how to act, behave or live our lives, but They can't do it for us.
* They can ask other people to do stuff for us or to tell us things. They can arrange Co-incidences by directing us, but we still have to realise their significance.
* They can ask other people to help us, but we still have to let others help us.
* They are the makers, the *Shifters*, the *organisers*.
* We are the *doers* in the physical world.

Lee read though the list and nodded. Tara continued, 'The Guys cannot physically prevent bad stuff from happening, but They can *guide* you *around* the bad stuff as much as possible.'

'If we're Listening.'

'Yep. The Guys can warn you. They can help you. They can hide you or help you find safety. They guide you and lead you out of tricky situations as quickly as possible, and They can warm and comfort you. The Guys are the knowledge, that in all the bad, there is *always* a light, there's always a way out, but it's up to us to take the initiative.

That's often the reason why there is still a lot of suffering in the world,' Tara said.

'Hang on, I think I missed something, how can that be?' Lee swallowed hard.

'It's because we're often either not Listening or not acting. **You know, no matter how much people want to, The Universe can't be blamed for what's going on in the world. The hardships on this planet are all directly or indirectly down to us humans.** Neal Donald Walsh wrote a fantastic paragraph in one of his books that goes something like this: "God, why do you let people starve, why do you allow wars, why do you let this happen and that, the list went on." God Listened patiently and when the questioning was over he just said: "All of that? That's got nothing to do with me, you humans are doing all that to yourself. I have given you enough food, you're just not sharing. I have given you enough land, but some of you are greedy. Natures catastrophes are not helped by you messing up the world!" - God was pretty sarcastic, but he spoke the truth,' Tara grinned.

'Wow, good point. Three cheers Neal!'

'That's what I thought when I read it. The reality is, that The Guys can direct people till They're blue in the face, but if people choose *not* to Listen?' she shrugged her shoulders.

'Yeah, but if the family grows... slowly, slowly. Ha! Or with a huge bang!' Lee hollered, throwing his hands up in the air.

'Exactly.' Tara grabbed Lee's hands and sing-sang, 'Let's try to change the world *top* to *bottom*. We've tried it the other way round for eons, that never worked. Let's do it different, let's do it big. Let's just do it! Let's make The Guys at the top *happy*!' she grinned upwards.

Cults? No Way.

'**W**hat if people worry about becoming part of some kind of cult?' Lee asked a little worried.

'That's actually really important to talk about. I personally try not to believe anything willy-nilly. If I hear something that resonates with me, I try it. If I love it and it makes my life fantastic, hey, who am I to argue? I personally would always stay away from anything that requires any kind of make-believe, blind trust or just believing what somebody says.'

'That'll rule out religion, politics, new pharmaceutical drugs...,' Lee said dryly.

'Well, yeah. You obviously do have to draw a line somewhere, but even with regards to those organisations, a bit more public discernment might be useful. Anyway, there are individuals and groups out there that brainwash people, and that is a risk. Some people find it easier than others to tell an honest teacher, a truthful method or a bona-fide organisation from a manipulating and exploiting one. Some organisations are unbelievably clever and people might accidentally slip into unpleasant situations and then can't get out. Yep. Happens. I don't have a miracle cure for that either. All I can say is, use your Intuition and some common sense. If you're part of a group or if you're following a method, if it's all unconditional and it's your free choice to come and go, and deep down you *feel* free and happy, that's important, then you're cool. If you find a teacher, whom you respect and who you *choose* to learn from, even though it might mean some sacrifices, that's cool too. But if somebody or something tries to change you against your will and against your better judgement, it might not be right. If you're becoming dependent on anything or anybody, you're not free anymore. That's not so cool. If you're supposed to give somebody all your money, or all your time, if you don't feel comfortable with that - don't.

I think the long and short of it is that if somebody tries to make you do something that you don't like, if you feel uncomfortable, distressed or scared or you're not sure if it's right, or if it goes against your moral and ethical beliefs or your common sense, then there's Doubt and therefore alarm bells should be ringing. It doesn't mean you're in trouble, but you should at least pay some closer attention to what's going on, maybe enlist some friends to help you out with some advice. But my number one advice, always Listen to your Intuition. And I need to keep stressing, that that obviously only works once you *know* your Intuition!! **Failing that, check periodically if you feel Free and most of all if you're happy. If you're not? Change it. Cult or not.'**

'Good speech and very true. Very applicable for everything in life. Jobs, relationships, commitments, the lot,' Lee said thoughtfully.

'You got it. Let's write down some more specifics with regards to The Guys and cults.'

This is the list the two Cosmos travellers concocted.

The Guys and Cults:
- The Guys don't want us to become open and loving, not dependent.
- They don't want to influence us, They want us to realise that we are masters of our own lives.
- They don't want us to believe anything, they want us go out there, get our own proof, make up our own Minds and grow.
- They don't want us to become numb, They want us to become Aware and active and Conscious.
- They want us to learn from other people, from the past, from many different kinds of our own experiences.
- They want us to develop our inner strength *independent* from outside influences, situations and people.
- They want us to be responsible for our own actions.

- They don't want us to become slaves to something we believe to be higher, better or more all knowing than ourselves. That is the duality that has created all this mess in the first place.
- They want us to think for ourselves (no pun intended).
- If all of this sounds good too you, great, if not, maybe The Guys aren't for you.

'That was the cult speech. I rest my case,' Tara fell back exhaustedly.

'Well rested,' Lee dropped his pen into his lap.

'If I talk anymore, I shall surely collapse,' Tara moved her jaw around, but she knew that her jaw had more to do, much more, at least for a little while.

Is Listening To The Guys Following Fate?

"Humans are so much more entertaining -
since we've given them Free Will!"
- God (in a newspaper cartoon)

'So, do you think that Following The Guys hints and tips is following our *true fate*? Is that The Perfect Line?' Lee asked another of his probing questions.

'Oh man,' Tara raised her eyebrows, 'that's far too philosophical for me, I think everybody has to figure *that* out for themselves.'

'Fair enough. But still, do you believe in Fate?' Lee asked.

'I strongly believe that everything happens for a reason yes, but I don't believe that our Fate is inevitable. I don't believe that there is only one way for our lives to be, that there is a fixed outcome to our lives or that we can't change anything. From my experience, we can hop on and off the perfect- and the off-lines as we choose. A friend of mine said to me once: **life has it's own flow regardless, but each person has it's own predisposition and tendencies towards it.'**

'Wow, that's a cool quote. Give me a second with that one,' Lee requested. After a minute or so he said, 'So that basically means that life goes along it's path, but people just see it in different ways?'

'Yeah, that's pretty much it. But it's not just how we see it, it's also how we physically *react* to life. Some of our actions fuel certain situations, whereas others disperse them. Sometimes it's cause and effect which we're responsible for, sometimes, well, sometimes the shit just hits the fan, something happens that was outside of our immediate control, and we have to act the best we can. **Are events in our lives fate? I have no idea, but I do know that we always have a choice of how to look at things and how to deal with them,**' Tara paused for a second. 'For me, the word fate, means predestined. For me the real question is: is life predestined by the Universe or is it predestined by our *own actions*? What we choose to do?' Tara said with great internal strength. 'Is it fate that we keep choosing bad partners? Or is it *just* a bad choice? Is it fate that we don't make the right choices? Could we turn our fate around if we'd meet the right people? If we'd learn how to make better choices in life? If we'd find some get up-and-go energy and took our lives into our own hands? Was it fate that we were or were not able to do that? You know what?' Tara said shrugging her shoulders, 'I have no idea.' Lee grinned appreciating her honesty. 'Is it fate that the man died of a heart attack? Ehm, actually, let's not ignore that he's been abusing his Body for years with drink and bad food. Was it fate that he did all *that*? Well, he probably knew that he shouldn't do it because it made him sick and aggressive. He might not have liked that, but he did it anyway. Was it fate that he couldn't say "no" that very first time when he let his better judgement slip? Again, I don't know. What I *do* know though, is that often, The Guys or Fate for the matter, don't have anything to do with the fact that things don't work out for us. Not always, but often it's our Free Will to ignore Them and *choose* to go off the perfect line even though we might know *or sense* that it would be better not to.'

'It's the typical: 'Oh-I-know-it's-not-good-for-me-but-I-can't-help-myself syndrome',' Lee said.

Tara nodded, but didn't respond for a few minutes, she was thinking. After a little while she said, 'You know, when we *always* Listen to our Intuition one hundred percent, when we Shift, we're pretty damn close to the perfect path, the perfect line. I just don't believe that this is just one line from birth do death. I don't think that there *can* be only *one* perfect path and therefore only *one fate* if you want to call it that. I feel that there is *a* perfect path for every *moment* in time, for every person. I think that there are numerous perfect lines that change every moment with our life circumstances, individual situations, our surroundings and every single decision we make. **Life is a constant flow, a constant opening and closing of doors, a constant change of outside influences. The perfect line is *always* there, in any moment, in any situation, the Goodness is *always* around us, we just need to learn to see it and to become aware of it. So I think 'good fate' is out there, if we have enough tenacity to look for it and never take "no" for an answer.'**

'Wow, what an answer to such a simple question.'

'Sorry,' Tara blushed.

'No, please don't apologise, I love it.'
'Oh, good.'

Lee

'**A**fter all of this, what ever could be next?' Lee asked expectantly.
'We're still only at the beginning, you know?'
Lee's jaw wanted to move downward again, but he caught himself just in time. 'Man, I keep forgetting that you always say that. This is *still* the beginning? The beginning of what?'
'The Shift. The Shift is what's *truly* great. Compared to the Shift, everything we've talked about so far is Mikey-Mouse stuff, Peanuts.'
'You're not kidding, are you?'
Tara shook her head slowly and steadily, her gaze holding Lee's, 'Do you want the rest?'

A whole range of Emotions made themselves know within Lee. It was a mixture of overwhelmed-ness, excitement, curiosity, Trust, Doubt and terror, all at the same time. He had always wanted to know what's *really* out there. What the potential of the human Mind was, what the interrelationship between humans and the Universe was, how the Universe *really* worked and how Humankind could work *with* it? How, How, How? Was he really about to find the answers? Was this real? He pinched himself and winced. Oh, yes, it was real all right. Ouch! He felt as if somebody had offered him the Red Pill and he had to choose. Take it and change your life forever, or refuse it and remain blind, deaf and ignorant to the vastness of life's possibilities.
Lee had already noticed a new level of Awareness tiptoe its way into his every waking hour, transforming every minute of his life - and he'd only been doing this stuff since yesterday! He couldn't even begin to imagine how his Being would change after a week or a month or even a year! He knew it was good, he knew it was necessary, he knew it was right for him. But still... he pushed any last Doubt away and made a decision. He knew that actually, he had chosen long ago - Red!
He felt like a warrior, getting ready for his big battle with the unknown. He had put on his armour, tested it's fit. He knew he had trained and refined his mental and physical strength as far as he could have done up to this point and now, now he was ready to fight for the new Reality he'd prepared for all his life. He breathed in deeply, grinned, and laughed out loud. God, the stuff in his head. But no, it wasn't a battle at all. It was a quest. A quest for knowledge and answers to questions he didn't even know yet. His horizons had been blown into new dimensions, a new era. He knew

515

that Tara was right when she said that this was just the beginning. He looked at Tara's face and into her eyes. She looked back at him with clarity, strength and a bouncy little sparkle. There was no judgement, no battle, no terror. There was just Now, with a big fat smiley rainbow around it.

He remembered when he had first seen Tara, the impression that her serenity and contentment had made on him. He had noticed that this balanced and blissed expression had never left her Being, no matter how excited or involved she'd got during their chats. He liked that. It was something that was dearly missing in his life. He was silently thanking The Guys, The Dudes, God, Angels, Fairies, Wind, pretty much anything he could think of, for slamming his door shut that fateful morning, yesterday.

He casually checked through the cult-list he'd made earlier and was glad to see that he felt perfectly at peace, free and happy with everything. This was not cult stuff. He didn't aim to be like Tara, he knew that that wasn't the point. **The point was not to become like anybody, but to become his own person. He also knew that their conversations were vital in his process of becoming a better person, a better man.** They were as vital as many amazing future conversations with other people would be, but he also knew that in the end, everything was down to his choices and actions alone. And one of the choices was to be made now.

He felt strongly that his life had been directed this way, that he had to meet Tara to respond to the more and more urgent requests he'd made, to … something. He *had wanted* to know more. He *had asked* for it! Gosh, he thought, how many people were lucky enough to Listen just at the right time - without having even known about Listening - and just stumble across the answers? How many people were out there, that were doing bits and bobs of this stuff and didn't even realise? How many people knew that they were doing something right, but didn't know that they could increase it's effectiveness? How many people were out there that didn't know how to share their experiences? How many people didn't know that they were *not* weird? How many?

Then again, whatever. Dots and Squiggles. The point was, he was here, right now, with a freaking red pill under his tongue, still asking how and why. Within a second he ceremoniously swallowed it. His Intuition screamed: "Yes!" - his Rational Mind screamed: "How will I ever cope?" - as his mouth opened and confidently said the words, 'Ok then, give it to me!'

Tara had sat quietly, observing Lee's face going through the motions, giving his Thoughts away. She'd been there, she knew what it was like, but also she knew that he could take it, that he would love it. She smiled, tilted her head to one side, tilted her chin down and looked up at him from under long curly lashes and asked with the sweetest voice, 'All of it?'

516

By now Lee's grin was matching Tara's. He took one last deep breath and said, 'As good as you've got!'

PART 10

28 THE SHIFT

How Far Have We Got?

'Ok, then, The Shift,' Tara announced dramatically.

'Shift full Power ahead,' Lee dared her.

'I shall duly oblige,' Tara began. 'Now, everything we've talked about so far, are the steps to prepare us to *Shift, right?* Before we go on though, let me do one last summary of what we've talked about up till now, so that we've got it all straight and clear in our Minds.'

'Great,' Lee said enthusiastically.

'Let's do it. As we said right at the beginning of our conversation, a long, long time ago,' Tara began in an old woman's story-tellers voice, 'the current state of affair is that a lot of people, who've had any involvements with Co-incidences, are currently at a stage, where they are looking out for Co-incidences, but where they're not sure what they are really supposed to be doing and how. They have no idea if a Co-incidence is significant or not. They follow random events, hoping that somehow they're eventually going to strike gold. Sometimes they're lucky and happen upon great things, sometimes they get nowhere at all. Generally, they're pretty much wandering in the dark, stumbling across the occasional spot of light.' Lee nodded in agreement as Tara continued, 'Some have managed to get a step further. Either through experimentation, or because somebody told them, they got to know about a few of the things we've discussed. Either way, they have started to ask The Guys questions and to ask Them *for* stuff.' Tara took a deep breather, wanting to summarise the most important aspects of their conversations as thoroughly as possible. 'As we've discussed, through becoming more Mindful, by diverting our attention to only *one* thing at a time, by becoming more Now, and by slowly emptying our warehouses of the unnecessary, constantly interfering roller-coaster Emotions and Thoughts, we become more Aware and more Conscious of *Everything*. By actively increasing our Awareness of our environment, inside and outside of us, we learn how to follow the little hints, hunches and Intuitions that are related to what we've asked for. With practice, we learn how to communicate with The Guys, how to notice and follow Their Physical, Mental and Intuitive Signs. The more we practice Listening and analyse past events and Co-incidences, the more we get to know our Intuition. The more we get to know our Mind and our Intuition, the more we'll be able to tell them apart, and the more we'll start to see The Guys' help everywhere. We become aware that significant Co-incidences happen constantly, and that it's up to us and us alone, to notice them, to realise their significance and to act upon them. By practicing to follow our Intuition and The Guy's messages, we learn to distinguish the significant from the random events in our lives. We begin to increase our Co-incidence hit-rate, and to our surprise but also great relief, we notice that it's all true! That it works!' she smiled at Lee. 'We realise that everything suddenly starts to work out. Co-incidences, events and meetings begin to feel as if they've been arranged in some mysterious way, just to suit our needs. The more we do all of the above, the closer we get to the perfect lines in our life. At the same time we've learned to accept that sometimes "shit still just happens". We're comfortable in the fact that we know how to deal with it, how to stay balanced, grounded and happy, no matter what happens,' Tara drew a deep breath, closed her mouth and looked at Lee.

'You really don't have any doubt about any of this at all, do you?' Lee already knew the answer.

'No. That's exactly the point. No doubt! Learn to trust your Intuition and follow it. *Always*. When you get *your own proof* that your Intuition is *always* right, then your doubt will explode into a million little multicoloured butterflies. And when you Shift, you can fly just like them too,' Tara made cute little fluttering movements with her arms.

Lee smiled softly as he drew a million little butterflies on a separate page of his notebook. Then with a broadening smile he added another little detail to the drawing. Only if you would have looked very, very closely, would you have seen what it was. It was the tiniest little male stick figure, flying in amongst all of the butterflies. Lee knew he was ready, he wanted to fly.

Tara had looked across the grass and the little pond and the swans swimming with their offspring. When she looked back at Lee, she watched him finish his drawing. At first it looked like doodles, then she saw the picture that emerged. She sighed. What a wonderful man she had been allowed to bump into. Silently she thanked The Guys. She gently took Lee's hand into hers, looked at him for a few second without saying anything and then slowly, ever so slowly Let Go.

Both had their own little Thoughts. They had to do with life, The Guys, The Shift and - with each other.

The Shift is Different From Anything You've Ever Experienced

After a while Tara said, 'Now to The Shift. You know when I said that everything we've talked about so far is only the preparation? I meant it. Everything so far is only a stepping stone, the entry exam, to enable you to go out there and play with the *real* toys,' Tara winked at Lee. ' The Shift is the culmination of *everything* we've talked about so far. It's as far you can take this stuff. Well, as far as I know that we can take this stuff anyway,' she said humbly. 'When I said earlier that compared to the Shift, all the things we've talked about so far are Mikey-Mouse stuff? I meant that too. Everything we discussed before could be pretty easily understood, right? Most of the time, you had some kind of reference point as to what I was talking about, some kind of relevant experience. How to do what we talked about was in the end just a set of logical consequences, a logical set of next steps. The Shift is slightly different there. We can get hints and tips and ideas from others, but the gist is that we can talk about it and describe it, but without actually experiencing it ourselves, it will always be a great story, but we'll never truly understand it's reality, that it *is* real and how it feels like to live within that reality! With that I'd like to stress that I'm not only talking about the is-it-real-or-not kind-of-reality, but about actually entering a *different* reality, a *new* reality, about actually living in a different *dimension*. A reality, a dimension, which is just ever so slightly Shifted from the one we know, how we experience life and ourselves at this moment in time.'

'Wow, that's an interesting introduction to get my head around,' Lee said with raised eyebrows.

'That's why I'm not talking about just *believing* it, but about *seeing* it, *living* it, *experiencing* it and *being* it! Actually *doing* it and *feeling* it. It's amazing to notice the difference to how you felt before The Shift, how the world behaved before, how you interacted with it and how it's all slightly but ever so magnificently different once you've Shifted. Things get turned on their head, in a magically, wondrous way! The Shift is different from anything you have ever experienced. That's what makes it so tough to explain. You might logically understand the theory behind it, but the doubt, that it's just too far out to work or to possibly be true, will always remain. With the theory of The Shift, your imagination will be stretched to it's limit. The Shift is an experience so far out, so unbelievable and incredible, that a simple description will never do it justice. Ha,' Tara smiled knowingly, 'and once you have experienced it, it becomes *your own* mad story, and *you* can go out and try to explain it to people,' Tara sparkled at Lee.

'Believe it or not, I'm looking forward to it,' Lee grinned.

'A man just after my own heart,' Tara said happily. 'But still, let me just mention a few more things, because it's nearly inevitable that you'll be uncertain at some stage. Uncertain about where The Shift will lead you? If you should maybe rather stick with what you know? Different realities? That's creepy, too X-Files. But it will still just feel so right to you. You'll ask yourself: "Aaargh, am I going nuts? Is this real? It's fascinating and it works and I'm getting results - but man, it's so weird." But don't worry, because there's one thing I *can* promise you. Once you start to play with The Guys and *really* test the boundaries and you get your own proof. *Nothing* will sound weird anymore! After that The Shift is once again just the logical and natural next step!'

'Ok, I'm sold, what do I have to do?' Lee didn't have to think twice. Curiosity was written all over his face and he was getting impatient.

What To Do?

'**As** I said, it's difficult to explain the Shift with words, therefore it's easier to explain *how* to Shift. By describing *how* to get there, you can logically follow my arguments and my train of Thought. Like that I will try to get the *experience* of The Shift across to you, rather than just a bunch of theoretical concepts. With a bit of luck, something inside you will click, and you'll get it. If it does, something inside of you will change and you'll *know* it's reality. Then, if you can keep your Rational Mind switched off just for a little while longer, if you can experience without your Rational Mind telling you you're crazy, if you can Let Go of any preconceptions, conditionings and expectations, and if you can find just the smallest glimmer of Trust within you, the smallest hope that this could really be true, then you might actually get to go out there and *live* it rather than just *know of* it.'

'I'm intrigued.' Lee tilted his head to one side.

'That's the point,' Tara said grinning.

'Go on then, hit me with the list,' Lee said expectantly, glanced once more at the butterfly picture and turned the page to write the next few points Tara was only too happy to provide.

The Shift:
* Get your own proof by doing it - Intuition works
* Trust - no Doubt
* Stop asking
* Everything happens automatically
* Be Now

- Be Continuously, Consciously Aware
- No resistance of Free Will
- No resistance with the Rational Mind
- We Shift by offering no Resistance - at all

'Let's call this list "The Shift List" for easy reference,' Tara suggested once Lee had finished writing. 'How about we tick off the points on this list as we go along?'

'Sounds good,' Lee nodded and earmarked the page for future reference.

Get Your Own Proof By Doing It - Intuition Works

'Now, the most important pre-requisite for the Shift and for everything we'll talk about now, is that you have played around with your Intuition and telling it from your Thoughts, that you've learned to *Trust* your Intuition and that you have become more Consciously aware of what's going on inside and outside of you. Also that you have dabbled with Co-incidences, Mindfulness and Nowness, and most of all, that *you got your own proof* that everything we've talked about so far is actually true, real and that it works. You have to *know* for yourself before you continue! You have to know from your *own* experience! Once that has is the case, everything else, including The Shift, happens automatically. And I'll of course tell you what that will be like.'

'Whoha, hang on, The Shift happens automatically? I thought you said it's difficult.'

'Ah,' Tara raised her finger with a twinkle in her eyes, 'I never said it's difficult to *do*, I just said that it's difficult to *believe* without having experienced it.'

'Oh good, I thought it would all become really intense now.'

'Intense? Me? Don't be so silly darling!' Tara cuffed Lee with played outrage. 'It's supposed to be fun, remember?' she laughed.

Solid Trust - No Doubt

'The important thing with all of this, is to build up Trust.'

'Trust in what?' Lee grinned. 'Ha, I remember this was my first question to you. If I would have known what an innocent little question like that would lead to... At our first meeting I so innocently asked you: "Trust in what?" and you said: "Trust in being looked after."'

Tara smiled, 'Yep, and that's still the answer. **To Shift you have to build up Trust. You have to turn your initial *believe* and curiosity into *knowledge* and then *Trust* that everything we've talked about works.** You have to *know*, not just believe, that you *can* tell your Intuition from your Mind - every time. And you have to do it. You have to *know* that following your Intuition is good for you. **Through your own experience you have to build up *Trust* that it works, even though you can't explain it with your Rational Mind. Trust that The Guys really have a couple of answers or two. Trust that when you're in the Now, when you Listen to the Guys and when you follow Their messages, that They will always lead you perfectly along the perfect line for you. Trust that you are being looked after! It's has to be a *solid* Trust and, I'll stress it one more time, it *has* to be based on personal, first hand experience rather than blind belief. Only then are there no more But-s, only then there's no more Doubt.**

> *It's Trust that The Universe will Provide*
> *Whatever You Need – Without a Doubt.*

Once you have developed this Trust,' she wrote into the little notebook:

Solid Trust:
- You don't care anymore how it works or if somebody else's story sounds believable or not, or if other's believe your stories or not, because you've got your *own* proof. You've seen the Signs and had the guidance and you know. That's all that matters.
- You'll still be amazed, but not surprised anymore about the amazing events that are happening in your life. You accept this to be the new 'straight line' you have chosen for yourself.
- There is no doubt, no But-s anymore, only Trust.
- Now you know.
- Now you Trust.
- You Trust that Nowness and Listening is safe, useful and amazing.
- There are no more But-s. There's no more Doubt.

'As you keep playing with The Guys, and as your Rational Mind interferes less and less, with time, this total Trust will manifested itself in your *Conscious* Mind. There it will become solidly rooted and anchored.

Eventually, the more your Conscious Mind becomes involved with this Trust, you will reach a stage, where this Trust also floods into your *Subconscious* Mind. **As this Trust becomes rooted in your Subconscious, noticing, recognising and acting on Signs and significant Intuitions will become automatic, as none of it has to pass through the Rational Mind anymore.** At that stage, your Rational Mind has finally gotten the message and has given way to your Intuition, which can now play it's Cosmic role freely,' the information came through Tara in a steady flow.

'Oh yeah,' Lee's head shot up. 'That's what I asked about yesterday. **Now the Subconscious acts *immediately*.** Trust bypasses the Rational Mind. It doesn't question any longer! **Now we can't miss out on Intuitions anymore, because they get *automatically* put into action.** This is amazing!' He flicked through his notebook and crossed out the reminder not-to-forget-to-ask-about-things-bypassing-the-Rational-Brain.

'That's it,' Tara nodded content. 'At this stage, there are no Doubts anymore, no questions weather to follow a hunch or not. It's just obvious, it's crystal clear that it's an Intuition and *not* a Thought. It's clear that it's significant and your Being follows it without arguing about it. There are no evaluating Thoughts anymore, as **Listening to and following Intuitions becomes automatic and thus an inherent part of your life, an intrinsic undercurrent in all of your daily actions. That's Solid Trust, without Doubt.'**

'Well, that's still a little way off for me,' Lee said dreamily, 'even though I have to say that the last couple of days have been pretty Mind-blowing in the proof department. I think my Conscious Mind is slowly getting convinced, but I my Subconscious will need a wee bit more time, I think,' Lee said.

'And that's fine.' Tara said encouragingly. 'You've picked up this stuff faster than anybody I know already, so don't rush yourself. It'll all come in it's own good time.'

'I know. I just need to make sure that I really *internalise* everything and play with *experiencing* it, rather than just become a professional at accumulating your words and knowledge. I *really* have to drop *all* doubt, not just theorise about it!' Tara nodded approvingly at Lee's vigour. 'Even the tiniest, niggliest doubt that might tell me that it sometimes works and maybe sometimes it doesn't has to be convinced and dropped. I have to play with asking for stuff and following the Signs until it becomes automatic. There's still some playing too be done for me! Gosh, this is all so exciting.'

'There is always more to play with, for you, for me, for anybody, but the point is to enjoy the ride, and I can see you doing that anyway! You know, it really is like a fun fair ride! You don't just want to get to the destination, do you? The whole point is to enjoy the ride!'

'Yeah, otherwise you could just stay at the start of the rollercoaster ride and never even leave to go on the ride in the first place, as you end up where you started anyway,' Lee grinned. 'Anyway, that's a nice piece of wisdom right there. Enjoy the ride! *All* of it! That'll make the getting-to-The-Shift fun too.'

'That's the point,' Tara smiled.

'Fabulous.'

Stop Asking?

'Let's get to the juicy bits, shall we? No more delay!' Lee skimmed through the *The Shift List*. 'Now, what on earth is the "*Stop*-Asking" point on this list all about?' he'd only just noticed it. 'First we spent all this time learning *how* to ask questions and now you say that we need to stop it?' Lee was bewildered.

Tara grinned happily, 'It will all makes sense in not time. If you remember, the asking-thing is an aid to help us to notice Co-incidences, hints and Intuitions, right?'

'Sure I remember. We said before that asking for things helps us to *train* ourselves too look for Signs related to what we've asked for. It helps us to ensure that we *perceive* significant events, simply because we're actually looking out for them.' Lee was surprised how he could just rattle off all this new input.

'Right. Now we go a step further. As we said, the asking-thing is a Mental crutch to help us become more aware of our environment. Over time and with practice, as we're actively looking out for the Signs, and are becoming more aware, we begin to pick up all sorts of stuff by default. We start to pick up Signs, hints and Intuitions about stuff that we did *not* ask for. Basically,' Tara paused, 'we didn't ask for those things, simply because we didn't know yet that we needed them.'

'Woha, something just hit home,' Lee barged in, '**once we have Shifted, we are on-par with The Guys, aren't we? We know everything They know. We are continuously tapped into the Collective Consciousness, so we don't *need* to ask for Intangible things anymore because we know anyway, and we don't need to ask for any Tangible things anymore, because we are automatically following the Signs and therefore we get everything we need.** We don't *need* to ask anymore. We don't need the crutch anymore. Wow,' Lee's mouth gaped open. 'Now I'm truly flabbergasted!' he fell silent, he needed a few minutes to digest this one. Lee wanted to really *get it*, not just *understand* it. Slowly he repeated his realisation in his Mind, again and again:

> **"We're so Aware,**
> **that we see all the Signs and get all the Messages.**
> **We get everything we need,**
> **so we don't need to ask for it anymore.**
> **We know everything we need to know,**
> **so we don't need to ask for it anymore.**
> **We don't need the crutch anymore.**
> **We can stop asking!"**

'Man, this *is* big stuff,' Lee brushed a few strands of hair out of his eyes.

'Yep. You asked why we spent all this time learning *how* to ask questions when we stop it now? Well, do you understand now why we *had* to learn in the beginning *how* to ask for stuff?' Tara asked.

'Oh I do. Quite an ingenious little trick that.' He winked at Tara. 'We needed the initial questioning process to learn to *Trust* that the process of *Listening* actually works. Without the asking thing we would have not been able to do that.'

'Good man!' Tara still couldn't believe how quickly Lee could apply his knowledge. It had taken her ages to figure all this out. 'Great, so besides the fact that we simply don't *need* to ask anymore, if you really think about it, by asking for anything, we actually *always limit* ourselves.' As Lee's face quite obviously showed a question mark, Tara continued, 'No matter how carefully we phrase the questions, we will never be able to ask for *all* the wonderful things the Guys can give us, or *all* the fabulous ways The Guys can use to show us stuff with. Our little brains will always think in earthly ways, with earthly restrictions.'

'Ah, good point. Asking for stuff, in the end, is like trying to tell a Genie in a bottle how to do it's job.' Lee grinned and lovingly rubbed his empty Orange Juice bottle.

Tara smiled, 'Exactly. Once you've Shifted, you don't need to ask the Genie for anything anymore. He already knows and provides you with what you need all by himself. Actually, I have another example. It's a bit like being in a restaurant, that always knows exactly what you want for dinner, without you having to order,' Tara said. 'Most of the time you won't even know how much you wanted or needed a particular dish, until they give it to you, and then you're surprised by how perfect it is. They have fabulous surprises, you know?' she grinned, remembering all the astonishing things The Guys had dished up for her.

'That's so cool! The Guys know what I need and what I want. They know *everything*. That's handy!' Lee sniggered at this understatement.

'Actually Tara, d**o you still ask for stuff?'** he wanted to know.

'Mmh, not really, well, sometimes I do. **I still ask for guidance from time to time, but all in all, I hardly seem to ask for stuff anymore.** You know,' Tara went on, 'it's funny, sometimes we ask for stuff just because we need to feel to be involved. Sometimes we want to make double sure that The Guys are actually Listening, you know, when we're really desperate for an answer? **There's obviously no harm in doing that, we can still ask questions if we want to. But the point is that it's not *needed* anymore.** If you ask anyway, or if you check up on a question you asked a while ago for which you still haven't received an answer, often all you get is: "Patience".'

'Ha, that's funny! That's why The Guys didn't give you the answer yet in the first place, because there was nothing to tell you yet. You had to be patient.'

'Exactly. So there was no point in me chasing up, right?' Tara grinned broadly. 'But it'll take you some time to figure that out and trust it fully. I personally, through my own experience, I know by now that I'll get the answer, because I know how to Listen to Them. Well, occasionally I still say: Guys, it would be really nice if..., but mostly that's just for making conversation you know? It's nice to chat to Them,' Tara said fondly.

"Her face was always so bright and happy," the Thought only rested in Lee's synapses for a few seconds. Just long enough for the corners of his mouth to curl upwards into a little smile. 'Something just occurred to me,' Lee said, as another question popped into his warehouse. **'When do I know when I'm ready to *stop* asking?'**

'That's an easy one. **When your life is full of magic Co-incidences without you having had to ask or look out for them. When you continuously get things that you didn't ask for but really needed, when you notice all the good things around you without even trying, when it begins to look that somebody is running around you, and dropping everything you *need* right into your lap.** Trust me, you will know all by yourself when you're ready,' Tara said happily. **'Mmh, come to think of it, when you're ready, you just kind of automatically stop all by yourself. There's just no need for it anymore. I mean, why would you ask for something you've already got?'** Tara asked rhetorically.

'Fair point. Fabulousness!' Lee gave the thumbs up.

'Remember though, you get what you *need*, not always what you *want*, and there might be a difference.'

'Yeah, I remember, thanks for reminding me though. I've got a whole bunch of notes in my little friend here,' Lee patted his notebook.

Manifestation And The Art Of Time

'You know, The Shift is not just about being aware and not asking anymore, it's about Shifting Dimensions! For real!' Tara said.

'Cool,' was all Lee could say.

Tara cleared her throat dramatically and said:

"Time is the space between an event and the perception (the awareness, the knowledge) of that event."

'Woha, come again? I need to write that one down.' Lee waved his pen in readiness. Tara repeated the last sentence and he dutifully wrote it down.

'Let me give you an example to explain what I mean,' Tara began another chapter. 'Imagine you're walking on the beach and you want to write a message into the sand for a friend and you ask The Guys for something to write with. You walk around for a bit and you find the perfect stick half way down the beach.

Now, by asking for something to draw with, you've increased your *Awareness* of your environment, which assisted you in noticing the event, i.e. the stick, right?'

'Ok, I'm with you.' Lee nodded slowly.

'Now, **the closer you get to The Shift and the better your Listening gets, the shorter the time span becomes between you asking for something and you getting it, i.e. the significant event itself.** That means that after a bit of practice when you ask for a stick, The Guys just *tell* you where to find it.'

'So, the time span gets shorter because I don't have to wander around looking for the stick anymore, right? I can just go and find it, already knowing where it is, because I've actually been told. There's no trial and error anymore. Wow.'

'Exactly. They can tell you with a Mental message like: "over there in the shrubbery, darling", or they might tell you through an inexplicable pull towards a *particular* bush. The better you Listen, the shorter the time span becomes. Once you get really good at it and The Guys want to tell you something out of Their own accord, instead of having to warn you quite some time beforehand to make sure that you get the hint, They can now just tell you to watch out *immediately before* something significant happens.'

'Get it. So, at that stage, me asking for the event, my knowing about the event and the actual event happening, i.e. me finding the stick, are all really close together,' Lee summarized.

'Full points!'

Time Lapse Equals Zero - Immediate Messages - Instantaneous Manifestation

'Now, if you become even better at Listening, The Guys won't have to prepare you at all anymore, They can just tell you *as* the event happens and you'll perceive at the same time,' Tara said.

'So, that would be like needing a stick, asking for it and the stick being already right in front of us, sticking out of the sand.'

'Right. The time lapse between you needing something and you getting it, is reduced to virtually nothing - zero. Manifestation happens *instantaneously*. This is what happens to you *just before* you Shift.'

'Wow, instantaneous manifestation, that's nuts!' Lee clapped his hand excitedly like a little boy, his tousley hair falling over his eyes.

What Could Be Faster Than Instantaneous Manifestation? Pre-empting...

'I agree that's already pretty cool, yeah?' Tara had one of her knowing smiles on her lips again. 'This is pretty much as good as anybody could wish it gets, right? Instantaneous Manifestation. Not bad, ey?' she said casually, then her grin broadened.

'But you can top that?' Lee said, knowing by now how Tara announced her little gems.

Tara grinned, 'Well? What *is* better than instantaneous Manifestation?'

'Oh God, getting something *before* we even know we need it?' Lee blurted out. He had no idea where that Thought had come from.

'Exactly! Once you Shift, you find the stick *before* you know you need it. You might walk along the beach and you pick up this stick without even thinking about it. And *then* you think that it would be a great idea to write a message into the sand for your friend,' she paused for a moment. '**Do you** understand now what I meant earlier, that when you Shift, things get turned upside down?' Lee nodded carefully. **'The Shift is a** *different dimension.* **It's like a glimpse in the Matrix. It's one step up from instantaneous manifestation, it's** *pre-empting.* You'd get a new pen, just before you notice that your old one ran out and you had to write a very important note. Somebody offers you a lift, without you knowing that you'd already missed the train that you were going to take. Somebody offers you to look after your cats just before you get called away on an urgent trip.'

'The Cosmic Restaurant gave us a dish before we knew that we wanted it.'

'Actually, it's more like home delivery just seconds before you decided you were hungry,' Tara smiled.

'Ah,' Lee was stunned.

'After the Shift, the world becomes truly magic. Wait till you experience it, it'll knock you over, it's just crazily fantastic. **This is when time doesn't exist anymore! You ALREADY HAVE.** You ALREADY KNOW!'

'Pfffft. I can only begin to imagine,' Lee shook his head, picked up his notebook and wrote:

The Shift pre-empts your Needs
Time doesn't exist anymore!
You ALREADY HAVE. You ALREADY KNOW!

Four Phases Of Listening

'Actually, let me go into a bit more detail, to make sure that you don't just understand it intellectually, but that your really get a *feel* for it.' Tara said thoughtfully. She knew it was easy to get and just as easy to loose it again. 'So, there are basically four phases to how well you Listen and how that affects your perception of events around you, with the last stage being The Shift.'

Lee had his pen ready when Tara began to go through the four stages:

4 Stages of how well we Listen:
- If you're really deaf, the coconut falls out of the tree and kills you.
- If you're Listening a little bit, you look up and see the coconut *just before* it hits you.

- If you're Listening pretty well, you look up and *step aside* just in time and the coconut lands next to you - a lucky Co-incidence.
- Once you've Shifted, you wouldn't be anywhere near that tree when the nut comes down. Just a blissful happy day without any hick-ups...

'Ah,' switches were getting flicked in Lee's brain as he beckoned Tara to continue. These are the other examples that were put on paper:

General:
- With mediocre Listening, you ask and you find in round about ways.
- With better Listening, you ask and They can *tell* you exactly where to look.
- With really good Listening, you ask and it's *already there*. Manifestation is instantaneous. You perceive the event *as* it occurs.
- With The Shift, They *pre-empt* you, you get what you need before you need it.

'See, at this last stage, you don't even need to look anymore. You just flow, do your thing, which always just happens to be *exactly* what you need to do. There's no looking out for Co-incidences or Signs anymore. You don't have to decide anymore or listen to your Intuition, it's just what you do, naturally. You'll be riding the wave of the Universe, you'll be flowing and dancing with The Guys. Yipee!' Tara threw in simply.
    And another list emerged.

The Stick:
- You have to go an look for a stick.
- They tell you where the stick is.
- You look ahead and the stick is right there.
- You find *and take* the stick before you know you need it – The Shift.

'I think I have a list of my own,' Lee grinned and began to write:

The Warehouse:
- If you can't listen, a big fat red box gets delivered into your warehouse, but you can't find it in a million years amongst all the jumble.
- Then, the more you get to know your Mind, the more you clear out, and the better you can Listen, one day, you walk into your warehouse, and you see the big fat red box, right in the middle of the main storage area screaming at you: "yoo-hoo, here I am, me, me, me".
- Then, with more practice and even better Listening skills, you get a telegram telling you that you've had a delivery and you just go to the delivery entrance and pick it up.

- And finally, all I can say is: HOME DELIVERY!

Lee's face glowed. He threw down his pen, sat up straight and snapped his notebook shut. 'This *is* bonkers,' he said, slightly taken aback, 'I think I'll need a bit of time to get my head around this. It makes perfect sense when I see it in a list like that, but man, this is like seriously far out. My Rational Mind is going crazy here.' He saw Tara smiling a mischievous but loving I-told-you-so-smile. He huffed, 'Man, does this really happen?' He saw Tara nod. 'Gosh, that would mean that our life is *actually physically* changing when we Shift, *not* just the way we *look* at it. We *really do* enter a different reality,' Lee held his head in his hands, rubbing his temples.
'Yep, that's it. Take all the time you need. Ask questions if you have any,' Tara said calmly. She knew that this stuff could be a little overwhelming, especially if you *knew* deep down that it *was* all true. The good old Rational Mind always needed a little longer.'

Manifestation or Foresight?

After a few minutes of mulling things over in his head Lee asked, 'You know you mentioned the word manifestation before. Mmh, I wonder if asking for something *creates* an event that would *not* have happened otherwise. I mean, do we actually *manifest* an event - or does the act of asking just raise our *awareness* to a level to be able to perceive an event which would have happened anyway?'

'I can't answer that question, and I don't think we'll ever know for sure, but I do have my own opinions,' Tara ventured.

'Let's have'm,' Lee invited.

'When you get good, asking for things works so incredibly well, that it sometimes *does* feel as if you *are* creating, as if you *are* manifesting something out of nothing. But come to think of it, for me the question is not if I *create* an event or if I become more aware of an *existing* event. For me the question is: is it Premonition and Foresight, or is it Manifestation.'

'Hang on, I'm lost. What does Manifestation have to do with Foresight?'

'Well, it's a little like what you just asked, do you *create* an event or do you become *aware* of an *existing* event. I asked myself that question too, and from that I went on to ask: what comes *first*, the *wish* to manifest something, or the *existence* of that future event itself?' Lee still looked at her blankly and Tara paused. This was new territory for her too. She had never really discussed this before and she was thinking while she was talking. Actually, she was *Listening* while she was talking, and her *thinking* had just gotten in the way, as it sometimes did when she got excited about stuff The Guys said through her.

Anyway, Tara cleared her Mind and Their words came back again, nice, clear and loud, just as she was used to. She had stopped thinking completely by the time she said, 'Ok, the usual definition of Manifestation would be that you ask for something first, then the requested event happens and *then* you perceive the event. Right?' Lee nodded. 'Well, I have a different suggestion. What if: a requested event is going to happen in the near future, The Guys tell you about it *before* it happens, and you perceive it as a *desire*, which *prompts* you to *ask* for it, then the physical even happens which you then notice.'

Lee's mouth slowly opened. Something had just made click. He scribbled into his notebook, waving at Tara to stop talking for a minute. When he was done he read out loud, 'In different words: manifestation could mean that we don't create an event which would not have happened otherwise, but that we just get a premonition or a foresight of an event which is going to happen in the future? Like getting a glimpse of a future event? Like a vision?'

'Yes, you could call it that. But instead of perceiving it as a *vision*, we perceive it as *desire* for that event to happen.'

'That is so clever!' Lee marvelled, giving The Guys a little appreciative wink skywards. 'It could be seen as another way of The Guys giving us Messages. Making us think we manifest stuff. Sneaky little buggers. Ha! Actually, that makes it much easier for the Guys too!' Lee laughed.

'How's that?' Tara wondered out loud.

'Well, it's simple, because **out of all the things that are *already* happening, The Guys just need to tell us where we can find the ones that are significant to us, so They don't actually have to *make* anything happen at all.** I hadn't thought about that before.'

Tara just winked at him, 'Dude, you're unbelievable, that's a seriously good point! Isn't it great? Effortlessness all round!'

'Tara, is this really how it works? I had never thought that stuff like this could be explained this rationally.'

'All I can say, is that this is what simply starts to happen once you Shift. You be able to observe it yourself once you get to that stage. And then remember? No Doubt?'

'Oh man,' Lee looked away and grinned broadly.

This is As Far As We Can Get In Our Everyday Working Lives

'Want more?'

'What a question!'

'Ok then, this is probably as close to The Shift as we can get in our everyday working lives,' Tara said. 'Once you have Shifted, you are in Nowness all the time. **Once Shifted, there's no need to think at all anymore. You just ARE. That's The Shift. You just Listen and act, all automatically - until you get to work.' Tara laughed out loud.**

'Oh bloody hell,' Lee rolled his eyes. 'Ok, I can see now why it would be tricky to be Now all the time, with 2.4 children, a job, a dog, a lawnmower and a crazy neighbour. **I guess in a normal life, the most we can strive for is to be as *Mindful* as possible, to be *as Consciously Aware* of as many of our Thoughts, Emotions, Behaviours, actions and our environment, to consciously *observe* as much as we possibly can.**

Phew, I guess the torch example is the most useful,' Lee continued, '"On" when needed, "off" when it's not. And come to think of it, of course, when the torch is on, to be always be *constantly consciously aware of every Thought* in our head.'

'Well said. **Once you're able to do that, you spend most of your time on the Perfect Line. That Shift in itself will change your life beyond anything you could ever possibly imagine. But, you'll still be thinking from time to time and you'll still be trying to make decisions or plan, right? And like that you might still hop to an off-line from time to time.'**

'Ok? And?' Lee was waiting for an answer.

To Shift Permanently - No Resistance

'Wanna go a step further? Dare ya,' Tara twinkled at him. 'Not many people will want to do this though. It takes a lot of commitment and some possible adjusting of life style too.'

'Of course I want more. More! Faster! Bigger! Higher!' Lee laughed loudly, noticed other people around them looking slightly disturbed and quickly sat down again.

Tara stood up, not a care in the world and announced loudly for everyone to hear, 'This is Lee. My friend, and I'm proud of it.' She sat down again, ignoring all the baffled people around her, who were desperately trying to look as if the most interesting thing in the world was in the top braches off some nearby tree.

Lee grinned even wider than before and said, 'After your admirable public pledge of friendship with a total loony, am I going to hear more or what?'

'I think we can oblige,' Tara whispered.

'Ok, hit me with it then!' Lee's skin was covered in goose bumps. He felt something *big* coming on.

'Now then, to Shift *permanently*, you have to *completely* DROP your Rational Mind.'

'Right,' Lee laughed at Tara.

'I'm serious.'

'You are?' Lee asked hesitantly, but Tara held his gaze. Yep, she was serious. Shit, that *was* big. That was crazy too. *Completely dropping* his Rational Mind? Wow, hang on, wasn't it our Rational Mind that lifted us above the animal world? Wasn't it our Rational Mind that made us human? How could he just drop that?

He heard Tara talk to him again from very far away, 'We have to drop *all* Thoughts, Conscious and Subconscious. We have to stop resisting with our Rational Mind and at that, also with our Free Will. To Shift we have to drop *all* Resistance. **The Shift is total Surrender to Intuition. It's total Letting Go of our Mind.'**

'Ok?' Lee really couldn't say anything else.

Tara went on comfortably, 'Do you remember, when we said earlier that every Thought is a wire in a pipe with water gushing through it? That every Thought offers Resistance to the water of the Cosmic flow?' Lee nodded. **'Now, when we catch a glimpse of the Shift, we *take out* the wire, we take the Resistance out of the pipe for that moment,'** she paused deliberately, **'but when we Shift *permanently*, we get rid of the wire and of the pipe too!'**

'Oh Shit,' the lights had finally turned on. Lee stared at Tara.

'All there is left over, is the water, the life force flowing through the Universe - Effortlessly, without any Resistance *whatsoever.*'

Lee mumbled, 'Bloody Hippies,' and sheepishly looked away, just to scribble franticly so that he wouldn't forget.

No resistance:
- No resistance through Free Will, and therefore.
- No resistance with the Rational Mind.

- Let Go of the wire *and* the pipe.

'It's like the "pot-example" we don't just get rid of the steam, but of the steam *and* the pot!' Lee said thoughtfully.

Why We Don't Need The Torch Either - The Ultimate Shift

'Yep. Now, **when we can Let Go of the wire *and* the pipe, then we're in *constant* Nowness. That's The *Ultimate Shift*, the Black Belt, the hard-core dedicated version of the Shift, the permanent move to the Perfect-Line. When you do that, you drop The Torch!'**

'You drop the Torch,' Lee repeated slowly. He had never in his wildest dreams imagined this to be possible.

'You Shift, because you realise that the torch was a crutch as well! A crutch you needed, because you were scared to walk barefoot in the dark! Once you Shift, you Trust that even in the darkest darkness, even when everything in your life goes belly up, you will be looked after. That's when you *confidently* walk barefoot in the dark, with your head held high, your heart wide open and a huge smile on your face. *That's the last challenge. To drop the torch. Drop your Mind. Be Now. Fully*,' Tara paused again to let her last few sentences sink in.

Lee quickly wrote:

The Ultimate Shift:

- That's the last challenge. To drop the torch. Drop your Mind. Be Now. Fully.

Lee began to fidget with his notebook, 'But man, would anybody actually dare to do that? I mean, completely dropping the Mind? It's obviously fabulous, but man. Isn't that a bit drastic?'

Tara said reassuringly, 'First, if people dare, that's each person's own choice. This is as far as you *can* get, it's the potential, the Ultimate, but you obviously don't *have* to go this far. What you do in the end and how far you take it, will always remain your choice.

Second, if you play with all the preliminary stages to The Shift, by the time you get to The Shift itself, it will *not be* scary anymore anyway.

536

You'll have *already* realised that following Their Signs is better than your Free Will could ever be and you'll have acquired doubtless Trust on the way. **Right now it might still sound far out, but by the time you get there, it will be the logical and automatic next step. It will feel comfortable and safe and really bloody good fun.** If you dare, you can always play with it, and if you don't like it anymore, there is always a way back out,' Tara challenged softly.

'Ah, I assumed there must be. What is it?'

'You think, think and think,' Tara waved her hands franticly.

'Ah of course!' Lee suddenly grinned. 'As soon as we think, our Rational Mind will only be too happy to oblige. If our Rational Mind talks, we can't Listen anymore, and once we stop Listening, we go straight back to our normal little Dotted and Squiggled existence.'

'Easy,' Tara said simply.

Lee wasn't completely satisfied yet, 'But hang on. By this stage Listening and following the Signs has become automatic, hasn't it? How can we stop something that has become automatic?'

'Ah, good question. You have to actively stop Listening, by either actively chattering in your head so that you can't Listen, or by ignoring anything that you do hear. After a while, the messages will stop. Once you stop Listening, the connection to The Guys is severed again, and therefore the automatic-following stops too. If you feel really fruity, you can even just to tell The Guys to stop talking to you. They might need a bit of convincing though."

Lee grinned, 'Fair enough, all that makes sense. I guess it's just retracing the steps and burning the bridges behind you.'

'You could call it that,' Tara nodded. 'But you can always rebuild the bridges, in case you change your Mind,' she grinned.

'Like you did before? When you asked The Guys to stop talking to you and then missed them?'

'Yep. Happens.'

'Cool, I feel much better about it now. It really does sound amazing and I'd love to play with all of this, but man dropping your Mind completely? Well that'll take a bit of time to get my experience around,' Lee smiled visibly amused by his play of words. 'Ha, and now that I know how to start, pause and stop how I please? Well, there's nothing to be worried abut anymore, is there? So, Nowness, here I come!' Lee announced happily and enthusiastically took hold of pen and paper to write:

When you Shift:
- You Let Go of the pipe.
- You drop the torch.

- If you want to go *back* to pipe-and-wire-land, just pick up the torch again.

Lee added the last point with a confident smile.

The Shift Summary and Why You Don't Need Shoes

'I think it's time for another notebook summary,' Lee said, wanting to make sure no details went amiss.

They sat together for a while making a long list of everything they'd discussed about the Shift. When they were done, it looked something like this:

THE SHIFT:

To Shift, we need to maintain Nowness.

In Nowness, we Shift our Consciousness to a new state of Awareness.
We Shift our Consciousness from I-haven't-got-a-clue-what's-going-on, to Constant Conscious Awareness of the Now and being in touch with everything!

If we are constantly in the Now, we become aware of all sensory input at all times, of all of our Thoughts, all of our Emotions, Behaviour and reactions - not just the little tit bits approved by our Rational Mind.
In the Now there is no Rational Mind to hide anything or mask anything.

Our whole Being is in the Now, In the moment where Everything happens.

Nothing inside or outside of us happens anymore without us being constantly consciously aware of it.

After The Shift, Listening is 100%. We are totally connected.

We see all the Signs, we notice all the messages. In Nowness, The Guys can talk to us whenever They need to.

We stop trying to do anything with our Rational Minds, as our lives become guided along the perfect path automatically. We know what to do and we actually do it, we don't think about it anymore, we don't decide it anymore, we just do it.

538

We Trust and follow our Intuition - always. It has become second nature. Through Trust, our Rational Mind allows itself to relax, it does not feel the need to intervene anymore. It feels Safe!

When we follow the Messages automatically and when there's no conscious effort involved anymore, when we are fully Now, we Let Go of the Wire and the Pipe and we drop the Torch.

There is no more Resistance of the Rational Mind.

Listening is Automatic. Following significant Signs and Messages happens Automatically. No Thoughts are involved in this process anymore. Even though we've dropped the Torch. We feel safe. No matter how dark it is.

There is no more need for Asking or Manifestation. The Shift pre-empts our Needs. We Already Have. We Already Know. There is no Conscious effort involved anymore.

Once we let life happen without constantly trying to interfere with our heads, it suddenly all just works out. Everything just falls into place. Our lives become guided along the perfect line automatically. In Nowness, we are and stay on the perfect line.

People start to notice how happy we are, even when things seem to go wrong. People notice that we never stare at a closed door, but excitedly and curiously look around for the next one to open. People notice how 'lucky' we are, as help always seems to be at hand just when we need it. Everything becomes effortless, as we stop worrying, as we begin to accept whatever comes our way as impermanent.

We stop Trying to Actively do Anything or Be Anything.
We Shift from 'Trying To Do' to 'Just Doing It'.
We Shift from 'Trying to Be' to 'Just Being'.

No Judgements. No Worries. Easy. Light. Free. Fun.

When they were done, Tara said, 'Well, as we're summarising...,' she gently took the pen out of Lee's hand and, with a big smile, slowly and carefully began to write:

Why You Don't Need Shoes:

When we Shift:
We are fully connected to Everything and Everyone,
To The Guys and the Universe.
After the Shift, we become One with Them again and so
We become an inseparable part of Everything.
Now, that we are a fully Conscious part of the Cosmic dance,
That's when we can really join the Party.
As we stop trying to Be anything or Force anything,
As we stop defining ourselves to be only a part of something,
As we finally Let Go of the parts, we become Whole.
As we become whole again,
We become One.
One with our Body, Mind and Spirit,
With Nature, with the Cosmos.

Once we've Shifted, we don't just think that we are One,
We ARE One.
We experience Oneness.
We become Oneness.
We're looked after. Always.

We enter a new Reality, a new Consciousness,
A new Dimension so full of happiness and love and laughter,
We would have never believed it could exist.

We are Carefree and Light, yet Grounded and Real.
That's the stage of 'Just Being it'.
Solid, Strong, Powerful,
Playful.
That's the SHIFT.'

That's Why You Don't Need Shoes.
That's why you can walk barefoot - in the dark - without worrying.
That's why you can Trust one hundred percent
That the Universe looks after you.
As you are One with It. You are It and It is you,
Nothing can hurt you anymore,
As nothing would hurt itself.

Tara put the pen down. Silently Lee picked it up and added in strong meaningful letters just a few more words:

Strong, Powerful, Alive, Happy. Clear. Yeah!

'Ha!' Lee thought. He knew he'd been onto something when those words had popped into his Mind a few years ago. Now it was all beginning to make sense. He smiled.

Loosing Nowness - Lee

While they had been writing, an interesting feeling had overcome Lee. It had started in the centre of his stomach and had evenly spread out across his torso and to his limbs, till it had permeated every single part of his Body, right to the tips of his fingers, his toes and the top of his head. At first he was unsure what it meant, but when he looked at it closer, he realised that it was an unmistakable feeling of strength and certainty that he was on the right path. He realised that his Rational Mind had become quieter. It was beginning to accept. Lee *knew* that the Shift was real. He didn't just *believe* some pretty girl. In fact, his entire Being was screaming: Affirmative!

Then, totally out of the blue, his Rational Mind freaked out: And what the hell do you think you are you doing? You're not a Hippy! You have a job! What's with this talk about the Universe? Have you lost it? And that girl? She's crazy! Isn't that obvious? And anyway, what's with all this No Doubt stuff? I'm doubting, you hear me?? I AM DOUBTING! His heart was beating faster.

As he scanned his Body for tensions, he noticed that he was breathing high up into his chest, rather than into his belly. With all the excitement his Rational Mind had provided him with, he'd lost his centre. He was surprised by how clearly he could feel it! Gosh, how quickly you could loose it! Take your Mind of it for one second! Slowly and deliberately he concentrated on breathing into his stomach again. As he moved his Awareness back to his centre, the feeling of strength, certainty and of connectedness grew stronger. "Interesting," he thought, he could *feel when* his Being was switched on. It felt different when it was Conscious and when it wasn't. It was as if he could feel different intensities of his Being, depending on how Aware he was. And man, it was crazy how the Rational Brain had a life of it's own, how it was constantly trying to throw obstacles into the path he'd cleared. He marvelled to himself for a few moments and decided to tell Tara what he'd just experienced.

'Ah, that's what it was,' Tara grinned.

Lee frowned. That was not the answer he'd expected - uh - expectations - anyway, 'What do you mean?' Lee asked surprised.

'Your energy just changed a few seconds ago, your posture changed, *you* changed. You've just turned into a *man* again. Your natural masculine edge just came back. You'd lost that there for a while.'

'You noticed?' Lee was taken aback.

'Of course.'

'Why didn't you say anything?'

'Well, I don't really know you.' They looked at each other and burst out laughing. 'Well, it's not my place to tell you stuff like that without being invited to,' Tara said unassumingly.

'Fair enough,' Lee appreciated Tara's discretion, but still found himself curious wanting to hear how she could have picked up on something so subtle. Gosh, she really was perceptive. Did Nowness make you more aware of this kind of stuff too? She'd said he'd just turned into a man *again*? So if the *man* hadn't been there, *what* had he been? He prepared himself for the answer. He breathed. 'When you say I lost it, what was I like?' Lee asked.

'Eh...,' Tara hesitated.

'Come out with it, I can take it.'

'Well, wimpy.'

'Wimpy? Oh man!' Lee leant forward. 'Promise me something,' he looked at her firmly.

The new power, the clarity and the sparkle in his eyes was an interesting combination, Tara thought. 'What?' She asked, stirred by his intensity. She knew that such a change in energies only came with heightened Awareness.

'When that happens again,' he said, 'please promise to tell me.'

'Are you sure?'

'Absolutely. Besides that I don't want to be wimpy, compared to being Aware and Conscious, this frantic rollercoaster the so called Rational Mind puts me on really sucks. I actually noticed the change myself. I'd been struggling for a word for it, but wimpy is a good description. I lost my power because I wasn't present. I was in my head. I felt out of touch. Out of touch with myself and, actually, come to think of it, I felt out of touch with you too,' Lee was venturing on thin ground, was it ok to talk to Tara like that? Kate would have freaked out long ago.

'Yeah, I noticed that as well,' Tara said without hesitation, surprising Lee once again.

She wasn't only cool but she was also interested in this conversation. 'Actually, I think you changed too,' Lee said carefully and then added quickly, 'I'm not just saying that to counter what you've said to me, I really mean it.'

'Yeah, I know, don't worry. It's good to talk like this. It's good to point out to each other when we loose our connection! It's important! That's how we learn. We learn faster together. So, how do you feel I changed?' Tara asked.

Lee smiled, she wasn't only dishing out, but she was also prepared to Listen. 'Mmmh. I think you lost your softness.'

'What do you mean?' Tara asked genuinely interested.

Lee thought for a second, 'I guess you lost your softness, your roundness, your wholeness, your womanliness.' Tara looked thoughtful, but she was still Listening, Lee observed to his relief. She really wanted to know. She wanted to learn about herself. It still amazed him to see again and again that Tara was for real. He thought for another second and then said, 'I think both of us were so focused, we were so in our heads, you trying to explain, me trying to get it, that we weren't really Now.'

Tara wanted to object. Of course she was Now, she had to be, otherwise the information wouldn't flow through her. But then again, she had felt a change too. Come to think of it, he was right. Within all that Nowness, she realised, she'd also been eager to make Lee see, to make him understand, to get as much information across as she could before she had to leave. He was right. She had been Now, but not fully. Not enough to maintain total connection. She had become a little edgy. God he was right, she *had* lost her softness. She'd gotten his edge and he'd gotten her softness. And it didn't fit neither one. They had reversed roles to balance each other. She told Lee what she'd just realised.

'That's incredible,' Lee said and looked into the distance like he always did when he was thinking. 'I guess, I lost my masculine essence and you lost our female essence, you know? Who we *truly* are, and we became something else. And it didn't feel comfortable, for ourselves or for each other. That's the best I can put it.'

'Wow,' Tara was gobsmacked. 'Did you just make that up?'

'I guess so,' Lee shrugged his shoulders.

'That's *really* interesting.'

'I lost mine, you lost yours. Are we connected too?'

'Yeah.' Tara was beginning to like Lee more and more... the stuff he came out with...

'It feels like the more Present we are, the more Now we are with each other, the more connected we feel.'

'It's because in the Now our Vibrations increase,' Tara ventured.

'What?

29   The Party

'There's something else that happens when we Shift,' Tara began to explain.

'What's that?' Lee asked.

'Our Vibrations change,' she said casually.

'Aha?'

'Basically, the closer we get to The Shift, the longer we stay on the perfect line, the higher our Vibrations rise. For a lack of a better word, I call them *Dimensional Vibrations*. But let me explain. Every Dimension has it's own Vibrations. The head-in-the-cloud human being vibrates pretty low. The more Conscious, switched on and Aware we become, the more Now we are, the more our Dimensional Vibrations increase as a result.'

'Ah, so you're saying that if both of us are Now, we vibrate on the same level and thus feel more connected? To the Universe and to each other?' Lee tried to clarify.

'Yes.'

'Now that explains what just happened to us. That *Vibrational* change is so significant that we can even feel a *physical* change, a change which others can notice it too. If they pay attention that is,' Lee added with a wink.

'Exactly.'

'Now that's pretty cool. Can you explain *everything* with The Shift?' Lee grinned at Tara.

'Quite a lot, yes.'

'Well, shall we see if we can stay Now together,' Lee challenged her with a mischievous smile.

'Deal.' They shook hands. 'Actually, that leads me nicely to The Party.'

'What Party?'

'Well, if our Vibrations have reached a certain level, we slip into a new Dimension that is just slightly, ever so slightly Shifted or off-set too the one we're currently in. When that happens, it's as if we've gate crashed a Party in a new Dimension, only to realise that we'd been invited all along. Everybody is smiling and everyone is having an awesome time. All we need to do to stay at the party, is to stay Now. If we're not Now permanently, at least we might get to go every weekend, or every Wednesday,' Tara smiled.

'Or whenever we manage to stay now,' Lee stated insightfully.

'Exactly.' Suddenly another one of her knowing smiles flashed across Tara's face, **'Anyway, everything we've talked about so far, is as far as we can get in a physical Body.'**

She playfully examined and blew over her fingernails, as she looked at him out of the corner of her eyes for his reaction. His mouth had dropped once again. Nice. She grinned.

And so did he.

The Party Above the Party

'What do you mean, this is as far as we can get in a physical Body?' Lee asked as his grin widened.

Tara looked at him, 'To get your answer you only need to focus on your breath, raise your Awareness and Listen.' That was all she said. She closed her eyes.

"Fancy that," Lee laughed to himself. He closed his eyes and Listened. Slowly his smile broadened more and more. Lee marvelled at the clarity of his Thoughts, the ease with which the words came to him. Words he had never thought about before, Thoughts he really shouldn't be having, slowly but steadily flooded his brain. He opened his mouth, and Listened to himself talk, 'Once we die, our Being is not bound to the limits of our physical Body anymore. Our Beings' Vibrations can finally increase to it's full potential, until we enter a Dimension, which is even higher than The Shift. A Dimension, in which we *fully transcend* into the higher Consciousness.'

This time it was Tara's turn be amazed. She had to consciously bring herself back to the Now, to support their mutual Vibrations. It was often easier to do this together. **It was as if you could help raise each others' Vibrations when you were together, but for that, *both* of you had to be Now for it to work.** She confidently returned to Nowness.

Lee continued without drawing breath, keeping his eyes firmly shut, 'Once we've Shifted, we can get glimpses of the new Dimensions beyond what we can normally perceive and imagine. That's The Party above The Party. That's The Party, that is beyond your wildest dreams, where you'll party like you've never partied before!' Lee opened his eyes. They shone brightly. Brightly but sanely. An uncertain smile showed up on his face, but he ignored it. Uncertainty didn't exist in the Now. He closed his eyes again and Listened once more, and talked, 'The Shift means that we have perfected our ability to live in a physical Body, in a human life. We are in *near* continuous Nowness.' While this came out of Lee's mouth his Rational Mind asked loudly - "Hang on, what you mean with *near* continuous Nowness, I thought we said that when we throw away the torch, that we are in constant Nowness?" - he brushed the Thought away. Slowly, the words - that were not his own - came back to him, 'As long as we have a Physical

Body, we will never be able to be in *Perfect* constant Nowness, where we don't have *any* Thoughts *at all* anymore - *ever*.' Lee's Rational Mind butted in again – "What, not even the holy hermits in their caves?" - The box with the answer stood out clearly in his Mind and he spoke out loud what he saw, 'Not ultimately, no. **Even if we could go and live in a cave in the Himalayas or sit in a Monastery until our days pass by, even if we could somehow cut out all Thoughts from our ordinary life and enter Nowness as much as humanly possible, that would only work until,'** Lee paused dramatically - had he heard that right? - yep. He added with a cheeky grin, '**until we have to pee!'** They both laughed. 'Or eat. Or sleep or wake up for that matter. **Even though these sensory impressions might bump right off the fringes of our Consciousness, in that moment our awareness is still called back into our Physical Body, even if only for a split second, and our Vibration drops enough to get kicked out of the Party above the Party,'** Lee stopped talking and slowly raised his right hand to his mouth. Behind his hand, his jaw dropped. 'Bloody hell, that came straight through. Shit, talking like this already feels like a different dimension!' Lee said through his fingers.

Tara laughed loudly at Lee's aghast expression, 'How did you like your first visit to The Party?'

Lee shook his head vigorously to snap his brain back into the earthly dimension, 'This stuff is Nuts.'

'Yep, nuts, with chocolate ice-cream, fudge sauce and rainbow umbrella on top. Super yum,' Tara licked her lips.

Lee felt his own Thoughts flood back into his Mind. Yeah, that was better. More familiar. "The other stuff is cool – really cool – as long as it stayed in small doses, at least for now Dudes, please. Effortlessly please thank you. Oh, and with fun!" Lee thought tentatively.

As Lee breathed he suddenly felt a tiny, soft, ever so gentle voice saying something in a far off corner of his Mind, 'No problem, small doses it is. Let us know if we get too much for you. Until then, enjoy!'   Lee looked up, shook his head and this time, roared with laughter.

The Red Pill - A Choice Now, On The Deathbed Or Instead Of Extinction

After this good laugh, Lee was back to normal, whatever that meant now. He was ready for more. He focussed on his breath again and it didn't take long for more to come through. This time he spoke the words-that-were-not-his-own more confidently, 'At the moment of death, we vibrate so fast, that the physical Body isn't needed anymore. **At that precise moment, where our Being leaves our Body, we will get a choice where to go to.** It's like taking the Red Pill all over. The Guys will make us the offer to move beyond anything imaginable *and* stay Conscious throughout (!), or to take the blue pill and drift off to Unconsciousness! Some people are aware enough to choose the option to leave their Body and transcend while they are still alive, but the rest of us will get that choice at the point of death. It's like the choice to move into the brightest light when we die. **To dare and boldly walk towards it and to not be distracted by all our Thoughts, Emotions, grudges and fears, but to stay Now, even when we die.** To stay Conscious!' Lee was cautiously shaking his head again.

Tara put her hand onto his knee, leant forward and said gently, 'If it freaks you out, stop, otherwise, enjoy! I've learned most of what I know about these things, by speaking words-that-were-not-my-own, stuff that came straight through.'

Lee took a deep breath, pushing the Thought - that he was currently getting right into the middle of some of the most extreme Hippy Shit he could have ever imagined, and that he was absolutely loving it – out of his head. He opened his eyes and his tone of voice became more relaxed again, 'We have no words or experiences or feelings that could give us any point of reference to even begin to describe or even understand what it will be like to take the Red Pill, to join the Party above the Party, the stage, where our physical Being will be no more and where our Cosmic Being begins it's new existence, where we truly merge with Oneness, although some of the finest meditations can come close,' he finished, visibly stunned. 'Boy, that's fascinating. I'm coming out with all this interesting stuff which I don't even know anything about.'

'Great ey? It's so useful! I couldn't have put it any better myself. Are you ok?' Tara clapped her hands.

Lee nodded, 'Yeah, I'm fine. Wow, this takes a bit of getting used to though. Dear Dudes, can you please do this a bit more light hearted next time, pretty please thank you, effortlessly and all that? That was a bit intense.'

'No problem,' a friendly male voice said. Lee looked around there was nobody there.

Lee looked at Tara who looked straight back at him and shrugged her shoulders, 'Don't look at me.'

'Bloody hell, you heard it too,' Lee was shocked.

'I told you this happens, didn't I? In Nowness we connect to the same place.'

'Well, yeah, but knowing and experiencing is just ever so slightly different,' Lee said, shaking his head more surprised now than overwhelmed.

He was getting used to it. It wasn't that tough really, all he had to do was *stop* thinking that it was weird, or that he couldn't do it, and be Now instead. Click, click, done. As if by magic. Grin. But man, if anybody would have told him a few days ago that he'd be channelling The Dudes,… he laughed.

'Shall we move on?' Tara bounced in on his Thoughts.

'Sure. **Actually I have a question first,' Lee said, 'is there another reason why we might want to Shift to any of these Cosmic levels during our life time, besides the obvious fact, that it would be really cool and exciting to find out what it's like?'**

'Good question, and yes there is. The Shift is the next stage on the evolutionary ladder. **We become higher Consciousnesses and besides that, it gives us a way out.'**

'What do you mean a way out?' Lee scratched his chin.

'**Well, if the world and Humankind in it, ever becomes confronted with extinction, when this physical world gets destroyed and with it all the physical bodies within it, or if we just die out due to natural causes, the only alternative to BE, is in different dimensions.'**

'I see, it's the life after death thingy,' Lee's Rational Brain raised an eyebrow.

'Yep. **The people that have Shifted during their life time have learned to Trust, and they will have the *courage* to take the Final Red Pill at the point of Death. They will have the courage to say, oh yeah, that's *familiar*, I've heard that before, I don't need to be scared, I just go back to the Now. I know it's not threatening, I know *that* Party will be fun,'** Tara said.

'Ha, imagine if the world, or even this Universe would end and instead of being scared, we'd all be looking forward to get VIP tickets to the Party above the Party? That'll be a surprise. Can you imagine if *everybody* would turn up at the door? That'll be some almightily weird Party. Skater Boy, Suit Dude, Hippy Girl and Buddha meet Starship Enterprise, Klingons and ArtuDitu. That'll certainly be worth sticking around for,' Lee laughed. 'I wonder what food they'd serve. Hamburgers with weird green slimy stuff?'

They both chuckled, noisily imitating suppertime for various alien species, for the onlookers in the park. It was so nice not to care about what other people thought.

'So basically,' Lee summarised, still holding his fingers in the usual Trecki fashion, 'preparing to Shift, prepares us for *life* in the higher dimension, including the highest dimension after Death. So, when the shit really hits the fan on this beautiful planet, we get a way out.'

'Exactly.'

'And even if the Shit doesn't hit the fan, the preparation is such fabulous entertainment value and anyway, it makes life *on* this beautiful planet so much more fun. Well, beats telly any day,' Lee said with a smug grin.

'I dare to agree with that.'

And After That?

'You know Tara, whenever I thought so far that this must be as high as we can go, you always said that there was more. **Wow I wonder what's above the Party-above-the-Party**,' Lee asked rhetorically rather than expectant of an answer.

'Well, there are always further Shifts.'

'Oh, of course,' Lee grinned.

You see, Shifting is like climbing a mountain. When you get to the top, all proud, thinking you got to the end of your endeavours, you realise that all you got, was a better view of the rest of the Himalayas.'

'Oh,' Lee swallowed.

'It's like the story of the man who saw Buddha. He got up and danced, thinking he was finally enlightened, that this was as far as he could get. He looked at the Buddha and was just about to sit down, when slowly, ever so slowly, he saw a hand materialise around his Buddha. And then an arm attached to that hand. And then a Body attached to that arm, until another Buddha, a much bigger Buddha had materialised, holding his, now very little Buddha in his hands.' Lee grinned knowingly, but Tara motioned that the story wasn't finished yet. 'The man was shocked at this set back. He sat down and tried to get his head around the enormity of this vision - what it meant for himself and for humankind, and about how he felt that he wasn't *'there'* yet after all, that he had to start all over, - when slowly, very slowly, a hand materialised around the bigger Buddha, and then a hand around that arm and then *another* Body... Seeing that, a twinkle came into the man's eyes. First he smiled and then he laughed, and laughed and laughed...'

'What a wonderful and very poignant story,' Lee cocked his head to one side, and his fringe fell into his eyes again.

'Yeah, it's another of my favourites,' Tara said. 'You know, during all these years, there's one thing I've truly learned: whenever I think, "Ok, that must be it, now I know it all", or "now I really have experienced it all", something new finds me. And all I can say is thank God for that, at least it never gets boring! It's a bit like getting to the Party above the Party, and meeting lots of other guests, who all have their own lives and their own realisations, their own discoveries, and actually, they're all off to another party afterwards, and they invite you to come. I mean, would you not want to go, simply because you're so disappointed that this party isn't the *only* one? Or not the *last* one? What a silly Thought!'

They both laughed.

'Oh Tara,' Lee had tears of laughter in his eyes.

Tara went on unperturbed, 'You know, there's always *more*! Not just with regards to the Shift, but with *everything* in life. There's always a 'Party above The Party', and *another one above* that. There is *always* more beyond what we're able to perceive. And all we need to play higher, is to know the rules. And Nowness is the cosmic rule book. In Nowness you suddenly get invited to all sorts of Parties!'

The Rainbow - or - The New Ying and Yang

'**Y**ou know,' Tara continued, 'after The Shift, the world is a fantastic grey ball of fun!

'Eh, *grey* doesn't sound very fantastic,' Lee chuckled.

'Actually, grey is happiness a la carte.'

'And how might that be my dear?'

'You know, everybody is into black and white, Ying and Yang. But that's so extreme, so intense. Once you're flying high, you have to come crashing down again. It's a continuous roller coaster.'

'Yeah, so we have a boring old grey instead?'

'Not boring grey*! Perfect* grey. True balance between black and white, true harmony and bliss. And to make sure it doesn't get boring,' she winked at him, 'there's a huge, great, big, fat rainbow around it. That's Effortless Fun.' Tara first drew a traditional Ying and Yang symbol, then an arrow pointing at another picture she was about to draw. She drew a circle which she shaded grey, with a few bigger circles around that one, shading them with different lines to simulate colour. Then to finish it off, she drew a big fat smiley face into the grey centre area.

Lee laughed out loud in disbelief, 'Tara, you're freaking mad. You've just turned the whole of ancient Chinese philosophy on it's head and you know the maddest thing? It works! That's such a cool way of looking at things. The fun way. *That's* why the Buddha is laughing!'

'Bingo. Oops, it's time to go. My mum is waiting,' Tara said jumped up.

Lee noticed that Tara had not checked her watch, in fact, she wasn't even wearing one. 'How do you know?' he asked her. Tara looked at him in surprise. 'Oh, right,' Lee grinned.

'Shall we meet here again in the morning? Around ten?' Tara asked as she was packing up her things.

Lee quickly computed, Sunday, ten am, yep, that'll be cool. 'Sounds fabulous,' Lee said getting up to say good-bye properly, but Tara was already running down the street.

'See you then,' she turned once more, her braids flying around her face, waving back at him.

'Yeah, see you tomorrow,' Lee garbled. One second she was there, the next she was gone. He rubbed his eyes. Nope, all real. The remains of his little picnic proved it.

He packed all remains from their little get together, folded the blanket, stuffed everything into his shoulder bag, picked up the rubbish bag which they had dutifully used all morning to dispose their trash of and wanted to walk home, when something made him stop and check his watch. It was five to three. Tara would be just in time. She was supposed to meet her mum at Angela's. Bemused he looked up and mumbled, 'Well, well, well, you Dudes seem to be useful for all sorts of stuff. You're even an in-build alarm clock.'

'We do what we can.' Lee heard a quiet voice say. He shook his head and went on his way.

Margaret

Tara had run straight to Angela's where her mum, Margaret, had already been waiting. She hugged her and sat down opposite her at the little table. Seeing the glow on her daughter's face her mum had asked, 'Have you been telling fairy stories again?'

'Mum, they're not fairies. They are called The Guys,' Tara answered her mother's question for the millions time. She looked at Angela who had just stuck her head out of the kitchen, for support.

Angela just shrugged her shoulders as if wanting to say, 'Don't worry sweetheart, some people get it, others don't.' Angela gave Margaret a fleeting glance, and then looked at Tara again, 'Even if she's your own mother,' her look seemed to say. When Angela went back to bustle in the kitchen, she gave Tara a mischievous nod and a nearly imperceptible nod. What was she up to, Tara wondered.

Margaret changed the subject and talked about flowerbeds, seedlings and vegetable gardens, when Angela appeared back at their table with the Specials-Menu. 'I have a very special Specials-Menu today,' she announced, proudly presenting her daily menu to both of her guests. She had glued a yellowish picture from a magazine on it, together with a handwritten description of a posh desert creation of chocolate sauce, waffles, fruit and many other things that Tara had only faintly heard of. Angela ceremoniously handed it to Margaret, who ritually placed it onto the table in front of her.

Margaret crossed her fingers as she always did, arranged them on the table in front of the menu and ceremoniously bent over Angela's piece of art. She was used to Angela's little oddities and was only too happy to play along. When she looked closer at the menu, she stared at it with total incomprehension. She looked at Angela, then at Tara, as if she was wondering if this was some kind of joke. 'Where did you get this?' Margaret asked Angela visibly taken aback. Tara had no idea what was going on and shrugged her shoulders.

Angela looked at Margaret trying to sound surprised, 'Well, The Guys told me yesterday to look at some of my old Magazines, so I did. This recipe literally jumped out at me. It's 18 years old. Isn't it great? There are so many strange ingredients in it, but my supplier was amazing and managed to get them all by yesterday afternoon. Somehow I double ordered though, so I guess I have to pass some of the ingredients on to someone before they go off,' her voice trailed off. 'Anyway, I made it this morning and it turned out so well, that I decided to put it on the menu. I impressed myself,' Angela chirped.

With stiff fingers, Margaret pulled a Magazine clipping out of her dark green suede-leather handbag. She had marked a section with a yellow Marker Pen. It was a recipe. The same one as the one on the board in front of her. The same picture. Only, the date on it was *today's* date. 18 years later! The magazine had re-used the same recipe, 18 years later! Margaret had seen it today for the first time. It had looked absolutely fantastic and she was planning to cook it for her dinner party next weekend. The ingredients were not that easy to get and she had wondered if it was worth the trouble to try. She would probably have to try out the recipe beforehand too, as she certainly didn't want a botched desert when the Bottichelli family came for dinner.

She had decided only yesterday that she didn't really have time to hunt for the ingredients and do a trial run. Shame, it would have been perfect. Well, she was just going to make Tiramisu again. That was yesterday. And now, the same day she turned up with this piece of paper, Angela just happened to pull an 18 year old version out of some dusty old box? And what was that about The Guys telling her? What a strange Co-incidence. And Angela had double ordered *and* had enough to giver her the exotic ingredients she needed for her guests? For a split second Margaret saw how the Universe connected to help her, how Co-incidences worked, how it was possible for Angela to know that today was the right day to try an 18 year old recipe. How Angela could give her some of the ingredients and tell her how she had made the dish. It was crystal clear, total common sense. Skirting past the horizon of her Consciousness she briefly, every so briefly noticed a faint voice.

It was a very pleasant, very polite little voice, 'Hi there, we're The Guys. You know, the ones your daughter is always talking about? Try Angela's special. The Bottichelli family will love it.'

An instant of clarity, of recognition flashed past Margaret's eyes. A split second of ancient remembrance. Her forehead wrinkled, her eyes questioned, then it was gone.

Tara caught Angela looking at Margaret expectantly. Tara tried not to gape at Angela when a realisation hit her, 'Oh you cheeky minx. I can't believe you just tried that,' she scolded Angela quietly in her head.

Tara and Angela and The Guys looked at Margaret. 'Gosh! *Nearly*!' They all thought at the same time. They had *nearly* got through. Margaret *nearly* got it, but she just wasn't able to hold on to it for long enough.

'Worth a try,' Tara heard a faint giggle of her favourite Universe representatives echoing of the walls of her warehouse.

She chuckled, 'God, you're so naughty!'

Angela and Tara felt the buzz of the Universal connection, whereas her mother calmly looked back at the Specials Menu as if nothing had happened. 'Wow, I'll try that! That just sounds fantastic. I was going to cook that myself next weekend, you know? What a fluke. I can't wait to try it. What about you,' she looked at Tara, 'will you have the same?' Tara nodded in disbelief, gosh, her mum was a tough nut to crack. 'Great twice please and a coffee for me,' Margaret ordered happily without further ado.

'Ice tea for me please Angela,' Tara said.

'Oh, and Angela, I'd love to buy some of those extra ingredients from you if you don't mind, I had trouble getting them and if you need to pass them on anyway?' Margaret said while packing away her recipe and simultaneously handing Angela her menu back.

'Sure, no problem,' Angela replied, grinned at Tara like a little school girl, and shuffled back into the kitchen.

'Now Tara, your little brother,' Margaret said seemingly oblivious to what had just happened, 'he's just impossible when I'm trying to weed. He runs around me, picking the weeds out of the basket and tries to stick them back into the ground. Talking about Universal Laws and all that. Not being greedy and not hurting anything. Now, what's that all about?' she looked at Tara questioningly.

Now it was Tara's turn to gape, where did he get that from? Tara hadn't told him. She looked at Angela who had just happened to appear back in the door frame. Angela's look clearly stated, 'Nothing to do with me, hun.' Then who had, Tara wondered. She dived into Nowness, asking what the hell was going on. She heard a faint giggle, 'Well, kids have it much easier to Listen you know? Kids Listen from birth, remember?' The Guys said cheekily. 'We didn't tell him about the weeds though, he made *that* up himself. You wait, soon you'll be learning from *him!*'

Tara looked up at Angela who was standing in the doorway laughing at her. Yep, they were tuned into the same channel. This was insane. Tara wanted to scream and laugh at the same time. The Guys were impossible!

'Touché,' Tara thought. She leant back in her chair and looked forward to the 18 year old Chocolate **Blanche Neuveaux** she had just ordered. As she was letting her mothers ceaseless chatter pour over her, she caught herself awaiting the day when her little brother could talk coherently, when he was old enough to tell her what was really going on in his little head. She looked up and winked at The Guys. And well, whatever had been going on in her mum's head before, she had a little smile on her face now too.

When Angela returned with her magic concoction, Margaret took the plates out of her hands and examined the presentation of the dessert, wondering how she could improve on it for the Bottichelli's important visit.

Reality Check!

The alarm clock rang. Eight o'clock. Lee's first sleepy Thought was, 'Oh no, I'm doing a Bobby, I'll be coming out of the shower in a minute, realising that it was all a dream.' Reality check!

He turned onto his side, pushed the blanket away, half frantically, half resigning to his fate and scrambled for his notebook. It was where it always was, on his bed-side table. He hurried to open it and let out a sigh of relief. It fell open on one of the last bullet points they had written. He saw Tara's unmistakable girly lines, and underneath his own sturdy writing: STRONG, POWERFUL, ALIVE, HAPPY. CLEAR. YEAH! Good! The last couple of days had not been a dream, they were real.

Great! And what was best, he had arranged a whole bunch of extra time to play with The Guys at his leisure, *and* to get some first hand experience. When he had left the park, he had called his office and left a message that he was going to take another couple of days off. He knew there wouldn't be a problem with that. There was nothing particularly urgent that had to be seen to. He would send an e-mail to one of his colleagues to hold the fort on the Dillons deal and that was about it. He loved the flexibility of his job. It was unusual in his kind of work environment, but the official arrangement was that all employees covered for each other. I scratch yours, you'll scratch mine and so far nobody had taken undue advantage of it. So, Monday and Tuesday were at his mercy. And now, now it was only Saturday.

Saturday? Hang on, why was it Saturday? The digital display was unmistakeable. But why wasn't it Sunday. He'd slept, it was eight o'clock. It was a blur. Lee rubbed his eyes strongly with his hands, that always helped him to come back from the sleeping world. Slowly the fog began to clear. Oh yes. He'd come home and gone straight to bed, he'd been so tired after all that talking. Lee looked at the alarm clock a bit closer and laughed. Ah, it was Saturday eight *pm,* not eight *am.* Right, that made sense, that also explained the fading sunlight outside too. "Sunset, not sunrise," he laughed. Fantastic, he didn't have to get up. He pulled the duvet back up to his nose, his pillow was soft and warm as he snuggled back into it. His last Thought before he was just about to doze of again was how strange it was that the alarm clock had rung.

"The alarm-clock didn't ring for nothing, you know?" Suddenly Lee was wide awake. "Yep he got it," he heard. He sat up straight in bed and turned around. Nope, nobody there. Of course there wasn't anybody there, he was in his apartment, he scolded himself. Suddenly a memory hit him as hard as a brick: A voice-which-is-not-your-own. It will stand out. You will know when it's a Message. He looked up and said out loud: 'Dudes, are you playing tricks on me?', but he didn't hear any more voices. Deep down he felt though as if something was giggling at him. Not viciously but cheekily and kind of happy and very, very pleased. At the same time his Rational Mind told him that he had finally lost it, whereas his Intuition told him: "No Resistance!". He amusedly observed the little angel and the little devil on his shoulder arguing for a while, when he finally decided to interrupt them, 'You know what? You can go on like that as long as you want to, but I'm getting up! It's not a life and death situation. It's just about getting up. Why, I don't know, but even that's not such a big deal.' The devil and the little angel evaporated with a puff. He pushed the blanked aside once more, threw his legs over the edge of the bed, stretched himself thoroughly and wondered what he should do now.

'Park.'

'Pardon?'

'Park.'

'Which freaking park?'

'Park.'

'You don't make it easy, do you?'

'Use your brain,' the little voice said boldly.

'Excuse me?' Silence. Lee laughed out loud. 'Use your brain? How cheeky is that? First I'm told not to use it, then to use it. How can I ever know what to do?' The voice didn't say anything else, so whatever, he didn't have anything to loose. He got up, had a shower, got dressed, all the while mumbling to himself, 'No Resistance, No Resistance, you're Nuts, No Resistance, you're crazy.' He briefly thought about food, but dismissed it as quickly. He wasn't hungry yet. All those nibbles in the park where still filling his stomach nicely.

Without further commotion, he found himself standing outside of his front door with his keys and his notebook in his pocket, wondering where to go. The only park he could think of going to, was the one he had sat in with Tara, the one with the lovely big tree. Well, that's the park, "Any objections?" he asked silently in his head, half serious, half amused. No objections came. As he didn't feel any sense of urgency, he allowed himself amble along merrily. Nearly at the park, he passed a small shop, and all he could suddenly think of was milk. Now that was odd. He didn't usually drink milk and it was also not precisely logical to buy a pint of milk on the way to the park at half past eight at night, was it? He analysed the Thought. Was it a Thought? Had he prepared it? No. Was it out of the blue? Unrelated to anything? Yes. What did it feel like? It didn't feel like a nagging puppy, but it felt like a strong feeling, that milk, right now, was essential. 'Oh sod it,' Lee swerved a hard right into the corner shop and, still shaking his head at himself, handed over his money to the shopkeeper in turn for a pint of milk, faintly noticing that he still had no idea why he was going to the park - with a pint of milk. He grinned. Life was certainly becoming more interesting.

He briefly thought about buying some food, so he didn't have to worry about it later in the park, but he dismissed the Thought, as *now* he suddenly *did* feel urgency. Spurred on, he literally ran to the park and towards the tree. When he saw what was under the tree, he didn't know if he should scream, laugh, cry or just run away. He threw his hands into the air, 'This is a film, right? Tell me I'm dreaming!'

Tara got up and hugged Lee happily, 'You're in a film and you're dreaming. Good evening to you too. Nice you're here, ah, and you brought the milk. I hope you haven't had any dinner yet.'

'What do you mean - Nice you're here - *and* you brought *the milk*,' Lee squealed.

'Well, I was wondering what the reason was myself, and now I know. After meeting my mum I went home and after an hour or so, I was told to come back here. I guess The Guys thought it was too nice an evening to waste.'

'You're kidding me, right?' Lee asked stupefied. Tara shook her head innocently. 'And you asked Them to tell me to bring milk?' Lee asked flabbergasted.

'Ah, no,' Tara said, 'I only just noticed that. But I told you They pre-empt you, didn't I?'

'I have to sit down,' Lee slumped next to Tara and started chewing on the carrot, Tara had handed him. After a few minutes, he looked at Tara, then at the carrot. He carefully put the carrot down on the blanket and examined the scene he found himself in. Tara had arranged a few food containers, some cutlery and some crockery on a nice little picnic blanket, which she had brought this time. He noticed that he wasn't even surprised, that there were two cups of hot, steaming tea, when he arrived. Not nearly cold tea, or *no* tea, but his very own cup and still hot.

Well, he was certainly getting in tune with *something*, he thought, he'd had two messages this evening. He had trusted them, followed them, and they had gotten him here, into the park, *with* milk.

Tara listened avidly, when Lee put her in the picture about the evenings happenings so far. When he was finished, she giggled, 'Man, so much excitement, I don't know how you cope.'

'Cheers. Anyway, that was me. Now, how did *you* know that I was coming?' Lee wanted to know. 'It's *you* that had the tea prepared and everything. I mean, it's still hot! Did you see me coming?' as soon as he asked the question, he knew that Tara couldn't have seen him, he had come up from behind.

Tara replied truthfully, 'No, I didn't see you, but you know, you got 'park' and 'milk' and I got 'park' and 'tea', simple really.'

'And you brought food and two cups, just in case somebody was going to join you?'

'Yep. Well, I assumed I might get company, but no, I didn't know. By the way, are you hungry?' Tara asked simply. She didn't seem to think any of this to be the least bit strange.

'I am now. I thought about it earlier, but it felt I had to come to the park instead, quickly, so I didn't stop for food. By the looks of it I'm just in time for piping hot tea and a picnic,' Lee grinned. In the back of his head he remembered the sudden feeling of urgency to come to the park, when he'd thought about food in the corner shop. He ticked off his check list. Another Intuition well followed.

They sat together drinking tea for a few minutes while Tara told Lee, to his great amusement, what had happened at Angela's with her mother. Lee was still laughing, when Tara opened a container with leftovers her mum had given to her earlier. At the sight of a packet of dried plums that was perked on top, Lee nearly fainted. Not only were they the brand he always bought, but also, it was the kind he loved most, the ones with the stones still inside of them. Lee looked up and screamed into the evening mist, 'I believe, alright? Yes, I get it! I'm convinced! I *Trust!* I do!' he shook with laughter. Silence came in response. Silence with a tiny little sparkly twinkle.

Tara grinned broadly at the nightly spectacle in front of her, 'Isn't it strange, that it really takes some time to get used to so much goodness?'

'That's so true. Weird really. If everything would have gone wrong today, I might have been pissed off, but it wouldn't have been such a big deal. But everything going *more* than perfect? Now that's overwhelming! It's a freaky world!'

'Welcome to the world of the Shift,' Tara leant forward and whispered into Lee's ear, 'Welcome to the *real* Party!'

'Well, thanks for the invitation,' Lee said. 'But,' he paused, 'how come that all of this worked out. Me being here I mean. I'm not even close to Nowness yet.'

'Well, some people are just lucky and get the messages really quickly. But also, you and I have a pretty special connection, which helps too. We raise each other's Vibrations.

Actually, The Guys just happened to have demonstrated nicely what I was going to talk about next. Are you up for more? Despite the late hour?' Tara asked.

She held a small bowl of salad and some kind of stew out to him.

Lee nodded and took the dish gratefully, as he pondered that 'special connection'.

They munched and gorged themselves, finished off the plums, drank tea - with milk - and within minutes they were back deep, deep into a highly cosmic conversation.

PART 11

30 Shifting Together, Playing Together, Party With Your Friends

'Do you remember when I said that The Shift is like climbing a mountain?' Tara asked.

'Sure.'

'Don't you think it would be pretty boring to sit up there all on your own?' Tara pulled a slightly lost face, looking around.

'Oh, that's such a sweet picture. You finally got there and then you're all alone and bored.'

'Not so sweet when you're up there and you haven't got anybody to play with and nobody to talk to, who doesn't think you're crazy.'

'I can see that.'

'That's why it's so nice when people *around us* Shift too, because then we can *share* the full magic of it. I mean it's great on your own, but it's so much more entertaining with more people, just imagine what it could be like if a whole bunch of us Shift and play?'

'That would be incredible,' Lee couldn't wait to experience that.

'Actually, that's what you got a taste of this morning and this evening! With both of us following messages related to each other.'

'Are you telling me that I've Shifted?' Lee looked at her sceptically.

'I wouldn't go quite that far, but you certainly managed to pick up a bunch of messages. You still had to follow them consciously, so, that action hasn't become automatic yet, but what you *did* do, was enough to fulfil Their plan.'

'I guess I just had my first taster of the They-tell-me-where-the-stick-is stage, or better the where-Tara-is stage,' Lee grinned.

'Yeah, I'd say so too. That's what happens when you're in tune with somebody else, when you are part of each other's Co-incidence. When more and more people are switched on, when it's snowballing and spreading fast, that's when it gets really fun. It's the apple thing again, remember? When people are throwing them to each other?' Tara pretended to dodge apples that were being thrown at her. Lee laughed. 'Oh, did you bring your notebook?' Tara asked.

'Of course,' Lee said and took care of the first list of the evening, as Tara was happily dictating.

To Shift together:
- We choose to *actively* and *deliberately* become part of each other's Co-incidences and to help each other out.
- We *know* what we can do for each other and we actually *do* it.

'We help others and others help us. This unconditional big family includes strangers as well as friends,' Tara concluded the list.

'We really are all in this together, aren't we?' Lee said enchanted.

'Absolutely. The Guys are so clever at interweaving our lives, that when we all Shift, we all have a sack of apples that constantly keeps refilling, as we're giving them away,' Tara gently threw Lee a real apple.   He caught it with a smile and took a hearty bite. She buys the same apples I do, he noticed.

'This Shifting Together business means, that somebody actually *can* come to your door with a silver tray, and give you what you need,' Tara smiled happily.

'Man, if all my friends would be game for this? Just the though of it balls me over. I can't believe that we're not all doing this already,' Lee said.

'Well, the numbers are rising fast.'

'I'm so glad. By the way, **so, I guess you do this all the time then?**'

'Of course,' Tara said without batting an eyelid. Not big headed, just confidently. She was stating facts. She grinned, 'Why do you think I'm telling you all this stuff? Or why do you think that I can answer all your questions? I wouldn't be able to answer half of your questions, if I wouldn't have asked them all myself, and gotten some decent answers, would I? I've done it, I'm doing it all the time, and so are lots of my friends and other people I've met. There are a lot of people in a whole bunch of different stages of the Shift, and the word is spreading fast. People are beginning to understand what they are doing, rather than stumbling around blindly in the vastness of the Universe. Newcomers are getting into it big time and the old hats are refining their connections.'

'Dudes, where have I been?' Lee asked the sky above himself.

'Where pretty much ninety percent of human kind is right now. In a huge great big grey cloud.'

'Ouch.'

'Sorry, but it's the truth, and I've been there too.'

'I know, I know, it's just so unbelievable that something so big could have been ignored for such a long time.'

'Well, lots of people have dabbled with it, but many got stuck somewhere or lost interest. And to be honest, society doesn't exactly endorse or promote this kind of thinking.'

'Yeah, sad but true, and as it seems, a lot of the dabbling took place on an individual level,' Lee could see the limitations of that clearly now.

'Exactly. But now? Now it is time to come together and *play and experiment more actively with each other.* Together we learn so much faster.'

'Yeah, I remember when we pointed out to each other earlier when we lost the connection. It was great to do that together. I can see how useful that can be.'

'It is invaluable. It really is. You can point out all sorts of stuff. Judgements, Emotions, expectations, roller-coaster Thoughts. You can help each other catch yourselves out, help each other to analyse Co-incidences and Intuitions, and on it goes. You can talk about what you want the other person to do for you and you can give each other permission to call each other on your shit. You can be Aware for each other and you can help each other grow! Of course only if you can be open, share your experiences and your insights. Just like you and I did earlier. You can learn from each other and have ridiculous amounts of fun with all of this!'

'Yeehaa,' Lee grinned.

How Do You Recognise Like Minded People - How Do I know, If I'm Supposed To Talk To Somebody?

'How do you recognise like minded people though? I assume I'm not going to meet all of them in the street as easily as I met you?' Lee cuffed Tara lovingly. He hoped that there would be lots more people out there to play with. **'Maybe, maybe not, but either way, it still is always a bit like you and I met.** You connect and you know,' Tara said.

'Oh, of course,' Lee remembered, 'when I met you, I saw your eyes, and just *knew* that I had to talk to you.'

'Same here. That's a good example of how two people connect and know that they need to get together. **It's like an Intuition.** It's a strong and urgent pull, a clear Message. **You can't really do anything but follow.** Even if you can't explain it.'

'Yeah, I knew that I had to talk to you and my Intuition just wouldn't let it go. Come to think of it, I was strangely certain that I'd be missing out if I wouldn't talk to you.'

'And then I caught you staring,' Tara laughed cheekily.

'Eh, yes. But I was just figuring out a way of how I could talk to you without having to say, - excuse me, but I have this strange Intuition that I need to talk to you. - That usually doesn't wash too well with the girls.' Lee laughed. 'Remember? This stuff is still all new to me.'

'Yeah I know, just teasing.'

'That's all right then,' Lee smiled at the memory.

'Getting back to your question though,' Tara picked up her train of Thought, 'some people come into your life through oddly random situations. You bump into them and just know that you have to talk to them. Others you look at, and you know that you have something in common and you start talking and things develop from there. **Like minded people are really easy to spot.** You've probably been in situations, where you've known that you've met a like Minded person, even though no words had been exchanged?' Tara looked at Lee for confirmation. He nodded. 'Great. So, let's say you're in a group of strangers and you say something which *you* think is really bizarre, but nobody else seems to think so. **Then you catch the eye of a person across the table, and your eyes meet for a split second, both of you grin, raise your eyebrows and nod.** There it is! Recognition! You might not know each other, but you just recognised each other as thinking the same way. **You know that you're on the same page.'**

'I know what you mean. I've had situations when I've recognised that twinkle. I've inexplicably felt drawn to talk to somebody, simply because we clicked just looking at each other. Usually we end up having a really good laugh or a very interesting conversation.'

'That's exactly what I mean. And when you have stuff in common, you might just randomly start to talk about stuff that interests you and then as a natural consequence, hey presto, you're talking about cosmic stuff. You can gently try it with your friends first. You might be surprised, the most unlikely people can be more approachable then you think, but then again,' Tara added consciously, 'you probably know best who to talk to.'

'Well, I have some in Mind, that's for sure. I shall report back,' Lee grinned.

'Can't wait,' Tara laughed. 'Actually, it's not only interesting to talk to different kinds of people, but it's also useful to play around with *how* you talk to people about this stuff.'

'What do you mean?' Lee wondered.

'Well, for some people you might have to adapt the wording a bit or *the way* you talk about it. If you can connect with somebody usually depends on if you have something in common and if you can communicate in the same language. The Shift fascinates a lot of people - especially when it makes sense, but your language can make a lot of difference.'

'Yep, I can see that. Actually, you just said that you might start talking about stuff that interests you to somebody and then as a natural consequence you'll start to talk about cosmic stuff? I'm not so sure about that. **I mean, I don't think everybody can dive into it just like we did.'**

'Yeah, I guess that's a fair question.' Tara thought for a while. 'Well, there are numerous ways. Maybe you were involved in somebody's Co-incidence or something and you had an amazing conversation afterwards, which helped both of you enormously. **Maybe both of you happen to realise that the meeting was pretty significant. At that point you could just ask: "Why did you actually come to talk to me?"** Now, there are two scenarios. One, the other person might say: "I guess I just knew I had to talk to you." Or: "It just felt right, even though it was a bit weird." Or: "I thought you were a fruit cake, but you seemed so genuine,"' she grinned. 'Anyway, if the other person says something like that, it's obvious that they have just followed something like and Intuition. Second, if on the other hand they say: "I don't know," then you can probe a little. Some people are just not used to analyze themselves like that. A few pointed questions usually open them up and allow them to see the connections.

So, in both cases, you could ask: "What kind of a feeling was it? Was it like a Thought or an Intuition, a feeling or a knowing or a mysterious feeling drawn to, did your Body maybe just move on it's own accord?" Then you could ask them *what* it felt like. Try and describe each other's Intuitions to each other, how you felt like, *when* you had it, how clear it was, was there a forewarning that you should talk to that person, or was there even a warning that you should talk to that person, but maybe only *later*? You know, you can ask all the stuff we've talked about before with regards to Co-incidences. There are all sorts of little nuances to our Intuitions and you can play with figuring and pointing them all out. The more you talk about it and compare your insights with others, the better.'

'Sounds like the Co-incidence analysis to me.'

'It is, just done with another person. I've had some crazy conversations doing just that. **But I guess the simple answer is just: trust your Intuition.** Whenever you feel that there's a person that you'd like to talk to or share with, check in with your Intuition and if it feels right, act. Trust and *don't* hold back and can *always* be bothered. Do it! Don't contemplate or generate resistance with the Rational Mind. Do not create any But-s and don't initiate any: but-what-will-the-person-think-of-me or: but-I-can't-say-that or: but-I'd-rather-do-something-else, or: what-if-they-say-no, or what-if-they-don't-understand, or what-if-they-think-I'm-weird. *Don't think, Just do it!*' Tara said with emphasis. 'I guess that's what distinguishes the Shifted people from the non-Shifted people. **The non-Shifted people succumb to the But-s in their heads, the Shifted** people go beyond them,' Tara said meaningfully. **'But all in all, if you keep your eyes and Intuition open, you'll meet plenty of people to play with.** Oh,' Tara grinned, 'and there are people you'll especially want to watch out for, they're the ones you can have some real fun with!' Tara said.

'Oh yeah? Which ones are they?' Lee was curious.

'They are the ones with that special little twinkle in their eyes. **A twinkle that people get when they are Aware, Present and Now. In their presence you feel their humble knowledge, a relaxed energy, a simple understanding, a good natured mischievousness, a playfulness, an openness, a sparkle, a light-heartedness and warmth, which is solid, grounded and present.** Those are the ones that already get it. They might not have Shifted yet, but they get it, they're on their way.'

'Yeah, I know what you mean,' Lee saw that twinkle in Tara's eyes and knew that he was feeling it more and more within his own eyes too.

'You know, those people are really not that hard to find. It's just that different places around the world have different densities of Conscious people. Some places attract them, some don't. If you don't find so many where you live, venture out. Go on holiday, go travelling. Find them,' Tara suggested.

'Yeah, I remember that. Backpackers in Asia were particularly switched on. Well, most of them.'

'Yeah, I experienced the same thing. But there're in cities in the West too, it's just that some are easier to find good people in than others. But go and find them! Go on the Internet to find good parties, talk to people in cool shops, get 'What'sOn' magazines, go to performances, exhibitions, courses and shows where you feel like minded people would got to. **Look into people's eyes, learn to recognise the look of somebody that is Aware.** Ask people that are switched on where they hang out. Wander, find all the little hidden nooks and crannies in a city, the hidden spots. *Actively* find out. *Research* if necessary. The Internet has *everything* on it. Look up Consciousness or Awake or Aware or Alternative Communities or whatever. **There might be lots of stuff that's not for you, but keep looking, you might get surprised. And most of all,'** Tara paused and looked deep into Lee's eyes, 'ask The Guys to guide you.'

'That's fine advice thank you. Don't wait for the 'cool people delivery' at your front door**, but go and find them. Ask and follow the Signs.'**

'Right. Just ask for it! **If you ask for it, you *will* meet Conscious people.** Make sure to stay open though, because those people

564

come in all sorts of shapes and sizes. You might also find them in a rather unlikely place or person. They could be much older or much younger than you, or not your preferred sex, they could be friends or strangers. So stay open to all possibilities, don't limit yourself with expectations. Practice, learn and play with many, many people.'

'Yeah, and then we'll all change the world together!' Lee threw his arms wide open with wild enthusiasm. 'I can do that. Think-Big has always been my motto. I always used to say that if you think Big and you get half of it, you'll still get quite a lot. If you think little, well, you might as well forget it.'

'You're right,' Tara smiled. 'Think Big, and with Biiiig Nowness we *can* change the world.'

Lee waved his pen in agreement and wrote:

Playing together:
* Now it's time to come together to *play* and *experiment* more actively
* *Ask* for like minded people.
* Trust and *don't* hold back.
* Can always be bothered.
* Analyse and contemplate together.
* Share experiences.
* Learn from each other.
* Have ridiculous amounts of fun!

Communication Made Easy

'**Y**ou know the good thing?' Tara asked. 'The Guys like it easy. **They make communication with other people *easy*.** All we ever need to do is learn how to Trust our Intuition and Listen, and of course *act* on it. Then everything else is simple and will happen naturally. So, don't worry, everything will be aww-lright,' Tara hummed the last word to the tunes of the old Beatles song. 'By the time you're on your way to Shift, this will all be peanuts anyway. Oh, and don't forget to ask The Guys for somebody to practice with,' Tara gently reminded him.

Without warning, Lee screamed from the Top of his lungs, 'Guuuuyyyys! I'd like to meet lots of people to practice with. I reeeeaaaallllly liiike it!'

Tara stuck her fingers deep into her ears, to stop her brain from bursting. Lee grinned, leaned over and softly pulled Tara's fingers out of her ears.

She smiled, 'Watch this spot, one day *you'll* come and tell *me* some new stuff.'

'I sure hope so,' Lee said, gently Letting Go of her hands.

Tara shook her head and waved her freed index finger at Lee, 'Hoping leaves you hoping.'

'Oops,' Lee grinned.

Now it was Tara's turn to scream. She raised her head and shouted, 'Everybody! Let's get on with it, shall we? Let's Shift and Paaarrrrrrdyyyyyy!!!'

'Yeeeahhh.'

They bounced about juchzing and laughing, bumping into each other and eventually falling over in a heap like two little children. They hugged and looked at each other.

'Nice to have bumped into you,' Lee said.

'Yeah, same here,' Tara grinned back at him.

It was nice to recognise that sparkle in somebody else's eyes. Especially when it was mutual.

Passing Their Messages On To Others

'**O**k, so far we've said that it's important and fun to share your experiences and insights with people, right? Well, it's also important to become an active *part* of each other's Co-incidences, and the easiest way of doing that is by giving each other messages.'

'Sounds great, but how do I know what to say? You said earlier that I might have to adapt the wording a bit or the way I talk about it.'

'Easy. The Guys not only *act* through us, but they also *talk through* us.'

'Is that the same as channelling?' Lee asked.

'That's a fancy word for it, but yes, it is. It's nothing special though, everybody can do it. Remember? You did it earlier.'

'So I did,' Lee's eyebrows went up in a look of surprise. 'Bizarre, I always thought this was just for the mad old woman dressed in blood red lace, with a huge wart on her nose and a black cat on her shoulder.'

'Gee, thanks, I take that as a compliment,' Tara grinned, stroking a pretend cat on her shoulder. She turned her face down and sideways, to shyly try and hide the wart. They both laughed. Tara looked up again and said with exaggerated relief on her face, 'Lucky, warts are not a pre-requisite anymore.'

Lee grinned, 'Yeah, otherwise, you'd have the nation running to plastic surgeons, asking them to sew the warts *on*, rather than to *cut* them off.'

'Just the Thought of it,' Tara laughed loudly. 'Where would you like it madam, on your left or on your right nostril?'

'The long curly hair on it, costs extra though.'

'Uuurg, that's horrible,' Tara turned her head in disgust.

'So, if all of that wart business isn't needed, then what is?'

'You tell me, you did it earlier!' Tara prodded Lee.

Lee cast his memory back to the moment when he was speaking the words-that-were-not-his-own. 'Eh, that was weird. Well, at first anyway. It was like I was Listening to stuff in my head and speaking it out loud at the same time. It felt different from my own Thoughts too. Actually, I wasn't even thinking, I was just talking. I didn't have to think or prepare the next sentence, it just came *through* - I guess that would be the right word to use - without any doing from my part. The words were simple and straight forward and there wasn't a word too much. It's like my mouth just talked of his own accord,' Lee said. He realised how good it was to put these things into words, to analyse his experiences and to explain them. Talking to someone about them, to someone who understood, helped in knowing that it was real and not just a figment of his imagination. Tara was right, it was good to do it together.

'That's how I feel it too,' Tara said. 'To be able to let The Guys speak *through* you though, you have to Trust Them and Their words enough to *dare* to speak out loud what you *hear*,' Tara pointed out.

'Absolutely, and I agree. I was weirded out at first, but what I was saying, well, what they were saying through me,' Lee corrected himself, 'was so fascinating that I just went with it. With practice I guess one begins to trust Their validity and usefulness more and more, and Their flow can go on unhindered.'

'Full points,' Tara held up ten fingers.

'Oh, I noticed something else,' Lee remembered. **'Whenever I was beginning to think, I lost the connection, I couldn't hear Them anymore.'**

'Because you can't Listen to The Guys and your own Thoughts at the same time,' Tara explained.

'That's exactly what I found. Whenever I got stuck, I realised that I was *thinking* or getting *freaked* out or feeling *amazed* or whatever. **I had to consciously clear my Mind again, stop my own Thoughts, and only then did the words come back.'**

'Yep, that's how it works. So, to answer your earlier question, **if your Intuition told you to talk to someone, the right words will come to you too. If you *let them*!'** Tara emphasised.

'Cool, so now, if we're supposed to give somebody *else* a message, *we* get a Message through just like before, just that this

time it's not for us, but for somebody else? And we just pass it on?' Lee recapped.

'Precisely. Sometimes its like wham, wham, here's what you need to know, goodbye, whereas sometimes the messages are a little more elaborate. Sometimes the meeting is over so quickly, that you don't even catch each other's names, whereas sometimes you become best friends, and sometimes, sometimes you find a soul mate over it,' she smiled at Lee tenderly and continued before he could reply. 'Oh, and sometimes The Guys get really clever and your conversation with somebody just happens so that somebody *else* can over hear you, so that they get the message!'

'Now *that is* clever!' Lee never stopped to be amazed by The Guy's craftiness.

'I know, it's so funny to notice what They come up with. Anyway, sometimes you pass on a message and that's it, whereas sometimes you get a message in return. Sometimes only one of you notices and gets something out of it, and sometimes both of you notice and are amazed. But, you know,' Tara pointed out, **'don't always expect an earth shattering revelation or some mad channelling every time you feel drawn to somebody. Some simple messages can be passed on through normal everyday conversations, you know, like that the shop down the road is closed, but the one up the street is still open, something like that.** Sometimes you get an Intuition to talk to somebody, but you don't get a message to pass on. **If that happens, just start talking about anything and the conversation will develop naturally, just as it did with us,'** Tara smiled. 'It's important not to have any expectations about what needs to happen. You could channel or you could just have a chat.'

'The way to go is - with the flow,' Lee cut his hand through the air in a wavy motion. The flow.

Tara grinned, 'Right on! Now, if you do get a message through, there are a few useful things to keep in Mind. **Before we pass on a message, we need to make sure that it actually *is* a Message from The Guys and not our own Thoughts.'**

'Oh, yes, that's important. Our Mind could be making up all sorts of stories. Our *own* Thoughts and opinions, our *own* judgements. And they could be wrong, or at least not what that person needs to hear at that moment in time,' Lee laid on his stomach and propped up his head with his hands.

'Precisely. Always remember, it's *not* our job to go around and lecture people, it's not our job to change people. It's vital that we don't give help, advice or whatever, because we *think* we know better than others, but only because we *know* that it's the right thing to do, because it *feels* right! Intuitively! That's important,' Tara emphasised.

'You really have to know your Intuition for that though.'

'Of course, that's the point.'

'Mmh, maybe that's why you didn't tell me earlier that I'd lost my connection,' Lee thought out loud. 'Maybe it just didn't feel right at that moment.'

'Yeah, I guess so,' Tara thought back. 'Actually, now that you say it, I *did* check in with my Intuition and it said no. Maybe you had to figure it out by yourself.'

'That would be a good explanation. It really would be actually,' Lee caught himself checking in on himself, making sure that he wasn't just agreeing to stuff willy-nilly. He wasn't. 'I think I learned a lot by analysing myself and coming to the conclusions I did,' he said finally.

'There you go. It always works. And thanks, because that's good confirmation for me again as well,' Tara smiled at him. 'There's also something else that's useful to know about, cause otherwise it could confuse you,' Tara remembered.

'What's that?'

'It's when you get told to pass on a message, but - not yet. If that happens, just wait till you get the green light. Easy. Don't try and make it happen, just wait and be aware of the Signs.'

'Check,' Lee ticked of an imaginary list in the air.

'Another thing that can be a little strange at the beginning,' Tara said, remembering some of her own little trial and errors, 'is when you get a message through and you hear yourself saying stuff that is actually different to what *you* think might be true, what you think might be needed or even appropriate, or that is different from your any other of your own opinions.'

'Right, but then again, half of the time you wonder where all the stuff that seems to be spluttering out of your mouth comes from anyway, so that wouldn't really surprise me,' Lee said.

'Excellent! Just thought it's worth to mention just the same. And you're right, with practice, you'll recognise pretty quickly that the messages are always spot on, *and exactly* what that person needed to hear. So no matter how crazy the stuff you're saying might be, nothing will surprise you anymore. Well, it'll surprise you forever, but it wont' stop you from passing on the messages,' Tara added with a knowing undertone.

'Well said. I think I'll have to play with that more to reach the absolutely no doubt stage,' Lee nodded slowly. 'It's easy with you, but with others? I'll practice,' Lee said with resolve.

'The more the better, that's for sure,' Tara sat up and stretched her back as she always did. She looked over the grass for a while and seemed to remember something. 'And when you do play, besides knowing how to keep the flow going, and making sure that you pass on Their messages, rather than your Thoughts, there's something else that's super important to keep in Mind when you're channelling The Guys.'

'I'm all ears,' Lee pulled his ears to the sides.

'It's to recognise when you're supposed to *keep talking*, and when you're supposed to *stop talking*, when you're supposed to shut up.'

'Ah, yes.'

'Sometimes, *while* we're passing on messages, The Guys suddenly stop talking to us and there's a pause. You can still feel Their presence within you, but no more words come through. It can feel a bit abrupt at times and if you're not used to this, this is often the moment when you feel embarrassed because all of a sudden you stop talking mid-sentence.'

'And embarrassment clogs up the Mind, which makes it more difficult for the rest of the message to come through,' Lee said, feeling it to be the common sense thing to say.

'Right, and worse, you might keep on talking with *your own* opinion, just to keep on talking.'

'And that's not good.'

'Well, I don't know, it might or might not be. All I *do* know is, that it's *not* The Guys talking anymore, but *you*. With practice you will see for yourself quite quickly that there's always is a good reason when The Guys stop talking like that. The other person might need some time to let things sink in or maybe they need some space to ask a question or prepare something to say. **So, if The Guys stop, wait quietly in Nowness until They start again. And if The Guys are actually done talking, you'd know that too,'** Tara said.

'Yeah, I felt that earlier. It felt as if my own Thoughts were flooding back into my Consciousness.'

'That's a good way of putting it.'

'Cheers. **So I can deduct that it's not only important to watch out for the *beginning* of Their messages, but also for the *end*.** Phew,' Lee thought out loud, 'you really have to know your Intuition pretty well to feel comfortable with all of this. But hey, practice makes perfect, right?   I have to do it to learn it and to improve. So, even if I might get it wrong a few times, if I might feel a bit stupid or catch myself out when I'm passing on my own opinions, who cares, it happens. Mmh,' Lee paused, 'I could even point out to the other person that I need to stop for a second to find my thread again, or that I need to correct something I just said. Great, it's really not that difficult.' Lee beamed.

'Ha! You're getting good at this,' Tara applauded. 'Basically, be honest and open and have fun with it, and after a while it's child's play.

Some people love giving messages, others don't. Play around with it and do whatever you feel comfortable with. If you don't like passing messages on, or if you just want a break, you can tell The Guys that too,' she suggested.

'I think I can do that. You know, all of this doesn't sound so bad anymore. I was ok with it earlier when I actually did it and back then I didn't even know what I was doing. **Come to think of it, it was even fun in some weird way, once I got used to it. In fact, it was absolutely fascinating, I was learning *from* myself, *while* I was talking**, that was pretty cool.'

Lee grinned at how he had just gone with the flow, how he had spoken the words in his head, just because it had *felt* right. His colleagues would die laughing if he'd tell them. God, how would people in the *real* world react to all of this was anyone's guess. Lee shook his head and smiled to himself at the though. He looked across the park, at the people walking by. How would he feel to walk up to anyone of them and tell them stuff from-The-Guys? Just the Thought of it made him cringe. But then again, he wouldn't talk to random people, only to the ones his Intuition would draw him too. Yeah, that was cool.

'How do *you* feel when you pass on Messages?' he asked Tara.

'I'm used to it now, but I used to get a bit freaked out too, especially at the beginning,' Tara said frankly. 'It can be strange to find yourself telling a total stranger things that makes the Mind boggle. **I've thought many times: "who am I to tell them stuff like this?"** You know, sometimes the Messages can get pretty extreme. **But, through experience, I learned to Trust.** Now, if The Guys want to talk through me, I'm confident that I can distinguish between The Guys' and my own Thoughts and I know when it's the right time to do, and I know that I'll always have the right words. And anyway, if you're spot on, if you're hitting the right buttons with the other person all the time, it shows, and that reinforces your knowledge that you're doing the right thing. Oh, I just thought of something, do you want a funny story about this?'

'Of course, we haven't had any stories in a while.'

'Well, this one will make up for that. It's a good one,' Tara twinkled and took her story teller pose. 'I remember one day when I was in a café for some breakfast. This dude walks in and all I have in my head, is to tell him about his posture.'

'His posture?'

'Yes, you know, how he held his Body, particularly his back. The dude was there with his wife and didn't not look very alternative to say the least and I wasn't sure how he'd react if I'd come up to him correcting his physique.'

'What did you do?'

'I ignored my Intuition, ate my food and talked to my friends.'

'Really? You ignored your Intuition?'

'Yep, it still happens from time to time, but wait,' Tara lifted her hand, 'I'm not done yet,' she grinned mysteriously. 'The Guys wouldn't leave me alone, and went on and on for me to talk to them, so that eventually, I thought: "whatever!" What did I have to loose? Finally, when the couple was about to leave, I got up and walked over to them. I apologised for approaching them like that, and asked him if he would mind if I would help his back ache in a minute or so.'

'You didn't,' Lee looked at Tara with a perplexed look on his face.

'Funnily enough, that's exactly how he looked at me,' Tara laughed. 'I could see straight away that just by asking that question, I had struck a note. He obviously had problems with his back. He looked at me and silently nodded. His wife somehow looked strangely encouraging. I mean, they were normal people, in a restaurant and this strange girl comes up to them and asks if she can sort his back out for him. Not asking him *if* he had backache, but telling him *that* he did. Well, I certainly had their attention. The couple gave me the go ahead and I told the guy how he shouldn't cross his arms like he always did, which caught his attention even more, and went on about how that put stress on his upper back, I even touched the area on his back to show him where it hurt - after asking permission obviously. I had both of them flabbergasted. Then suddenly his wife goes off on one, how her husband always has problems just where I touched his back, and how the doctors only ever give him pills but never sort out the problem. Well, I showed him a couple of posture corrections (by the way, I really know bugger all about posture and muscular things), and another few tips on relieving the strain in his back. Then I added: "well, please try it, if it helps that's great, if not, you'll have a great story to tell your friends about this mad woman talking to you in a restaurant",' Tara laughed. 'It's always good to tell them that they can take it or leave it.'

'What happened next?'

'Both of them looked at me, still a bit bewildered, but he said to me that he will definitely try what I had suggested. It was funny really, he nodded so vigorously, I knew that something had hit home. Hard. They both shook my hand, thanked me and left. Outside I could see him paying attention to his posture, pulling his shoulders down and backwards, and tilting his hips a little forward. His wife even playfully slapped him a little further down the road when he crossed has arms again. It was quite comical.'

'Well, I guess they really did Listen to you.'

'Not to me, but to The Guys. I had nothing to do with it.'

'Yeah, kind of, you were the channel though.'

'True,' Tara said humbly.

Lee sat back against the tree once more. 'I can see now that the messages can be...,' he tried to find the right word, '- interesting.'

'Yeah, interesting,' Tara laughed at the understatement of the year.

Lee glanced at his watch and jumped up, 'Oh is that the time? I'm sorry Tara, but I need to go. Can we still meet tomorrow?'

'Yeah, sure, but lets make it a wee bit later, what about ten o'clock? Here again?'

'Sure, ten it is. Shall we have a picnic breakfast?'

'That sounds great,' Tara smiled.

'Fabulous. See you later,' Lee leant down, gently squeezed Tara's shoulders and gave her a quick peck on the cheek. Before she could respond, he was up and off.

'Oh, and thanks for your mum's gourmet leftovers,' Lee shouted back, already running towards the street.

Tara looked after him smiling, her face a tiny shade of darker red than usual and her belly buzzing with little million little butterflies. She felt certain, that if she would have looked a little closer, she would detect a little male stick figure in amongst them. She closed her eyes and enjoyed the feeling.

When Lee woke up the next morning, his head was thumping. He'd met his friends for last orders in his local bar last night and he felt a little worse for wear. The day with Tara had been pretty hardcore mentally and he'd thought there was nothing better to clear his head and help him digest all that information, than a nice fresh beer. Unfortunately that hadn't worked. Instead of clear, his head felt as if he had banged it against the fridge for last twenty minutes flat, and his stomach felt as if he'd drunk a litre of washing-up liquid. He wasn't in top form to say the least. But, he was going to the park, there was no arguing with that. He dragged himself out of bed, made his special hangover breakfast, a glass of milk with a raw organic egg in it, had a long shower, shaved, brushed the murky taste out of his mouth and slowly began to feel better.

Last night. The memories came back. That didn't go as planned either, that was for sure. His mood was still tainted from what had happened. He didn't want to mull over it again just now though, he had to leave. Leave to meet Tara. Lee was determined not to let his disappointment over last nights events tarnish his mood this morning, and he made sure to catch himself out whenever the disappointment returned, and instead, to direct his Thoughts to look forward to meet Tara.

573

He went into the kitchen and rummaged through the cupboards and the fridge for something nice he could bring for breakfast. He found some of his favourite whole wheat crackers topped with delicious sesame seeds, a jar of olives, some goats cheese in garlic and chilli oil, a bottle of wine, maybe for later, half a pack of left over cranberry juice and a few nice big and juicy oranges. He grabbed a large bottle of water, a couple of plates, wineglasses and knifes, stuffed everything into his backpack and went on his way. The walk was nice, but uneventful. "No messages for you today, sir," he smiled to himself.

Shit It All works

By the time Lee was leaving the house, Tara had already sat in the park for a couple of hours. She'd gone to bed early and woken early. She loved the time of day when everything and everybody was still asleep. She had enjoyed a quiet walk to the park, and an hour of stretching exercises that made her feel satisfied and happy. She felt like purring as she looked into the morning sun. Contentment, soft, Now, what more could she possibly want?

'Tara, Tara,' she heard her name being shouted from far away. She stopped and turned to see a young man in a light checked coat run towards her, barefoot. She recognised Ed and waved back. Tara had met Ed a year or so ago on the bus to work, when her car had been in the garage for repairs. As things happen, they somehow got into a conversation about The Guys and The Shift. Ed was so fascinated by what Tara was talking about, that he had started to play straight away. Over the months his excitement and curiosity never changed. They still met regularly to talk about their weird, wonderful and far-out experiences.

When Ed finally stood in front of her, totally out of breath, he hugged the life out of her and said, 'Tara, man, bloody hell, it's all true.'

'Of course it is,' Tara said, her playful smile broadening.

'It really all works!' Ed said, still out of breath.

'Well of course, that's the point! You've done this for a year now and you're still surprised?' she laughed.

'Tara, I know we've talked about so many of our little adventures, but the longer I'm practicing, the more everything around me changes. It's crazy, my life is so different now, suddenly everything flows. My life is more exciting and fun than ever. My Being is full of happiness. I can still hardly believe it,' he hugged her again. Ed caught his breath, 'Phew, I guess I'm a bit overwhelmed and excited right now, it all came back to me at once, just seeing you here. I might be a bit incoherent now,' he said apologetically, 'but when I'm on my own, I'm actually more balanced and present than I could've ever imagined, and The Guys really helped with that. It's just so good. Tara, you've truly got something big here.'

'I know,' Tara said serenely.

'But how can you stay so calm about this?' Ed looked at her intently.

'Because I'd go nuts otherwise,' Tara shrugged her shoulders.

'You? How could you go nuts?'

'I'm only human. If I think about this too much, I would go nuts. So I just accept that it works, because I know it does, and I stay calm.'

'But you twinkle inside, I can see that. It's bursting to be free,' Ed said.

'That goes without saying,' Tara smiled at him. 'I know that I've discovered something madly fabulous, something so fantastic and mind-blowing that it will rock the world. But it will happen as it needs to happen. The Guys are doing a pretty good job already, I'd say,' Tara grinned broadly.

'But how can you stay calm? All I want to do is shout it from the rooftops and make the world Listen. This is something so fantastic, everybody in this world should know about it!' Ed persisted.

Tara smiled, 'Shouting stuff like this from the roof tops in today's world, would probably get you into a straight jacket within minutes.'

'But it works! How can anybody deny that? If they'd try it, they'd know. It really *can* change the world!'

'Sure it can, but people don't believe it. And unless they try it, they never will. Jesus, Buddha, and a bunch of other guys can tell you a story about this one too. They've been trying to talk to a brick wall for centuries, and the world's still not getting it. The world doesn't *want* to Listen.'

'That's why it needs more of us,' Ed said excitedly.

'True, but that will be a natural progression. Others will start to see people like us. People who are always happy and carefree, but also responsible and reliable, intelligent and most of all grounded! They will become curious and will ask us how we do it. The ones that come and ask are the ones that are ready to take responsibility for their lives and Happiness. They are the people that are ready to stop all the excuses, pull their finger out and to start to concentrate on taking their lives into their own hands. They don't want to be the victims of our society's reality anymore, they will want to create and shape their own!

They are the people that know that there has to be more to life, and those people will find us and they will start to ask questions. That's when we share. If they go and practice it in the end or not, is not of our concern. We planted a seed. That's all that we can do. Be open and enthusiastic. But don't preach, don't create a cult, don't create a religion. We can only show people how to go, play and teach themselves,' Tara smiled at Ed remembering his impatience. 'So, until you meet the right people, work on yourself Ed and *Be* yourself.

Whenever the opportunity arises, get guidance, give guidance, exchange your experiences and learn the words to describe them and to talk about them. Ask questions, and follow your Intuition without being shy. Learn with others, point out Co-incidences, Signs and Intuitions, do the analysis we've talked about. Help each other, support each other. Analyse, discuss, throw mad ideas around and reassure each other that this stuff really is real. When you're done with words, Merge Souls.' Tara made a mental note to talk to Lee later about Merging Souls. 'You can bypass a lot of slow Rational learning by *experiencing*. **Sharing, and of course planting the occasional seed, is the best way to spread the Shift, to grow and to speed up all of our development.** The more people get switched on, the higher the critical mass rises, until it finally becomes significant, and then, as if by magic, more and more people will suddenly switch on naturally, all by themselves,' she finished gently.

'Thanks for reminding me of that,' Ed said gratefully. 'Phew I can sometimes still get a bit carried away, you know? All this can be a bit overwhelming at times, you know.'

'Of course I do, I used to feel the same, but you know, ...'

'I know, overwhelmed Thoughts are still just Thoughts,' Ed finished Tara's sentence. She smiled at him. 'Oops,' Ed said a little surprised, 'I just noticed something! My Vibrations have just picked up, haven't they?' Tara nodded. 'Gosh, I still need to keep working on staying grounded,' he breathed out in one hard gust and shook his head to clear his Brain.

Suddenly they looked at each other, smiled and nodded. Lee's face had flashed past their Minds eye. Tara turned around, just the second Lee hugged her, lifted her bare feet of the ground and squeezed her. 'How did you know I was behind you?' he asked slightly out of breath.

Tara giggled, 'Not to be patronising or anything, but some of us have been talking to The Guys for a little while longer you know?'

They all burst out laughing.

Lee looked at Ed, thinking he recognised that coat from somewhere, when a pang of jealousy hit the centre of his chest, but as if he'd never done anything else, he caught himself out, realised how silly that feeling was, and breathed instead. With a big smile he held out his hand to Ed, 'Hi, my name is Lee.'

Ed bypassed his hand and gave Lee a strong hug. 'Hi, I'm Ed. Nice to meet you Lee. Nice to bump into you Tara, but I need to go, I'm late already. Eh, then again,' he mumbled, 'I'm sure I'll be perfectly on time.' He looked up with a smile, winking at The Guys, looked at Lee slightly uncertain, and added, 'eh, whatever, you now what I mean.'

Lee nodded at him with a wide grin, 'I think I do.'

Ed smiled back at him in recognition, hugged Tara, gave Lee a pad on the back and run off shouting, 'See you later,' over his shoulder.

Once Ed was out of sight, Lee asked politely, 'Eh, did I disturb anything?'

'Na, you're cool. Ed is a good friend of mine. He talks to The Guys too.'

'Cool, he seems like a really nice bloke,' Lee said, remembering the warm hug from the stranger. 'Wow,' he said without further ado, 'you've prepared quite a spread here.' Lee looked at the blanked Tara had laid out. There was a little basket next to her, baguettes, apples, tomatoes and cucumbers and some yummy looking cheese nicely arranged on a big plastic plate.   Perfect.

PART 12

31 The Real World, The Hurdle Of An Advanced Nation, How and Why

Lee sat down next to her, added his own culinary delights to hers and together they admired their fabulous breakfast collection. They were both starving and happily helped themselves to the goodies. As they munched away, Tara asked carefully, 'Wanna talk about it?'

'Talk about what?' Lee asked surprised.

'What happened.'

'What do you mean?'

'Well, you told me to tell you when you're not connected. Well,' she hesitated, 'you're not. You're preoccupied.'

'Gosh, you *are* Intuitive, aren't you?' Lee said surprised.

'It's my job,' she grinned.

'I thought I was doing a good job not letting it affect me. I already feel much better now than when I woke up this morning,' Lee said a little evasively.

'You don't have to talk about it if you don't want to,' Tara said considerately.

Lee hesitated and then said, 'Actually, I think it would be good to talk about it,' he took a few seconds to think about how to approach the subject. 'Well, basically, I know now what you meant by sitting on that mountain on your own.'

'Why is that?' Tara raised her eyebrows.

'Because people don't get it. They don't understand it. Either they don't *want* to understand it or they think that I'm nuts,' Lee said gruffly.

'Ah, I see, that's what happened last night,' Tara nodded in recognition, remembering the conversation she'd just had with Ed. 'Funny, how Co-incidences work,' Tara grinned, 'that's just what Ed and I talked about.'

'You did?' Lee hung his head, 'at least I'm not alone.'

'You never are, trust me.' Tara said reassuringly. 'Most people go through the same stages, doubt, rejection, euphoria...,'

'Thanks, that makes me feel better. Mmh, you know, just the little I have experienced with you so far, has given me enough proof for myself to Trust. But I find it's so difficult to tell other people about it. You see, I met my friends last night, and they just didn't want to know.' Remembering the previous night, Lee felt sad and angry at the same time.

'You know what?' Tara sweetly pushed up Lee's chin, looked deeply into his eyes, winked, then took the notebook from his lap, opened it and wrote with tidy, swirly letters:

Remember:
* Not everybody has to get it.
* Remember to Listen to your Intuition. You will know when to talk and when to be quiet.

Lee read the list, nodded and looked back up at Tara. It was good to know that Tara had similar experiences.

She smiled softly and said soothingly, 'You know, you can't be angry with them. A lot of people haven't had any contact with this kind of stuff at all. I mean imagine! Vibrations? Healing? Psychic stuff? Co-incidences? Switch off your Rational Mind? I mean, get off it, that's magic, humbug, stories, sailor's yarn. Some people gobble it up and get really switched on, but others?' she just shrugged her shoulders. 'This is all far to new and weird for most people, and many think it's fairytale stuff. Most people have absolutely no concept, no reference point for any of this in their lives. I mean we've spoken intricately for hours and you've had a lot of experiences already to get a glimpse of it's truth, but how long did you talk to your friends about this? Ten minutes? Twenty?'

Lee pondered for a few moments before replying, 'Fair enough. You know, everything about the way we've been raised, is about Reason, about our Rational, analytical and scientific Mind, and that side of us always finds a Yes-But. We always say 'No' first. We're sceptical of anything that doesn't comply with the norm and of people that do things differently. That's how a lot of us grow up. We *don't* Trust,' Lee finished on a dramatic note.

Tara nodded, 'I know. We've had generations and generations of Humans asking *why* and *how*. We've used intellect and the Mind instead of our Intuition for a long, long time now. That's what made us Human,' she added as an afterthought. **It's funny that it's exactly *that* brainpower, which created the hurdle of runaway Minds, worries, Doubts, disbelieve and suspicions, which our Advanced Nation faces now.** We've proactively been breeding those 'qualities' for eons.'

'*Why* and *how*,' Lee murmured. 'Why shall I do this, will it be worth it? Why shall I love? Will they love me back? Why shall I give? What will I get in return? Why shall I trust? How do I know this is true? We need a reason for everything. We need to know *why* we should do something, and *how* things work. **We want all the theory, all the reasons, all the**

proof *before* we start anything. Unless we can see it, touch it, rationally or mathematically explain it or at least scientifically prove it, we won't believe it and certainly not try it,' Lee was on a roll. He was venting all the Thoughts he'd had last night, 'People are so set in their ways. The idea of fully trusting and following an Intuition or an inexplicable feeling is just beyond them. They simply can't overcome their rigid Mindsets, they can't even imagine it, don't *want* to imagine it. Actually, it's worse, a lot of people can't even see that their Mind set is rigid in the first place.'

'Sounds like my mother,' Tara said ruefully. 'I know what you mean. The desperate need to feel safe with what we're used to, shuts people off from breathtaking new insights and experiences.'

'Yeah. **Our Rational Minds and our conditionings really do a wonderful job to stop us from even *trying* to fly, sometimes even from *dreaming* to fly.** The Rational Mind doesn't like to be open minded and flexible,' Lee drew a deep breath. 'I can see now how the constant reasoning of pro-s and con-s, should-s and could-s, clogs up our Minds, holds us back and cuts us off from our Intuition. And what's funny, a lot of the questions we're asking often don't lead to final answers either, but only to more questions, which then create even more Thoughts, more loops and more Dots and Squiggles, more distractions,' he said with sincerity. 'Man, it really takes quiet something to break out of all of that, out of all the conditionings we've been loaded up with and dare to just go for it. To play with unconventional stuff, to be curious enough to want to try things for yourself, rather than just dismiss them. And of course, to actually stick with new stuff long enough to get some results!

Actually, I have a nice example of a friend who managed to break all conventions,' Lee said. 'One of my friends packed up his well-paid job to open a dive shop on a Pacific Island somewhere. Everybody told him that it was a silly thing to do, and what about his future, and what if he gets ill, what if, and why and how and bla, bla, bla, but for him it just felt right. First he worried and then finally stopped Listening to all the But-s, and did what he'd wanted to do his entire life. He made the jump, and it worked out! Three years later, he had a good business, a local wife and a beautiful little daughter. He was happier than he'd ever been in the city he'd lived in before, living a normal life, working a conventional job.'

'That's a good story and there are many, many like it, but you know what? Sometimes things *don't* work out the way we expect.' The spark in Tara's eyes betrayed the warning tone in her voice.

Lee caught on quickly, 'Of course, but then at least we can die happy, knowing that we've tried, never regretting that we didn't. And I'm sure we learn lots of really useful stuff on the way. And anyway, I've just learned not to limit myself with expectations, but be open and notice whatever else comes along. And anyway, if something goes in a different direction than planned, maybe it wasn't supposed to work out, maybe something else was to come our way instead.'

'You're really digging this stuff, aren't you?' Tara laughed heartily. She really *had* found a like minded Soul.

Lee nodded, much happier now than he was just a few minutes ago. His headache was slowly easing off too. Tara's company was good for him. In more ways than one.

Shall We Spread The Word? We Teach By Example

'Still, it is frustrating that we can't *make* people believe.'

'Well, forcing our opinion onto others would bring us right back to the point where we don't want to be.'

'Oh, I know,' Lee threw his hands into the air, 'but you know what I mean.'

'Of course I do. I used to get frustrated about that myself. In the beginning, when I discovered how incredible the Shift was, I wanted to go out and preach to the world, I wanted to tell everyone, make everybody understand. I wanted to try and speed up the process, to try and actively help to raise people's Vibrations. I felt that this stuff was too good for people not to know about. I told people about my amazing experiences, the fascinating messages I followed, the incredible situations I'd found myself in, the luck I was having, the things The Guys told me, the helpful knowledge I received, information I couldn't know about in a million years. The necklace thing, the Cancel India story and many more. The list went on and on with bizarre, weird, wonderful and often incredibly useful occurrences. **I tried to *make* people Listen,'** Tara shrugged. **'I guess everybody who gets involved with The Shift wants to do that at some stage, it's only normal.** But you know what? **These stories don't help convince anybody.** They are just too unbelievable!'

'And that's where the chicken and the egg comes into it,' Lee interjected. 'If they don't have proof, they won't believe and thus they won't try - and if they won't try, they won't get the proof.'

'Yep. That's it unfortunately. Unless they experience the total far-out-ness for themselves, but of course in a grounded and balanced way, they will always think that you're nuts or that you are making it up to make yourself look important. They simply don't believe it's true. Actually, many *cannot* believe it. Their Mindset simply won't allow them.' Tara paused for a minute and then continued, 'So, I know how you feel, Lee, I've come across exactly the same frustrations.'

'Well, how did you deal with it?' Lee asked his gaze still disheartened.

Tara shrugged her shoulders and said, **'I guess I've just come to realise that it really doesn't matter to anybody else if *we* believe that something real. If somebody else doesn't *want* to know, *our* experience and Trust counts for nothing.** It doesn't count that *we* know that it's real and that lots of people are doing it and using it. What matters to people is only what *they* know or believe, or better what *they want* to know or believe. We can give examples and explanations, hints and tips, until we're blue in the face. We can drown people in theories and stories, but all we'll achieve, is put them off. You see, you can lead a horse to water, but you can't make it drink. In the end it's all down to individual choice. You know, we're not better than others, we don't have the only valid answer, we're just doing things differently. And that's *our* choice - and like that we have to respect *their* choice too.'

'So, you would never even attempt to try and actively change anybody's Mind? You would never preach or try to convert anyone or try to make somebody see your point of view, no matter how true or good you think it is?' Lee asked sceptically.

'No. There's no point. If they don't *want* to Listen, we can't make them. And you know what? **As I said before, it's not for us to judge that we do the right thing and they don't. Our way might not be the right path for everyone. Everybody has their own freedom of choice and we have to respect that.'**

'Oh, I know, but my experience last night was so frustrating. No matter how much I explained to my friends that they have to try Nowness for themselves to experience what I was talking about, to get their own proof, they were not even prepared to think about it.'

Tara patted Lee's shoulder, 'It will never be possible to convince anybody one hundred percent of *anything* unless they *want* to find out about it and that's all there's too it, no matter how much we like it to be different. Unless the incentive excites them enough to drop their doubt, they will never do the first step. And without that first step, they will always find a yes-but. I've tried with my mother for years. I've planted seeds, told her stories, but it just never sunk in. She can't even accept that it's *my* world. She still believes that I live in fairyland,' Tara suddenly giggled, remembering what happened in Angela's café the day before. 'You can drop the occasional hints, plant seeds and stuff, but you can't make them grow. **So don't make a nuisance of yourself. Nobody likes a preacher.**

But you know, it's not all doom and gloom, you'll be surprised, how many situations you'll find yourself in, where the subject comes up naturally, where people *want* to know. For me personally? **I'm not looking to preach or convert or desperately spread the message. I just live it,** I don't just talk about it. That's it. As a result, people that spend time with me or that observe me over a period of time, usually notice that I do things slightly differently - and simply because of that, they often come ask me questions about it. *That's* when I tell them little bits and bobs. When I talk about Intuitions and being able to distinguish them from your Mind or how to follow Co-incidences, people are usually pretty interested. If they are curious, I keep on talking. If they ask questions, I answer them. I respond rather than push. This way, people can take as much as they want, rather than what *I* think they should have. It's easy this way. It's on *their* terms rather than on mine. **Listen to The Guys and not your Ego!**

Sometimes just quickly pointing out how to watch out for Signs or how do a Co-incidence analysis in a few words, can be enough for them to be able to go and play with it for themselves if they like. Even just such a little thing can change people's lives, believe me!' Tara emphasised. 'A lot of the time you're just planting seeds and let the choice to grow them or not, up to each individual. More often than not people come back and ask for more, once they noticed that the little thing you told them worked wonders.

To be honest, it's like with everything else. If you're good at fly-fishing, people see you and might ask you about it. You tell them, and if they're really interested, you tell them more. It's exactly the same, just that I'm good with the Universe and crap with fish,' Tara laughed.

'Sure, but fly-fishing is hardly going to change the world, this stuff could. Don't you ever proactively do anything?' Lee probed.

'I don't go round randomly evangelising the world, no. But I do use my Intuition and follow it. I was at an Open-Mic(rophone) night once and The Guys told me to get up on stage and say something. So I did. I talked for three minutes about how you can tell your Mind from your Intuition by analysing Co-incidences.'

'Really? What was that like?'

'It was fun actually. I made a real show out of it, with jokes and everything. Out of fifty people one person came up to me afterwards and thanked me. He said he really enjoyed me talk. That was it.'

'That was it?'

'Yep. But it was worth it. I don't always need the recognition. I don't think: will it be worth it? I told fifty people about The Guys, in an unobtrusive way. I assume that some people laughed about it, some quietly took it away to think about it in the comfort of their own homes, some maybe just put it in a box for possible future use. Either way, the seed was planted and maybe, when a situation comes up where they need some help, maybe they'll remember. The long and short of it is that I talk about this stuff when it feels right, and sometimes that's really often, and sometimes I don't talk about it for ages. When I trust my Intuition, I usually find the other person or the situation relaxed and approachable. I go with the flow and never try to force things.'

'If you're forcing, you're doing, you're trying and thus you're thinking how to do it best. It's you, not Them,' Lee said scratching his chin. 'Now that I'm thinking about it, I think I *knew* that I was banging my head against a brick wall last night, but I ignored it. I ignored my Intuition! Oh man, that's it! I knew and I tried anyway! Shit, I knew!'

Lollipops and The Cosmic Drill

'Ha, did you just notice that?' Tara suddenly leant forward.

'What?'

'Your Being just brightened up. Just the second you said that.'

'Woha, I think I know what you mean. I just felt like a tiny Shift inside of me. My Body suddenly feels lighter. It feels as if I just jumped out of a grey cloud,' Lee sat up.

'That's exactly what I felt too,' Tara said excitedly.

'Bizarre that you can feel what I feel,' Lee said still not used to experiencing the new dimension. 'So, I remember that Vibrations drop when I leave the Now. I guess by *accepting* what happened last night, by realising that it was nobody's fault and that it was actually alright, I stopped the dots-and-squiggles, and went back to being Present instead. **My Vibrations rose again, I could feel the Shift inside of me and so could you. Man, these changes within me are so subtle. If you wouldn't keep pointing them out, I probably wouldn't even notice. Well, I might have noticed at some stage that I felt better, but not really why. By analysing it like this, I can find out *why* such a Shift happens. This is so fascinating,' Lee's eyes were bright and clear, reflecting his new state of Mind.** 'If I look back at past events, my drops in Vibrations have all been because I slipped out of Nowness, because I lost my Mindfulness on whatever I was doing. That proves to me that when I *am* Mindful, when I *am* Now, I'm happier, more relaxed and balanced. Now,' Lee lifted his index finger in a scholarly fashion, 'by figuring out what makes me slip *out* of it, I can watch out for those things and either avoid them, or on the other hand, develop a blue-print of how to deal with them and *get myself back* into Nowness. Wow. This stuff is cool.'

Tara grinned happily, and started to poke around in her shoulder bag. 'Lollipop?' she asked waggling a lollipop in front of Lee's nose.

A look of amused disbelief showed on Lee's face as Tara handed him a little round sweet on a stick. 'Lollipops? I haven't had one of those since I was a kid!'

'Really? They're an essential accessory for me. They're magic you know? They sweeten up my life, they put a smile on people's faces, they're fabulous to entertain and soothe kids, and they're a fabulous tool to make you Mindful.'

'Oh yeah? How so?'

'Well, have you ever tried to get the wrapper of the freaking things?' Tara produced another one for herself and began to fiddle intently with the wrapper. 'It takes *all* of your concentration!'

Lee burst out laughing, all his miseries about last night forgotten. 'You know, your happiness *really does* all depend on *how* you look at things. It really *does* depend on what you tell yourself in your head! If you tell yourself it's fine, it's fine, if you tell yourself it's not, it won't be. **If you're in a cloud and you know it, you can *actively* pull yourself out. Just looking at you struggling with that lollipop, makes me see and forget all those stupid thoughts I had before,'** Lee looked at Tara **lovingly. 'When you concentrate on just one thing - even just opening a lolli, then you simply can't think of anything else. *Consciously noticing* this suddenly makes it so much easier for me to understand. I really get now what you meant by *always* being Mindful - even when opening a lolli!'** Lee rubbed is face, **kept his eyes closed for a second and then said, 'Funny, now that I'm out of that cloud, and I can look at the situation in the pub last night, without being all emotionally wrapped up in it, I can just laugh about it.** It's so silly, how I tried to explain this stuff to my friends, and how disappointed I got when they weren't interested. Daft really! Sure it's a bummer that that they didn't get it, but either way, *I* learned something. I learned more about my Intuition,' he nodded to himself. 'And anyway, my friend Simon is into clay pigeon shooting, and *he* doesn't get all in a huff just because *I'm* not interested! He just mentions it from time to time, in case somebody changes their Mind and wants to try it after all, but otherwise, he doesn't preach clay-pigeon-hood, it's just what works for him.'

'Clay pigeon-hood?' Tara could hardly contain herself.

'Well, you know...,' Lee grinned. 'You know, when I think about it, **this morning I felt like this lollipop,'** Lee wriggled his banana-chocolate flavoured candy on a stick. **'I was all emotionally wrapped up, and the only way to open me up was with Mindfulness and concentration.'**

'Yeah, or with rude force,' Tara dug her teeth into the plastic wrapper and ripped it with her teeth.

'Well, I guess nobody's perfect,' Lee laughed out loud, his eyes warm with affection. He watched Tara lean back against the tree, contently sucking her strawberry and cream lollipop. **'It's amazing how talking about feelings and Emotions in relation to my connectedness and my level of Nowness, can really help my work through stuff and see the cloud so much faster. I somehow just seem to pop right out of it as soon I *see* the cloud, once I simply recognise that I *am in* a cloud.** Hach, that's better.' Lee opened his lollipop wrapper with one simple, gentle pull of his thumb and forefinger, and with a smug smile leant back against the tree to join Tara, who looked at him dumbfounded.

'Well, you did say that I was a master student,' Lee giggled, shrugged his shoulders, stuck the lollipop into his mouth and began to suck loudly.

'How the hell did you do that?'

'Practice darling, practice. I used to eat ten of these a day, you know?' Lee looked all pleased with himself.

'There you go,' Tara laughed, **'with *practice* you can open up any emotional lollipop wrapper in no time and get stuck back into the sweetness of life.'**

'Lollipops and the Cosmic drill. What can I say. Cheers to that,' he smiled at her. She really was amazing.

Inspire Through Action

'**O**ey-enogsh-avout-ouiops,' Tara said.

'Ey?' Lee grinned.

Tara took the lolli out of her mouth, 'Ok, enough about lollipops,' she smiled and put it back in.

'Ah, so now what?' Lee asked.

Tara tried to say something else but thought better of it. She took the lolli out again and said, 'You might be surprised you know?'

'About what?'

'You might have planted some seeds last night. I mean, there was a reason why you talked about the Shift last night.'

'Interesting, that hadn't occurred to me, I just thought that it was a terrible disaster.'

'The Guys sometimes work in mysterious ways you know, and the reasons are not always obvious straight away. You might be surprised if not one day one of your mates might get back to you and ask for some more details.'

'Funny, I was so upset last night, I actually forgot that Shane did seem to want to ask more questions, but I think he felt kind of embarrassed because everybody else was making fun of me. So maybe I'll stay open, and maybe one of them will ask questions.'

'And if not?'

'Yeah, yeah, then that's cool too. One down to experience,' Lee smiled genuinely. 'But, maybe Shane will put it into his warehouse for further use as you said before.'

'Nicely put,' Tara said enthusiastically.

'I guess you're right. Sometimes people might not want to be seen to be into Hippy Shit. It might not be very professional or laddish or cool for that matter. But sometimes there might be a more open personality hidden behind the pretence,' Lee said, thinking that this described the people from last night pretty well.

They were not his closest friends, more his drinking buddies, and talk was usually about football, rugby and politics. Rubbing shoulders rather than Minds. Perfect for after work senselessness and chill out and he loved them for it, but they never talked about anything too personal, let alone far out. But surely, each one had a hidden side outside of the pub personality, just like himself. Lee decided to wait and see, maybe one of them would come and surprise him.

'Ha, all the big Executives, Lawyers, PHDs, CEOs and all the other acronyms out there, are probably all just closet Hippies with big sunflowers on their underwear and socks,' Tara laughed, pulled down her skirt and tried to hide some imaginary sunflower socks.

'You might be more right than you think, you know? Don't you think we're in a new era?' Lee looked up into the trees branches. 'Preachers don't work anymore. People don't want to Listen to do-good-ers or people trying to convert them. They'll only listen when they *want* to listen, be it out of curiosity, boredom, interest or whatever else. Some people only Listen when they hit rock bottom, when they get desperate, when all the traditional methods don't help anymore, that's when people know something *has* to change. *That's* when they are *prepared* to cast the Rational Mind away and try something new. They've seen it work for others, so sod it, why not try it? They've got nothing more to loose.'

'Exactly. For us that means that instead of preaching,' Tara picked up Lee's threat, 'just being around and doing what we do in the new and different way we do it, means that we become a part of some people's natural progression. We're there for others when they need to talk about these things, but we don't preach or impose or go on people's nerves. And for the sceptics? **If people only believe what they see? Well, let's show them.** If we're *all* doing it? Like *really* doing it? If we're all *living* it? People are going to see it, right? And that's going to draw attention sooner or later, right?' Lee grinned happily as Tara went on, '**It's not a time for preachers, but for** *guides*. **It's a time for people who actually get of their bottoms and really** *do* **what they talk about. People that** *live* **the strength, the balance, the power and the playfulness of the Shift. People that inspire with** *actions* **and the solidness of their Beings, rather than through words and empty promises.**'

'Three cheers,' Lee clapped. 'You know,' he sucked on his lollipop, cherishing the flavour in an intense moment of Mindfulness, 'if you *really* concentrate on the weird chemical taste of these things, event that would be a good way to be Now. Mindfulness on tasting.'

'Ha, I said they were magic,' Tara said, focussing on the strawberry zest, wondering how on earthy they could reproduce a fruit artificially.

Lee nodded, bent forward and caught up with his notebook duties.

Teach by example:
* People observe, then they ask questions.
* You can drop a couple of little tit bits out into the world just in case - you can plant seeds.
* We teach by example.
* Inspire through actions and the solidness of your Being, rather than through words and promises.

32 A Brief Earth History, How Did We All Forget?

When Lee was done with the list, he leant back again and looked across the park, 'Funny, Listening to you, I suddenly see all those people in front of me who tried to change the world for the better. People that talked about helping each other, supporting each other, not hurting each other. I mean, hel-lo? How many people have tried to tell us this simple, simple message? How many books have been written? But we're still not getting it. Man, it's such common sense. I read a little booklet once called "Vision". Somewhere in it, it said that:

"It feels like such a joke.
We have been given the gift of life
and the opportunity to do whatever we want with it.
The opportunities and joys are endless.
But we are just scraping at the bottom of the barrel,
just ticking along,
while there's so much greatness and wonder out there."'

'Wise words,' Tara said appreciatively. 'I guess the people that wrote them, might have known about The Shift too, ey? In fact, it sounds very much like something The Guys said to me once. They asked me: Man, your existence could be so beautiful, so perfect, so easy, so full of happiness, joy and love. How come, that you Humans don't want that? We just don't understand! - When I said I didn't know, They told me what has been happening with Humankind since existence began on earth. How we continuously chose to move away from Them.'

'The world history? Straight from The Guys?' Lee was fascinated.

'Yep. They sat me down and told me the story. Do you want to hear it?'

'Of course.'

Tara cleared her throat for effect, sat up straighter and began, **'A long, long time ago, the Beings on earth were all intimately connected to the Universe and Mother Earth.** Their way of Being together was purely by *merging souls* with each other and with their environment. There were no words, only knowing. **There were no secrets as all shared the same Mind.** They *chose* to only see the good in everything. **They lived in harmony with Nature, they respected the world and everything within it.** They were individuals but they all worked harmoniously for the common good. They lived unconditionally with each other and their surroundings. These were the First People – before greed, status, wanting and with that, *Thoughts* took over their hearts.'

'How did that happen?' Lee was moved by the feeling that seemed to come with the story.

'After many years, some of the First People began to interpret the natural forces for their own personal benefit. These individuals interpreted Nature and so called messages-from-the-Gods to suit their needs and to gain control of others. They began to manipulate the core of other Human Beings. If there was a drought, people were told that they did wrong, and that the drought had come to punish them. If it was black moon, people were told that they had to perform a ritual or give offerings to ensure that the moon would come back. The Sun shining, the Water flowing, the Earth warming and feeding, all of Natures natural cycles became conditional and dependent on humanities' subservience to its leaders. Over time Humankind forgot that the Sun and the Moon, the Heavens and the Earth had always been there for them, no matter what the humans did or didn't do. They forgot that they were always looked after and loved - unconditionally.

As conditions were imposed onto Nature's Unconditional Love, the way humans loved *each other*, changed too. Love, giving and living in general became conditional. **Humanity's Heart, which was once pure and clean, was taken over by competition, hate, anger, pain, jealousy and desire.** A society, which used to be based on un-conditionality, love and sharing, had been ripped apart to create desire for Material status.

Conditions and expectations started to trickle into all cultures and began to take over the hardening hearts of Humans. People stopped helping each other freely, and began to swap and sell their skills instead. People accumulated possessions, and wanted more. Greed was born. Hierarchies and class systems emerged as an inevitable result, putting values on Souls, raising some above others. **When people started to use their Minds for their own advantage rather than for the common good, the Base Human Vibration split into many different individual Vibrations.** Slowly people became more and more distant, and after a while, a merging of the Souls was no longer possible and with time people could no longer see into each other's souls. People lost their ability to deeply share their feelings and their love for each other. **As the shared heart crumbled, distance, secrets, and misunderstandings grew.** Over time Humankind forgot the beauty of the Souls and the closeness they used to share with each other, other Beings and their environment. **They forgot how to live with each other in a peaceful, harmonious world, One with the Universe.'**

'I want to cry,' was all Lee managed to say.

'I already have,' Tara said sadly.

The World Is Changing

They sat in silence for a little while, feeling the beauty and the sadness of the story Tara had told, when Tara slowly shook her head, 'The Guys could never understand why Humanity preferred a disconnected unhappy existence instead an abundant and joyful one. They kept trying to tell us, to remind us, for centuries, but we've forgotten the ancient teachings, we've forgotten how to listen and how to Trust. We've hit a trough. The world's a mess.'

'I agree that the world as a whole is in tatters,' Lee said sombrely, **'but then again, overall, Spirituality is on the increase,** isn't it? I mean Yoga, Meditation, Ayurveda, Reiki, Tai Chi, Shamanism, Acupuncture, Alternative Medicines and Practices, all that stuff is in the up and coming, or not? It's all becoming more and more mainstream, more trendy.'

'Well, yes, but that also depends on where you live. Also, it's worth to keep in Mind, that the true messages of those disciplines have often been filtered out. I mean, who in the West does yoga for self-realization? It's used as aerobics, as exercise,' Tara pointed out.

'Yeah, that's true, but I can still see things changing even for people that are more scientifically poled. I mean, **look at Modern Quantum Physics being at a loss of how to explain some of the new phenomena that are being discovered, and finding the answers in the ancient scriptures.** Multiple Universes, Matter, Anti-matter? Yeah, oops, sorry, you were right all along, we are all connected, yep, we are all One. Yeah, ok, you win, there really are Alternate Universes out there,' Lee grinned. He had read *a lot* about this stuff and it had fascinated him endlessly. 'It's funny really, the sheer speechlessness of all those great scientists, when their experiments were coming up with answers that they simply couldn't logically explain, when results were one hundred percent contrary to anything their logical Mind could comprehend. Quantum Physics has begun to confirm what the Ancient Ones were talking about since the beginning of time. And strangely... how did they know back then? Without microscopes and modern measurement equipment? They put themselves into an altered state of consciousness and just asked questions! And if Scientists believe it or not, they got the answers! That's how the ancient Yogis did it, Zen, Aborigine, Shamans, all of them. **They found out Biology, Chemistry, Psychology and, and, and, sometimes just through Meditation. The accuracy and the detail still baffles our Scientists. But somehow they're still reluctant to recognise that one doesn't need machines and equipment to do all of that! It's weird really, Humankind seems to have a strange, strange reluctance to go into their own Brains to explore it's potential. Mmh, I wonder what's up with that?'** Lee scratched his chin thoughtfully.

'You're right,' Tara had done her own fair share of reading on the subject, 'it seems that the ancient teachings and techniques are beginning to be taken more seriously in the West and they're slowly coming back to life. Quantum Physics is certainly making people take notice, well at least the ones that are interested in that kind of stuff. And it's true that more and more people revert to alternative medicine where traditional medicine has failed. Reiki has become a household name and proved that hands-on healing is not just for Jesus, but for anybody and everybody to learn. A lot of people trust it today, they practice it, teach it, you can even get insured for it!' Tara giggled, 'That would have been unheard of a few years ago, it wasn't even an accepted healing art, and now you can get insurance for it! Mmh, maybe it's just so that you can pay tax on it?' Tara's said ironically. 'Anyway, yes, the word is spreading. More and more people are doing courses to find the meaning of their existence, ways to be happy, and how to create the life they want. Personal coaching for executives, managers and staff is on the up. A happy employee is a productive employee. In some more progressive cities, it's not so hidden in the underground anymore or seen as the workings of sects, communes, gurus, charlatans and gypsies. It's not just something for the Hippy community anymore, in some areas it's even becoming an accepted management tool.'

'Because it works,' Lee threw in.

'Right.'

'Another thing I've noticed is that **Western students from ancient Eastern masters are beginning to reveal secrets that have been deliberately kept hidden by Asian traditions for a long, long time.** With that new knowledge, old scriptures are being newly translated, misunderstandings and distortions, which had been made for personal or political reasons, are being corrected, and complicated contents are made more accessible for the layman,' Lee said.

'**But unfortunately, with the advent of all this new *old* spiritual knowledge, it has become another consumer product. We've materialised Spirituality,**' Tara said. 'We buy the knowledge, but forget the wisdom, we buy the title rather than the ability. We put outer beauty before inner beauty. Spirituality has become something to *become cool through*, something to own, something to become the best at, have certificates for, do as much as we can in as little time as possible. Quantity counts over quality. We're not actually concerned with *getting* it, with understanding what we do deeply and sincerely, and with that, we actually miss the point.'

'I know what you mean. I met a so-called Healing Master once, who had never actually practiced, but for two sessions on his mum and one on his sister,' Lee shook his head at the memory. 'I also met a dude whom I had an interesting conversation about Tai Chi with. He knew all the masters, the schools, the names of the forms, all of it. It was fascinating. The way he talked, he must have had years and years of experience and practice, but when I asked him how long he'd been practicing for, he said that he wasn't. It was all theory. He was fascinated by it, he knew all the benefits, but he never actually did it, he never actually experienced all the incredible changes the Mind, Body and Soul undergoes through Tai Chi, it was all hearsay,' Lee added slightly cynically.

'True, and to a certain extent it's fair enough, I mean we can't do *everything*. But the point is that some people don't really *do* anything. Sure, some people are just interested in the theory, but others use it to show off or make themselves important. Education is imperative right? If you use your knowledge seems to be secondary.

Some people go to courses or Gurus and teachers and love it. They're fired up, until they realise that the results take some work, practice or simply time, then they mysteriously forget to do it or they simply can't be bothered. So they do the next course, hoping for another instantaneous result. When that doesn't happen, they move on to the next guru, or teacher. They become Guru Hoppers and Course junkies, **but they never actually take the time to *do* the work,**' Tara said with regret. **'Our society sells these vast concepts and ancient traditions as a quick fix, give me money and you can own it.'**

'Ha, and the more money you give me, the *faster* you can own it,' Lee said sarcastically. **'But it doesn't work like that. Unfortunately, in their ignorance, people dismiss the practices as useless if they can't *own it* with significant result after just one weekend. It's such a shame.** Spirituality is not about certificates or knowledge or status or organisations. It's not something to buy. It's something to experience, to do, to live. To Be.'

'Agreed,' Tara nodded vigorously. **'Spirituality is about taking responsibility for our own development and our role in society.** It's not just about becoming a happier person, but also about becoming a *better* person. **It's about learning about ourselves, and we can't *buy* that. We have to work on it ourselves. It takes determination, effort and a bit of time.'**

'And if at all possible, some good guidance,' Lee emphasised, winking at Tara.

Tara smiled back, 'Thanks sweetie. You know, even just having somebody to kick this ball around with makes a whole load of difference.'

"And having somebody really *Cool* to kick the ball round with is even better," she added silently in her head. "He really is a wonderful person," Tara thought. "He gets it, he's sexy, he's sweet and funny. He gets it!" her Mind repeated one more time. He wasn't only politely interested because it was the stuff that *she* was into, he was really tuned in. He thought the same way she did. He even understood the significance of the "Brief Earth History". He understood why it was so sad. And he understood the modern changes in the world too. This was all a bit too good to be true. She hadn't met anybody like this in a long, long time. And boy, he *did* have nice hands. It took Tara a whole two seconds to catch herself out. Gosh, she thought, you could think a lot of stuff in two seconds. Where had she left off?

Oh yeah, nice hands - no! She grinned to herself. Before that! He seems to feel the same way? Yum... nice, a warm wave slowly moved up her Body. Tingly. Lovely.

Lee filled the silence before she had a chance to remember, 'Well, I hope that at least the sheer volume of alternative ideas and practices out there now means that *a* different message is sinking in, and that people's mindsets will begin open.'

'Oh, I so *hope* so! **I think the most important thing is that people realise, that there actually *is* a different way.** That it's not all drop-out or Hippy stuff, that you're not all weird, only because you're not working nine to five, but that it's a perfectly *possible* and *acceptable* way to live a different life.'

Tara took a deep breath, which Lee took advantage of, 'I think more and more people are beginning to see that, you know? So many people are disillusioned with their hectic full on and little fulfilling lives that they begin to want something different - and they're looking for it. **I think some people are starting to see through the materialistic direction that their lives have taken them into. People are seeking something *new*, something *deeper*. They are beginning to ask questions. People are beginning to wake up,'** Lee popped another bit of goats cheese into his mouth.

'Agreed. People in all walks of life are realising that the way we're going at the moment is not making us happy. Not having any time to spend our money on fun stuff, having to spend it on convenient food or transport or entertainment instead, or simply not having the time to enjoy our possessions, really isn't in anybody's ideal picture of life. **We're stressed, angry and hurting - Physically, Mentally and Emotionally.** Modern medicine cannot cope with diseases of the Body, which are linked the Mind and our Emotions. We can no longer treat the symptoms with lotions and potions, we're beginning to feel that we have to get down to the root of the problems, but what a lot of people don't know is that finding this root is not about Psychiatry and couches and stuff, but about Awareness of ourselves. About Constant Conscious awareness of what we do and how we think, what we put into our Body and how we look after ourselves. Our Body, our Mind, our surroundings, our friends, our job, our partner, it all plays a role. More and more people are beginning to understand that. More and more people are waking up to that simple fact, not just theoretically, but practically. The Mass Shift has already begun,' Tara said with certainty. 'More and more people, from all walks of life are beginning to cotton on. More and more people are familiar with one or more aspects of the Shift. The most unlikely people are beginning to talk about it. It's bizarre actually, I keep picking up the most fabulous messages in *conventional* books, in *conventional* everyday literature, nothing spiritual at all. Romances, silly teen novels, butch-boy football books, they all suddenly have these really profound little messages in them. Little realisations that people had, just thrown in by the by. And that's the great thing about this day and age. Today you don't necessarily have to read hardcore enlightenment books anymore, you can get it all neatly wrapped in a nice little story.'

'Three cheers for that,' Lee himself remembered a few of those wonderful little books that got him started in his spiritual enquiries.

Chemical Hobgoblins - Artificial Openings

'**M**an, I just had a Thought,' Lee said. There's quite a significant proportion of youths out there nowadays, a whole generation in fact, that has been deeply influenced by Psychedelics, Ecstasy and other drugs. **A lot of those people have experienced feelings of Universal Love and Oneness, feelings which they had never felt before.'**

'Yeah, and others flipped out and lost their marbles,' Tara toyed.

'Well, of course, it takes all kinds. But you know, some of them stayed grounded. **Some people had experiences, which were so powerful, that they changed their lives drastically to live according to their new understandings of the world.'**

Tara nodded thoughtfully, 'That's very true. I always wondered why so few people implement their positive drug experiences into their everyday lives. I mean, if you've seen the top of the mountain and it's freaking fantabulous up there, well, are you just going to sit at the bottom, twiddling your fingers, waiting for the next chemical hobgoblin to take you back up there, or are you going to start to find a way up there by yourself? I mean, it's the logical thing to do, isn't it?'

'You like your mountains, don't you?' Lee grinned. 'But yeah, I agree with you. Luckily though, there *are* people out there, who have seen the top of the mountain and they have managed to implement those experiences into their daily lives *without* the drugs. They managed to live more wisely and aware, without having to run off with the Hippies or emigrate to a desert island far away from all civilisation, to practice what they've learned.'

'**True,' Tara nodded, 'those people don't need to pop another pill for them to tell anyone that they are beautiful, they just do it. They don't need to take any substances anymore to marvel at a caterpillar or a butterfly or a flower. They remember the experience and *just do it* in every day life. They catch themselves out when they're *not* doing it, and *just do it!*'** Tara's voice trailed off. 'Remember? The *doing it* is not the difficult thing, *the remembering to do it* is! **We can decide that we want to behave in a certain way, and we can just do it! We can go and tell somebody they're beautiful, we don't need pills for that! You just need to remember. Drugs might take our inhibitions away, but hey, in Nowness, we don't have any Inhibitions either.**'

'And the come down is much easier too,' Lee grinned.

'Now there's a point,' Tara laughed. 'Maybe we should bottle it, we'd make a fortune.'

'Ha, happiness, two pounds fifty. Brrr, scary Thought. But seriously,' Lee said, '**the people that *did* get it through the Chemical Hobgoblins? They are now growing up. They are becoming heads of companies and teachers and politicians and their experiences influence the way they live, work and relate to other people.** If you really look at it, the last 50 years were marked by an ever increasing influence of Travelling, Learning about the Eastern ways, Meditation, Soul Searching and drugs of all kinds. And for the first time, people on a larger scale, experienced peacefulness, love, freedom, harmony and weird and wonderful Mental and Psychic connections with other people, nature and the Universe.'

Tara picked up Lee's flow, 'Some have had their heart chakra or their psychic third eye opened. Some experienced the knowledge that can be accessed in Nowness first hand. Some even briefly opened the final seventh cosmic chakra and got a glimpse of the Party above the Party,' Tara swayed her hips a little, dancing at the Party above the Party.

Lee smiled, 'Yep, and some were only opened up temporarily, others were blown open and stayed that way, but either way, each one of them knows that there is more out there. More than what we experience in our hectic Business world, home life, school, relationships and in the constant demands that are being placed on us by the world around us,' he said. 'For the people who had these insights through drugs, interestingly these profound new understandings usually stay long after the drugs have worn off. And that's because they make sense, because it's true. The drugs just open people's eyes to that fact!'

'True, but for people who find it difficult to cope with their insights, with trying to change their lives and trying to integrate their realisations into their everyday living, The Shift and The Guys can help with advice, guidance and explanations,' Tara elaborated on Lee's Thoughts.

'Good old Guys. Ever helpful. You know,' Lee had a sudden realisation, 'those people would probably find it easy to Trust,' Lee said, carefully balancing an olive on a cracker he'd prepared with tomato and cheese.

'What do you mean?' Tara wondered.

'Well, to anybody who has survived and enjoyed a psychedelic experience, or who has entered some of the far out dimensions of our Mind and the Universe through Meditation or whatever else, to those people, the far out stuff we've talked about probably won't seem quite as unusual as to the average person, would it? I mean they've probably seen and experience much weirder stuff working just fine, right?' Lee grinned broadly.

'Well dear world, get your backside Shifted! It's free!' Tara said cheerfully to nobody in particular.

'And at least as much fun,' Lee added.

'Amen.'

People Changed

'Actually,' Lee shared his Thoughts. 'Actually there are other types of people that had similar experiences, to drugs or some parts of the Shift.'

'Oh yeah? Who?'

'People that had major life changing experiences due to an accident or a trauma. **A lot of people change their lives or attitudes drastically once they've looked death into the eye.**'

'That's very true. They suddenly realise that there's more to life than what they've seen so far, they get that they really don't have to take silly stuff so seriously.

At the beginning they might be shy to talk about it, but as they begin to accept their strange and often inexplicable experiences as a reality, they begin to speak about these phenomena in a carefree and down to earth manner. They know what they've seen and they don't care anymore what others think. Some of these people have like minded friends to share with, others often find support in the Spiritual communities that do understand.'

'But whichever way,' Lee said, 'naturally or chemically initiated, people that used to think that they were going crazy, are now finding reassurance. People that thought they were different or alone, because they could heal people, see auras, talk to spirits, channel, be telepathic or know stuff that they couldn't know, are noticing that they are *not* alone, that it's really not all that weird, and that actually there are lots of people out there doing it - they're even *teaching* it,' Lee smirked, still amazed that the same thing applied to The Shift.

'True,' Tara agreed. 'Personally? **I feel that there's a strong Cosmic revolution on the horizon. And it's coming fast. Over the past few years, there has been a noticeable change in the Vibratory levels of the world's Consciousness. Awareness *is* increasing.** But,' Tara said with a warning undertone, 'the ones that are waking up and are trying to use it for their own greedy advantage? They're the ones to watch out for! But note, those baddies won't stand a chance if everybody else works to raise Trust and Love, and with that the higher Vibrations of this planet. So far it has taken world after world and generation after generation to just produce a few people that *got it.* Some transcend to higher Dimensions, others chose to conscientiously keep coming back to the rest of us to help us raise our Vibrations as well. Sure, it will take time to build up Trust again, but we're getting closer. Since the *First People*, we have never been as close as we have now. It's about to explode. It needn't be many more generations - maybe we even live to see it,' Tara said with a confident look in her eyes.

'The Party above the Party is sending out invitations as we speak...,' Lee grinned.

'I certainly want to get an one, that's for sure. I would so love to meet a KlingOn,' Tara laughed.

It's Not Just About Us

'**There's still more to be done though until the Cosmic Revolution can really take off,**' Tara said. '**We** have to *remember who we are.* **We need to remember that we're all *connected* to the Universe and Mother Earth, that we once lived in harmony with Nature and that we respected the world and all beings within it.** We have to remember and *act* on the knowledge that we're not an individual part of an *ego*-system, but rather a common part of a big *eco*-system. I really like the way you put that before,' she smiled at Lee. 'At the moment we only look after ourselves and we're destroying everything around us in the process. We need to remember the role we're supposed to play in the Universe. You know, look after everything, to allow everything to look after us? You know? Have some respect.'

'I know,' Lee said. 'It's sad but true. **We behave as if everything on this planet is unlimited.** We pollute the Air, the Water, the Earth. We cut the Trees which clean our Air, we leave Mountains of rubbish everywhere, we waste precious Water, and oil, till it runs out and we act all surprised. We rob the Planet of it's reserves, and when we have used up one resource, we just go to the next, regardless of the future. **We don't *live* with Nature, we *use* nature.**

We have changed the planet so much that it's hard to recognise it in places. Seasons are changing, rain is stopping or starting, unimagined heat and frost waves are hitting the world, so are floods, draughts, hurricanes, typhoons and earthquakes.'

'A friend of mine said once that it's as if we have put Planet Earth into a straight-jacket of cement, metal, plastic and glass. We're walking all over it, pinching it, tickling it, stabbing it and digging into it. Over the years the Planet has accepted it, but of late it felt more and more uncomfortable and it started to jiggle. It has begun to move inside the restraining jacket.'

'Yeah, and it will not be long before the straight-jacket tears and we're wiped off it's back. Just like we would wipe off a fly off our sleeve if it's pestering us,' Lee roughly flicked an imaginary fly of his T-shirt.

'Phew, looking at the big picture,' Tara said thoughtfully, 'if we keep on going like we have, it's pretty inevitable that this is going to happen one day. Nobody knows how long from now that will be, it could be many life times and generations till planet earth finally decides that it had enough, but I think we can feel that it has already started. But people ignore it. Whole governments ignore it. It is known that large multinational companies are pressuring the government not to change laws that infringe their profit margins. It's publicly known, and it's *still* ignored! Helllooo!' Tara said with a faintly worried undertone. 'And governments go along with it, hoping that if it's not immediate danger, why worry? I mean, the oil reserves are running out, does anybody really understand the significance of that? They really are running out! It's not a fairytale. Yoo-hoo! Anybody hooome?!'

'Yeah, and then everybody freaks out when the shit hits the fan, even though we've been ignoring all the more than obvious Signs for years!' Lee said cheesed off. **The governments think: Why panic the nation, why risk elections, why risk the law and order we have established?** Let's ignore it, it's unlikely that this world will go under in my election term, isn't it? Or what about the one where the government let things go belly-up on purpose, so that they can be the saviours or lets put it differently, the rulers of the chaos?' Lee said, feeling truly at home with political discussions.

'Right! But people don't think that far, people just won't learn from history! People still believe that if the world's situation would be serious, the government would do something about it, which then of course justifies them to sit on their butt and twiddle their thumbs.' Tara poignantly. 'It really is messed up.'

'And the truth is that the mess is speeding up! The way things are going, we might actually live to see the world go up or down, you know? At least parts of it. Large areas of the world are already being devastated by freak catastrophes.'

'And as the natural disasters are beginning to move to the *Western* world, rather than conveniently staying in third world countries, people are actually beginning to take notice,' Tara added cynically. 'And for heaven's sake, what is all of this crap about not-in-our-life-time? What about our children?' for the first time Tara's voice got a little louder. 'They might live in a world with constant hurricanes, ice everywhere, no natural resources, a messed up ecosystem. *Our* children! Not some weird distant future generation! This is an immediate threat! **But that argument doesn't work with people either.** People don't seem to care enough about the children or even *our own* old age for that matter to act now! Isn't that bizarre?' Tara really couldn't believe the sheer stupidity of the world's inhabitants. 'But what *will* work, is when the Earth begins to rumble even more and when it begins to make our lives truly miserable. *Then* we'll frantically try to make up for our ignorance! So, why not just wait for that? That's much more comfortable, much easier, isn't it? But man, for every second we wait, our remedies will have to be more revolutionary. Because when it hits the fan?' Tara shrugged her shoulders.

'It really does,' Lee filled in the blanks.

'Yep,' Tara sighed.

An Advanced Nation - Desensitised - The Other Extreme

'It all comes back to the fact that us Humans think that we are the most advanced of all creatures,' Tara said, 'which in turn of course, makes us better than everything else on the planet, and therefore, we can do whatever we want, right? **But actually, what gives us the right to feel so superior?** Because we have a brain? Because we understand Physics and Biology? Well, look at ants. We call them primitive. An interesting description for a species which has perfect colonies, which is structured to works for a common good, which can create natural air-conditioning, farms lice for milk, doesn't take more than it needs to survive. So, why are we so much cleverer again?' Tara looked genuinely confused. 'Sure there are ups and downs with all species. They have to defend themselves or kill for food, but still, their fundamental make-up is not to take more than they need. Even the squirrel does something good by not finding the excessive nuts it buries,' she laughed. 'If we really look at it, are we truly better than them, just because we understand Mathematics and because we can build computers? How can be so much better than Nature, when we so desperately rely on it? What gives us the right to rape and pillage our vital environment?'

'Because we have a brain and hands to build Technology, and because we *can*,' Lee said scornfully.

'Right. And you know what's ironic? We think that Technology gives us Freedom, when actually, it removes us further and further away from that Freedom. We're becoming more and more dependent on the tool itself. I mean can you imagine a life without computers now? Or the phone? Or the Internet? Or,' a shock of mock horror flashed across her face, '*Electricity?*'

Lee scrunched up his face, 'Phew, no way.'

'I know, it's impossible for most of us. Most of us *can't survive* without those things! They'll starve! Isn't that crazy?

That's just the physical side. On top of that, most Technology removes us from ourselves, from Nature and from other people. **The more we work with computers, the more we forget how to communicate between Beings.** Sure, the Internet connects us, but at the same time, Computers don't need feelings or sensitivity or Hugs, even Honesty, Integrity and Truth. The more we deal with computers, the more we become like them. **Our reactions become mechanical, our activities without heart, our Emotions desensitised.'**

Lee interjected quietly, **'Because we sit in front of a computer all freaking day!'**

'Right. We talk through computers and SMS messages, rather than on the phone or by meeting up. Computers are replacing human interaction more and more. There's a huge difference between communicating via a computer or face to face! Many children in the Western world spend more time in front of the telly or the computer, than with their friends, their parents or in Nature. And when they do play with others they compete, rather than *support* each other, play *with* each other or *share*. **Our ability to communicate and interact with each other naturally and intuitively, is dissolving in a computer interface.** Slowly, we become computers ourselves.'

'Oh yes, what an Advanced Nation we are. Advanced and Desensitised,' Lee said sullenly.

'And you know what's worse?' Tara asked dramatically. 'As we're becoming more like computers ourselves, we are being programmed to *become* the same as each other. *Look* the same, *act* the same, *do* the same things.'

'Run the same software,' Lee threw in.

'Yep. I know that this can all sounds a bit radical and extremist, but it's true and obvious to see if we look around us or watch the news.'

'Well, a uniform flock of sheep is much easier to herd.'

'I know. Often our lives are not ruled by what *we* really *like* doing, but by what we think we *should* be doing to fit in and to comply to our society's expectations of us. Even though most of the time we don't like the rules or don't agree with them, we comply anyway, simply because that's what people do. We shave our legs. Drink branded water. Have a car that drives faster than any speed restriction would ever allow us to. We own lots of stuff we never use. We upgrade our mobile phone every 6 months. We need better Internet all the time to save another millisecond. We do all these things because that's what we think we need to do. That's what the telly tells us, the papers, the magazines, the adverts. That's what we're being told makes us attractive, accepted and loved. All around us we see pictures of all these perfect people with perfect outside shells and that's what we want. Of course. We want to be accepted and we want to fit in. We've already talked about some of this when we talked about self-judgement.'

Lee rolled his eyes, 'Yeah, I know, but it's so true. If it wouldn't be so sad, it would be hilarious. The worst thing is, that we're all falling for it. We've been falling for it for decades. **We're *all* playing the game. The game of society telling us to jump, and us asking how high and us giving them our money for the privilege.** Then we go out to earn even more money to do it all over again, when they changed the game-rules for us to do just that. Business is so clever. It's a constant cycle of greed, short-lived temporary satisfaction, and then wanting more. It's a high speed consumer society.'

'And what's so weird is that we know it, yet, we still do it!' Tara added shrewdly. 'You know, sometimes it seems that *we* don't consume the goods, but that our society is *being* consumed *by* the goods.'

'Scary Thought. On that note,' Lee lifted his index finger to command attention, 'let me quote a fabulous book, Mutant Message Down Under: - **The goal of business is to stay in business, regardless. - You see, most of the time it's not about helping people or making them happy, it's about being and staying in business to feed all it's members.** And we all play our part in it,' Lee pointed out.

'Isn't it crazy that we're just not learning? Even though we know all this, even though a lot of us don't like it, we're still playing the game.'

Onions

'So *why* are we playing society's game?' Lee put out there.

'Because society tells us that we're onions and that our layers aren't good enough. Therefore we have to go and get different layers. Some whiter ones, darker or more colourful ones, or less hair or more hair, or bigger or faster. Just so that we can all look like all the other Onions and be accepted. It really is as you said, society tells us to jump, and we ask how-high every time. We're insecure, we feel that we are not good enough or we don't have enough. We need to be different or own more stuff. And of course, *only* if we achieve all of those things, *then* others will love us and *then* we'll finally be cool, and *then* we'll finally be accepted, and *then* our mum's and dad's will finally think that we're achievers!'

'Yeah and sadly, often it even works, well to a certain extend. I mean have you ever noticed that Onions attract Onions?' Lee grinned. 'I mean, a lot of people really believe that somebody with a big car is cool or that an expensive dress is important or that the right brand of tennis shoes or bike or shampoo or freaking toothpaste will really make them feel like a different person and help them become who they want to be - and I'm sure a lot of their friends agree, that's why they're their friends.' As an afterthought Lee added, 'Of course I'm not trying to argue weather some goods are better quality than others, the point is what is going on in our heads.'

'I agree,' Tara said, '**the point is that we have so much, but we're still not be happy. You know what most of us want? Really deep down? A cuddle. But an unconditional one! Not because of our money or possessions or our prestige and status, but a deep, loving and true hug, because we're being loved. Somebody softly cradling our head and telling us that it's all going to be ok. That's what we can't buy. Tenderness, gentleness, true affection.** But hey, we get what we put out there. If all we want is materialism, that's what we're going to attract. People that want our material things. If we think that we can buy people with money, we'll get people that *can* be bought with money.** If we want material things, that's what we get. Material. Not love or heart or gui stuff, but bolts and screws and plastic,' Tara said flatly.

'Some people of course argue: but it's not like that, it's not that bad. But, if we really look at it closely? In a lot of places, it really *is* like that, isn't it,' Lee agreed.

'I know. Sure, there are also lots of happy, independent people out there too, but what we're talking about, *is* the other extreme the world is moving into. **We're seeking refuge in material things because we don't know *how* to be strong or happy *without* all of those things.** People are self-conscious, self-critical, they feel too fat, to small, to tall to thin, to ugly, to poor. People feel unappreciated, taken advantage of, they crave more and more, and when they get it, they want more of something else. Most of us feel pressured by society's expectations. **Many people don't feel good about it, don't feel fulfilled, but we're still all complying - because we just don't know *what* else to do,'** Lee stressed.

'**Or *how* else to do it,'** Tara added. '**Well, the Shift will give them a pretty good idea.'**

They both drew a long deep breath and looked at each other in astonishment. What a snowball conversation, back and forth, back and forth.

'I can't believe how similar we think, it's nearly weird,' Tara said, scratching her head in a gesture emphasising her point.

'Yeah, I know. Did you notice that we finish each others' sentences?' Lee grinned. 'We even seem to *read* the same stuff. I couldn't believe it when you knew about Quantum Physics earlier. Nobody ever knows any details.'

'Are you kidding? I love that stuff!'

'So do I!'

33 Lee, Tara and....

Lee watched Tara play with a long lock of her hair. He loved the red shimmer of her curls, how they reflected the sun, how they framed her face, how they fell all the way over her shoulder blades, tousley. He kept wanting to ruffle through it. He liked women that were natural and sunny. Kate had been all about perfect make up, perfect hair and he'd loved that too. Girls that were made up also had their attraction. But too often it was all look-don't-touch. He'd missed playing with hair and kissing without having to worry about destroying the painting. He caught himself looking into Tara's eyes. She returned his look, also lost in Thought somewhere. 'Maybe she's lost in the same place as I,' Lee thought, as a warm, familiar feeling spread in his belly. A warm feeling of what-if?

Tara looked at Lee. She was enjoying his company so much. She caught herself looking into those dreamy eyes and noticed him returning her look, also lost in Thought somewhere. 'Maybe he's lost in the same place as I,' Tara thought, a warm, familiar feeling spread in her belly. A warm feeling of, what-if?

They smiled at each other, somehow knowing that they knew each other's Thought, that their bellies were tantalizing them with the same sensations.

Lee winked at Tara, ever so slightly and saw a little spark ignite on the other side. He felt bashful. What a strange feeling. It was self-consciousness and shyness all rolled into one. At his age?

Lee smiled to himself and turned his head to looked across the grass towards the pond, enjoying the moment, when his peace was unexpectedly shattered into a million little pieces. "Bad timings of bad timings," his Thoughts gasped. Kate was walking straight towards to him, she was already at the pond and would be with them in just a minute or so. "Oh God, here we go," he thought apprehensively.

'Hi Lee,' Kate said to him, then looked at Tara. 'Hi, my name is Kate.'

'Hi, I'm Tara,' Tara looked up in surprise.

'Sorry to interrupt you guys, but could I have a quick word please?' She looked at Lee. 'In private? It'll only be a minute.'

'Sure,' Lee and Tara answered in unison. They looked at each other briefly.

'I'll be back in a minute,' Lee said to Tara, got up and feeling slightly awkward, walked over to his ex-girlfriend. Together they walked a little way into the clearing, until they were out of hearing distance.

'Sorry too disturb you,' Kate said genuinely, 'I just saw you and I thought now is as good a time as any.'

Lee noticed that she felt a little awkward too.

'I just wanted to tell you that I picked up the rest of my things today,' Kate said. 'Marc came with me to help. I hope you don't Mind. I rang the bell, but you weren't in. I used the keys.'

'That's cool Kate. Just as well I wasn't there. I'm not so sure I'm up to meeting Marc again yet,' Lee said surprisingly calm.

Lee remembered Kate introducing him to her ex-boyfriend before it had all happened, little did he know what was going to take place so soon afterwards. He pushed the Thought aside. He wanted to tell her, "I have found something over the past few days that really sorted out my head and my Emotions about this whole thing," but decided not to. In fact, there was so much he wanted to tell her, but it wasn't his place anymore. In the back of his Mind he noticed that he was fine with that. Lee felt like a different person now. He remembered the continuous catching out he'd done when Thoughts of Kate had infiltrated his Mind. He remembered dealing with his feelings, the retracing of Co-incidences, trying to see the good in it all, seeing the reason for which it had all happened. The second Tara had told him about catching out, his Being had screamed YES and he'd been at it ever since. Constantly. Under the tree, in the pub, at home, walking the street, making dinner and so on and so on. He even thought he'd woken up one time, feeling as if he'd caught himself out in a dream. There had been so much anger, so much disappointment, so much jealousy and so many hurtful feelings of betrayal, but he had spotted them all. He had stared them right into their naughty little faces and decided that he didn't want to feel that way anymore. He had realised that his head was creating stories that weren't real, and even if some of them might have been, he understood that his Emotions were holding onto a reality that was no more - and that he had Let Go, that he *wanted* to let it go - knowing that nothing he could do within his head would change the situation. The more he had played with his Mind and Emotions, the more it had dawned on him that he hadn't even wanted to change the situation anymore. He knew it was for the best! In fact, he'd known for a while! Deep down he'd known all along that splitting up had been inevitable, it had always just been a matter of time. Right from the start. Kate and he had loved each other dearly, but they were never made for each other, and they'd both known it. So, it was just as well.

Learning to observe his Mind had helped him to tell reality from silly made up stories. He'd even learned to laugh at it all his cumbersome, unwieldy and awkward Thoughts and Feelings. He had laughed sincerely and truly, from the bottom of his heart. *That* in particular had taken him by surprise. He couldn't deny that he'd been genuinely entertained by the sheer ridiculousness of the stories his head had made up about Kate. He knew that what had happened between him and her could have taken him ages to get over, had he not been assisted by a few little Cosmic Helpers. Lee smiled to himself. He had only just met The Dudes and they had already taken up a full time job. And They were doing Their job well! Even his Behaviour right now, he noticed, with Kate standing right in front of him, was different than it would have been a few days ago. He felt calmer, more controlled and relaxed. They were a good team, The Dudes and him.

'You look much better now,' Kate said.

'Yeah, I am,' Lee took comfort in noticing that this was true. This was the first meeting with Kate since she'd told him that she was getting back with Marc, seconds before she had walked out of their apartment. 'I'm glad we're talking,' he said honestly. 'Sorry to have lost it before. It all took me a bit by surprise. It was all pretty sudden.'

'Yeah, I'm so sorry. There's never an easy way,' Kate seemed to be sincerely apologetic.

'I know. In retrospect,' Lee said, 'I know it's best for both of us. You really love Marc, I guess you always have,' he tried to sound more cheerful.

'I'm so sorry things turned out the way they did. I guess we can't predict where cupid hits us,' Kate looked at him warmly, a reminder of her affection for him.

'Yeah,' Lee said with a tiny smile, glancing over at Tara.

Kate's sharp Mind didn't miss the secret gesture and her eyes followed the direction Lee's were moving to. A beautiful young woman sat on a blanket, wearing a flowing long skirt, which played innocently with the shapely outline of her legs. Her top charmingly revealed soft shoulders and toned arms. Such bright colours, Kate smiled, taking in the rainbow of colours that made up Tara's possessions. She felt an unusual warmth towards the stranger as she saw Tara braiding her hair into long pigtails, looking happy. She seemed playful, yet enticing and interesting, exciting even.

Kate knew straight away that Lee and this girl were made for each other. They even kind of looked like each other, they felt alike in some strange way. She felt a tiny pang of jealousy, but then remembered why she had made her decision in the first place. She loved Marc. Lee was right. She'd never stopped loving her previous boyfriend. She still deeply cared for Lee and she never wanted to hurt him, that would have been the last thing she'd ever wanted, but she loved Marc. With all her heart.

It had taken her so much effort to come over to talk to Lee. She wondered how she had felt seeing her ex-boyfriend having a pick-nick and deep conversation with another woman, but that didn't matter anymore. She was with Marc, and she loved him. She had felt apprehensive though, not wanting too disturb, not knowing what Lee's reaction was going to be, but she'd known that it was the right thing to do. It had finally felt like the right time. Now, looking into Lee's eyes and talking to him, she knew that she'd been right. She was glad to see that he looked good. *Very* good in fact, she noticed with some surprise. Something within him had changed. It was quite noticeable. He looked much stronger, much more settled, much more alive. Clear even. Powerful. More masculine. "More so than he'd ever done with me," she recognized, feeling a tiny pang of jealousy and relief at the same time. Separating had been the right decision! "For *both* of us," she reminded herself. The most important thing now, was that he was well. And he was. He looked happy. Kate felt a huge weight taken of her shoulders. Things were ok now. She could feel it.

Kate and Lee looked at each other. 'Thank you for finding me,' Lee said.

'Thank you for talking to me,' Kate replied.

He took her hand, held it, closed his eyes, and opened them again. As their eyes met once more, he saw her soul and for another moment, he allowed her to see his. He gently lifted her hand to his lips and kissed it softly. 'I hope you'll be well.' He Let Go, of her hands and of the Past.

'Thank you, you too,' Kate said, clearing her throat. She held his gaze for another second, gave him a quick peck on the cheek, looked at him one last time, took his left hand, put a set of keys into it, closed his fingers over them, squeezed his hand briefly, smiled and walked away, not turning.

Tara watched them talk. It seemed to be a serious conversation. The woman looked very different to herself, more formal, expensive clothes, nicely made up. She had straight blond hair, about shoulder length, a lovely smile and a kind, open face. 'Lee's got good taste,' Tara thought to herself. She could feel the attraction between the two. But there was also something else. She didn't want to pry, but the feeling came of it's own accord. A feeling of conclusion. At first she felt anxiousness between them, a wall, then she saw the energy between the two hesitating for an instant, then merge for a few moments. Unison. Comfort. Then their energies slowly separated again, leaving both of them looking much calmer, content even. They'd come together looking slightly edgy and tense, and they had left each other looking soft and relaxed. Tara liked the way their interaction had felt. *Conscious* was the word that came to her Mind. She just witnessed a *conscious* meeting of two souls. "How wonderful," she thought.

Conscious. That's how she felt now too. She hadn't been a few minutes ago though. She fondly reflected on the last few moments of goings-on in her head. Initially, the second Tara had laid eyes on the other woman, her Mind had exploded with the most fantastic stories. Lee's got a girlfriend, they are in love, they'll get married and she will never see him again. She thought about the strong connection she and Lee had shared, and wondered if her Intuition had really fooled her? Surprise had turned into jealousy, which had turned into disappointment and then into doubt. All of that had taken at total of thirty-two seconds. It took Tara thirty-two seconds to catch herself out and to stop her Thoughts dead in their tracks and start laughing to herself. "Wait!" she had told her Mind, "Be quiet! You don't know anything yet! You'll know what's going on soon enough, and then, *that's* the way it *is*. Nothing you can do right now will change that, so shush!" Tara felt strength and comfort flooding back into her Body as the truth filled her warmly.

The picture of Lee kissing the woman's hand came back into her Mind. Another puppy begging for attention. She petted it for a split second and saw it slowly disappear, as soon as she withdrew her attention from it. She felt relaxed and calm.

"Thirty-two seconds, give or take. Not bad. She's getting real good," she faintly heard The Guys skirting on the fringes of her Consciousness. She smiled. She was surprised to see how much she cared for Lee.

Tara saw the woman kiss Lee goodbye and then walk over to the pond, where a young man in a casual suit and tie waited for her next to a tree. Tara didn't think Lee had seen him. Lee had already turned away to look across the lawn towards the forested area of the park. He seemed lost in Thoughts. The man by the pond on the other hand, looked anxiously towards the woman. When she reached him, she hugged him, they exchanged a few words and the man visibly relaxed. Tara could literally see him let out a huge sigh of relief. He looked at the woman lovingly, took both of her hands and kissed her. He put his arms around her, she put her arm around him and together they walked back towards the path. After a few steps the man leaned over her, he seemed to whisper something into her ear. Quick as a flash the woman slid out from beneath his arm and tickled his sides. He jumped aside, with a smile on his face, trying to fend of her arms. They seemed like nice people, Tara thought. They were in love.

"Good," a puppy slipped in sneakily. Tara smiled at it.

Lee watched Kate leave for a moment, turned and looked out towards the small forest that framed one side of the park. He stood silently for a few minutes, trying to clear his head.

'Co-incidences,' he thought to himself. He smiled now. What had been the chances of him meeting Tara, just the day he needed to hear about The Guys? What had been the chances of him becoming available just the day before meeting - his soul-mate? He caught himself out at the words soul-mate. It was time to go back, he had kept her waiting long enough.

He slowly walked back towards Tara, wondering what he was going to tell her. They had a strong connection, there was no doubt. They had flirted, even if only playfully. Then another girl comes along, demands a private audience and drags him off. He could only imagine what that must have looked like. Any other girl would have looked anxious or jealous or at least miffed and expectant for an explanation. Looking at Tara, he was reminded with a pang why he why he felt so attracted to her, because Tara? Tara was braiding her hair, smiling, as if to herself, a long pigtail already caressing her back. She seemed genuinely relaxed. When she saw him approach, she patted the spot next to her on the blanket, inviting him to sit down. Gratefully he sat. He could feel that she sensed that something was up, but she didn't push him. She looked at him warmly, sensing his apprehension and returned her attention back to her hair, patiently waiting till he was ready. He so liked this quality about her. She gave him time. He always needed a bit of time.

Kate was slowly leaving his Being, but he knew that he would need just a little while longer to deal with the engagement ring that he'd just felt under his lips.

Lee sat quietly for what seemed an age, looking at the forest, the trees, the sky, the birds within it. Strong, Powerful, Alive. His mantra came back to his Mind. Free! He drew a deep breath, feeling his belly expand and the words flood through his Body. Returning to him the familiar feeling of Strength, Power and Life. Tara had changed so much for him. Beauty. Love. Happiness - Engagement ring. Phew. Puppies! Absentmindedly he took one of Tara's pigtails and played with it for a moment. He noticed that she had not fixed it with a rubber band. He wondered how it stayed together. Taking one last deep breath, he gently dropped it behind her back to join the other one. He struggled to find the right words. **He hadn't told Tara any details about Kate yet.** One didn't tell a girl that you just met, that your ex-girlfriend has just split up with you to get back together with her ex-boyfriend, did one? But it had been on his Mind and he felt that it was time to talk about it. He owned Tara an explanation. He wanted to be open and honest. And most of all he thought, a little smile crossed his face, he wanted to put *her* mind at rest!

First slowly and hesitantly then more easily he told her. Tara Listened. Her Being not judging, but open and receiving every word. Lee finished off by saying, 'And I was kind of worried what you would think, because I really like you and I don't want you to feel uncomfortable,' Lee stocked.

Tara was surprised by the intensity of the relief she was feeling. He cared! He likes me! Yes! 'Lee, it's ok. I feel the same way,' she said quietly, feeling grateful for their mutual, gentle honesty. Lee looked up. When their eyes met she said, 'Thank you for telling me. I did have a few puppies to play with, but it's fine now. Very fine.'

It was funny, Lee looked as relieved as she felt. She knew that he had dealt with the situation in a remarkable way. She also knew that it was time to take *his* Mind of things now. She stopped her own Thoughts and Listened. She heard something. Not a worldly sound, but something within. Her smile grew broader. It was laughter.

Tara took his hand into hers, 'We've talked about grownups, do you want to talk about children now?'

'Children?' Lee nearly bit off his tongue, trying not to choke.

34 Children, Parents, Society and Relationships

Children

'**W**ell, this is the fabulous world of adults,' Tara laughed at Lee's reaction, 'adults who should know it all. Adults, who have a *choice* about how to live their lives, a choice about what to do and how. **So here we are, us wonderfully stable, strong and balanced people, and most of us haven't even half sorted ourselves out by the time we have children!**' Tara winked at Lee cheekily.

"Ah, that was the missing link," Lee thought, following Tara's train of Thought now. He was still a little distracted, as the feelings and Thoughts he'd been dealing with over the past few days trying kept to compete for his attention, but he appreciated Tara's attempt to take his Mind of things with her skilful diversion. Gladly he went along. He took Tara's hand, held it and thought: "Thank you. Let's go on, but gently." Tara understood, even without words. Little by little his brain sped up, grateful for the new focus.

He continued Tara's sentence, 'And here we are, sadly incomplete ourselves, procreating to share our 'wisdom' with our children,' he winked at Tara, she smiled back. Everything *was* ok again. Lee tuned back in and continued, 'By not knowing any better ourselves, we fill our children's heads and hearts with our own confusion, unbalance, insecurity, conditionality, self-indulgence, greed, and other hang ups.'

Tara nodded and picked up happily where Lee had left off, 'Most adults still partake in constant emotional roller-coasters and head games. They continuously try to change themselves to be accepted. If we really look at it, adults are just older children and when it comes down to it, some were lucky enough to learn how to live life joyously and harmoniously, and others weren't, and as a result, a lot of grownups are everything *but* balanced, strong and grounded. Isn't it great? That's what we teach our children!' Tara said sarcastically. **'Our world seems to have forgotten that children are empty warehouses, blank sheets of paper and that *we* as a society and parents, fill that warehouse and draw on that paper. Kids *become whatever* we put in into their warehouses,'** she said. **'Our children learn *everything* we say and do. Not just what we *consciously* and deliberately teach them, but *everything*.** Stupid, slow, big nose, bickering, fights, insecurity, fashion or materialistic desires, priorities, dominance, anger, how to treat fellow human beings, how to learn, what to want, what to have, how to judge, how to measure, how to think, what to be happy about, how to Be, everything.'

Lee shared Tara's sentiment, as the last half an hour of events faded into the distance, 'It's sad really, all we seem to know about, is how to improve our children's *Brains* and *Minds*, their intellects and their I.Q.-s. We do that in kindergarten, at school, at work, with books, telly and games, but we forget to develop their *Hearts*. **Our society is geared towards creating *useful* people, not happy and good people.** Surely parents must want to do something about that?' Lee relaxed back into the flow of their cosmic exchange.

He felt comfort in hearing Tara's voice, in exchanging Thoughts with a like minded Soul. It made him feel at home. Understood. He was thankful that Tara had managed to stir his Mind towards new and exiting things rather than wallowing in the past. It was time to look ahead again. "Wanna talk about children," she had asked. Cheeky. She really had him going there for a second. They would have beautiful babies though. The Thought shocked him back into the present moment. He looked up at Tara who was waiting for him.

'Children,' Lee scolded her amused.

'Children,' Tara replied.

A warm feeling overcame them. "Happy, wild and wonderful children," they both thought, only slightly aware of the peculiar remembrance that was occurring in their brain, an ancient connection to the other..., but now wasn't the time for that.

Parents

'Where were we?' Tara tried to clear her Brain and pick up the conversation.

'Parents' responsibilities towards their children. We said how difficult it is for parents that are still struggling with themselves to pass on a balanced and strong personality on to their children,' Lee picked up where they had left off earlier. 'Now, obviously not all parents are having a hard time, some parents are great. Some are fantastic role models to their children,' he said, thinking of his own mother. She had brought him and his sister up on her own. She had never had it easy, and heaven knew, they hadn't made it any easier for her either, but she'd done her best. The best she could, as best she knew. He hoped to have learned from her. 'I was just thinking, I guess a lot of great parents probably had great role models themselves. Mmh, then again, maybe not. But, whichever way they get it, be it from their own parents, through books or friends or 'on-the-job' experience, those parents would know how to develop children's Minds *and* Hearts. Or they'd at least know that it's an important thing to do.'

'That's true, but no matter how engaged parents are, how they've figured out how they want to raise their children for the best, they often become involved in a battle against a society where a lot of their values are not lived out. Children subject to the *other* world outside of the 'ideal' home, as soon as they set foot out of the front door. I mean, how can *we* teach a kid to play outside, when all it's mates play computer games? How can *we* teach a kid to wear any old tennis shoe, when he's getting teased at school for not wearing brand names? How can *we* teach a kid which food is healthy, if it's not cool, if they can't get it at school and if hardly any adults eat it either? How can *we* teach kids good moral values if people in the world out there don't follow them? How can *we* teach them anything, if society breaks the rules left right and centre?'

'That's true. We can't *say* one thing to our kids, *do* another, and expect our kids to listen to us. Nobody learns like that. It doesn't work, and if you try to make them, the kids won't like you for it,' Lee knew that from his sister's experience with her two children. 'Even the best parents will have a hell of a job to do if they intend to go against peer pressure, junk food, soft drinks, television, computers, bad adult and peer examples, mass marketing and advertising aimed at children. It's all constantly in their faces, and scarily, children are taught at least equally as much by their surroundings and their environment and peers, as they are by their parents, if not more.'

'Hello you cute little ones?' Tara put on a high-pitched witches voice, 'Welcome to the real world! Let's show you how it's *really* done! Ha, ha, haaa.'

'Uoh, creepy,' Lee cringed. **Isn't it bizarre how no parent wants to play the game, but how they still all do it? They play it for themselves, and they play it for their children too.** There just doesn't seem to be another way. There is a lot of pressure from society and advertising to Be, behave and live in a certain way. And that's what the kids learn too. So, even if the parents 'get it', it's still a challenging task to get the kids follow in their footsteps,' Lee remembered the thoughts he'd had before about how he would raise children in this modern world.

'I feel the same way,' Tara said sadly. 'You know what the other important element that distracts in us raising our children with the attention, love and affection that they deserve is? One element that is actually under our control? One that we choose?'

'What's that?'

'It's our busy lifestyle. Man, in a working family time is so limited and there's always something else that needs to be done, rather than spend quality time with our kids. We simply can't spend twenty-four hours with them. We need to go shopping, cook, clean, work, organise, pay bills, look after relatives, deal with single parenthood or both parents working, deal with an entire life, and all that, while having a child being dependent on us all day and all night long.'

'Yeah, and besides time for the children, what about time for the parents?' Lee threw in.

'Gosh, you're right. It's such hard work for any couple to stay sane without *Us*-time. Time for *us* alone.' They looked at each other. Tara continued, 'It's challenging to be a parent. You need to concentrate while being drowned in screaming. You need to relax, while they won't sit still and want your attention. You need to have a conversation with your friend, while your child wants to have a conversation with you. You say yes, they say no. They don't think it's fair, you thing it is. You don't want to ground them, but you don't see another way to make your point. They want to go to a music concert on a school night, you don't want them to because their studies are important. Then you remember how you always wanted to go to concerts when you were a kid. Then you don't know what's right anymore.

The list goes on. It's difficult to always be loving and caring to the children, so yeah, sometimes the parents need a break too,' she finished.

'And of course, the modern solution to that problem is to bombard our kids with outside entertainment, because *we* haven't got the time to look after them, or because *we* need our own space. We sit them in front of the telly, let them play endless computer games or surf the net.'

'And that cuts the kids off from natural human interactions,' Tara said sorrowfully.

'We can't judge the parents for that though,' Lee said seriously. 'Personal space *is vital* for every human being's sanity, I mean a lot of what we've been talking about requires some kind of space, even if it's just Mental space.' Tara nodded unhappily. 'And, things need to get done in a busy life and it's nearly impossible to include children in everything. It's not like the olden days where you always had family or community around you to help out. A lot of parents have to cope by themselves.'

'You're right,' Tara agreed. 'Parents have to cope in an environment, where *we* are allowing the cutting of budgets and the closing of social projects, kindergartens, schools, play groups and youth centres. Money is running out for community programmes, scout and sport facilities. Places where kids could learn how to communicate properly, rather than just press a couple of buttons or pull some levers, become less and less. Places, where kids have to become aware of and take responsibility for their actions and the cause and effects of their Behaviour, rather than just press *replay* to get another seven lives or a new playmate.'

'Everything, which would give children a sense of community, belonging and togetherness is being budgeted down. Parents have to deal with all of this, and a lot of them don't know how,' Lee said regretfully.

Tara nodded again, '**What most forget is that parents are only grown up kids themselves, nobody taught them how to look after kids**. No matter if young or old, people are often really not prepared for what it's like to be a parent and it's usually quite a shock. Sure there are play groups and pre- and ante-natal classes etc, but hey, actually having a kid? Nobody *really* teaches us the truth about it. **How do we suddenly cope with having so much extra responsibility? A little creature needing us 24 hours a day?** From one day to the next. Of course children the most wonderful thing in the whole wide world and we love them dearly, but how do we cope if they scream all day long, or if we have to get up five times a night, are exhausted and don't get any peace during the day either? What if to top all of that we have difficulties in our relationship? Or when the closeness in the father-mother relationship dwindles without *Us*-time? Or if we are given 227 different solutions for the same problem we have with our child, and we don't know which one is best? Different books, different opinions. How can we know what's right? Do we say 'No' to the child, or does doing that break the kids spirit? Should we be strict or forgiving? Shall we risk huge side effects of inoculations or shall we risk the disease? We have a teenager who drives me up the wall. We're going crazy. It's not easy having children. **Kids don't pop out with an instruction booklet and to be honest, in the end, it's all trial and error.** Isn't that scary?'

'That's not only scary, **it's plain ridiculous,**' Lee said honestly horrified. **'Raising the next generation is more or less based on trial and error.** That's insane! Parents can do whatever they want to, good or bad, deliberately or out of pure ignorance. No wonder we're all so messed up! Happy families, content, well balanced and cool children are really not the norm. If you are one of them, count yourself lucky, but if you really check it out, most people have one or more serious issues.'

'Ridiculous is a good word to describe this situation,' Tara agreed. 'It's one of those situations which would be funny if it wouldn't be so sad. **You know, we have to take a test to be allowed to drive a car?** We have to have a pilot licence to fly a plane, we need to have all sorts of certificates to do pretty much anything nowadays. I mean you even need a licence to have a dog! **But anybody can go and have a child not having a clue.** There is no curriculum. **It's the luck of the draw if the kids get taught fundamental life skills or not.'**

'This is mind numbing. The fundamental make-up of our society is neglected right from the word 'Go', because we as parents, simply don't know any better ourselves,' Lee said with despair.

Schools Lost their Higher Meanings

'You know, the ancient teachings of love and joy and community have become so diluted and forgotten, that they're mainly left to Religion and alternative organisations to be distributed,' Tara continued.

'True, but they usually communicate in a way which is far too removed from our normal day to day lives. The language they use simply doesn't fit into our new scientific way of thinking. The vocabulary is not hip, the messages aren't trendy. Most people switch off as soon as they hear the word Religion or Love. I feel that it's not the *core* messages that the people don't like, most people agree with not killing or stealing or whatever, but it's the *way* it's being taught that doesn't switch people on anymore, they just can't relate to it,' Lee brushed his hair back. This was fundamental stuff.

'True. The stories read to us in church are set in a time so different from ours, that even adults have difficulties to apply the messages to their lives. In the age of business, skaters, hip hop, drugs and parties, stories about the Romans, Fish, mountains, holy men and temples just don't pull any weight anymore,' Tara shrugged her shoulders.

Lee picked up, 'You know, it's sad really, Religion, Jesus, Buddha, LaoTsu, Krishna and all their friends have been talking about this stuff for centuries. They talked to Spirits, they healed with their hands, they received messages, they followed all the Universal Laws, they loved unconditionally, and instead of thinking: "Oh wow, that's so cool, I wonder how I could do that," we just think that: "Well, these were the olden days," or "it's probably not true anyway," or " even if it was, true, it's not possible anymore in our day and age" or well, that's them, *I* wouldn't be able to do that." I think we're missing out,' Lee said with emphasis.

'I think so too,' Tara said. 'Even though the world and time moved on, the teachings didn't. People were still mostly taught in the old traditional ways but they simply couldn't relate to the messages anymore. Over time the relevance to people's lives got totally lost in the process. With time even the teachers forgot *how* to teach and *how* to get the message across to people of the Modern World, to Children, Teenagers and Adults alike, people from *all* walks of life. **As a consequence, after a while, even the teachers themselves forgot the real meaning behind the words they were teaching, and thus passed on a long line of diluted, empty messages.'**

'It's actually quite bizarre,' Lee frowned, 'all the main subjects we learn at school: Mathematics, Religion, Philosophy, Physics, Chemistry, Biology, **they all initially had one aim in Mind, to examine the marvels of the world. They were all inherently about trying to explain the Universe. They were sacred sciences. They were about the major realisation that there was an innate connection between everything, that everything is made out of the same material, that it all vibrates, that certain Vibrations create certain shapes. Even boring old Maths was used to create buildings in sink with Nature and to affect people in certain ways, simply through their shape and dimensions. And from History? We were supposed to learn not to repeat our mistakes, rather than regurgitate dates and names.'**

'Well, that didn't work,' Tara said grimly.

'No it didn't,' Lee threw his hands into the air and dropped them again, 'and that's because we don't teach those higher meanings of the subjects anymore. And what's worse, the few beautiful teachers that *do get it*, are bound and restricted by the **schools curriculum, which emphasises learning the *details*, rather than understanding the *whole*.** Religion for example, which should all be about love and compassion, is often reduced to dates, places and learning stuff by heart,' Lee said. 'And like this, the *real* messages get lost in the details.'

'If the kids manage to stay awake for them, that is,' Tara managed a smile. 'But even if the big subjects such as love or compassion are being talked about in school, they are usually being discussed as abstract concepts or are characterised as saintly qualities, rather than as a virtue which *all* of us can aspire to. We see them as exceptions, rather than something wonderful that *everybody* can attain, and there are therefore usually no *practical* hints and tips of how to actually achieve any of those qualities within our lives. Do we really not care?'

'Well, there are some alternative schools out there that make a point of teaching those things, but they are few and far between. They're also not accessible to everyone, financially or due to location. Besides, this stuff should really be in the main stream schooling system.'

'I second that,' Tara nodded vigorously.

'So, all in all,' Lee began to summarise, '**the ancient teachings don't work in their original form in our modern society anymore. The messages nonetheless are as relevant as they ever were**. If we could find a way to have the existing classes at school teach the original subject's meanings again? Now that would really begin to change the world. Putting the focus back on the inside rather than the outside? On working with Nature, rather than owning it?' he thought for a second. 'But hey, fat chance! **You can't run a business with teachings like that, can you?**' he said cynically. 'It's so much better to teach Maths for Business or Chemistry for the Pharmaceutical Industry or Biology for cloning or History to learn how to become more powerful, than to look after people's most fundamental needs, Love and Happiness.'

Society, Love and Relationships

'It's all so frustrating,' Tara sat up straight and crossed her legs. '**Our entire educational system has been put in place so that we can learn how to become a valid member of the Business society, rather than a humanitarian society. We learn how to become good *business* people, rather than how to become *good* people,**' she threw her hands up in the air in a gesture of despair. 'Who in our educational system, or afterwards even, teaches us how to become a *good* person? How to help others? How to care for others? How to love? How to have relationships (be it platonic or sexual)? How to communicate? How to forgive? How to relate with others unconditionally? How to deal with our Thoughts and Emotions? Nobody.'

The Thought horrified Lee. He drew a long breath, 'It's unbelievable that our basic human needs are not part of the national curriculum, whereas Maths is. Our world really is messed up,' Lee finished.

'You know what? I just thought, that it's not just about children and parents anymore,' Tara said, **'but about society as a whole.** Hardly any of us have actually been taught how to have a successful relationship or how to communicate well with other people. Nobody taught *us* how to experience bliss and harmony. Nobody taught *us* how to love or how to be unconditional with another person. Nobody taught *us* how to stop worrying so much, or how to deal with our insecurities. Once we're adults, nobody teaches us anymore anyway, unless we actively go and seek it. Friend can sometimes be of help, but they often can only pass on their own experiences of hurts and failure, with often very little practical advice. Real practical advice, not just: "pull yourself together," or "don't worry about it," but something with a bit more meat, can be hard to find,' Tara said harshly but truthfully.

'Good point,' Lee could identify with that. All of his friends had their two cents to give after his break up with Kate, but nobody had been able to give him any practical step by step advice on how to deal with his Thoughts and Emotions. He had to meet a total stranger for that. And boy, he was grateful. 'Man, nobody tells us how to deal with a break-up, or how to get a loving and fulfilling relationship in the first place, or even how to *stay* in one and achieve *contentment* in a relationship,' he said. 'I think many of us learn about Love and relationships from television and films, soap operas and dramas, but they feed us ideals or nightmares of love and relationships, which are usually of little *practical* use.

Sure there are books out there and self help seminars, but many people don't go to them. Some simply can't afford them or don't know about them, some people think it's embarrassing to have a problem, rather than knowing that it's normal. People see it as stigma to need counselling. Some people don't even know they have an issue that could be changed or solved, they simply think that that's just the way life is or the way they are. Others do seek help, but the help doesn't address their issues. Man, all this stuff really should be part of our general education.'

'Agreed, but a common argument against that is: "but Love and relationships *are* experimental and everybody has to find their own way. Nobody can teach that." - And of course that's true to a certain extent, but it's also a cop out,' Tara said sternly. **'So many divorces, personal problems and unhappy relationships could be avoided, if somebody would just explain *how* to relate, but not just *after* the problem occurred, when it's to late, but as a norm, as a preventative technique, as part of our education system.** But it's not done, even though we're expected to relate to people all day long.

Nobody teaches us *how* to communicate, even though we're expected to communicate all day long. **Nobody teaches us *how* to love, even though we expect of ourselves to be in loving relationships *and* love ourselves.** Many of us feel like failures if we can't do it right.' Lee shook his head in disbelief as Tara went on, 'I really find it incredible that we have to learn about all of this by trial and error. Every single one of us, every single time, over and over,' she smiled vaguely. 'For some people the learning phase is more painful than for others, some learn quicker than others, some never learn. Some are lucky and get good advice on the way, others don't,' Tara was exasperated. 'Here it is again, as we said before, isn't it odd that such an advanced species leaves the most important things in life to every single person's trial and error? Without even offering far-reaching guidance?'

'The closest we get is sex education at school,' Lee said sarcastically.

'Yeah, great, very useful,' Tara shook her head, her braids swinging and coming to rest on her chest. 'We learn how to put on a condom, if we're lucky, we learn how sperm gets to the egg, but not how to communicate about feelings. It's *sex* education, not *relationship* education, not *communication* education, not how to *love* or how to have *equal, fulfilling* relationships. We are not taught *preventative* methods for relationship problems, we're not taught to address issues *before* they take over our lives. **Our society is set up to deal with *symptoms*, but not with *causes*.**'

'Yep. Agreed. But you know, besides school, what about afterwards? As you mentioned earlier, as soon as we've left school, we're on our own. We have to find our own teachers! Some people are incredibly lucky and find the right people to help them along the way, and others are not so lucky,' Lee looked at Tara. 'You know, looking at all of this, I'm beginning to realise something. **We can't blame society or teachers or even parents for any of this, because they've all been taught in the same system! They don't know any better either!**' Lee said with horror.

'Exactly, and we can't teach what *we* don't know, what *we* haven't been taught,' Tara stressed.

Lee pushed his hands through his hair and scratched the back of his head, **'You know, I wonder if we're not teaching it, because *nobody* actually gets it.'**

'Well, there are people out there that *do* get it. Actually, one would have thought, that by now the leaders of this world would have clogged on to all of this and would have started to get those people together to teach this stuff in schools, wouldn't one? I mean they're supposed to be clever people up there in government,' Tara nodded upwards, 'but they're *not* doing it. **Nobody teaches these life essentials to the world.** Why? I just don't know! **Could we not be happy and balanced and still be**

obedient?' **Tara said with a firmly sarcastic undertone and a wicked twinkle in her eyes.**

We're All different

'Well, maybe it's not that bad?' Tara supposed. 'But then again, if it isn't, how come then that we have to have an entire social system that's trying to catch the unloved children and adults of our society? It's great that we do have those facilities, but once again, we are treating the *symptoms* of society, rather than the causes. Prisons, youth facilities, counsellors, psychiatrists etc, they're all treating the symptoms and they're overflowing with 'inmates'.

What we need to do instead, is to take a step back and look at the *big* picture, find out why all these kids and grown ups getting messed up *in the first place*, and then find a way how to *prevent* it. But that's not an easy thing to do, because it's difficult to find a fix that fits all.'

'That's *because we're all different*. We all have different stories and needs,' Lee emphasised and quickly made a note on a fresh page in his book:

Help society:
* Find what the causes of problems are.
* Find a way to *prevent* them.
* Why is it so difficult to find a fix that fits all?
* Because we're all different.

Tara waited for him to finish and then said, 'So, why are we so different? Because we all grow up in different environments, with different parents, with different social status. We live in different countries, towns and cultures, we have experienced different standards, rules and regulations. Different people *think* differently. Everybody has a different way of relating to problems, concepts and solutions, people solve problems from different angles and look at life situations from different perspectives. What is common sense for one, is totally beyond understanding for another. The perfect day for one could be a nightmare for someone else. We all get fed different ideals, different ideas of love, relationships and of how to Be with other people. None of these things are ever one hundred percent the same for any one person, even if they come from the *same* background,' Tara emphasised. 'All of those factors, and more which I haven't mentioned, make us who we are. **Every single human being is *different*. Not just the way we look, but the way we think, process, relate and feel.**

We're all different and we all have different ideals and principles which we believe to be good and true,' she took a long breath. 'Gosh, that was good to get out.'

'Oh man, something just clicked,' Lee talked quickly not to loose his Thought, 'we think that we are the way we are, full-stop, and that nothing can change that. It's what we were made into, but even though we understand that other people are different, simply because of *their* upbringing, we don't *really* understand that this means that if we change our circumstances, we can change ourselves too, right? There might be some existing ingrained in us patterns already for sure, but with new influences, we can create a new future, right?' he beamed at Tara, who smiled back at him, equally happily. 'Man, we believe that our boundaries are *set* in stone by our education, by our background and role models. **We are simply not aware that we can change those boundaries at whim, that there are other ways of thinking, living or behaving out there - other people are living them already - and that they can be learned and adopted. That we can choose.**' Lee continued with vigour, '**We are what we learn. We strive for ideals which were taught to us, we were taught reference points which we use to judge and create opinions of the world around us. But we can re-learn! We can change, create and reinvent ourselves anew, just the way we want to be,**' Lee breathed in deeply, looking at Tara.

'Exactly,' Tara nodded enthusiastically. 'For example, **if you've learned right from when you were little,** that: you're always right. Or: everything is yours. Or: you don't have to Listen to anybody. Or: if you want something and the other person doesn't want to give it, you just take it anyway, if necessary by force. Or: if you don't get what you want you just scream or get in a huff. Or,' Tara expanded, 'if you've learned or have been told that nobody likes you. Or: that you will never be good enough for your parents, or whatever. ***That's* what you will believe, *that's* who you will be, who you are,**' Tara paused dramatically and then continued, '**until you start to believe *differently* or until you *actively* decide to change,**' Tara recalled her own experience.

'Right,' Lee thought for a moment. 'The only problem is that if we were never taught this, we'll never know that it's even possible. We'll never know that life *could* be different, that *we* could be different. We'd never know an alternative. One that's actually truly possible for us to achieve. We have no idea what to aspire to or what we *could* become,' Lee paused. '**Essentially, we could try and explain to a delinquent, under-privileged, beaten child until the cows come home that there is love out there and caring and beauty. The kid will not even begin to be able to understand what we're talking about, because it has never experienced love. It has no point of reference.** Nothing to relate it too. If somebody has learned something for their entire life, and then somebody else comes along and tells them, that it's all wrong and they have to do it differently now? I mean, it's not surprising that there'll be problems. It takes time, experience and patience to reprogram us!'

'It's like an alien coming to earth,' Tara said in all seriousness, 'an alien, that has never seen the colour "blue" or felt "heat". **Unless the alien experiences these things, they are not part of it's reality. It can understand the descriptions and it might clarify things a bit, but in the end, they remain words.**'

'Right, and out of that very same reason, the delinquent kid might truly not understand that a certain Behaviour is bad, simply because it just doesn't know any different,' Lee said.

'True. We might think that the kid or the adult is stubborn or unwilling, but in fact it might not be. It might just not understand. I'm not trying to come up with excuses for messed up kids or try to play down crimes they might have committed. All I am trying to say is that *our kids learn by example*,' Tara looked at Lee more firmly. '*What we teach them is who and what they become.*'

'Affirmative,' Lee said and started to scribble profusely. While his pen danced across the pages once again, a little neuron in the far corner of his brain noticed that the more his Body and Mind relaxed and the more he opened up, the easier the words seemed to appear out of the tip of his pen, as if by magic. He didn't even have to really think about them anymore.

Tara smiled, looking at Lee writing like a madman. He was sitting cross-legged, his back straight and his head just slightly bend down, looking at the pad. His hair had fallen over his forehead, as it usually did, and he looked as if he was taking down a dictation that was just a tiny bit to fast. His writing was slurring with speed. When he finally finished, he looked up satisfied and showed Tara his list.

We're all different:
- We think differently.
- We feel differently.
- We interpret ideas, situations and conversations differently.
- We have different expectations.
- We believe different things to be true.
- We believe different things to be worthy of our attention.
- We have different ideals.
- We have different ideas of love and relationships (platonic or sexual).
- We have different ideas of how to Be with other people.
- We solve problems from different angles.
- We look at life's situations and developments from different perspectives.

- We have different logic and feelings of common sense.
- We have different reference points.
- We reason differently.
- We have different opinions.
- We want and need different things to be happy.
- We need different things to feel loved and understood.
- We communicate what we need differently.
- We interpret Signs we receive differently.
- We behave and react according to what we learned in our lives, all of which is and has been different.
- We set our personal boundaries according to what we learned in our lives, which again is different for every person.

'That's a pretty conclusive list man, well done,' Tara said impressed.

'Thanks,' Lee smiled broadly. 'This Listening business is great,' he said pretty impressed himself, 'you don't have to think, it just comes.'

'What can I say?' Tara grinned happily, flopped herself on her back and looked up into the tree in silence.

At Ease

Lee joined her. He was acutely aware that he'd gotten used to the little silent moments they shared. Normally, in situations with other people, silences killed him, they were just too uncomfortable. He opened his eyes and saw Tara peacefully lying next to him. He turned onto his side and looked at her. With Tara it never felt uncomfortable. He wondered why. Gently he diverted his attention to his breathing. While his Thoughts were slowing down, answers came to him. He noticed that with her, he never tried to figure out *why* she was silent. He didn't think about reasons. He didn't wonder if she was bored by the conversation or if he had said something to offend her, or if he should try and say something to bridge the silence. Instead, his Mind just switched off and rested. He knew that when she was ready, she would resume the conversation, and so would he.

Lee looked at Tara, her hair, the contours of her hips, her shoulders. He realised how easy it was to be with somebody, if he himself wasn't constantly trying to figure out what the other person was thinking. From now on, he resolved, if he wanted to know something, anything, he would just ask, rather than make up stories, even if he wanted to know was going on in another person's head. If on the other hand he decided that it wasn't important to know, he would *stop* thinking about, but if it *was*

623

important, he would *act*. Easy really. Strange that he hadn't come up with that himself before. Well, he had now. He smiled.

Snippets of their conversations flew by his observing Mind and one word stood out distinctly. *Experience*. Ah, that's *why* he suddenly understood. Because he'd been *experiencing* this Mind stuff by hanging out with Tara. He wasn't just regurgitating theory, but he had already began to *do* it. Through his own *Experience* it had begun to become *part* of him. He didn't have to just believe anymore, but he could comfortably trust *his own* truth now, it wasn't just somebody else's words anymore.   He turned back onto his back and stretched himself contentedly. With a smile in his eyes he looked up into the sky and silently said, 'Thanks Dudes,' and went back into that wonderful warm space which Nowness had become for him.

They laid just like that for another while, when Thoughts slowly began to creep back into Lee's Mind, bouncing up and down on the outer reaches of his Awareness. Slowly he redirected his Consciousness from his Breath to give the new arrivals in his brain some of his attention. The images that appeared in his Mind told him that now, as he began to understand himself more, the fact that everybody was *different* seemed to strike him even harder. **He began to appreciate that the clarity of Nowness, which people shared at birth, became clouded with everybody's own little flavours as we grew up. These individual flavours made us who we are. That was beautiful, Lee thought, but at the same time, peoples differences tended to create conflict, sometimes just because people were misunderstanding each other.** Lee mulled the Thought over for a minute. **There had to be a way of how to relate better with others, while still retaining who we were, while retaining our individuality.** Lee's Thoughts abruptly finished. He tried to continue his ideas, but his Mind was empty. Once again the peace and calmness that he had come to know over the past couple of days, descended over his Mind and Body. No Mind. Now. A gentle smile spread over his face. When he finally opened his eyes, he found Tara looking at him, her gaze felt loving and open.

'Hi,' she said.
'Hi,' he replied affectionately.

Tara liked the warmth they shared, the silences. She loved looking at him, his face, his Body, the serene expression on his face, his smiles. She laid on her side now too, leaning on one elbow, with her head propped up in her hand. As looked at him closer, Lee's hand slowly bridged the space between them. It hesitated for a second, then came to a soft rest on her waist.

624

Gently, he pulled her closer to him and held her warmly. To his surprise and delight, she snuggled up to him.

'Come here,' he said, tightened his hold and drew her even closer, finally smelling the sweetness of her hair. "Perfect fit," he thought, feeling happy and content.

"Yippeeee," was the Thought that danced around in Tara's Mind, as she buried her face in Lee's chest.

Love and Unconditional Relationships – The Real Thing... – How It Really Works

'**O**k, now then, we're all different, parents mess up their children, we don't know anything about love or relationships, so, **how can we sort all this stuff out?**' Lee asked, playfully pinching Tara's side.

Tara squealed cutely and turned her head just enough so that she could speak comfortably, 'Well, in my humble opinion, it all starts the same way.'

'You don't say,' Lee grinned. 'And that way wouldn't happen to be Nowness, would it?'

'How'd you guess?' Tara grinned back at him.

'Absolutely no idea,' Lee giggled. ' But man, I'd love to see you solve the world's problems with it,' he smiled genuinely. 'So, how does it work?'

'Well,' Tara began, 'when we become more Mindful about our sensations, feelings, actions and reactions, and once we stop feeding all the millions of puppies around us, then we can maintain Nowness. And in Nowness our Mind is Balanced and strong. Nothing ruffles our feathers anymore. Whatever happens around us, we're as solid as a rock and nothing pushes us over anymore. Other magnets can come and be in our field, but it's not a big deal anymore. We can just Be, anywhere, anytime, with anyone.'

'Yeah, I know all of that, and?' Lee tapped his fingers impatiently.

'Well, **when we have achieved such a state of Being, we can overcome the differences within ourselves and with others. *That's* when we're ready for *Unconditional* Relationships. In the Now, nobody *expects*. In the Now, nobody *judges*. In the Now, nobody projects their own opinions onto the other. In the Now, we all have the same rights.**'

625

'More?' Lee beckoned Tara to continue. He propped his head up a little and looked at her more intently.

'By following the Universal Laws and through Nowness and Mindfulness of our Thoughts, actions, Behaviour, Emotions as well as cause and effect, do we become fully Aware and fully Conscious of ourselves and others, which in turn enables us to have Unconditional Relationships between two Equal Beings. Two *whole*, *strong* and *balanced* Hearts, unified in happiness and content, enriching each other's lives,' she paused briefly and scrunched up her face a little, **'rather than two half hearts, trying to make each other whole, two Beings just ticking along, because they don't want to be alone.'**

'Uhm, yeah,' Lee agreed whole heartedly. He knew those kinds of relationships. They weren't fun.

'Actually, let me clarify something,' Tara said as she slowly pulled herself out of his arms to sit up again.

Lee smiled. She had stayed close enough to maintain contact with his Body. He looked up at her as she spoke.

'Of course a loving relationship fulfils, right?' she said. 'But what I'm talking about though, is the *intent* behind entering a relationship.'

Lee nodded, waiting. Were they indirectly talking about how to have a relationship, or were they still discussing cosmic stuff? Kind of both, he smiled to himself. A comfortable tingling spread through his belly.

'Ok, I think I've just lost you,' Lee turned onto his front, 'come again?' His focus had waned and he wasn't sure if Tara had something else.

'Oh, sorry,' Tara said slightly blushing, 'ehm, well, let me explain how I perceive the common view of love nowadays, and then in turn what Love *can* actually be like, and with that I mean the purest form of Love, not some idealistic dream stuff, but what it can *really* be all about. What it can be like if two *Whole* and *Equal* Beings come together.'

'Go right ahead,' Lee thought he knew what Tara was going to say, he'd had experiences like that, but still, he was interested in hearing Tara's take on it.

'Well, the prerequisite to feel whole and fulfilled in a relationships is that we have to feel whole and fulfilled *before* we enter it - exceptions as always proof the rule, but still, unconditional love is based on two *whole* Beings coming together. A *whole* person finding another *whole* person. Two whole hearts joining side by side, enriching each others lives, growing together, being there for each other. Accepting and loving each other unconditionally.'

Lee was glad he'd listened, 'I think that would be amazing, but I think that particular idea is not commonly practiced yet. There are shit lots of people out there having relationships that are far, far away from what you've just described. I mean like not even remotely close to it,' he said sadly.

'I know. Today's relationships are unfortunately not based on that kind of love. It's more like: half a heart finding another half to make each other whole, and then, when we're without a partner, we're just half a heart again. We feel incomplete and keep looking for another person to make us whole again. In fact, we *expect* the other person to make us whole. Sometimes that works, but to achieve true symmetry and harmony this way, the other person's half a heart needs to be *exactly* the *same* shape, size and shape of *our* half heart, otherwise it won't fit. It would be crooked and that wouldn't feel right. It would be out of balance. I guess it's obvious that finding that perfect fit doesn't happen every day. So, what do we do?' Tara asked.

Lee sat up all of a sudden, looking intent, 'Gosh, we try and *make* it fit.'

'Exactly. The normal kind of sequence of a relationship today is: meeting a wonderful person, and with time, realising that they are different from us. Then trying to change them, then getting angry or frustrated because they don't. Then trying harder. Then getting disillusioned or pissed off because it's still not working the way we want it. Then separating or going on bickering, fighting, nagging and moaning and generally becoming even more unhappy. Of course there are lots of happy times as well, but all in all? Sorry, but that's not what I call being fulfilled.'

'I certainly see your point,' Lee nodded, sharing Tara's sentiment.

'And you know what the worst thing is once such a relationship stops?' Tara asked.

'What?'

'We're two half hearts again! Half, unfulfilled and weak. And guess what?'

'The whole story starts all over again. Bloody hell!' Lee cocked his head to one side.

'Yep. Obviously there are always exceptions, but generally, that's the typical cycle in today's relationships, no matter over how many years they might go on for.'

'I guess most people simply don't know any different. They think it's normal, to be like that,' **Lee said, wondering how he shaped up against all of this. He didn't think he was quite that bad, but then again..., and, what about Tara herself, he silently questioned.**

Tara seemed to have read his Mind, 'You're right, and man, I'm not perfect myself, but I count myself fortunate that I at least *see* this trend, that I am *aware* of it, and in a relationship, I would want somebody that can see it too. I live for the openness, the Nowness and the commitment to be as Now as I can, *and* therefore have that reciprocated in a relationship. I want to be able to point out to each other when we loose connection,' Tara added quietly. 'I really want to be Now. Together. Well, I'm working on it,' she added even more quietly.

'I'd love to try,' Lee whispered nearly inaudibly. They looked at each other for a moment, each surprised by their own little Thoughts.

Tara broke the silence, 'We think it's normal to have millions of expectations of our partners. I mean,' she added sarcastically, 'the other-half has a job to do, right? A duty to fulfil. The job to be *our* other half, to be the right shape and size to make *us* whole. To do what *we* want them to do.'

'Yeah,' Lee said thoughtfully. 'Our relationships are usually not about just *Being* together, but about *Shaping* each other. We try to make fundamental changes to the way a partner behaves or acts or does things. The classics are the way they talk or dress or look, the toothpaste cap, the toilet seat, being more considerate, remember Birthdays, do more of this and less of that,' Lee remembered his own fare share of nagging girlfriends - some more justified than others. 'Other favourite bones of contention are about the children or the mother in law or the car or the job or the food or the washing up, the shopping, the trash, or maybe just little ticks like scratching or sniffing or fiddling or forgetfulness or untidiness. The list goes on. These are just a few things that people get hung up on,' he looked serious. 'I guess it's obvious how the care-freeness in relationships gets lost this way. It might be there from time to time, but it's not the constant undercurrent in many relationships. I guess,' Lee remembered a previous example, 'it's like being two magnets with differing energies and one is pulling this way and the other is pulling into a completely different direction. We're competing for each other's energies, both trying to align the other's bits to be just like ours. It's a constant struggle, a constant demanding and giving in. People live *off* each other, deliberately or subconsciously. Some more extremely and obviously than others,' Lee drew a long breath.

Tara nodded, '**In Unconditional Relationships on the other hand, both partners are *equal*.** If we are whole within ourselves, we are like magnets with strong, self-contained energy fields, we don't disturb others and others don't disturb our bits. **We can rely on our strength, which comes from a core deep within us.** That's when two Wholes come together. Two equals. **We can still be different magnets, two individuals, but it means that we are happy and content with who we are and that we love ourselves just the way we are.'**

'**And that's what allows us to love and accept the other person just the way *they* are,**' Lee picked up Tara's sentence. 'We wouldn't want anybody to come along and change us, so we are prepared to grant the other Being the same right. We can be with each other without expectations, unconditionally. We can live *together* and not *off* each other. We have a companion, a best friend, a play mate, a partner in crime,' he drew breath and felt another warm tingly feeling, this time around his heart **'a person to grow with, to share with, laugh with, learn with and from. Two people are together, because they *want* to be, not because they *need* each other to make each other whole.'**

'Exactly. There is no taking, only giving and receiving. It's an intuitive balance. There are no expectations and there are no demands.'

'But come to think of it,' Lee thought for a second. 'two whole hearts still have issues or not? I mean, nobody is perfect. **How would you work with this on a practical level?** You know, every day life kind of stuff?'

Tara answered without hesitation, 'Partners in Unconditional Relationships, deal with issues is differently.'

'Oh?' Lee Listened closer.

'When Whole Hearts love, it's not about wanting to change the other person, and it's not about just putting-up with things that disturb us either. **Relationships are *not* about becoming a martyr, it's not about Being with somebody that you really don't get on with and just hope that in Nowness it disappears.** No. **It's about *working* together.** *Talking* to each other and *Listening* to each other and *consciously* trying to find a way to be together and grow. Compromises have to come from each person themselves. There needs to be a mutual understanding of what can or can't, or what each person wants to or doesn't want to change. Change needs to happen because the individual *wants* to change, not because the other person is nagging or demanding the change.'

'Because that can create resentment,' Lee said, shifting around a bit to make himself more comfortable.

'Exactly. It has to be a combined effort between two *open* Beings, with a *mutual* commitment to *stay open* with one another. And if something needs to be done, *both* have to work on it. You don't nag, you don't moan. You take action. And you agree what this action needs to be. On both sides.

If we can't accept the other person the way they are, if the other person really disturbs our energy field so bad that we really can't live with them, well, then maybe we shouldn't be with that person, because obviously?'

'We'd rather have a different one.'

'Precisely. We should not be in a relationship because we *can't* be alone, or because we don't *dare* to be alone, or because we don't know *how* to be alone.'

'Yeah, sometimes it's better to part than to desperately stay together,' Lee said, his Thoughts wading through his memories. Tara nodded, aware of her own memories flying past her. She shook them off, started to write and began to read out loud a few bullet points as she was jotting them down.

When Whole Hearts have issues with each other:
- They look at themselves first and check why something is causing them a problem. Is it really such a big issue, or is it a silly little puppy wanting attention just for the sake of it?
- They are Mindful and spend time in Nowness. They know that in Nowness, they are fully *connected* with their partner.
- They recognise the insignificance of most problems in the light of what's *really* important.
- In a Whole Heart relationship, both partners look at themselves first. They never accuse or blame the other for their own unhappiness. Both understand that each person is responsible for his or her own happiness.
- There is no struggle, but openness and understanding. There's no stubbornness, greed or ego, but Strength, Wisdom and Unconditionality.
- They are aware that different reference points, experiences and the use of words (which limit our expression) can create possible misunderstandings.
- They don't make any assumptions about anything the other person says. If they're not sure, they always ask to clarify.
- They don't try to guess what the other person is thinking, they don't make up silly stories about what the other person *could* be thinking! They ask and verify.
- If they feel that the other person said something that's strange or unlike them, they clarify it *every time*, just in case!
- There's open and honest communication. They don't hold back feelings, but discuss problems open and lovingly.
- They don't bottle up, but discuss issues as and when they occur.
- They know that Love is not about believing that we know better than the other, or that we have more right to be the way we want to be, than the other.
- They work on issues equally, with the aim to make each other happy, rather than to get one up on the other.
- They work on problems together. They understand that no problem is one sided. There are *always* two sides to the coin.
- If one person has a problem, the other Listens and tries to understand. They don't defend a point of view, but accept that the other person *feels* that way. If that is the way it is or not, doesn't matter, it's the way they feel.
- They *actively* try to find a solution together.

- They understand each other, because they talk about *the way* they *want* to relate to each other.
- Each tells the other about the things they can't help themselves doing, what they've been trying to change about themselves, basically things they know the other partner should know about themselves. They try to make sure that each persons' issues are laid bare. Each can then decide for themselves if they want to change or if they want to stay the way they are.
- Each partner can decide for themselves if they want to have assistance in changing.
- They talk to each other about problems in previous relationships to try and avoid any similar conflict in the current relationship.
- They give and receive equally and naturally.
- They *want* to make each other happy and they actively do things for their partner, just because they like it.
- They can always be bothered.
- If they want to be Now together, they point out to each other when they loose their connection, and find out why they lost it.
- They have to be brave enough to bare yourself open.
- They want to be a whole heart in all relationships, sexual or not.
- They are relate-ionships. It's about *relating* to one another. Relating means connecting, interacting, cooperating. Working *together*.

Lee read the list as Tara was writing. When she was done she said, **'You know, when you come down to it, Unconditional Relationships are about *Awareness, wanting* to make each other happy, and *actively* working on doing that. It's about doing nice things for each other, simply because we know that it makes us and them happy.'**

'Yeah, when we spend time with a partner, we know what the other person likes or needs,' Lee thought out loud.

'Precisely, so we just give because it's nice, not just because it's needed.'

'Good point. If we know what the other enjoys, why not just do it?'

'Exactly. But it's about doing that all the time, not just in the first few months of courtship. **It's about being an *active* part of the relationship, it's about being Aware, about observing and seeing what needs to be done and doing it without having to be asked.** He's sweeping, get the dustpan. She's making a cup of tea, get the milk ready. He's looking for a lighter, help him find one. How often have you observed somebody and knew exactly what they needed, but you just couldn't be bothered to help? Whenever that little twinge comes like: well, I know I should. Well, *just do it*.'

'It all sounds a bit idealistic, but it sounds absolutely wonderful,' Lee said dreamily.

'It is,' Tara said. She'd been working on her relationships for a while now and she'd discovered a whole new world of wonderfulness when both partners shared the same ideals and when both were willing and set on evolving and growing together. Tara looked across the grass and said, 'But of course, it's not about going and taking the first best person from the street, marry them and trying to make it work.'

'It's NOT?' Lee sat up dead straight looking horrified, only the twinkle in his eyes giving him away.

Tara laughed out loud. She was so glad that Lee had such a sharp Mind, it made flirting so much fun. She blushed slightly once again, 'Well, that depends, of course,' she smiled sweetly, 'you never know what you might find on the street,' she said as she winked at him, then added quietly, 'as long as you happen upon somebody who wants the same thing.' Her voice became a tad more serious, 'To really make this game work, it needs two emotionally mature and whole people who are prepared to open up and talk about *everything* and not hold back *anything*. Otherwise Unconditional Relationships will always remain just a nice dream,' her voice trailed off.

'You never know what you might *have found* on the street,' Lee echoed silently, a smile spreading across his face.

They sat looking at the tree, the sky and the grass, each feeling the warmth of the moment and each other.

Headspace

This time it was Lee who broke the silence, 'You know, even though I agree with all of that, I think that unfortunately a lot of people have no idea that such a dream could be reality, that it can be achieved, that it could even exist. They have no *reference points* of how something like that could look like or work in a practical sense.' Tara nodded in agreement as Lee went on, 'I guess, we often confuse passion with love, and infatuation with attraction. We know all about quick satisfaction without the relationship angle, and on the other hand, about the endless trying to make relationships work. But we don't know how to just *Be* with somebody. And that's in sexual or even just normal everyday relationships. Man,' Lee rolled his eyes, 'isn't it crazy? All those behavioural cycles we're in and don't even notice.'

'I know, it's nuts. But all it needs, is just one switch to be flicked. It's so straight forward,' Tara emphasised. 'Even if we can't change all the other magnets around us, we *can* at least change our *own* headspace, and that in itself is going to make a huge difference! Just being Aware, Conscious and Mindful of *our* way of relating is a great step on the way. *Everybody* can become Aware and Conscious of all of this. *Everybody* can implement this into their lives. It just takes practice. And it's so worth it.'

'But it always takes two,' Lee pointed out, 'and finding that significant other is never that easy, is it?'

'Well, that depends. When you think that you're truly ready for this, *ask* for someone to practice, share and grow with and then be prepared for The Guy's magic. It will come!' she smiled. 'You know, people always grin at me and say: "wow you have high standards." Well, yes I do, but I wouldn't want to go for anything less, I just wouldn't be happy. So, I'd be happy to wait for that person, simply because I'm actually also very content and happy alone.

Anyway, until that special one person arrives, each and every one of us can start with themselves. All we need to do is to become Aware of ourselves first, of what *we're* doing and how *we're* relating to others. We need to understand that we're all different, that we're all in a different headspace, and we need to accept that we cannot expect everybody to be in the same headspace *by default*. And then we need to know that if we both want to, we can enter the *same* headspace together with another person,' Tara's eyes began to sparkle brightly. 'And for that we don't need to wait for *The One*, we can practice that with anybody, even best friends.'

'And when we do that,' Lee was connecting the dots, '**when we consciously enter the *same* headspace, all the stupidity, all the bickering, all the differences people have disappear and we can actually *see* the other person for who they *really* are, without all the silly Thoughts we made up about them or the stuff we expect from them or all the past experiences and ideas that we attached to them. Ah, and that's where Nowness is the link,' Lee was making the connections easily, 'because in Nowness, we're all in the *same* headspace.'**

'Exactly,' Tara nodded. 'By simply *understanding that in the Now, we're all the same,* we can stop judging and expecting, and instead we can begin to understand and develop love compassion and kindness towards each other. We can understand that Unconditional Love is Letting Go. That it's Letting Go of any preconceived ideas, that it's pure experience, untarnished by Thoughts and Emotions. The purest form of love does not require words. When we love like that, our level of vibrations is connected with Oneness. We can feel it. We feel comfort, content, happiness, bliss. We feel it on our own, we feel it when another person joins us, we feel it the other person leaves us again. We feel it, because that's who we have *become*.'

'**Ah, and when we *are* that, that's what our children will experience!**' Lee said. Things were clicking into place. Suddenly the idea of having children didn't seem so outlandish anymore.

'Exactly! Let them *experience* the love and balance. Let them *experience* a solid base and a strong reference point for what Love really is, rather than just learning about it through words. Once again,' Tara added meaningfully, 'we teach by *example*.'

Lee nodded, 'So, in Nowness we can eliminate any existing differences, but the real trick I guess, is *prevention* wherever possible,' he said firmly. 'The prevention of insurmountable or even just niggly differences to occur in the first place. Sure, family life is not always easy, as we've pointed out,' he raised one eyebrow to emphasise the point, 'but by being aware of how fulfilling Unconditional Relationships can be, and by actively working towards that, we can set an example to help our children remain in touch with Nowness, to remain open and to *not* forget how to connect with others in the same headspace, in the easy times and the more trying ones. Wow, marathon sentence, anyway, like this children will grow up to be strong inside, balanced and calm, because that's the environment they're exposed to, that's what they learn and that's what they will absorb.'

'Exactly!' Tara said happily, 'Of course there will be a few little rebels out there,' she added lovingly, 'but at least they'll have a good foundation.'

'Tara. Never one to leave out the juicy bits,' Lee grinned.

'Well, you've got to be realistic, but all in all, **if we relate to other people in this way, we can make a hug impact *now*, and if we relate to our children this way, we can affect an *entire new generation!*'**

Tara turned another page in Lee's little book and wrote with beautiful swirly letters:

Love is Nowness.
Just Being. In Nowness.
We accept ourselves and each other the way we are.
In Nowness the Mind is quiet, the Ego doesn't exist.
Harmony and Unconditionality are the result.
Our children learn by example.

PART 13

35 Experiental Teaching and Learning, Cosmic Ways To Communicate

Lee made charmed uh-ing and ah-ing sounds about the beauty of Tara's words and then said, 'You know, I just thought of something. After what we've said so far, I wonder how it would actually be possible to have a relationship in the Now. I mean sharing information and experiences with words is a major part of being a human being and thus of being in a relationship. And, well, I guess in the Now you can't do that.'

'You're right, but there are many different ways to communicate,' Tara said simply.

Lee pricked up his ears, 'Sounds intriguing, tell me more.'

'Well, we have *three* different *things* we can communicate *with*, and *three* different *ways* to communicate *through*,' Tara's eyes twinkled with excitement when she took hold of pen and paper once again.

We can communicate *with:*
• Words
• Vibrations
• Intuition

We can communicate *through*:
• Our Rational Mind
• Our Intuition
• Merging of the Souls

'Merging of Souls? Isn't that what you mentioned in your story about the First People in The Brief Earth History? Isn't that how they used to communicate?' Lee said excitedly after reading Tara's notes.

'Exactly.'

'Now that sounds interesting,' Lee said appreciatively.

'Oh boy, it is.'

'Go on then!' Lee requested curiously.

Limitations Of Communicating With Words

'Well, let's start at the beginning,' she tapped the first point on the list with Lee's pen. 'When we communicate with words, our Rational Mind *prepares* and *interprets* the meaning of the words for us. It compares them to our Ego's experiences, opinions and views. Each point of comparison depends on our upbringing, our conditionings, life experiences and of course on external factors,' she said. 'As we already said, as everyone has a different point of reference, everyone interprets what is being said slightly differently.'

'So if we rely on the Rational Mind for communication, even though we think that we're talking about the same thing, that's not necessarily the case. It's usually always ever so slightly different,' Lee said.

'Yeah, ever so slightly, or hugely! And that's what causes us problems. For example, if two people talk about the colour blue, both think that they are talking about the same colour, until they are asked to pick the shade of blue out of a selection of colours. Then they'd see that they both had an entirely different shade of blue in Mind,' Tara paused. **'It really is that drastic. If you believe it or not, we *constantly* misinterpret and misunderstand each other and the scary thing is that we don't even realise.** Most of the time it never occurs to us that it could even be that way. We just expect that everybody understands *exactly* what we're talking about, *exactly* the way *we* understand it.'

'When in actual fact, every person hears what they *want* to hear or what they're *used* to hear, rather than what's actually being said,' Lee added.

'Right. The word Family for example has a very different meaning in different cultures. Let's say,' Tara paused, 'traditional Asian values as compared to the average Western ideas of the word Family. Both cultures are likely to understand it as a unit of blood-related people, but each one will have a different *concept* of Family in their Mind.'

'A slightly different shade of blue.'

'Right. Both will have different associations with the word, depending on their cultural upbringing, social imprint, moral priorities, way of life and responsibilities. Each of which will give the word Family it's own special meaning.'

'I know what you mean. I've actually got an Asian friend who simply can't get his head around the fact that young people in the West disrespect their elders or put them into homes when they get old and sick,' Lee said.

'Whereas for us that's just the way it is.'

'Sadly so,' Lee agreed. 'So different cultures' values of loyalty and respect can be really different. I guess, even people which grew up in the *same* cultural environment can think different. One person might have had a

636

sheltered life, another might have grown up in a neglected environment. If two people with such different experiences and imprinting come together to talk about a subject where the definition of the word Family is vital, misunderstandings might occur, customs can be offended and friendships broken. Well, at least if these differences in reference points are not known beforehand, or identified and clarified during the conversation,' Lee added.

'Which they often aren't,' Tara pointed out.

'Right. Come to think of it, I can see a whole bunch of barely discernible differences in the way all of us see the world. I can see the million and one ways we can attribute different meanings or slightly different nuances to the words we use. It's like speaking different languages,' he thought out loud.

'Well, not really. If we'd speak a different language, it would be obvious that we're *not* communicating on the same level,' Tara said. 'What I'm talking about, are more subtle differences in *understanding*, which people are often not aware of.'

'Good point,' Lee nodded thoughtfully.

'So, the first limitations of using words are misunderstandings, right?' Lee nodded again. 'The second limitation is that we can't even be begin to communicate a lot of the stuff in our heads. Words simply fail us.'

'Exactly. Sometimes words aren't enough to express what we want to say. Words are *so* limiting,' Lee shook his head exaggeratedly. 'But seriously, you're right. When we talk about big cosmic stuff, we try to talk about phenomenally far out ideas within the restrictive parameters of the human alphabet. We try to describe *Universal* events with the limited scope of *twenty-six* letters. Silly really,' Lee laughed. 'Man, sometimes just describing how I *feel*, seems impossible. I just don't have the words to describe things like that properly.'

'Right, and it doesn't help that we usually don't even think in words.'

'Oh,' Lee grinned. 'I just remembered when you told me to think about America. That was so naughty.' He winked at her. 'Man, I remember the millions of impressions flashing past my brain. I knew exactly what I felt and Thought, but I just wasn't able to describe it adequately in a million years. The concepts and impressions that hit my brain were just too many, too fast, whole words of concepts tumbled in on me within seconds,' Lee shook his head to clear his Mind of the intensity of the memory.

'That's exactly what I'm talking about. **Concepts are a space of fuzzy information flashes in our heads, flashes without defined boundaries,'** Tara made a few squiggly motions with her hands in front of her, **'it's difficult to grasp and confine them.** *That's* **why words limit us so much.'**

'I think I can see something coming,' Lee said with a huge smile on his face.

'Oh yeah?' Tara leant her head mischievously to one side, imitating one of Lee's favourite gestures.

'You're going to say now that **if we share the** *same* **headspace, we can see the** *same* **fuzzy flashes, right? That we can experience what the other person does? That we can bypass the words by a** *direct* **brain connection?'**

'Wow, did you just make that up?' Tara was gobsmacked.

'Eh, yeah? Well, that just seems to be the logical next step, or not?' Lee grinned daringly.

'Actually, you've just jump one step ahead,' Tara praised him. 'What you just described would be what I call Merging of Souls. So, full points to you, you're making the right connections, but there is one step in between, which might be worth to mention first,' she pointed at the last list.

'Oh alright then. Let's have it ma'am,' Lee laughed at Tara's meticulous adherence to her lists, but he knew that there was logic to the sequence in which Tara talked about things. He sat back patiently and regally motioned for Tara to continue.

'It's how to communicate with Vibrations to *support* the words,' Tara announced merrily. She was glad that Lee was happy to stick with her little system, this way she knew that she wouldn't forget anything, but also, from experience, it meant that there weren't any confusions or misunderstandings later.

Communicating With Vibrations

'**L**et me give you a bit of background info for this one.'

'Sure, background ahead,' Lee grinned lovingly.

'Well, everything inside and outside of our Body works with electromagnetic impulses, energies and Vibrations, right? I'll use the word Vibrations for all of those, just because it's easier, ok?' Lee gave an affirmative nod. After a seconds worth of trying to find an appropriate example to explain what she was talking about, she said, 'Great, now, imagine a Petry-Dish.'

'One of those flat dishes with a little rim that scientists use to grow bacteria in?'

'Yeah, one of those. Now stick thousands of tiny metal balls in into that dish and put it onto a vibrating surface and observe what happens.' Lee closed his eyes and imagined. 'First you'll see that the balls begin to move, then, with a little time, you'll see them align into a pattern.'

'I remember that from my Physics lessons,' Lee opened his eyes, 'some of the shapes are amazing!'

Tara nodded, she'd also seen some beautiful structures appear in front of her eyes. 'I assume that you also know about the next experiment,' she winked at him. '**The Vibratory-*pattern* of the little metal balls will stay the same until you change the Vibration.**'

'**And then the balls will re-align themselves into a new pattern that corresponds to the new Vibration. I know.** That's just the thing they do, there's no magic in that,' Lee's scientific Mind said, immediately remembering many, many classes of Physics. 'Actually, all the atoms in the Universe vibrate at a certain frequency. They all align to make specific shapes, not just flat arrangements in Petry-Dishes. If the atoms are very dense, i.e. very close together, their pattern creates matter, maybe a crystal, a snowflake, a rock, a plant, an animal, even a human Body. If we change the Vibrations of something like that, it will also change its shape, just like the little metal balls do. If we increase the Vibrations of a rock quite drastically, the rock will explode. Boom,' Lee threw his hands into the air. 'If we increase the Vibrations only minimally, nothing will happen. If we continue to raise the Vibration, over time, even though we might not perceive an immediate effect the rock will get brittle and eventually break,' he said, delving deeper into his memory. 'So basically *everything* vibrates, and the Vibrations of *everything*, affect the Vibrations of *everything else*,' Lee wiped his forehead in mock exhaustion. 'Actually, there's a nice example. This dude did a bunch of experiments where he subjected water to various words that were written on the bottles it was contained in and then examined the water molecules out of each bottle. The results of these experiments were crazy,' Lee said animatedly. '**The water molecules out of the bottles that had nice things like 'love' and 'compassion' written on them, had beautiful, harmonious and balanced molecular patterns, whereas the ones that had nasty stuff like 'hate' and 'kill' and stuff like that written on them, where unbalanced, chaotic and intense looking patters.** The differences were quite extreme. **My emotional reaction to the pictures was pretty intense too.** Just by looking at the printout of the molecular structure, I could really *feel* the kind of word that had been written on the bottle,' he shuddered at the memory of the picture that the words I-hate-you-I-want-to-kill-you had formed. 'The guy did all sorts of experiments. He measured the impact of sounds, words and much more. It's fascinating.'

'I've heard of those experiments,' Tara said, 'and incidentally, you've just hit the nail on the head with regards to what I wanted to talk about. The chap's name who did those experiments you were talking about is, Masaru Emoto and **he has shown that words, letters, pictures, sounds and even** *Thoughts, Intend, Prayers* **and** *Emotions* **affect water molecules**! **Now, hello! Our Body is made out of how many percent water?'** Tara asked just to make a point. 'So, of course we're affected! By all of those things! Big time! Some people might put this down as Hippy-shit, but in fact, there's a scientific side to this too. **Scientists can actually measure slight electromagnetic changes in our Brains when we think,** they can measure a slight rise or dip in our Vibrations.'

'Ah, I understand now what you're trying to get at,' Lee looked at her more closely. 'One object's Vibrations affects another, right? So that means that our Thought, Intent and Emotional Vibrations have an impact on other Vibrational-Entities around us. Such an entity could be another person, a thing or even just the Ether around us. Shit man, *our* Vibrations affect everything.'

'You've got it. Now, back to the point on the list. **After everything we've just said, it's common sense that besides the associated** *content* **of a word, each word also has a** *Sound Vibration,* **a** *Thought-,* **an** *Intend-* **and an** *Emotional* **Vibration linked to it, ok?'**

'**That means that each word doesn't only have an** *intellectual* **meaning, but also a certain Vibrational-Frequency-Meaning associated with it,'** Lee's mouth said as if by itself.

'Right, **and those can be picked up by an experienced Listener.'**

'Wow.'

'I know,' Tara grinned at Lee's amazement and started to write.

Each word has:
- Sound Vibrations
- Thought Vibrations
- Intent Vibrations
- Emotional Vibrations
- And probably much more which we don't know about yet

Thus each word has a:
- Rational/Intellectual/Content-ual-Meaning and a
- Vibrational-Perceptional-Meaning to it.

'Vibrational-Perceptional? Woha, big words,' Lee laughed. 'That'll be a great Hang-man! Nobody would ever guess that.'

'Hangman? Man, I haven't played that in ages. Yeah, I guess I'd win hands down,' Tara smiled.

'Big words or not, I think I know what you mean,' Lee said. 'The Rational-Meaning is how we *interpret* the word and how we *intellectually* understand it with our brain. Whereas the Vibrational-Perceptional-Meaning, is the *Vibrational* meaning *behind* the words, which requires a certain *ability* to *perceive.*'

'Precisely,' Tara said cheerfully. **'No matter how a word is pronounced or what the tonal level of the speaker is, every word still has a specific unmistakable Base Vibration, which is coupled with the Intend, Thought and Emotional Vibration of the speaker. The totality of those Vibrations, is the true meaning of the word. It's unambiguous. It cannot be misunderstood or interpreted.'**

'So, if we could Listen to the Vibrational-Perceptional-Meaning behind the words, we could drastically increase the understanding and thus the value of every word,' Lee clarified.

'That's right. But unfortunately most of us are not at the level of Awareness yet where that can actually happen.'

'So all we need to do is increase our Awareness?' Lee guessed expertly. 'In Nowness maybe?' he grinned cheekily. 'Oh, hang on, actually, that makes sense. In Nowness, we *can* Listen one hundred percent. There are no distracting Thoughts, no judgements, no plans, nothing, ziltsh, one hundred percent attention. Like that we *would* be able to pick up on the subtle Vibrations behind the words, wouldn't we?'

'You've got it! **In Nowness we can pick up on *and* understand the *totality* of the Vibrations associated with every word, and with that, the true, intended meaning of it. It's as if we can *feel* the meaning of the word.** It's like the molecular structures of water, that you just talked about. You said that you could *feel* the pictures. Well, it's the same here. You *feel* the Vibrations and you *subconsciously understand* the meaning of them, you can understand *exactly* what the other person wants to communicate.'

'Wow.'

'It's really not such a big deal you know? Wales do it all the time, They talk to each other with Vibrational signals, even the little ones. They go shopping with Vibrational signals, they go to the cinema. It's natural.' Lee laughed again at the Thought of a whale at the cinema. 'But seriously,' Tara said, 'lot's of creatures do it, whales, dolphins, bees, us humans are just a bit behind.'

'Can you tell me what that feels like for a Human though?' Lee asked.

'Phew, it's so difficult to explain,' Tara scratched her head.

'Limited by words, ey?' Lee grinned.

She smiled a beautiful dazzling smile as answer. 'I guess it's like knowing the meaning *Intuitively*. You just *know* what's being said. You don't *interpret* it or *think* it with your Rational Mind, it's just crystal clear without any mental effort. **Once you begin to pay attention to the Vibrations *behind* the words, you'll get to know them pretty quickly. They all have a certain shape and feel to them,**' she paused.

'Actually, I have an example of something you might have already experienced,' Tara said. 'Have you ever had the feeling that somebody had an alternate motive to what they were actually saying to you? That it felt that they really intended to say something else? Well, that's it. Kind of.'

'Yeah, I've definitely had that before,' Lee remembered vividly.

'Great, so we're on the same page. **Now, the trouble with only picking up on these Vibrations subconsciously, is obviously that you can miss some, but it'll also mean, that those Vibrations can *affect* us without us knowing.**'

'How's that?'

'Well, **positive Words with a *positive* Intent, have a high Vibrational Frequency, which, eh,**' Tara was trying to find the right word, '**well, they kind of rub off on us and as a result *increase* our Vibrations and thus raise our mood.**'

'**Oh, I see, aggressive words and on the other hand, sullen words, or words with a negative Intent, have low Vibrational Frequencies and can thus *decrease* our Vibrations and thus lower our mood.** It's like the water experiment again. Man, the Mind boggles!' Lee shook his head. '**Our Body is 97% water! Crazy! Our Being and Body must get just as affected by words as those water molecules do!** What a scary Thought!' Lee flopped back against the tree in amazement. 'So, words affect us all day long and we don't even notice it! Sure, the good ones would be cool, but the bad ones? Brrr,' Lee scrunched up his face. 'I just had another thought, to top all of that, not only do the words of the other magnets affect us on a much deeper level than I thought, but they affect us even just through their sheer presence, wouldn't they? Man, other people don't even have to say anything to have an effect on us!'

Tara laid back next to him. '**And now,**' she raised her voice dramatically, '**imagine if your Awareness isn't high enough to *consciously* pick up on these Vibrations!**'

'Oh man, that's even more scary.'

'It's crazy, isn't it? **That's why it's so important to be *Continuously Consciously Aware*. Aware of how we think and of how we feel, because only then can we become aware of any changes within us or of anything that feels out of the ordinary!**'

'Makes sense. So,' Lee spun that Thoughts further, '**if we consciously pick up on other people's Emotions or moods, I assume that as we notice them, we can Let Go of them?**'

'**Exactly. Like that we'll never end up with anybody else's energies.**'

'Sounds great, and how do you do that? Let Go of them I mean?'

'**We recognise that the Thought or Emotional Vibration or whatever is not our own, and then we Let Go of them, just like we discussed earlier with regards to Thoughts and Emotions. We Let Go of other's just the same way as we Let Go of our own.**'

Lee nodded, 'Makes sense, but man, I'm beginning to wonder how we can ever live a chilled out life with all of that crap constantly coming at us.'

'Well, a lot of people don't. They get affected left right and centre, their Emotions are being jumbled around and around and they have no idea why. A lot of people have developed some kind of way of staying sane in this crazy world though, be that consciously or subconsciously. And well, so have I.'

'Let's have it then,' Lee said with overplayed impatience.

'In the end it's all pretty straight forward. As you become more Aware, you begin to notice when you're feeling slightly off, even though there's absolutely no reason for it, but you know that you're still feeling kind of strange. That's the time to check your warehouse for any strange boxes that shouldn't be there. Find them and chuck them out.'

'I love it,' Lee laughed.

'Sweetie, I haven't even started.'

'Oh goody, goody! Go on then, go on then,' Lee bounced up and down, nudging her playfully.

'Nothing easier than that.'

'Oh, wait,' Lee stopped her flow, 'let me just write this one down.'

Word Vibrations:

- Besides the associated *content* of a word, each word also has a *sound Vibration*, a *Thought-*, an *Intend-* and an *Emotional* Vibration linked to it.
- Each word not only has an *intellectual* meaning, but it also has a certain Vibrational-Frequency-Meaning associated with it.
- You know the meaning *Intuitively*. You just *know* what's being said. You don't *interpret* it or *think* it with your Rational Mind, it's just crystal clear without any mental effort.

Vibrations affect us:

- Vibrations of people, environments etc affect us physically, mentally and emotionally. If we are Continuously Consciously Aware though, we can notice if something changes within us, or if something feels out of the ordinary, and once we notice it, we can Let Go of it. Like that we'll never end up with anybody else's energies.

(Authors note: The words in this book have been endlessly charged with positive Vibrations. To add their Sound Vibrations to your experience of this book, play with reading it out loud, maybe even to each other...!)

Dilemma Of Humanity

'**N**ow, even if we learn to Listen to all Vibrational-Meanings behind words, in the end, words are still just words and their meaning is still limited, even if we understand their *exact* meaning.'

'How can that be?' Lee was confused. 'I thought when we pick up on *all* the Vibrations behind the words, we understand *everything*.'

'Well, sometimes we want to learn something from each other where no amount of words will be enough, right? So even if we feel the Vibrations behind the words, that won't do.'

Lee thought for a second, 'Like feelings? Or experiences?'

'Exactly. **Words are often simply not enough to truly describe an experience to somebody. The other person might get a vague idea, or a closer one if they can Listen to the Vibrational Meaning, but never the *real* experience. It'll always just be a *description* of the experience, never the experience *itself*.**'

Lee thought about sky-diving and telling his friends about the exhilaration of it. He had really struggled to explain the actual *feeling* of dropping out of a plane at thirteen thousand feet. Tara was right. His friends got a *description* of the feeling, but not the *feeling itself!* He grabbed the pen and quickly wrote:

Words:
• With words you can only get a *description* of a feeling or an Emotion, but *not* the feeling or the Emotion *itself!*

Tara looked at Lee's scribbles and nodded, 'That's it. And when you come down to it, it's *experiences* that *really* change people! The 'nearly-there', never quite does the trick. If we really want to share with others who we are, or what we went through, or even what we're going through right this moment in time, we need to be able to *actively exchange experiences!*' Tara gently took the pen out of Lee's hand and began to write.

The Dilemma of Humanity:

We have forgotten how to teach Cosmic things,
As the Cosmic concepts cannot be taught with words.
Today we need words to understand,
But we cannot understand these things with words.
They need to be experienced to be understood.
To experience, we need to be Open.
But in Today's world, we can't just Be open,
We need to see goals and reasons for it,
But we cannot understand the reason through words either.

Even if we do experience the Cosmic Things,
we still doubt Their reality,
Because our Rational Mind uses Words,
And it just can't understand.

Tara finished sadly.

Lee nodded, 'You know what? I think that really is *The* Dilemma of Humanity'

'I know,' Tara said as she added another sentence.

So, bypass the Brain and Merge the Souls.

'Wanna play?' Tara dropped the pen and grinned at Lee provocatively.

'Sure,' Lee grinned, and grabbed Tara's hand impulsively, 'what do you want to play?'

'Merging of Souls?'

'Oh, absolutely.' Lee was suddenly acutely aware of both their hands interlocked in his lap, 'Is that ok?' He asked, looking at her from underneath his lashes, while holding her hand in a firm grip.

'Oh, absolutely,' Tara smiled at him. 'I can't even begin to tell you how amazing that is.'

'Might that be my handholding or the Soul thing?' Lee asked with a twinkle.

'Both,' Tara said surprised by Lee's directness.

'Well, let's have some of the other one then,' he squeezed her hand lightly, happy to feel her squeezing his in return.

Merging Of The Souls - Communication Without Words

'Alright, this is where it gets even more fun,' Tara announced. 'First you've improved your Listening to words and all the Vibrations behind them, and now we can talk about communicating *without* words.'

'Aha, finally, that's where we can bypass the words by a *direct* brain connection?' Lee blurted out.

'Not necessarily a *brain* connection, but a direct connection, yes,' Tara taunted sweetly. 'I think the best way to explain it, is to give you a brief idea of the mechanics behind Merging of Souls. Why it actually works and how,' Tara suggested.

'Ok, mechanic away.'

'You asked for it, so here we go,' Tara announced light-heartedly. 'When we are born, all humans vibrate on the same Base Frequency, the Human Frequency. When we grow up and begin to fill our warehouse, our Being slowly begins to vibrate differently. It's still has the Base Frequency of a Human Being, but each person develops it's own little distinctive sub-frequency. These sub-frequencies influence the way we perceive the world around us and how we communicate with it.' Tara drew an eight turned on its side onto the next page of Lee's notebook. 'Each Human Being's Vibrations can be described with this Sign.'

'Oh yeah? How can it do that?' Lee said surprised.

'Well, the base frequency on which each Human vibrates, creates a basic shape or pattern.'

'Like the little metal balls in the Petry-Dish we talked about before.'

'Exactly like that. **Let's assume, just for demonstration purposes, that the Human Base Vibration takes the shape of this Infinity sign,**' she pointed at the drawing. '**Now, due to the sub-frequencies each person has developed, the loops of each person's Infinity sign will always have a slightly different shape or size.**'

'And different Vibrations are like speaking different languages,' Lee was beginning to understand what Tara was getting at.

'Yes. We can't understand each other fully, because we don't or can't match our Vibrational loops,' Tara continued his sentence. '**We'll always have to try and bend or shape our loops to fit with other peoples'.** Sometimes that's easier than at others, and sometimes it's simply impossible.'

Lee thought for a second, 'But we can be on the same wave-length with somebody, or rather on the same Vibrational Level, or not?'

'Yes we can. When that happens, we vibrate on *similar* frequencies, but our loops are still not the same. Even though such similarities make communication much easier, it's still not flawless.'

'So, I guess there is a much easier way?' Lee said smiling, anticipating an 'of-course'.

'Of course,' Tara said and Lee burst out laughing. 'What?' she asked smiling.

'Man, you are so predictable. You always have an answer, don't you?' he held her hand lovingly in both of his now.

'Mmh...,' Tara didn't quite know what to say.

'I'm glad, sweetie. It never gets boring with you. Whenever I think I'm at the top of the mountain, there's always another peak on the horizon.'

'Darling,' Tara said with a huge smile on her face, 'we're standing at the feet of the Himalayas!'

'I love it!' Lee grinned broadly. 'So what's the easier way?'

'The natural way for all Beings to communicate, is through Base Frequency Vibrations *only*.'

'Right,' Lee nodded slowly. 'So all we need to do, is get back to the Base Frequency. Nothing easier than that,' he raised his eyebrows. 'Care to elaborate?'

'Sure,' Tara drew a bunch of Infinity signs of different shapes and sizes around the first one. 'Can you show me the Base Frequency? The one point all of these have in common?' she asked him.

Lee looked at the drawings, 'Oh, of course. Even though they all look different, at one point they are all the same,' his index finger quickly tapped the middle points of each of the Infinity signs. 'The centre point. Here, here, here and here. Perfect balance. It's the point where we're all the same, where we're all One.'

'There you go! What do I know, you know it all already,' Tara leant back with a happy smile on her face.

'And if we're all *One*, we don't *need* words to communicate anymore, because we're the *same Entity*. It's logical really,' Lee said, surprised by the fact at *how* logical it was. It was far out and wacky, but it made sense!

'And to become One, all we need to do is Be Now,' Tara said.

'Surprise, surprise,' Lee shook his head. 'Therefore, to match our Vibrations with somebody else's', all we need to do is meet in the middle of the Infinity sign, in Nowness.'

'Yep, that's the space where we don't need words anymore. **In Nowness, our Vibrations match at the Base Human Frequency, where our Body and all of our Consciousness vibrates at the same level.** We're in the space where we can all perceive and experience the world around and within us in exactly the same way. It's like we've literally become the same person! We don't have to change or adapt or pretend or prepare. We are just ourselves as we become each other. Naturally, effortlessly, simple. That's what I call *Merging of the Souls,*' Tara finished.

Lee was awestruck. This stuff was so beautiful. Merging Souls. His heart was warmed by the Thought of it. It was amazing how everything they had discussed so far, could be the answer to so many things. The answer was always the same. Nowness. Nowness. Nowness. The sudden realisation nearly made him cry, **Nowness wasn't about being alone! It was about doing it together! About playing with others.** *That* **was the ultimate.**

Nuts and Bolts for Merging Souls

'There are some prerequisites to be able to play with all of this,' Tara warned.

'Ah,' Lee said wearily, hoping that his little bubble wouldn't burst.

'For the Souls to merge in Nowness, there has to be *Complete Trust and Total Openness.'*

'*Complete*? Phew, I think it might be hard to allow oneself to open up that much to another person, you know, to allow them to come in and see one's very own deepest inner Being, raw and unprotected. I think there would always just be a couple of bits that people would want to hold back.'

'That might very well be, but that wouldn't work, because *that's* exactly what prevents us from merging. Remember the story of the First-People? When our Egos get involved with all it's feelings, Emotions, prejudices, judgements, opinions, insecurities, secrets, walls, barriers, anger, fears, doubts, expectations, holding back and all the associated Thoughts, then Merging won't work anymore.

To merge, there can't even be the smallest, sneakiest undercurrent of any of those things lurking on the fringes of our Consciousness. Even the tiniest one is still a box in the Warehouse, which resist the unhindered flow of Nowness. **This is why two people have to trust each other** *fully***. There can't be** *any* **holding back whatsoever. There has to be** *complete* **openness. That's the whole point of Merging Souls.** It's to *really* and *fully experience* the other person. It's about *not* having barriers or walls or limitations, but about totality, purity and Oneness. **That's why it's different to just Listening to the Vibrational Frequencies behind words in Nowness. There we just have to be very perceptive, whereas Merging Souls is about** *Total*

Letting Go and *experiencing* **each others' Souls** *fully*,' Tara paused to let this sentence sink in. Actually, do you remember the look-into-my-eyes example?' she asked.

'Of course.'

'Well, one has to be totally open there too, it's not so much different here.'

'Oh yes, I forgot about that one.'

'As with looking into each other's eyes, with Merging Souls there's really isn't anything to worry about. If either person wants to stop, at any time, all they need to do is *think***. Simply by** *thinking* **you** *will leave* **the State of Nowness and with that, the connection will be severed.** Just like that. Easy. So, you can pay with being open, and when you had enough or begin to feel uncomfortable, you just stop.'

'Good to know,' Lee made a mental note, just in case.

'Actually, when people try to Merge Souls for the first time, that's usually what happens unintentionally anyway,' Tara hinted.

'What do you mean?'

'Well, they open up for a short time, but then Doubts might come up, they might get scared or worried about what the other person thinks of them or do to them.'

'And that would severe the necessary connection.'

'Yep. Unfortunately,' Tara laughed, 'this usually also often happens just at the moment when things get interesting. As people go 'uh' and 'ah' and 'wow', they forget all about Nowness, and puff it's over.' Lee grinned at Tara's description. 'It's often too new and crazy and different for people to stay focussed. People usually feel the need to speak, to exclaim their amazement or to ask the other person if they are experiencing the same thing. People have reality-checks, where they wonder if it's real or not, if it's really happening.'

'Yeah, I can imagine that it can be a little overwhelming when you do this for the first time.'

'It can be. But remember, ...'

'Even feeling overwhelmed is just a Thought, I know,' Lee grinned, finishing Tara's sentence.

'That's my boy,' Tara said, padding his shoulder. 'So, the long and short of it is that the flute has to stay clear for Merging of the Souls to work.'

'What flute?'

'Oh sorry, haven't I explained that one yet? **Do you want a nice way to picture the way Nowness works?'**

'Sure.'

'Imagine that the unity of our Body, Mind and Soul is like a flute, and the Universe wants to play a Cosmic-connection-tune through it. It wants to teach us new songs, new dances and show us how to really party up there!' Tara pointed into the sky, 'I know it's corny, but bear with me,' she grinned as she saw the corners of Lee's move upwards slightly. 'Instead of joining in with the dance though, we're far to busy clogging up our flute with our Egos, our idea of our personality, constant thinking, our Emotions, etcetera, etcetera. Most people are so clogged up, you wouldn't get a sound out of their flute it in a million years. As a result, Cosmic communication won't work. Not with the Guys and not between Souls.'

'Ah, but as soon as we Let Go of all of that grit, of all the dirt and cloggy stuff, that's when we can have a really good boogie to the Cosmic melody,' Lee said and amusedly watched Tara get up, wiggling her bottom ridiculously, waving her arms and hands like a cheerleader, and singing along to a little imagined cosmic tune.

Lee laughed out loud, watching Tara put on a show, 'Then again, I'm not so sure anymore that that's such a good idea.' He held his hands out to a giggling Tara, who quickly bowed deeply before being gently pulled down besides Lee.

'Come to think of it, it's the same as the pipe and the wire example we talked about earlier,' Lee observed. 'First we need too get rid of all the resistance within it, even the smallest wire that's still offering resistance, and with practice we can take the pipe itself, alias the flute away! Then the Universe is not trying to play *through* us anymore, because we just *are* it.'

'Yep, that's it. The minimum prerequisite for Merging of Souls is just a super clean flute or pipe though,' Tara said comfortably.

'Great. That sounds actually achievable. Ok, to summarise...,' Lee said and started another list.

Merging of Souls:
- Cosmic Conversations, or Merging of the Souls, can only flow if our flutes are entirely clean.
- We need to *believe and trust* in communication *without words*.
- *Both* parties need to have *total* Trust for each other.
- They need to be *fully open*.
- They have to be relaxed and their Egos, conditionings, worries and Thoughts need to dissolve in Nowness and stay in Nowness.

We merge Souls in Nowness when:
- We *vibrate* the same.
- We *are* the same.
- We *are* One.
- The flute and the pipe are totally clear.

'Ha, piece of cake,' Lee laughed slightly daunted.

Merging Souls - The Experience

'**Y**ou know, by the time you'll have played with The Guys for a while, this will *really be* a piece of cake. The more you play with Them, the more you appreciate that words are not necessary to communicate. Remember when we said that The Guys use words, to talk to us, but that They also use Physical and Intuitive Signs to talk to us?'

'Sure I remember.'

'Well, when we Merge Souls, we *Listen* the same way we Listen to The Guys. We use our Intuition. Our Intuition can pick up much more than our ears. Intuition can grasp pictures, words, feelings, Emotions, experiences, sensory impressions and much more, all at the same time. **Through Merging Souls, we can get a total and rounded notion of the *entire concept* that is being communicated, rather than just receiving the full meaning of a *word* like we would by using the Vibrational Listening to words alone.**'

'Hang on, that makes Merging of Souls sounds like telepathy,' Lee observed.

'Well, not the way I would define telepathy. I would say that telepathy is the transferring of words from one Being to another. Merging of Souls goes a step further than that. I'm talking about transferring or sharing entire *concepts* and *experiences* between Beings. Shapes rather than points. **Communicating between Souls is about *perceiving* the concept of the word Family or America *exactly* the way the other person *experiences* it, rather than just getting a verbal interpretation of what that person *thinks* of it.** As you said earlier, it *bypasses* the Rational brain. **It's *pure experience*. It's communication in a different dimension.**'

'I'm speechless,' Lee said amazed.

'Now, there's an understatement if I ever heard one. Dude! This is unbelievably, incredibly out of this world!' Tara said excitedly. 'Actually, I have a great example to compare this to. Chinas' and Japans' written languages are made up of beautifully drawn characters, yeah? Each stands for a whole load of meanings, entire concepts in fact.'

'Yeah, I know. That's why there are such big problems with translations. Unless you understand the subject matter at hand, you won't be able to grasp the meaning of the characters fully, let alone put it into words to translate it. To make matters worse, a lot of the meanings have also been lost over time. We can still see the characters but we don't understand the concepts they represent anymore.'

'Exactly, and Merging of Souls would be like going back into the brain of the person who wrote a characters in the first place. I don't just mean *understanding* the characters, but understanding, or better *being* the *dude* himself as he wrote them! *Being* his Thought processes, his Intent, his Being. All of it. All the slight little intricacies! That's so much more than words!'

'I think I'm beginning to get the idea,' Lee marvelled.

They sat for a little while, when Lee began to want some more details, 'Tara, **how does it actually *feel* like when you Merge Souls**? It must be absolutely incredible. Do you get words or feelings or what?'

'It's a bit like Listening to the Guys, but different. **When we Merge Souls, it's like we *become* the other person. We experience *their* Thoughts, *their* feelings, *their* Emotions, *their* concepts *first* hand, just as *they* are experiencing them.** We experience a direct understanding of each other's feelings, Thoughts, Intuitions, wisdom and points of views. We *experience all* of it. **It feels as if *their* experience is our own.** We can see each other's shades of blue, we have the same feelings, we know and we understand. It's amazing. We could never intellectually grasp the immeasurable depth of other people's feelings in words. Through Merging Souls, there is pure Intuitive clarity and knowing of the other person's Being. There is no room for misunderstandings anymore.

I call it Merging of the Souls, and that's exactly what it feels like. Our Souls merge, they melt together. **As soon as they connect, we feel an immediate feeling of intense closeness, deep, yet soft and warm.** It's a much stronger feeling than having a close connection with a loved one. It's not a sexual feeling, but a feeling of heaps and heaps and heaps of unconditional love. Merging of the Souls is one of the most beautiful ways of showing each other, what's going on inside of us. How we feel and how experiences affected us. It's a wonderful way to learn about each other and to share our real Self. If you try it, you'll see how truly fabulous it feels to learn like that.'

'Sounds absolutely breathtaking. How did you feel when you did this for the first time? Did it knock your socks off?' Lee asked.

'That's a bit of an understatement... It's totally out of this world! When I first did this, people showed me feelings which I didn't even know existed. It was mad. I couldn't have even fathomed for anybody to feel like that.'

'What do you mean?' Lee asked intrigued.

'I remember one of my most striking experiences with somebody who had served in the war. Man, some of the stuff he went through was unreal. The anxiety, the fear, the anger, the frustration, the desperation, the claustrophobia, the despair. I felt it all, just as if I'd have been there myself.'

'Phew, didn't that get scary?'

'Kind of, but then again, not really. **You see, Merging of the Souls is soft. It can be intense, but it's safe.** It's not the real situation, it's just the *feelings* and emotions that *somebody else* had during it. We usually don't feel their physical pain, but we are *aware* of it. We share the reactions, the feelings, the state of Mind, the way the person *perceived* the world and the way it affected them. Often we can even 'see' the situation as it happens.' Lee was quiet. He was Listening intently. 'When I Merged Souls with that guy, for the first time in my life did I *really* understand what it means to be at war. Yeah sure, we get all the stories and we can imagine what it was like, but actually? No we can't! We haven't got a freaking clue! It's like having a tooth pulled without anaesthetic. Unless we have experienced it, we will never understand what it's really like. We might have some kind of idea, but wait till it actually happens to you, then it's a very different kettle of fish!'

'That's powerful stuff.'

'It's beyond powerful. By Merging Souls, we can *really* understand *why* a person is the way they are, *why* they behave the way they do, *why* they think the way they do, and how they look at the world from deep inside. We don't just intellectually understand the words somebody says to us, but we *know* because we have *experienced* the person *themselves*. When the merging is over, we might not be able to explain what we felt afterwards with words, but we *know*,' Tara paused.

'**Merging Souls drastically opens our horizons by getting an insight *into* other people.** We become aware of a completely *new* range of reference points, *new* Emotions, Feelings and perceptions of our world, which we could have never imagined before. Feelings other people have, which we've never experienced, which we never even knew existed,' Tara said, remembering some of her most powerful experiences. 'By being able to truly put ourselves into another person's shoes, we realise how different we all are, which in turn can help us to become more compassionate, *sympathetic, considerate, accepting* and *understanding* towards others.'

'Oh, this is so beautiful,' Lee sniffed.

'Yeah, I know, it is rather nice, isn't it?' Tara relaxed her hand in Lee's, which was still tightly holding onto hers.

'And you're telling me that anybody and everybody can do this?' Lee just wanted to make sure.

'Yep.'

'Fabulous,' Lee said already writing.

<u>Merging Souls</u>
- We *become* the other person.
- We understand each other from *within* our Souls, rather than from the outside through words.
- We *experience* the other person's experiences as they experienced them.

Tara read Lee's points and added:

- And besides all the learning stuff, Merging of the Souls is just really far out and ridiculous amounts of mad, mad fun.

Lee laughed, he loved how everything in Tara's world had to be fun. "And Common sense his little Rational Mind added." Woha, hang on, Lee laughed, his Rational Mind sounded pleased! Did his *Rational Mind*, begin to like this stuff too? Ha! Wonders never ceased!

Merging Souls - Practicalities

'The war thing was a good example, albeit a bit drastic,' Lee said.
'Thanks. You can obviously share anything, joyful incidences, traumatic or confused ones. You could share how you felt at your wedding day, or the birth of a child, or the stomach-butterflies on your first date, or a blissed-out travel experiences, an abortion, your first swim in the sea, a shocking experience, sadness, depression, child hood traumas, hopelessness, anxiety, fear, anger, amazing elation, adrenalin rushes, jealousy, anything. If you're really open, you'll get the other persons' experiences and feelings in whole concepts, in whole impressions, not just in little snapshots. You ask just ask each other: "show me how you feel or felt about this", or: "how you felt when you were in that situation", or: "how does this make you feel, or: "how did this experience affect you?" Go for it, try it out. It's educational *and* it's fun,' Tara said encouragingly.
'What a fabulous combination. School eat your heart out.'
'Yeah man, if modern teachers would know how easy it is to transmit information like this, they would drop their chalks and there would be silence in their classes for the rest of their lives, and faces of spellbound children.'
'Nice Thought,' Lee grinned. 'Although I can't imagine that you'd get a horde of adolescent, budding teenagers to spend forty five minutes in Nowness,' he said sarcastically.

'But...,' Tara waved her index finger meaningfully, 'if they could learn as much in forty-five minutes than they couldn't learn in an entire day, *and* be seriously blown away in the meantime?'

'Ok, you win,' Lee laughed out loud, 'that could be nearly as good as telly and video games.'

'Nearly,' Tara laughed with him. 'But besides that, there is a new generation of children emerging, that seems naturally more switched on. So, maybe one day...,' Tara looked dreamily.

'Well, not being one of those gifted children, but just a willing adult,' Lee smiled at her, 'are there any practical tips you could give me on how to start Merging Souls? I mean, do I just sit opposite another person and say, ok, let's start?' Lee asked.

'Well, kind of,' Tara took Lee's notebook and wrote:

<u>There are a number of different ways in which we can practice Merging of Souls:</u>
* Openness to anything that comes.
* Ask Questions before hand.
* Ask Questions during - out loud or in the Mind.
* The Shift.

'Ok, point number one,' Tara tapped pen onto paper. 'To start we sit together in Nowness and are completely open to *anything*. We're open to get a sense of the other person and seeing what comes up by itself. It's like both of you saying: "Ok, this is who I am, come in and have a look". This can also be a very powerful meditative experience, because being in Nowness *together*, is even more powerful than practicing it alone. You can have your eyes open and look into each others eyes, but it's probably easier to have your eyes closed. Personally I like sitting cross legged opposite one another and touching each others' knees, but in the end, all of that doesn't really matter.'

'Oh?'

'Remember when I said that TSC doesn't exist in the Now?'

'Are you saying that we don't need to be physically together to do this?' Lee guessed wildly.

'That's exactly what I'm saying,' Tara said with a twinkle in her eyes.

'Man, the potential of all of this is just Mind boggling,' Lee lost himself in an array of scenarios, dreams and ideas for a few seconds, but caught himself out, just when Tara continued.

'If we are physically together or not, doesn't matter. If we are in complete openness, all we need to do is enter Nowness. The Universe decides what needs to be shown.'

'Crazy,' Was all Lee managed to say.

'The second and third points on the list work exactly the same, just that you ask each other questions about *specific* things,' Tara continued with the bullet-points in the notebook.

Lee looked at the list, 'But if you'd ask a questions verbally *during* the merging, wouldn't that be disturbing? I mean speaking out loud and asking questions *while* trying to be in Nowness, that somehow doesn't seem possible.'

'Good point and you're right. Talking rips us out this peaceful state, rather brutally. It would therefore be more gentle to talk to the other person as we would talk to The Guys. That means, that we formulate a question *in our head*, rather than out loud. Asking questions like that takes quite a bit of practice though, because every time we think, we disturb Nowness and thus sever the connection.'

'Yeah, but even if we ask a Mental question, we're still thinking to prepare it, aren't we?'

'True, so the trick is to ask the question as quickly as possible, and to try to keep the Nowness nearly undisturbed.'

'Any tips on that?' Lee asked.

'Sure. It's common sense really. Let's assume that **we are in Nowness and a questions pops into our head. As in Nowness our Awareness is already heightened anyway, there is no need to do anything else. We've thought of the question once. That's enough and we can go straight back to Nowness.**

To be honest though, it's best to do all of that *beforehand*. If you want to share something in *particular*, it's easier to agree *before* you start who will share and who will Receive, and of course what you want to share. Once you've agreed, both people need to take a few minutes to fully relax, become Mindful and as Now as possible. Preferably the Receiver already enters Nowness. The *Sharer* then needs to direct his energies by having an Intent in his Mind, to feel and share the feeling or the experience he wants to share with the other person. **He does that by concentrating on the feeling or state of Mind he wants to share. By doing that the *Sharer* briefly *re-experiences* the situation. Sometimes all of this happens in a split second, that's why the Listener should be ready to receive, whereas some other time it can be a more drawn out experience.** During the sharing both people can think from time to time about the subject they want to share, but it's not necessary. We don't have to try to do make the Intent stronger by doing it over and over again. If the Intent has been put out there *once*, that's enough, the cosmic messenger pigeon has been sent out. The most important thing is to stay in

Nowness, rather than to clog up the flute with unnecessary further Intents. That's it. That's all the preparation that needs to be done.'

'Cool,' Lee said simply. 'Can you tell me a bit more about the Receiving part?'

'Absolutely. *Receiving* is a bit like Listening to The Guys. The communication doesn't happen with words, it doesn't happen by *talking*, but by *sharing silence*, by being empty, open and trusting. As with Listening to The Guys, we need to watch out for anything out of the ordinary in our Being, be it Thoughts, Feelings, Emotions, a sudden understanding of concepts and lots of other stuff. Actually, I just thought of something important,' Tara waved her index finger in the air, 'it's important not to expect anything in particular, because we often get feelings or impressions which we have never experienced before ourselves.'

'Because they're the other person's?'

'Right. So, it's important to stay open and just observe *whatever* comes up.'

'Wow, that's like channelling each others' Souls!'

'Oh, what a nice way to describe it. Yes, that's exactly what it is!' Tara said excitedly. 'Thanks, I like that one.'

'My pleasure,' Lee bowed. 'To summarise once again, the most important thing *while* Merging, is to keep the flute clean and to remain in Nowness. And,' he stressed, 'not to become impatient or angry because we don't feel anything - yet -,' he added insightfully, 'because those feelings are the *reason why* we don't feel anything in the first place, because they block up the flute. Funny vicious cycle really.'

'It's amazing when you really begin to understand this stuff. You know, the last two things that usually stop us from remaining in Nowness and thus to Merging Souls fully, are *Doubt* and *Trying*.'

'Oh yeah, *trying*,' Lee's voice trailed off. **That's what's so bizarre with this stuff, Lee thought, you** *couldn't try.*

'*Not* trying really takes some practice,' Tara guessed his Thoughts. 'You know, to some people this stuff comes naturally, others need to work on it. But *everybody* can do it if they *practice*, and...'

'If they put in the time and effort,' Lee anticipated the ending of Tara's sentence.

'Very true, and you know what? If you can't do it straight away? So what! Just keep on practicing the things we've talked about so far, and keep on playing till it happens all by itself.'

'And we do that light heartedly, while enjoying the ride,' Lee knew the drill by now.

'Full points,' Tara laughed out loud at her own predictability. 'You know, once people start to consciously play with this kind of thing, they might even realise, that they have always lived this way, that they have always had a strong connection to the Universe, that they have always felt comfortable with it, that they have always been able to pick up stuff from people around them, that they always somehow knew how other people felt. I've even had lots of fun with those people finding out that they can *actively* play with other people and they can show others how to do it too. Oh, and you know what? That's half the fun! Do it with a group of people!'

'What? Merging Souls in a Group?'

'Oh yes! Now, that really blows your Mind.'

'God, I can only begin to imagine. Tell me, tell me,' Lee bounced with excitement.

Group Merging

'**D**o you remember the story about me and my friend hearing the same messages from The Guys at the same time?' Tara asked.

'Of course.'

'Well, during Group Merging, everybody is in Nowness, right? And in Nowness *everybody* can become *aware* of the *same* "conversation". You can do it with as many people as you like.'

'Wow.'

'Yeah. **The more people Listen in the Now, and the more they *open up*, the more the Vibrations amplify and the stronger the connection becomes** and the clearer the messages and impressions become,' Tara shook her head, 'it's too mad to even begin to put into words.'

'Believe it or not, but I'm getting a pretty good sense of it, just talking to you,' Lee said with appreciation.

'Excellent. Man, I tell you, you're doing so amazingly well with my little Nowness crash course. Respect!' Tara bowed respectfully.

'If you say so, teach'.'

'Woha, stop right there! I'm just the messenger here. You're *your own* teacher!' Tara squealed with exaggerated shock and horror.

'I know, I know, just joking.'

'I know you are, but this is important. The Shift is not a teacher - student thing. It's an *Oneness* thing. *We* are all responsible for our *own* connection, development and growth. There should never be anybody that owns the exclusive rights to any of this stuff. Nobody should ever tell anybody when they're ready for the next stage or what the limits are. Everybody can try whatever they want to and they can play with it, just like their little hearts desire. Everybody can decide for themselves, have fun, enjoy, play, experience and practice. Everybody takes responsibility for their own actions,' Tara said avidly.

'Check. And yeah, thanks, it's good to keep pointing that out. There are always people out there in for a quick buck, inventing silly rules, trying to crate a following.'

'Very true. But hey,' Tara said now more light heartedly, 'we can all be teachers to each other. We can learn from everyone. When you meet a person with *that cosmic tw*inkle in their eyes, and both of you know that experiences need to be exchanged, try a bit of Soul Merging. When your Intuition tells you that the time is right? Off you go.'

'Yeah, right, like, hi there, do I see a cosmic twinkle in your eye? Would you care for a spot of Merging of the Souls?' Lee grinned, trying to look all cool and casual.

'Weirder shit has happened!' Tara laughed.

'Why doesn't that surprise me?' Lee rolled his eyes and asked mischievously, 'By the way, can you *still* top all of this?'

'Of course!' Tara repeated one of her favourite phrases.

Merging Of Souls After The Shift

'It gets even better once we've Shifted. **When we Shift, we *are* One and Now *all the time.*** That's true connection. **We are *always* Merging Souls with other people. All the time, by default!** We can see through everybody's masks and we have dropped ours. We exchange words, concepts, feelings and Emotions constantly. The exchange becomes automatic, there's no more involvement of the Rational Mind. There are no more misunderstandings, no more ambiguity. You know,' Tara said thoughtfully, 'it's not just about Listening to and Merging with other people, but about discovering a whole new world in Nowness. Music for example. We don't only Listen to music, but we understand the *Intent behind* the it, the story, the feelings, the *real* motivation of the composer. Books. We understand the Written Word with all its beauty, we feel the feelings the author had when he or she wrote them. We begin to learn on a completely new level! It really is a new dimension!'

Lee was amazed. Tara smiled from ear to ear and said casually, 'Oh, and don't wait with this stuff till you've Shifted! Get practicing and gather experience now! Just *do it*! Play! Be confident and don't ever let anybody put any restrictions on you! You might just get a lucky dip. The Guys are good like that.'

'Yeah, I remember, the world is my Oyster,' Lee said, reaching his arms out to each side and pretending to hug the entire world.

Communicating With _Everything_ - the Other Beings

'**M**mh,' Tara paused for effect, 'I think I might be able to top this one more time,' she said looking at Lee for his reaction.

'You're kidding, right?' Lee's eyebrows raised in surprise.

'Do I look as if I'd ever kid you?' Tara winked playfully.

'All right then, you win!' Lee shook his head. 'What's the top of the top, young lady?'

'Communication between _all_ Beings.'

'All Beings? What like, non-Human Beings?'

'Yep,' Tara nodded. 'We can communicate with _everything_ in our world that has Vibrations.'

'Woha, so that'll literally be _everything_,' Lee called out in astonishment.

'Precisely.'

'Shit!'

'Oh yes,' Tara's grin got wider and wider.

'You know, I thought about that earlier. I was wondering if we can just Merge with people. So, we can merge Souls with people, plants, animals, rocks, a cup of tea, the fridge, anything.'

'You are it, it is you,' Tara said grinning at the Thought of Lee Merging Souls with a fridge – one of those old fifty's style ones - gotta have style, she laughed, but this wasn't a joke, this was real. She continued more sincerely, 'In Nowness, we can perceive the _real_ Soul of everything. Obviously,' she had to giggle again, 'it might be tricky to agree with a fridge what we'd like to experience during a Merge, so I guess in that case, you'd just have to be Now, open and receive whatever comes. Be open, feel its feelings, smell it's smell, touch it's touch, think it's Thoughts or maybe even experience a completely new way of Being and perceiving. Experience _fridge-ness_.'

Lee looked at her and burst out laughing, 'Fridge-ness? Can't wait!'

'Hach, isn't it fabulous?' Tara stretched herself out contently on the blanket. Lee laid next to her, took his notebook and began to scribble.

Learning the Cosmic Ways:
- Merging of the Souls and Communicating in Oneness is the Cosmic Way of Teaching, Learning, Being and Knowing.
- We can merge with *every* Being, every Thing.

How Merging Affects Our Lives - The Sheer Beauty Of It!

When he finished Tara said, 'Merging of Souls can have a massive impact on people's lives, you know?'

'You don't say,' Lee smiled.

'Oh, I do,' Tara grinned, '**but the impact is not just from what we learn from the other Being, but also what we learn from the *process itself*.**'

'More?' Lee angled for elaboration.

'**Well, as we said, to allow the other person into our inner space for the duration of the Merging, we have to find it within ourselves to truly Let Go, to totally open up and fully trust the other person.** We have to completely drop our barriers, pretences and walls. Doing that for any period of time, and with another person, opens up a profound new dimension of Trust, Love and acceptance of ourselves and others. **As our Awareness increases, and we begin to understand that *everything* around us has a Soul, we begin to feel much *closer* to all other Beings around us. Once we experienced that, we not only *believe*, but we *know*, that *everything* deserves Respect, that *everything* has a right to live and be happy. Just as we do.**'

'Now there's a nice little side effect.'

'Yes, sir. By Shifting and thus permanently Merging Souls with everything, or even just by gaining little tasters of the Merging process, we begin to perceive the world around us in it's totality, rather than just in little bite size chunks. Our senses become heightened, our Awareness increases naturally, we perceive knowledge and wisdom from everything around us. We perceive the world as it is, rather than how we *interpret* it. We see the true reality rather than our own personal little Mental concoction of it,' Tara opened Lee's little book and wrote:

Merging Souls
is the natural way of communicating for all Beings

Lee read, hesitated and finally asked, 'Ok, so, this is it, right? This is as high up as we can go?'

'Well... actually... there's always a Party *above* the last Party.'

'So there *is* more?'

'Eh yes. Sorry.'

'Sorry? Are you crazy? Get on with it! I'm on tender-hooks here,' Lee urged.

Uoh, We're Getting It! And We're *Doing* It! Lee's Glimpse Of The Shift

Instead of talking, Tara closed her eyes and held Lee's hand. Lee swallowed his last Doubt and slowly closed his eyes too. Slowly, ever so slowly a feeling crept up on him. He felt an intensity of contentment and satisfaction rise within him, which he had never felt before. He felt clarity, purity and a powerful sharpness of his Mind, as his Awareness surpassed any level he'd ever known. Awareness without distractions, without puppies, just Now. **In this moment Lee felt what it would be like to Shift.** He wanted to open his mouth and tell Tara, but remembered that this would sever their connection. He needed to stop thinking. He put his attention back on his breathing and once again felt his Body responding to the heightened Vibrations. He felt warmth spread out from his belly to his limbs. He felt a slight tingling, as the atoms in his Body changed the way they normally behaved and aligned themselves to the flow of cosmic energy that was surging through him. He was acutely aware of every single molecule in his Body. His senses were crystal clear, he smelled the trees around him, he smelled wet dog. Wet dog? Yes, he clearly smelled wet fur. He opened his eyes for a split second and saw a dog all the way across the park, a good hundred metres away, his fur still glistening from swimming in the lake. Calmly he closed his eyes again, ignoring the bloody-hell-I-can-smell-things-a-hundred-meter-away Thought bouncing around in his head, and went back into Nowness.

Back in the space where *everything* happens, he became aware of all sorts of sounds around him, sounds which he'd never noticed before. Not because they hadn't been there, but simply because he hadn't paid them any attention. *Now* he paid attention. To everything. He felt the wind on his skin and the ground underneath his feet. **For the first time in his life, he felt that he was actually part of this world. That he was a Being that was part of something bigger, just like everything else around him, just like the tree above him or the rock he leaned against. He sensed a feeling of belonging that he never thought possible.** He breathed deeply. **All of a sudden he *knew* what it was like to be One.** Not because he understood the theory or the descriptions of it, but because he'd finally *experienced* what Oneness was. Tara was right. The feeling was grander and more outstanding than any words could ever describe. He felt elated, clear-headed, strong, powerful and alive. "Yes babyyyyyyyy!" - his Mind commented with excitement. Right on cue, Lee felt Tara's grip loosening. He opened his eyes.

Tara was looking right at him, grinning broadly, 'Not bad, ey?' The only thing that stopped her mouth smiling any wider, were her ears.

Lee laughed, 'Yeah, not bad, not bad at all!'

'Man, I can't believe how well you're doing,' Tara said in awe.

"Actually, *both* of you are doing well," the voice paused and then added with a cheeky snigger, "Babyyyyyyyy!"

Lee looked at Tara, Tara looked Lee, then both burst out laughing. Lee crooked his hand camply and purred, 'You're doing fabulously daahling, just fabulously.' Then he stopped short, suddenly looked more serious and then asked, 'Eh, hang on. Shit Tara, did you hear what I just heard?'

'Of course. We're One, remember? We always hear the same stuff, that's the point!'

Lee grinned at Tara's usual casualness, 'I really should stop asking stupid questions,' he rolled his eyes and shook his head.

While Lee grinned to himself at how rolling his eyes had become such an integral part of his Being over the past couple of days, suddenly, right out of the blue, Lee noticed a delivery in his warehouse. A concept this time. The perception of it came clearly and strongly. His Intuition understood it immediately. He looked at Tara and saw her nod. She was getting the same thing. She put her index finger to her lips, indicating silence, and closed her eyes. Lee followed her example. The concept unfolded in front of his Minds eye. He *received* a concept from The Guys, together with the profound realisation, that the concept was so vast, that it would be impossible to put it into words or to even discuss it with Tara. **This time he didn't only *know* the limitation of words, but he truly *experienced* it, the Cosmic way.** When it was over, he opened his eyes and looked at Tara.

She returned his gaze warmly. They stared at each other for a good while, until Tara finally said quietly, 'Sometimes it's just nice to Listen and experience. We don't always have to talk about it.'

Lee nodded slowly, still taken aback. He breathed deeply, squeezed his eyes shut a few times, rubbed his face vigorously and said, 'True, still, I think I'd like to try to describe what just happened.'

'Be my guest. It's good practice to share such information,' Tara agreed easily.

Vibrating Even Higher

Lee braced himself, suddenly there were mad, crazy puppies all over his Mind. The clarity and sharpness he'd just experienced, puffed up in smoke, his wonderful experience was being drowned in canines. His Mind taking over again fast, and all that was left, were the warm memories of a dream, which were disappearing rapidly. He breathed deeply and began to actively Let Go of his Mind again. When he knew that he was about to say something, he stopped himself for a second. He was acutely aware that he also needed to Let Go of any Thoughts that tried to prepare the sentence. He breathed once more, deeply, right into the core of his Being and slowly, deliberately, stopped *trying* all together.

He let the words flow out of his stomach, through his throat, over his tongue and out of his mouth, just as they came, 'Ok, this is the concept, the feeling that I just went through. Man, what an amazing experience,' Lee's Mind went back to the intense moments of connectedness that he was allowed to witness. '**Oneness is more than just an idea**,' he looked at Tara sheepishly, as if to say sorry-I-know-you-know-that,-but-that's-what's-coming-through, he continued, 'Actually, **we're *always* One, it's just that our Minds are so busy all the time, that we forget.** All we need to do to become One again, is to raise our Awareness. The more Aware we become, the higher we Vibrate. **Every time we become Mindful, we raise our Vibrations, every time we reach Nowness, our Vibrations increase even more. The higher we vibrate, the faster the little atoms *between* us vibrate, and as a result, the tighter our connection becomes.** Nowness, Mindfulness and Meditation get us back into a state of Being where we *can* experience Oneness again. Once we have Shifted, we *are* One again, *all* the time.' Tara only nodded, not wanting to interrupt Lee's flow, which now came out of his pen rather than his mouth. She watched him write.

> *We're One.*
> *All of us always touch.*
> *We touch an atom, which touches another,*
> *It bumps around until it touches you again.*
> *We constantly exchange atoms,*
> *With the Universe, the Atmosphere, with Food, with Each Other.*
> *There's no way we can be separated.'*
> *(Frank Herbert)*

Lee was amazed that he'd just remembered this quote in it's entirety. He looked across the grass, felt the sun on his skin and kept on writing.

Everything Vibrates:
- Our Body Vibrate
- Our Consciousness Vibrates
- Everything around us Vibrates
- Everything inside of us Vibrates

He laid down his pen, Listened and spoke, 'All Vibrations around us affect us and we, in turn, influence everything around us. By becoming more Aware of how the outside world shapes and changes us, we, in turn, can crate an environment for ourselves, which is conducive to our well-being and to raising, rather than lowering our Vibrations. **We raise our Physical and our Consciousness Vibrations by actively *generating* positive Vibrations within ourselves, by *surrounding* ourselves with positive Vibrations, and by *taking in* positive Vibrations.** We take in positive Vibrations by eating food in it's natural state, food which is not so processed that you don't even know anymore what it's made from. Food without additives. *Live* food like fruit and salads, food which is fresh and even raw, not food which has been boiled or fried or cooked or otherwise tortured for an hour. Basically, food which is *a-live*. If you boil or process a living thing? It dies. It's as simple as that.'

'Phew, harsh words,' Tara imitated Lee's voice. She enjoyed how the roles had suddenly reversed. She knew that one didn't *have* to go to such extremes, but what Lee was talking about, was what spending time in Nowness taught. And the more time one spent there, the more one knew that it was the right thing to do.

Lee continued unperturbed, 'Smoking clouds the Body and the Mind, so does Alcohol. Drugs sometimes open the Mind, but addiction closes it,' the words flowed effortlessly. He wasn't thinking or preparing anymore, it was coming straight through. He was Listening to himself while he was speaking and he was amazed to learn stuff he hadn't known come out of his own mouth. 'Surrounding ourselves with positive Vibrations is straight-forward. Friendly people, a caring environment, loving or friendly physical contact, positive words (be it Thoughts, verbal and written), positive thinking, good exercise, Happiness, carefree-ness, Integrity, inner power, positive affirmations, Meditation and Mindfulness. None of this is rocket science. **Positive Vibrations come from pretty much everything that makes us feel good.** Let's actively surround ourselves with it – as much as we possibly can. Hel-lo? Do it!' Lee giggled inside as to how much he sounded like Tara - well, they were tuning into the same station. The Thought only passed by fleetingly as his presence in Nowness became stronger and stronger. 'If we're not in a positive environment, we need to change it, even if it might take drastic measures, like leaving something or

665

someone behind. We can change our physical environment as much as our internal one.'

He breathed in the next concept, 'having our head in the clouds by losing Awareness, by not breathing properly, by rushing, by not paying attention, by being selfish, angry, unloving, full of expectations, aggressive, unhappy, by eating bad food, being sluggish, not moving much, not exercising, thinking too much and living in a Negative environment, these are all things that lower our Vibrations. And guess what? A lot of those things can be avoided if we *actively* and *consciously* work on them,' Lee quickly jotted down a few words, while still intensely focussing on his breath.

We raise our Physical and our Consciousness Vibrations:
- By actively *generating* positive Vibrations within ourselves.
- By *surrounding* ourselves with positive Vibrations.
- By *taking in* positive Vibrations.

'Positive and Negative Vibrations are all around us,' he continued effortlessly, 'and they affect us all day long, and of course, we happily go along with it - up and down like a Yo-Yo. Again and again. Surrounding Vibrations say *jump*, and we ask *how high*. Every time. Positive or negative. A nice hug or a nice smile can be enough to raise our Vibrations positively for a little while. We feel loved, safe and warm, we feel better, calmer, more relaxed, present, at peace and happier. It feels good. But raising our Vibrations that way, will only give us a temporary effect. **As soon as the word is forgotten or the hug is over, our raised Vibrations return back to the starting level. We cannot rely on the outside world to increase our Vibrations on a *permanent* basis. We have to *cultivate* our *own* Vibrations, from *within*** to become naturally balanced.' Lee made a mental note of that Thought for future reference and continued, 'Unless we do that, outside influences will always affect us and the Yo-Yo will continue.

The way out of this vicious cycle, is to build up and nurture our own level of Vibrations to be strong and steady. Personal Power and permanently raised Vibrations have to be *a Conscious decision* and a *continuous Intent*. When our Vibrations are healthy, strong and steady, so will be our entire Being. In Nowness there's clarity, strength and balance. In Nowness our Physical, Mental, Emotional and Spiritual Vibrations all vibrate at the optimum level. Once we're in *that* State, outside influences won't be able to pull our Vibrations down anymore,' Lee paused to take in another picture that emerged in his Mind. 'Now that's a good idea,' he mumbled and took his turn to draw into the notebook. 'Imagine a ball,' he said to Tara and drew a circle to symbolize the ball. 'The surface of this ball represents our current

Consciousness and Vibratory level. Below the line, i.e. inside the ball, is a field of lower Consciousness, a field of worry, anger, misery, unhappiness, too much Thought, bla, bla, bla. It's a field where our Personal Vibrations are low.' Lee waited for Tara to look up and nod, then he drew a bigger circle around the first one and shaded the area in-between with a few long strokes of his pen. 'This area represents a field of higher Awareness, Consciousness and thus Vibrations. In this area we experience peace and balance. The *surface* of the bigger circle itself, represents The Shift.

Now, whenever outside influences change our Vibrations, we leave our little ball of Consciousness and either move up into the shaded area of Higher Consciousness or we drop down into the ball of Lower Consciousness. As soon as the outside influence wanes, we switch back to the surface of the little ball, our initial state of Being. That Yo-Yo effect goes on all day long. Sometimes we don't even switch back to our initial state, because another Vibration has already influenced us again.

Lee was amazed that he could draw, talk and make sure Tara was still with him, all while he was Listening to something out there telling him stuff he'd always wanted to know. **He shook the Thought out of his head and focussed back on his breathing, 'When we start to cultivate our *own Positive* Vibrations from *within*, we start to *actively* venture out into the shaded area of higher Consciousness of our own accord. The more we practice, the longer we spend up there. As that happens, our Base Vibrational Frequency is raised on a more permanent basis.** As our current Awareness and Vibrations are amplified, the bigger our little ball becomes, and with practice and persistence, our Base Vibrational Frequency moves all the way *through* the shaded area and eventually reaches the bigger circle. That's the Shift!

At the beginning we can just dabble with higher levels of Frequency, because every time we leave the state of Nowness, we drop back to the little ball. That's especially what happens when we begin to practice Nowness and the raising of our Vibrational Frequencies during Meditation only, rather than including this Awareness into our every day life activities. If we do that, **the switch from the Meditational-state to the life-state can feel pretty harsh. That's why it's so important to learn to achieve and maintain this state during our normal lives activities. That is the ultimate goal! Not sitting in the corner and Shifting, but walking, talking and Being in this world. You could call it 'Practical Enlightenment','** Lee said, being amazed by what was coming out of his mouth. 'By learning to maintain Mindfulness and Nowness in everyday life, we start to maintain our increased level of Vibrations twenty-four-seven. That's when we start to spend more and more time on the bigger circle.

The more time dwell up there, the more we learn about this new State of Consciousness, and the more familiar and comfortable we become in this new field as a consequence. As we start to play in this new realm, we get to know how the Cosmic machinery works and what can be done with it,' Lee's gaze became clearer, as he became more comfortable with the novel strangeness that was going on in his head.

'What's most important, is that through our own experience of this new State of Consciousness, we gain the necessary Trust to allow ourselves to Shift for good. Once we've Shifted, our Natural State permanently moves to the higher Vibrational levels.

If for whatever reason we don't like that higher Vibratory level, we can simply drop back down by surrounding ourselves with lower Vibrations, and allowing them to enter our Being. Actually, even just lower Thoughts will do the trick just fine. So, it's safe to go and play as your heart contents,' Lee stopped abruptly. His Mind was suddenly empty. There was nothing. That was it. Or was it?

Tara was just about to say something, when Lee whispered, 'Hang on, I think there's more,' he hesitated, Listened again and nodded. 'As long as we have a Physical Body, the *surface* of the bigger circle, which represents The Shift, is pretty much the biggest Party we can go to.' Lee pointed at the outline of the big circle, 'this is where we can go to when we Shift, and this,' he drew a few rays radiating outwards from that outline, **'This is where we go if we *dare*!'**

Tara laughed.

"The Dudes are cool! There's always more", he smiled to himself and continued without hesitation. 'Once we've Shifted, we venture *outside* of the bigger circle, where a completely new dimension of Being lies. It's a new dimension of perceiving and existing. *That's* the state where our Infinity Sign is completely aligned with the *Cosmic* Vibrations - dot and loops and all,' he flicked through the pages to find the previous drawing. **'When our Vibrations are permanently in the Now, when there is no Human Mind left to interfere anymore whatsoever, that's the bigger Buddha holding the little Buddha,'** Lee held out his hand, lovingly stroking the head of a little imaginary Buddha. 'That's The Party above The Party,' he grinned, as the-words-that-were-not-his-own gently left his Brain. 'Boy, I so hope I get an invitation once that Party goes off!' Lee fell back into the grass, spread-eagled, flat out. 'Bloody hell, I guess I just had my question answered,' were the final words out of his mouth.

'Bloody hell indeed Lee! Don't worry man, your name is on the VIP list.'

'Yipee. Whoha, I think I've just had a peak through the door of the party hall,' Lee had a stunned look on his face, 'and man, I tell you, They're absolutely rocking up there!'

36 Why You Don't You Need Shoes

Lee laid there for a while, with Tara next to him still holding his hand. Slowly he Let Go of hers, turned onto his stomach and propped himself up on one elbows. As Tara followed his lead, Lee looked back through his notes for a while and recapped the immense amount of information he had accumulated over the past few days. He remembered how he and Tara met, the silly Co-incidence that had got them talking, both of them being barefoot and him asking Tara, why she didn't wear shoes. She'd said that she didn't need them because she trusted in the Universe. Gosh, had he known all the stuff he'd have to do just to be able to walk barefoot safely, Lee laughed to himself. He turned to look at Tara now and said, 'I guess you answered my question.'

'Which question was that?' she asked.

'The one where I asked you why you didn't wear Shoes.'

'Oh,' Tara grinned, that question seemed a million years ago.

'You know, I *really* understand now Why You Don't Need Shoes. We *are One* with everything, and nothing would hurt itself!'

Tara simply nodded and began to write:

WHY YOU DON'T NEED SHOES

In the Now you Trust.
In the Now,
You are in tune with yourself,
All living Beings, God, Mother Earth,
Nature and the Universe.
There are no more Doubts, fears or insecurities
Lurking on the fringes of your Consciousness.
There is no Doubt in your physical and mental abilities.
There is no Doubt in cause and effect.
There's no Doubt in Synchronicity,
Or that everything happens for a reason
There's no Doubt, that you are supposed to learn
from every experience in your life.
No Doubt that you are being looked after.
There are no But-s left in your Mind.
From then on,
You are One with everything around you,
And nothing will hurt you anymore,
As nothing would hurt itself.
You can throw away your shoes,
Be barefoot and walk with confidence!

When you know, from the bottom of your heart,
And with all your Being,
That You Don't Need Shoes ever again,
Then I cannot teach you anymore –
Because then, you SHIFT,
As then,
You are - ONE,

One with the Universe,
One with the Source of all Life,
One with all Beings.
You are One with Them,
as They are One with you,
as Everything just IS –
ONE.
NOW.

Tara put the pen down, picked it up again and added,

'Well, obviously, be practical with this stuff.

If it's freezing cold, don't loose your toes over it,
Be barefoot in your Heart instead!'

Lee finished reading, nodded, and slowly and deliberately took off his shoes and stuck them into his bag. He looked at Tara for a long time and eventually said quietly, 'Thanks Tara. I think I won't be needing anymore them for a long, long while.'

37   Nearly The End

- The End. -

Lee wrote, closing the cover. He looked at his little notebook with love. It had been with them over the past few days, like another person, faithfully recording their conversation.

Tara followed Lee's glance downwards and her gaze stopped on the little notebook she'd come to love so much, and for the first time, noticed the front cover. The words instantly etched themselves into her Mind. It was her language, more than anybody could ever begin to understand, but to her surprise, the words were written in a more roughish hand than her own:

STRONG. POWERFUL. ALIVE. HAPPY. CLEAR.
INTEGRITY. TRUTH. RESPECT.
FUN.
YEAH!

When she saw what was underneath those words she nearly began to cry. At the bottom of the page, Lee had carefully drawn a tiny stick figure, holding a teeny butterfly. When she looked closer, she saw that the little guy had two tiny little bare feet. She gulped. What she saw next made her heart leap. The little stick figure was holding out the butterfly to another little stick figure. A little stick figure with pigtails.

'We're so alike.' She met Lee's eyes and asked softly, 'Where on earth did They find you, Lee?'

'Same place They found you, I'd say,' he looked at her affectionately.

Tara hung her head, 'Well, I guess we finished talking. Now is the time to put it all into practice, there's not much more to discuss.'

'Actually, there's something else I'd like to talk to you about,' Lee said, clearing his throat. He leant over and lovingly pulled Tara closer.

Tara looked up, blushing slightly, 'Oh? What might that be?' the twinkle in her eyes betrayed the innocence of her voice.

'Us,' Lee said firmly, looking at her, their faces on the verge of touching.

'Now there's a subject that definitely requires further discussion,' Tara radiated.

Lee looked at Tara, tenderly touched her face, hesitated a moment and then, gently, ever so gently, placed a soft kiss on her lips.

38 21ˢᵗ October, A Few Years Later

'**D**addy, daddy!'

'Hello sweetheart,' Lee gathered up his daughter, who had flown into his arms, her tiny bare feet dangling above the ground.

'Daddy!' the little girl called again, nestling her beaming face in his chest. 'The Little Guys have been at it again.'

'They have?' he asked affectionately, looking into the bright blue eyes of the sparkly creature in his arms. Everyday she looked more like her, like that wonderful woman he'd met all those years ago. Barefoot. Not far away from here. He missed her.

'Where's your mother?' Lee asked, lovingly brushing a reddish curl out of the little girls face.

'Here I am,' she came up behind him.

Lee turned around. 'Just the woman I wanted. Are you ready to work on the next draft?' he dangled a little notebook in front of her nose. On the cover was a grey smiley face with a huge, great, big, fat, rainbow around it.

'Well actually, I have some *new* stuff,' Tara said, naughtily looking up at Lee from under her lashes.

God, he loved it when she did that, 'Again? Guys! What shall we do with you?' Lee rolled his eyes up towards the sky, a smile curling at the corner of his lips.

'Well, there *is always* more, *you* of all people know *that*,' Tara grinned, squeezing his hand passionately.

'Don't I know it,' Lee kissed Tara and placed a warm hand onto her belly, 'and I love every minute of it,' he quietly whispered into her ear.

- THE END -

MAY ALL BEINGS BE HAPPY

MAY ALL THEIR SOULS BE RUNNING FREE

Barefoot, without a torch.
and with a huge, great, big, fat smile on their
faces.

PART 14

1   AUTHOR'S NOTES

This is the end of the story between Lee and Tara. To follow are extra notes and additional information that I felt were important to be included in this book, so here it goes:

Everything In This Book Is True!

Everything in this book is true. It's not invented, it's not made up! It really works. You can really do it!

A Quick Word On Grounding!

When you begin to play with The Guys and The Shift, stay grounded! This stuff is going to make you fly! Co-incidences will start to happen all over, people will give you messages, there'll be *real* Signs everywhere. You'll be talking to The Guys, you'll be getting help, hints, tips and answers left right and centre, things will seem too good to be true. Sometimes you'll wish you'd have more people to talk to, sometimes other people will think you're crazy, you might feel lonely or loony, but you know it's the right thing to do, sometimes you'll be over the moon, sometimes you'll be scared, sometimes you'll just want to hide from what you uncovered in your Brain. But no matter what happens, you'll always know that you're not alone, that you're being looked after. The Guys are with you! Whenever you need help or assurance, they'll give it to you, keep your heart open and you'll hear and see. Oh, and Remember the Wow-journal? Use it.

Accept. Relax. Enjoy. STAY GROUNDED!
Ask for help, love, hugs or reassurance when you need it.
It will come.

A Quick Word On Re-reading the Book!

Re-read this book! Every time you read it, you'll discover something new. As you open up, as your Trust increases, as you shed your Doubt, you'll pick up new levels of information from this book - every time!

If you have questions, re-read the book. If you look closely, most of the answers are already in it.

You can even just open it from time to time and re-read a few pages as a "thought for the day".

Enjoy!

Re-read it!
Discover all the layers these pages hold.

2 Why You Don't Need Shoes Vision

A New Age

Human kind tried to heal the world many times:
- We tried it with enlightenment, but the concept got misunderstood. The world regarded it as something only a selected, special few dared to attempt, therefore hardly anybody did.
- We tried it with Yoga, but it got misunderstood. People used it to exercise rather than for physical, mental and spiritual harmony, to become One and reach enlightenment.
- We tried it with Philosophy, but we got lost amongst our own words.
- We tried it with the ancient teachings, but people couldn't understand or identify with the old ways of thinking. Teachers often withheld vital secrets and people never got the whole message, which always held them back in their refined development.
- We tried it through Meditation, but it got misunderstood, when people used it solely for relaxation.
- We tried it with Religion - I don't have to explain why that one didn't work either to unify the Souls on this planet.
- We tried it with self-help books and with Hippy-dom, but we never managed to reach the whole world.
- The world tried so hard to wake up, but it never really worked on a larger scale.
- Even if a few lucky ones did find the right teachers, their practices were often not something that the masses in today's world could make practical use of. Most teachings were arduous and lengthy, with many pitfalls. Often we needed to entirely give up or at least severely restrict

our lives to learn. Many people that tried, never got very far, despite years of intense practice, as good and trustworthy teachers were few and far between.

But This?

This is a new age! We don't have the time or the nerve for all this pfaffing about anymore. We need some action. We need something new. We need something simple, straight forward, easy and most of all bright, light hearted and joyful. We need something that we can do *during* our normal life, on our own, or in a large crowd, without having to set aside special practice time. We need something which *every single* Human Being can achieve, not just a selected few. Something which doesn't take years of practice or six hours every day. Something that doesn't need Gurus or Teachers or anything like that. Something where each and every single one of us is their own Teacher.

This is what Nowness gives you. There are no complication, no rituals and no special tools. Just Breathe. Bang. *Now.* In an *instant!* *You* teach yourself, you monitor your own growth. You practice whenever and wherever you want. It's *part* of your *everyday* life, and for a change, it's Fun!

The page with the Dots and Squiggles? Turn it around! That's what you want! An empty page! It's ready for you to draw your very own little Rainbow Smiley Face on it!

Be Now
It's a new message for a new area.
It's easy, straight forward and unambiguous.
It's in your face and crystal clear.
You cannot argue with it, interpret it or misunderstand it.
That's why this time?
It's gonna work!

Our world can only be healed with Love, unconditional living, and sharing without expectations. Our world and the Beings in it have experienced much suffering. We need action Now! Now is the time to switch off our heads and our Thoughts, to side step our Egos and start to play with our gut feelings and follow *every single* Intuition!

Being Now
is the most fun way for everyone
to exist together in harmony.

Let's Do It! Let's Change the World! Why The Hell Not?

So? Let's do it! Let's Change the World! Why the Hell Not? Big words? Sure, but somebody's got to do it! How can *you* do it?

How can *you* change the world!
- Everybody has to change *themselves* first.
- Then do something nice to for other people in your *immediate* surroundings, to raise their Vibrations. Make music, spread happiness, grow flowers, help out, surprise, love, whatever.
- And then, whoever feels the calling, do one *Big* thing. A *huge* thing that affects as *many* people as possible. (If you don't know what to do, ask The Guys.) Write a book, have an exhibition, give a lecture, raise a child. Whatever you do, do it with passion, love and respect. Do it well!
- All along, do your bit by just *Being*, Being who you *really* are and by Being Now.
- Teach by example.
- Get involved. Help. Don't ignore what's wrong with the world! Try to do what you can, without carrying the weight of the world on your shoulders. Keep your light-heartedness and carefree-ness, strength and balance, go out there and make a difference, no matter how tiny

Off you go. Be happy.
Go and Fly!
Change Yourself!
Inspire Others!
By just Being,
Now!

Why You Don't Need Shoes - Snippets

Walking Barefoot:

Reminds you to be Mindful when you walk!

You slow your pace, you don't rush, you take more care, you pay attention and take in your environment. Your Body, your Mind and your Breathing slows down!

You feel the ground and how it feels different everyday and every place.

You enjoy textures of the ground, leaves, mud and rocks!

You feel how different nature feels to artificial stuff!

You become connected to Nature and your environment!

It increases your Awareness and thus your Consciousness!

You feel a new and different kind of freedom!

You walk softly and thus respect Mother Earth. You don't mindlessly stomp around anymore, treading on things in your environment!

Touching the earth is a beautifully grounding experience!

As you are fully aware and thus connected, your Intuition will always alert you of danger!

As you treat softly, you will only touch the thorn, but you will always be able to pull back before it penetrates the skin!

You trust that you will be looked after. You are One, and nothing would hurt itself!

You have respect for everything, as you want everything to respect you!

You don't hurt anything, as you don't want anything to hurt you!

You gain natural physical balance - walking Barefoot aligns the knees, the spine and the bones in your Body. It creates physical harmony!

The foot-reflexology pressure points get a constant natural massage, which keeps your entire Body healthy and the Energies moving, inside and out!

You show that you don't need to comply to all of society's rules (have fun experimenting with all the places that won't admit you Barefoot... airports, restaurants, shops...)!

You can slip into everybody else's Shoes in a jiffy, which allows you to understand your fellow human beings better. Actually, as you become One, you are *already* wearing everybody's shoes. You *are* everybody!

As much as you don't need artificial soles on your feet to help you walk, you don't need anything outside of you to make you happy!

You can do everything you want to accomplish in life, with your *own* Body and Mind!

When you walk Barefoot you *have* to be Now, or at least very Mindful, otherwise your Barefootedness won't last long!

Be Barefoot, Be Mindful, Be Now!

Nowness connects you to Oneness and you *will* be safe!

Nowness

Nowness is the beginning to everything. Nowness is the entry exam to be allowed to play with the Cosmic Toys, to Shift and to change the world!

Excellent! We get to change the world *and* have some Fun.

With Nowness:

You realise that we're all pearls already, not onions!

You realise that we are all perfect inside, just the way we are!

679

You become aware of Cause and Effect and you become consciously aware of *all* of your actions and their impact on the world!

You realise that when you Trust, there's no need to *try* anymore

All Doubt disappears!

You become fully balanced, even in stressful situations!

You become fully aware of your surroundings!

Your Mind becomes clear, peaceful, calm and empty!

Your Being becomes balanced, powerful, strong and alive!

You know from *experience* that there is no anger, jealousy, pain, worry, craving or need to fight!

You experience everything Now as it *is*, not as *you think* it to be!

There are no interferences by the Mind at all! There are no descriptions, judgements, interpretations, comparisons or expectations.

You realise that everything can be unconditional!

You experience what it's like to just *Be*!

You *are* all of that by Being Now, by Being totally Present!

Our children will learn by Example…!

In The Now…

In the Now your life enters a new world, a new dimension!

In the Now our Physical, Mental, Emotional and Spiritual Body, are aligned and balanced!

In the Now Energies can flow freely and Energetic blockages will be resolved, as your Body is being nourished and purified!

The normal Dots-and-Squiggles-brain uses 30% of our entire Body's energies supply when it's resting, and up to 50-70% when it's active! Therefore, in the Now you free up tremendous amounts of energy, which can be used elsewhere!

In the Now you experience people, events, situations, sensations, feelings and everything else truly in the present, the space where *everything* happens!

In the Now there are no Expectations!

In the Now you live differently, you feel different, you experience the world differently. You might start to *feel* or *taste* colours, rather than *see* them. You might *feel* what somebody says, rather than hear it with your ears. You might see auras or discover healing abilities. You might taste music, touch Energies, hear Emotions or smell words!

In the Now you'll have knowledge that you didn't knew you had. That you couldn't have had!

In the Now you connect to people, plants, things and animals, like you didn't believe possible!

In the Now all your giving and receiving is unconditional!

In the Now you connect to everything and everybody!

In the Now you can sing, dance, drum, paint and write. You can do everything, simply because you're not thinking that you cannot do it!

In the Now you can find everything, as you are *always* Mindful about *all* your action, you will always remember where you put your things in the first place!

In the Now you can always remember people's names, because you were Mindful when you were told!

In the Now you don't pussyfoot around awkward issues, but you get to the point and get them sorted with unconditional Love, understanding and Integrity!

In the Now you feel Love every minute of every moment!

In the Now you have no concept of time! In the Now, time spent doing things you don't like, flies by. Long journeys, a trip to the supermarket, washing the car, decorating, they are all over and done before you know it!

In the Now, Time in queues, at the bus stop, or waiting for anything, disappears. In Nowness there is no perception of time or boredom!

In the Now, Thoughts that something is too difficult or takes too long or that you can't do it or that it is too cold or too hot or too heavy or too loud or too nervy or too scary, don't exist!

In the Now it's easy to do things you don't like to do, as you're not thinking throughout how much you dislike it. You just do it. In the Now you cannot dislike anything!

In the Now you don't think about doing stuff, you just do it. Suddenly everything gets done effortlessly in your life. Like exercising or eating your greens!

In the Now you're not love sick!

In the Now you're not moody.

In the Now you don't have any *cravings* for food, cigarettes, alcohol, sex or anything else!

In the Now there's no sadness, anger, jealousy, irritation, resentment, anxiety, guilt, worry, bearing grudges, impatience, shyness, frustration, roller-coaster Emotions, insecurities, heaviness, ugliness, *unnecessary* Thoughts, grieve, sorrow, resentment, blame, unfairness, pride, ego, embarrassment .... you can fill in the gap yourself!

In the Now, any Thoughts or Emotions that you don't like, need or want don't exist!

In the Now you are strong, confident, powerful, alive, happy, content and balanced!

In the Now you feel love, peace harmony and content in you life!

In the Now you don't expect. In the Now you don't have judgements, in the Now you don't have any projections, in the Now we all have the same rights!

In the Now you are aware of *all* sensory input. Nothing inside or outside of you happens anymore without you knowing about it, as you are *Consciously* aware of *everything*!

In the Now all you do is *observe*, you don't *react*, you don't *judge*, you see everything for what it really is!

In the Now you become part of your environment and it becomes part of you!

In the Now, Time, Space and Consciousness fall together!

In the Now there is no future and there is no past!

In the Now there are no time delays between events and your perception of those events.

In the Now you use your sixth sense, and all the ones above that!

In the Now you share concepts, direct Emotions, Feelings and experiences instead of words!

In the Now you can share information with others through Merging Souls and any other ways you can come up with!

In the Now everybody is in the same headspace!

In the Now we all connect!

In the Now we're all connected!

In the Now The Little Guys look after you, guide you and keep you warm!

In the Now you Breathe!

In the Now you *are* Now!

In the Now you live *every moment* to the full!

In the Now *anything* is possible!

Practice Nowness all day long, or use it whenever you want to. It's up to you.

Exploding Beauty and Respect

In the Now we start to see the beauty in the smallest things around us. In the Now the world suddenly becomes more interesting, more colourful, more fabulous, as we notice things we never noticed before. In the Now, beauty explodes all around us. Absolutely everything is a small miracle of creation. The ants, the tiniest flowers, the bark of a tree, sand, rocks, insects. They are all so fascinating if you look at them for what they *are*, rather than what your Mind has always thought them to be. A spider is not disgusting or icky or scary. It's intriguing and absolutely amazing to look at. They come in all sorts of different colours and sizes and shapes. They bounce and jump and swing. Some are even quite cute.

By being Now and by becoming consciously aware of our surroundings and fellow Beings, we become closer to them. Closeness and understanding helps us to develop consideration and compassion for our fellow creatures and people. We might not love them all, like the old mosquito or the guy down the road, but by recognising them for what they are, a little miracle just like us, it helps us to understand them, develop compassion and accept them the way they are. They are not good or bad, they just are what they are. Just as *we* are. They just do what they have been born to do or what society has made them to be. Just like us. In the Now we can treat everybody and every thing with the respect they deserve, with compassion and loving kindness, just as we like to be treated.

As we change our perception of the world around us, instead of being a distant observer, we become part of the world and the Universe again. As we begin to see the Cosmic plan and The Guys in every Thing and Being, we become more and more in tune with all living Beings, with God, Mother Earth, Nature and the Universe. As we become One, we wouldn't hurt anything, as we would not want anything to hurt us, then nothing would hurt us, as nothing would hurt itself.

The more aware we become of our environment, the more we notice how it changes. We notice when it flourishes and we notice when it hurts. The closer we get, the more we realise that in the end all Beings, no matter how different they look, are part of the same creation, the never ending circle of Nature. We realise that all Beings just want to Live and Be

Happy, and that we all deserve a little bit of Respect, love and tenderness. We all deserve to live in our own little way. We are all miracles. Nothing is better than the other. We are *all* special.

Trust

*Nowness
is achieved through
Trust.
Trust is based on personal experience.
Trust is what changes the world, not blind belief or faith.
Belief and faith imprison us in somebody else's system.
Trust gives us Freedom.
It's unconditional, flexible and adaptable to new experiences.
Go, play and experience it for yourself,
get your own proof!
Trust helps -
you individually, everyone else,
our planet,
and the Universe as a whole.*

Trust that the Shift can truly change this world!

Trust that there can be unconditional Love!

Trust that there can be unconditional giving and receiving!

Trust that all your actions can be unconditional!

Trust that all Beings can Be Happy!

Trust that Nowness is a tool to enable you to become aware of the world around you!

Trust that Listening to your Intuition works!

Trust that following your Heart works!

Trust that following your Gut Feeling works!

Trust that Listening to The Guys works!

Trust that playing with Coincidences works!

Trust that Mindfulness and Nowness enable you to become balanced, stable, peaceful, calm and strong and thus increase your Vibrations!

Trust that The Guys are out there for you - everywhere! - and *inside* of you of course...

Trust that you're always being looked after!

Trust that there is no good or bad!

Trust that everything is impermanent!

Trust that we can connect to other people in Nowness!

Trust that the Universe will provide whatever you need!

Trust that we're all in this together!

Trust that you help yourself by helping others! You cannot Shift by being selfish!

Trusting allows us to support the common good! By Shifting, we learn that if we do good, others will do good to us !

Trust that the more people Listen, the easier it will be to follow Co-incidences all round!

Trust that more mad and wonderful things will happen because you Listen and act *for* other people and other's Listen and act *for you*!

Trust that if we share with others, others will share with us!

Trust that if we give without expectations, we will be given to without expectations!

Trust that unconditional sharing is the key to everyone receiving! (It's the apple thing!)

Trust that if we love unconditionally, we will be loved unconditionally!

Trust that unconditional Living is Loving!

Trust that Love *is* the answer!

Trust that it's wonderful to make people happy or help them in a crisis!

Trust that it's amazing to give *before* being asked!

Trust that often *little* things make all the difference!

Trust that you can give physically (hugs and material things), mentally (wisdom, advice and examples) and spiritually (your energies, Being You) and whatever else you can come up with!

Trust that if something happens, even if it hurts, there is a lesson that can be learned!

Trust that maintaining Nowness and Mindfulness throughout your day, can help you to stay calm, steady and balanced in your Mind!

Trust that there *is* a perfect line out there for everyone!

Trust that if we're in the Now, we'll sit on that perfect line!

Trust that Nowness reduces the time between events and their perception!

Trust that Manifestation can be instantaneous!

Trust that They Guys pre-empt instantaneous Manifestation!

Trust that you can be, whatever and whoever you want to be!

Trust that you can create your own reality!

Trust yourself!

Trust yourself to take responsibility for our own happiness!

Trust that only *you* can change your life and make yourself happy!

Trust that all Beings can be Happy!

Trust that in Nowness everyone is connected *to* Oneness!

Trust that in Nowness everyone is connected *in* Oneness!

Trust that you Shift by becoming One with everybody and everything!

Trust that all this stuff works!

Trust that we need to work together to make this beautiful world more loving and Free!

Trust that we can change the world!

Trust that enough of us get of our backside and actually DO IT!

3   YOU. Final Word

Lots of people out there Trust already. They often don't know *what* they Trust in, but they Trust in something Good in all people. They Trust that there is something that makes life worthwhile, fulfilled and most of all Fun! Some people have been lucky enough to experience this first hand, others are slowly waking up to those possibilities.

Some played with Yoga, Meditation or healing arts, some just naturally became more aware of themselves, by riding a bicycle, surf or run. People have life changing experiences or get *significant* insights in many different ways. Some find it easy to implement their spiritual insights into their everyday life, some have found it not so easy. **May this book help and inspire all of you.**

If you have woken up *without* guidance, you might be worried that you are mad, strange or weird. Well, you're not! It's real, it happening and there are *lots* of people doing it. Right now! Ask The Guys to meet them!

Keep playing and never take yourself and your Thoughts too seriously.

And remember? You're being looked after!

If you're wondering how to practice, when to start, is it right for you? Stop thinking and finding excuses! Just *Do It!* Stop *trying* to make time for your practice, *just do it*. You can *always* be Mindful! There really is no excuse!

Be under no illusion that The Shift happens on it's own. It doesn't just happen. You *do* need to do it. You *do* need to practice. That's what all the exercises in this book are for. But hey, they're fun right? And you can do them throughout your everyday life. So, what was your excuse again? I think you're getting the point...

Play with the story in this book whichever way you like to. Try all of it if you want to get the whole experience or just do the exercises that you find most useful, but be sure to try some new ones from time to time or even play with all of them again and again, - you'll be surprised how your Insights change as your Awareness changes. There are always more doors to open and peek through, and more parties to attend. The Himalayas are vast!

This book is yours to play with. You can skip bits, laugh about some, disagree with others, or really get into *all* of it. Combine it, use it in whichever way your heart desires. That's all cool. This book is only a tool to get you started and to get you a VIP ticket to the Party. (Authors little side note: Once you've seen how the Universe whoops, grooves, boogies and really rocks, why not write a book about it yourself? It really isn't that hard, and The Guys will help you as much as They possibly can :0)

This book might change your life forever, or it might have just planted a seed. Even if you don't believe a word of it, try it anyway, even if just for entertainment purposes or for a bit of fun. And maybe, just maybe, you find out why you came across this book... And if you do? I'd love too see your face...

<u>Till then, always remember:</u>

The *Doing* it is not the difficult thing,
The *Remembering* to do it is.
If I would tell you right now To Be Now!
You'd be able to do it!
So,
Stop saying : "Oh, I know I should, but..."
Stop trying, Stop wishing, Stop hoping!
WRITE "BE NOW" ON YOUR HAND
And Just Do It whenever you see it!
That's all there's to it!

You only have one Life.
You can either be Happy or not.
It's your choice!

May All Beings Choose To Be Happy!

PART 15

APPENDIX

Dear Reader,

Whenever I meet with people face to face, they are fascinated and enchanted by the insights in Lee and Tara's story. Knowing how this world has affected us though, knowing about the Doubt and the scepticism this society has placed into our warehouses, I can imagine that there are people out there though who might still have difficulties in allowing themselves to Trust, no matter how intrigued they might be. So, for you guys I've added the following few extra chapters.

Xian
:o)

1 What, Dear Reader, You Still Don't *Think* It's *Real?*

What, dear Reader, you still don't think it's real? You still think that The Shift is all bogus Hippy-shit? You're still sceptical? Gosh, you're a tough nut to crack! You want more proof upfront? More incentive? Well, here it comes. I just happen to have anticipated your needs…

Now, do you remember Ed? Tara met Ed on a bus, Lee met him one afternoon with Tara in the park? Well, Ed and Tara had many fascinating conversation since they'd met, exchanging their stories and experiences. Ed had been so excited about The Shift and everything that comes with it, **that he played with The Guys and practiced Nowness from the word 'Go'. Despite his enthusiasm Ed was initially incredibly sceptical though, and it had taken him many back and forth-s to get his head around 'Trust'. So, to help you with *your* doubt, see how Ed got over his…**

Gödel and Einstein

Ed loved what he had heard so far, but despite his enthusiasm, his Rational Mind kept questioning things, and somehow there was still something that felt a bit strange. He approached the subject carefully, 'Tara, I'm fascinated with everything we have talked about so far, but I just think that it's all still a bit far out.'

'I know how you feel,' Tara said with understanding, 'and I'm glad you brought that up. When I first heard about The Shift, I felt exactly the same way. But you know, all this stuff is actually not that new. If you look at some of the scientific theories and the so called facts out there right now,' Tara waved her arms at everything around her, 'you'll realise that talking to the Cosmos and being One with it, is really not that bizarre. It's more like the logical next step. **Let me tell you about some of the great thinkers of our century, who've also been into pretty extreme stuff.** That'll put the far-out-ness right into perspective. Are you up for that?'

'Sure, but I'll keep harping on at you if I still think it's weird, ok?' Ed persisted. He knew that Doubt was one of the main hindrances of The Shift and he wanted to make double sure that he didn't have any left over - if at all possible.

'I wouldn't want it any other way,' Tara agreed freely. 'Well, let's talk about some of our *existing* knowledge first, shall we? Our so-called Scientific Facts. Facts, of which the average Joe Bloggs usually doesn't know many details, and facts with he usually doesn't question.

For many people facts are allowed to 'stand as a fact', simply because somebody called them a fact, maybe a *scientific* fact.' Ed grinned at Tara's sarcasm. 'Ok, now, in a nutshell, besides other things, Einstein said...'

'Einstein? You're kidding, right? Einstein talked to The Guys too?' Ed interrupted surprised.

Tara laughed, 'Well, I don't know about that, but he certainly did have some pretty outrageous Thoughts and ideas for his time, maybe he did have the occasional meeting with Them up there,' she smiled. 'What I want to talk about though, is that Einstein also suspected that there's something bigger out there, and anyway,' Tara's voice became a little more quiet, 'with the amount of substances he indulged in, he's probably seen and experienced a far out thing or two,' she winked at Ed. 'But besides all of that, the reason I want to talk about Einstein, is because he defined the *limits of man's perception* with part of his Relativity Theory. **Einstein said that our perception of the known Universe is limited by our *perception* of Infinity.'**

'That means that we can only grasp the vastness of the Universe as far as we can grasp the concept of Infinity,' Ed stated.

'Right. Einstein expressed mathematically how the condition (state/situation/circumstances) of the *observer* influences the things which he *can* perceive. That means that if the condition of the *observer* changes (that could be physically, mentally or spiritually, I might add), he might be able to perceive and observe *new* things or *existing* things in a *different* way.' Ed had actually managed to keep up and nodded, motioning Tara to continue, 'Another chap called **Gödel**, who was one of Einstein's contemporaries, went even further. He **made mathematic statements about the vaster realm *beyond* the limits Einstein had defined.**'

'Hang on,' Ed butted in, 'I know about Gödel. Gödel said that in any closed mathematical system, there are an infinite number of theories. These theories can be perceived, observed and measured. The complicated bit is that even though these theories are *contained* in and are part of the original system, they cannot be *deducted* from it or *proven* by it with *ordinary* logic. **In plain English this means that there are an infinite number of true things in the world, with no way of ascertaining or proving their truth.** All in all, there's stuff out there, which we just cannot understand or explain or scientifically prove or measure, but they still exist! They still work! They are still true.'

Tara clapped her hands excitedly, 'That's it. That was textbook stuff. I'm so impressed, hardly anybody I know, has ever even heard of Gödel, let alone been able recite his theories! I couldn't have explained it any better myself,' Tara patted Ed's arm. 'Now, according to Einstein, we are able to reach the limits of the known Universe with tools that are available to anyone that wants to use them. This means that if we can define and understand where we want to get to, with time, we can find or develop a tool to measure it and thus prove it.'

Ed picked up, 'He also says that **the Universe is infinite and that there are therefore an infinite amount of still undiscovered amazing things out there.** We cannot even begin to perceive the vastness of *true* phenomena around us or the vastness of tools that are still to be discovered, which, in the future, will prove even today's most far out theories to be real. Paraphrasing in my own words, Gödel basically said: "of course there's more out there than we know about". And Einstein said: "change your way of perception, and you will perceive". Basically, what both of them are saying is that we are still only scratching the surface,' Ed summarised expertly.

(Author's comment: Ed never took any notes, so, I'll take some for him - and you, :o) Xian)

Einstein and Gödel:
* *Known* phenomena can be reached with *known* tools.

- As we are not aware of the existence of a lot of marvels of the Universe yet, we obviously haven't developed the tools to reach them or prove them yet.
- For other still undiscovered phenomena, the tools might be starring us in the face, but we don't know how to use them, as we don't know yet what we could use them for.
- Some phenomena we *are* aware of, but we don't know yet how to make the tools to scientifically prove them.
- There are lots of unbelievable things and infinite amounts of true phenomena out there, which we don't know about yet or regard as weird and impossible, simply because they're not part of our current society's model of perception, or because they have not yet been scientifically rubberstamped.

'Gödel also described something else, which fits into all this perfectly,' Ed said.

Tara pricked up her ears, 'Great, what's that?'

'Gödel said that no Universe can be understood fully by *itself*. No Universe can be understood fully from *within*. To observe one thing in it's fullness, whatever entity does the *observing*, needs to observe from the *outside*. Therefore, it needs to be *bigger* or more *advanced* than the object that is *being observed*, be it physically, intellectually or spiritually. For example a computer, cannot look at itself as such, it cannot understand itself in it's totality.'

'Yet!' Tara threw in, loving the momentum Ed had build up.

'Yeah, right! Brr, scary Thought. Anyway, basically Gödel said that there *always has* to be something *bigger*. If you look at the Universe within *those* parameters, there's a humongous space and potential for far out stuff - *infinite* potential in fact.'

'That's exactly what I was trying to get at,' Tara nodded. 'You know it's funny really, everybody always shrieks if you mention Aliens, but to be realistic, we would be pretty naive if we would believe that in an *infinite* Universe, with *infinite* planets and milky-ways, atmospheres, dimensions and bla, bla, bla, that we could really be the *only* ones. I mean get real! That's not even make belief, it's logic. Einstein and Gödel could see that. And they're commonly *respected* scientists.'

'True,' Ed nodded, 'I guess the gist is that we have *no* idea what's out there and what's possible. Only because our scientists can't prove or explain a lot of weird phenomena, doesn't mean that they don't exist, it just means that the Geniuses of our world are a bit slow on the uptake of new tools! Ha, funny, I'm kind of answering my own question, aren't I?' he smiled. '**I guess keeping all of these things in mind, I have to at least agree with the *possibility* that there is something else out there**,' Ed thought for a second. 'And if I can get my head around that, then it's not that far off to imagine anymore that we could also communicate with it.' Tara was right, The Guys suddenly didn't seem so improbable anymore.

'Yipeee,' Tara squealed, she loved it when people saw the *inherent* logic of it all. They smiled at each other cheerfully.

More Far-Out Stuff

They spent a few moments in peaceful silence, both submerged in their own Thoughts, contemplating the weird and wonderful things they'd come across in their lives.

'Funny really, now that we're talking about it,' Ed said, 'I remember lots of things that Scientists can't explain, even though they most certainly exist. I have read about some pretty unbelievable phenomena in my time, which have utterly blown my Mind.'

'Can't wait,' Tara said curiously.

'I wonder if dudes E and G knew about those things too,' Ed pondered.

'Well, what?' Tara probed.

Ed obliged with a grin at Tara's impatience, 'Tibetan monks, for example. Some of them meditate in Himalayan caves in sub-zero temperatures for years. That's a feat in itself, but the amazing thing is that they are often naked, but for a loincloth!' he shivered at the Thought.

'Phew, sounds a bit nippy,' Tara hugged herself and rubbed her arms for warmth.

'Yeah, but besides the fact that it's freaking freezing, it's also pretty much scientifically impossible. The average person from the street would freeze to death within hours, even if they're used to the cold. But those monks sit there quite happily, doing their thing for ever and ever. Now, only because we can't explain it, doesn't mean that it's not true. They were and still are sitting there, that *is* a fact. I mean, they even teach how to do this stuff out there!' Ed shook his head and shrugged his shoulders at the same time.

'Amazing,' Tara said, Listening intently.

'I know, it gets better too,' Ed remembered a whole bunch of articles he'd read on the subject. 'There are monks in Tibet, that can increase their Body temperature at will to unbelievable degrees. Believe it or not, but they have competitions as to who can dry a wet blankets fastest on their back! The whole thing is called Tumo.'

'You're kidding!' Tara laughed out loud at the Thought of a bunch of scholarly, humble and noble monks doing a wet blanket drying competition.

'No, I'm not. They're really doing it, and there's more. There are Aborigine and even some African tribes people, that can run for up to a week at superhuman speed without eating or drinking. There's no magic in that, they've just trained themselves to do that. There are ways,' his voice trailed off. 'Then there are the Shamans. Shamans take herbal mixtures, which enable them to talk to plants and learn from them about their healing properties. We call it hallucinations or imaginations, but the fact is, that they have some incredibly complicated and effective medicines, which are made out of vast amounts of different ingredients, all prepared in their own little complicated way, combined in an even more complicated procedure. Western analysis showed that if only the smallest error would be made during some of the preparation, the medicine would be useless or even poisonous. I mean, how can they know stuff like that? They figured all this out without chemistry sets and scientific tests! *They* say the plants told them. I mean, why not? How else could they have figured it out? Scientists say its evolution by simple trial and error. With a medicine that has over 100 ingredients and more? I mean, get real!' Ed said with emphasis. 'To top that, there are tribes of Aborigine who communicate telepathically and think nothing of it! It's part of their *normal* everyday life. We can't explain that either, but they are still doing it! Only because we can't believe it, doesn't change the fact, that they *are* doing it.

The funny thing is, that most of the world thinks that these facts are just silly stories. They have no idea that this is part of everyday *normal* life in other cultures. These people didn't do the research, they didn't go to see those tribes, they didn't go and talk to the Medicine men, they just don't believe it because it doesn't fit into their normal way of how the world should work. Only if they see it, they say. So then get your precious backside off to Tibet, befriend an old age Lama who the Chinese have not yet managed to kill off, win his trust and see! Of course there are charlatans out there, but boy, some of them are for real! There's unbelievable stuff out there. But our scientists can't explain it, so they call such people *primitive*. Pah! The arrogance!'

'Pah! Indeed!' Tara laughed. Ed, surprised at his own animation, laughed even louder. Tara gently slapped Ed's shoulder, 'Ed, that was pure class! What a presentation! Gusto, zest, passion. What can I say, I'm in awe.'

'Thanks! Man, I'm not even going into the new discoveries of Quantum physics, I mean parallel Universes? Non-polarity? Shit, the findings baffle Scientists of today. So many of the experimental results are so intensely counter logical, it blows their brains, it's fabulous,' he grinned.

'They're beginning to admit that they really haven't got a clue. Thumbs up for them though, they're coming up with some fascinating stuff!' he nodded appreciatively.

'Yeah, I know what you mean, I've read heaps about it myself,' Tara agreed.

Electromagnetic Impulses and Conscious Thought

'**Y**ou know, besides the far out stuff that lots of people *don't know* about, what about some stuff much closer to home? I mean, what's up with Star Signs? Isn't it funny that *everybody* knows their Star Sign?' Tara asked.

'True,' Ed nodded thoughtfully, 'Most people know the sign and the basic characteristics of it.'

'Right. Now, hello, Astrology is about *stars* affecting *who* and *how* we are! Ever thought about how far out *that* is? But nobody thinks anything of it, it's part of our everyday life. Well, at least to a certain extend,' Tara shrugged her shoulders. 'We can go even *closer* to home. What about this little jobby up here,' Tara tapped her head. 'and all the things it's supposedly responsible for? I mean, what about Consciousness? What's that all about, ey? Have you ever thought about what Consciousness actually is? I mean, really thought about it? **The brain, which we believe to be the seat of our Thoughts and thus of Consciousness, all it is, when we come down to it, is a mass of constantly regenerating cells.** It's a lump of meat, like you buy from the supermarket. Just that it's a bit more alive.'

'Yeah, some more than others,' Ed grinned.

Tara giggled, 'Anyway, out of some inexplicable reason, this meat, people believe, can think and process sensory input. It can process feelings, touch, sight and so on. Man, I mean really think about this for a minute. It's a piece of meat! And it has Consciousness! **Now, *that's* far out!** Isn't it? And you were sceptical about The Guys?' Tara threw her hands into the air to emphasise her point. She rolled her eyes at him in mock despair.

Ed grinned, he loved it when his most basic beliefs were turned on their head with simple common sense, 'If you put it like that – the Brain thing really does smell a bit of science fiction. But I guess because our brain is part of our everyday life, we never question it. Strange really, it's such an obvious thing to want to know about,' Ed marvelled. 'Man, now I wonder at which moment in time a bunch of cells clicked from Stupid to Conscious,' he grinned.

'Yeah, or not,' Tara laughed. 'So,' she paused dramatically, 'what if our brain isn't actually doing the thinking?'

Ed nodded slowly, realising that he'd never really questioned a lot of the conventional education system he had grown up with.

'I'm not agreeing or disagreeing, with that idea,' Tara said carefully, 'but isn't it just a tiny bid mad that a lump of curled up substance can be happy about a present, fall in love, be jealous, judgmental or even just have a simple conversation?'

Ed recalled his Biology classes and said, 'Well, I learned at school that it all works with electromagnetic impulses. Scientists have done experiments, where they attached electrodes to the brain to make parts of the Body move in certain ways, even to affect our Emotions and stuff. So thinking must somehow happen in the same way.'

'Well, all that really proves is that the nerve endings for those reflexes are in the brain and that physical Emotional sensations can be influenced with electricity. Sure, there have been millions of experiments, allocating section of the brain to certain categories such as Emotions, creative Thought, Behaviour, reflexes and so on. With lobotomies, shock therapy etcetera, we can destroy whole Behaviour patterns. We have certainly proven that we can seriously manipulate human beings by tampering with their brains. But all we're really doing is fiddling with the physical side of the brain and it's reactions, we're not explaining Consciousness. **Even today, we still cannot *create Conscious Thought*.** Consciousness still defies all reason and explanation.

We've tried to develop computers that have Consciousness, but all we were able to do is program them with a method of deduction and of cause-and-effect according to certain rules. They *have* to operate along *those* rules, they are not able to *understand* their actions. They can compare options to given patterns, but they're not able to analyse anything outside of the realm they were programmed with. Hey presto, a Gödel I made earlier,' Tara giggled.

'Wow, Tara turns Information Technology consultant, I'm impressed, you sure are versatile.'

'Cheers,' Tara bowed. 'Now what I'm trying to get at is that Science doesn't really know how the transition between Electromagnetic Impulses and Conscious Thought happens. It's *that switch* you talked about earlier, the switch from Stupidity to Consciousness, or as I'd say it, from Nothingness to Consciousness and Awareness. Strange that nobody seems to make a big deal out of *that*! *That* totally bizarre fact we just live with every single day without having to question or understand it.'

Genius and Dim-wit

Tara's words were flowing easily, 'And what about the mad, crazy potential, the unknown possibilities of our brain? Have you ever thought about the Mental capacity you have and how much of it you're not using?' she paused, looking at Ed expectantly.

'I do know that some people use more than others,' Ed joked. 'The constant dilemma of Genius and Dim-wit. Actually, they can measure intelligence nowadays, can't they?'

'Yes there are tests. Well, intelligence tests, which are supposed to show strengths and weaknesses for a job for example.'

'Yeah, but they can be a bit silly though, can't they? In my opinion, somebody can score highly in one of those tests, remembering things, filling in the blanks of strange symbol sequences and so on, but to be honest, I think it doesn't say much about the person itself. They might have a high score in an intelligence test or a high IQ, but not an ounce of common sense. People that score highly might have *capacity*, but they might not be able to apply their fabulous intelligence in a practical life situation. They might have all the eggs, but they still need to know how to make the omelette,' Ed laughed. 'It's like saying, that only because you have a big brain, you must be mightily clever. Well, no. It's what you do with it that counts.'

Suppressing laughter, both of them bit their tongue at the joke that would normally be shared at this point.

'I agree. Sometimes life or work experience, sensibility, communication skills and some good old common sense can count for much more than a high IQ. In the end, the use of such tests will always be subjective, but hey, they have to use something to weed out thousands of applicants. But that's just my opinion,' Tara pointed out.

'An opinion with which I agree whole heartedly,' Ed nodded his head vigorously.

Tara picked up on her earlier Thought, 'I didn't want to talk about IQ test though, but rather the practical use we make of our brain.'

'Ok?' Ed asked.

'Well, for a start, we only use 10% of our brain, well, something like that. Some people say it's a myth, others are adamant that it's true. Either way, we certainly are not sure how much of it we really do use. I'm just going to use 10% as a number right now for the lack of a more accurate estimate,' Tara said.

'Yeah, I've heard about that 10% thing the controversy about it too, but sure, use it for now. Funny, I keep forgetting about that.'

'Yeah, that's what everybody does. They hear or read about most things like that, go wow and then forget it. Anyway, if you believe in the Evolutionary Theory of Darwin...'

'What do you mean *if* you believe?' Ed said surprised.

'Well, it's a theory, right? Just as any other,' Tara said simply.

'Hang on, that's what they teach in schools.'

'Well, sure, it's the *accepted* theory, and it's a pretty good one. But other people have used other evidence and have come up with *different* theories, and they're pretty good too, and they *also* have pretty convincing proof to back up *their* theories.'

'Actually, now that you mention it, I do remember some of them. Strange how our memory is so selective.'

'Yeah I know. So, assuming that we *do* believe in Darwin's Theory of Evolution, us Human Beings are supposed to have developed to be the best adapted creatures in our environmental niche, the top honchos of the animal kingdom. Now then, why would any human organism go through so much trouble and create something so complicated like a brain and then only use 10% of it - or something like that?'

Ed laughed out loud, 'Now that's a good point! It's like owning the Bat-mobile and only ever using it to go to the corner shop for milk. What a waste.'

'Fabulous example!' Tara grinned. 'It's like a builder building a house with one hundred rooms, knowing he'd only ever sell 10 of them. Neither builders logic nor the laws of Nature would allow such a waste.'

'Unless they could see a future potential or if they had memories of past potential,' Ed said.

'Ah, now we're talking,' Tara grinned.

'Which means,' Ed continued, 'that the builder might have either had a secret tip as to how to use the 90 rooms in the future or he might remember from past experiences, that there is a hidden use or potential, which people have forgotten about. One way or another, he knows that one day his rooms will be used. Woohoo, that's big stuff.'

Shit, we think, create, build, talk, we run our *entire* life with only 10% of our brain! It's absolutely amazing. We have *ten* times more capacity in our brain than we are currently using. For heavens sake, think of the *possibilities!*' Ed's mind boggled. 'Phew, can you even imagine what the remaining 90% could do?' Ed couldn't. 'I mean even if 10 % is the wrong estimate, even if would only be 50%, it'll still be mind-boggling,' he said with a mesmerised look on his face.

'I know, it's really far out, and that's also with us everyday and nobody thinks anything of it,' Tara added casually.

Tara loved how learned when she talked to other people. She often 'watched' herself talk about example that came out of nowhere, surprising herself at what came out of her mouth. The Guys were doing a pretty good job, she thought with a happy little smile, silently thanking them.

DNA Called Junk?

When another one of those Thoughts knocked on the doors of her Consciousness, she wasn't surprised. 'To add to the brain mystery – there is the DNA mystery,' she said, Listening to the words form in her mouth.

'What about our DNA,' Ed asked cautiously.

'Well, our DNA is categorised into 2 major types: functional DNA and Junk-DNA. Functional DNA is DNA, which scientists know or think they know of what it does, and Junk-DNA is the stuff they haven't got a clue about what it does. Funny, you would think that to class something as junk, it would have to be a very small, very insignificant amount, wouldn't you?' Tara asked.

Ed asked wearily, 'Go on, how many percent are Junk-DNA?'

'A staggering 95%.'

Ed's jaw nearly dropped to the floor. 'They call 95% of our data for life - Junk? Just because they don't know what it does? Bloody hell, there could be the gene for Enlightenment in there for all they know, and the arrogant world of Science calls it Junk? It might be the key to be Jesus or Einstein or Bach or freaking Superman, and they call it Junk? That's just unreal!' Ed was flabbergasted.

Tara nodded and said with a smirk, 'I guess I don't need to go through the builders example again to demonstrate that mother nature would hardly have given us an extra 95% of that stuff and not have any use for it! We are of course more than likely using a lot more than 95% already anyway, I mean, only because we don't know what it does, doesn't mean that we're not using it, just as with our Brain, right? But logically, it's not unlikely that there are a bunch of Genes, that have been laying dormant for a while, which we are not using yet, and that we haven't switched on yet!'

Ed's mind went back to his biology lessons. He told Tara about the Human Genome (HG) project, where scientists had completed the mapping of the Human Gene sequence.

'I have heard about the HG project,' Tara said, 'everybody was really excited about it.' She paused, 'Sure, it's an incredible accomplishment, but, as far as I know, it mainly is a snapshot of how the Genes physically fit together. It only gives limited information about what the individual Genes actually do, or how their actual function is interlinked. Scientists know about some inheritable diseases, and the impact that has on Genes, they know about some basic Behaviour, eye colour etc, but they still have a lot of work to do. What we know is still very limited. Actually, I explain the extent of our knowledge to myself by imagining the genes to be a motorway.'

'Can we have Bat-Mobiles on it?' Ed interrupted with a boyish grin.

Tara had to laugh. 'Sure! Anything you like,' she said, as a picture popped into her mind, 'man, wouldn't it be hilarious, if a scientist would look through one of his microscopes and see this big black thing with wings and a little guy with a balaclava and little pointy ears, waving at them? That'll teach'em, ha,' Tara wiped a laughter tear out of her eye.

Ed grinned, and stuck with the train of Thought Tara had started, 'So we have a ten mile stretch of motorway - and a bat mobile. Now what?' he wanted to hear more.

'Well, the HG project equals one humongous traffic-mug-shot of a *section* of a motorway, at a *particular moment* in time. We can count the cars on the snapshot, note the different makes of cars, spot the occasional Bat-Mobile,' she winked at Ed, who grinned back at her, 'notice colours, distances between the cars and how they are placed in relation to each other. But we have no idea, of how the cars *interrelate*. *Who* sits in that car, what kind of day they had in the office, what their mood is, if they drive well or not, what they can do with their cars, or if they are even supposed to be on that stretch of the motorway in the first place.'

'Gosh, what if some of the cars weren't even supposed to be on that road? Who can actually say that the person whose DNA they took for the HG, was the ideal person to use in the first place? Who said that *they* had the ideal genes? Man, I wonder who they took!' Tara nodded as Ed continued, 'We don't really know that much at all, do we? Imagine the big red Porsche. You would think that that's the most significant Gene, right? But what you don't know is that the chap in the Porsche can't drive for toffee and completely relies on support from his mate in the poxy little yellow Fiesta in front of him.'

Tara giggled at that analogy, 'It's getting a bit cryptic, but yes, I agree. Some Genes are interrelated and rely on each other, so maybe if just a tiny bit of one gets taken out or changed or 'crashes' or whatever, this could potentially have serious effects on all the other genes. If it's obvious, that's great, our scientists can work with that.'

'But if it's not,' Ed finished Tara's sentence.

'Right. We don't have all the information, but we still play God. Our scientists happily fiddle with the Gene pool, without really knowing or caring what the consequences could be. *That's* the daunting bit.'

Ed raised his eyebrows, 'The impact of such work could take many years or even generations to show up and by that it'll be too late to reverse it. Phew, that's worrying.'

'I know. Of course the HG project is a truly amazing project, and an amazing achievement, and I sure don't understand all of it, but what I'm trying to say is, that we are still far away from understanding DNA as a *Totality*. Even as our knowledge improves, there will always be a lot of unknowns. The subject is just too vast.'

'Wow, our brain and Body are as much a mystery to our scientists as any *alien* could ever be,' Ed said, shaking his head. 'I'd say that humankind still has an exciting time of discovery ahead of it, don't you think?' he looked up to see Tara nod in agreement. He thought for a moment and then said, 'You know what? It's funny, **until a few hours ago, I would have been very sceptical of a lot of your far-out stuff, but now? Man, there seems to be much odder stuff within our own Body which we quite readily accept without any questioning at all.** Strangely, I even knew about most of these things all ready, but I just never put it all together like this. I knew about the details, but it had never really clicked that yes, it is ridiculously far out what's going on up there and in there,' he pointed at his head and his Body. 'Odd how we know about stuff, but don't really recognize it's significance, isn't it? This certainly opened my point of view, thanks. And yes,' he grinned, 'talking to The Guys doesn't seem so strange anymore now either. Far from it, in fact.'

Truly Mad

Ed closed his eyes and thought of the amazing, unbelievable, mad potential out there in the Universe, in his Consciousness, in his Brain and his DNA. In a sudden realisation Ed said, 'I just got something. Man, our educational system, our entire knowledge about the fundamental bricks of life, is based on *Theories*! *Accepted* Theories, sure, but they are still all *Theories*. Not so long ago people believed the Earth was a plate. That was what *they* believed to be the ultimate truth. Back then they didn't have the tools to prove that theory wrong. Now we know that the Earth is round, we've proven it, and we've seen it from out of space, but what about all the other stuff? We have billions of so called scientifically-proven facts, but who says that *they're* the truth? Who says that nobody will develop more advanced tools in the future, which will prove *today's* theories wrong?' he laughed. 'See? I can make Gödels too.'

'A Gödel here, a Gödel there, a Gödel everywhere,' Tara whistled the Old-Mac-Donald melody.

Ed smiled and went on, 'Tara, this is just too huge *not* to know about, or rather to have been *allowed* not know about. **This is the stuff they should be teaching at schools!** Man, even though we fancy ourselves to be the civilised crème de la crème of the universe, we really don't have a clue. We think we do, but actually we could be proven wrong any day.'

'And that does actually happen every day!' Tara said seriously.

'Agreed, and on top of that? For *every* theory there is an anti theory, right? It's not unusual for scientists to be divided over subjects. Funny, it's still like it always was, the new and revolutionary discoveries get drowned out in scepticism, tradition, better lawyers, politics or more available funds. So, even though there are lots of really clever people out there, a lot of results and a lot of ground breaking discoveries will always only be as good as their tools or their means. Truly mad. What a great time we live in,' he mumbled sarcastically.

2   If It's So Cool, Why Are So Few Doing It?

It's Real Stuff

Tara noticed a sudden look of uncertainty on Ed's face. 'What's up Gov?' she asked carefully.

'You know, after this chat it's much easier to get my head around the fact that the Universe stuff we've talked about is real. I guess, I've always kind of known that anyway. I mean, I've read about meditation, about the paranormal, mystical and esoteric things, for years. I've always been interested in this stuff. But I always felt, that in the end, they were all just cool stories about what *other* people can do,' Ed said honestly. 'So far I've never actually met anybody that was actually *doing* any of it, somebody who's not just talking about it, somebody who was really getting something out of it. I've never met anybody that talks about *really* weird stuff, in a *rational* and *logical* way, that actually makes sense, and who is talking from *their own experience* rather than just regurgitating books. In fact, I've never met anybody like *you!*' he said frankly.

'Well thank you. You've just made my day,' Tara smiled humbly, then added cheekily, 'I'm glad we're outside, otherwise I wouldn't be able to get out of the door anymore, my head would be so big.'

'Big head, big head, big head,' Ed laughed.

Tara laughed, 'Thanks sweetie, you're very kind.'

'But I mean it, you know? I feel that I trust what you say and that's quite something. But that's not because I just believe you blindly, but it's because it makes sense and because I can go and get my own proof - you're even telling me to do that. Some of the things I've experienced with this stuff really surprised me. But,' Ed paused, 'there's one thing that I still have difficulties with. I don't know why, but as I said, somehow, even though I always believed that these things could be true for somebody else, it was never anything *I* would ever do. I can still easily believe that *you* can do the more outrageous things, but you are telling me, that *I* can do the really far out things too? I think that'll still take some time to digest.'

'I know what you're trying to get at, I felt the same way when I started out. But you know, it's not just me whose doing it. I'm nothing special. Lots of people are doing it, lots of people just like you and I. Some learned by themselves, others were taught. Actually, I've taught many people myself, ordinary people just like you and me, and they're playing now with The Shift too.

Of course, The Shift and everything on the way *can* be a special gift, just like playing an instrument or playing football. Some people might hardly have to practice, it just magically happens for them and they are fabulous at it, whereas others might really have to get their head down. But, as with everything, it can be a gift or a skill that has to be learned. Some people just need to practice a bit more than others, but everybody can get there in the end.' Ed nodded only slightly reassured. Tara noticed Ed's hesitation and continued, **We always believe that *other* people have more power than *we* have or that *somebody else* has a special ability. The strange thing is though, that it doesn't even seem to occur to us, that they might just be practising and that we're not, and that if we *would* practice it too, then we could do it as well!'** Tara put on a silly voice and said, 'Oh, really? If *I* put in the time, I could Meditate too?' she grinned. 'Well, yes actually. In fact, you can do anything that grabs your fancy, if you put in the time. It's about practice and *actually* doing it rather than just talking about it.'

'Easy for you to say, you are already doing it.'

'Yeah, but I wasn't always. I tell you, I was no more switched on or open than anybody else when I started off. I didn't know anything. I just met a few cool people, read a couple of great books and got ridiculously curious. I guess my luck was that I couldn't get any answers for my questions and therefore began to play around by myself. And of course, I never took No for an answer and kept on playing till I found answers I was satisfied with. In the end I just tried everything that sounded interesting. What I didn't know, I just made up as I went along and if that didn't work, I tried something else. You know, I practised and played with these things constantly, over years. And now I've got the hang of it.'

Ed nodded slowly, paused for a second and then asked, 'Well, who taught you then?'

'I didn't really have anybody to teach me. That's why it took me such a long time to figure out what I was doing. Which is a bummer, because I know now, that I could have saved lots of time with some proper instructions. But then again, at least now I've got knowledge about the potential, possibilities and methods through my own experience, rather than just through somebody else's theory.'

'That's why you *really* understand it, because you *experienced* and questioned *everything*. You have found your *own* truth. You don't have to try to *understand* the theory anymore, you *know* it. You've *made* it.'

'Yep, if I can say so humbly. That's why **I know all the in-s and out-s, and have answers to all your questions. Not because I'm so cool or anything, but because I've asked them all myself.**'

'I can imagine that you can get pretty persistent,' Ed teased.

'Well, I was always really curious, but I never made a mission out of it. I never got all serious or narky about anything. I just had a good laugh. If it worked out, fabulous, and if something didn't work out? So what? I had a giggle, I tried something else, and crossed the bit that didn't work of the list. Next.'

'That's so you!' Ed grinned. 'Nothing to serious, just having a giggle and happening upon some majorly profound and fundamental life changing tit bits on the way.'

'I know, it's great, isn't it?' Tara giggled like an excited little girl. 'You know, there's simply no point in taking it all too seriously. I mean, that takes the fun and the enjoyment out of it all!'

'Doesn't it just,' Ed agreed with a broadening smile on his face. 'And then? What's the point. If it's not fun?

Proof?

It was funny, deep down in his heart, Ed *knew* the truth behind Tara's words, but his Rational Mind was still seeking proof. It still wasn't convinced that *everybody* could do these mysterious things. He hesitated for a second and then said, 'We live in a suspicious world, don't we? We don't trust anything unless we can see it or touch it, and if we can't, it's fairy-stuff. Even though the results people have with Meditation and so on, really speak for themselves, we still don't believe them. We always doubt other people's accounts. Especially if they're a bit out of the ordinary,' he said rationally. Tara smiled at him. Ed was glad that she never took anything personally, no matter how sceptical he was.

'Good old proof. Essential, as always. In this day and age, we want proof, good, solid and tangible scientific reports. Facts, numbers, charts, graphics and statistics, *before* we get involved with anything. But, the fact is that hardly any of the truly far-out things *can* be proven, in the traditional sense anyway. That's why we have to *do* it and to *experience* it to get the proof *ourselves* rather than from hearsay,' Tara persisted.

'That's exactly the vicious circle,' Ed pointed out, 'no proof - no belief; no belief, no practice; no practice, no proof, and round it goes again.' Ed thought for a second and then said, 'The way I see it? **I think there's a real general confusion as to what is actually real and what isn't. There've been so many fakes, so many charlatans, we don't know anymore who or what to trust.** We've been trained to be practical and rational since we were children. By the time we've grown up, our Mind doesn't allow itself to believe in inexplicable things anymore, in anything that hasn't got scientific certificates or stamps of approval on it. You know, like: Stiftung-Warentest-Sehr-Gut, kind of thing.'

'True. It's also about what you want the proof for. I mean, I initially wanted proof for everything too, but at some stage I asked myself *why* I wanted proof, and exactly *what kind* of proof I was actually looking for. And believe it or not, I had some fascinating realisations.'

'I'm all ears,' Ed said.

'Well, I realised that we will never believe anything to be real, unless we really *want* to. No matter how much proof there is,' she said.

'Hang on, I kind of agree and kind of don't. Surely, if there are scientific reports and stuff, people do believe in them, or not?'

'Well, not always. Let me give you some examples to explain what kind of proof people are really looking for,' Tara offered.

'Sure,' Ed was curious.

'Meditation for example, can't really be proven, can it?' Tara asked.

'Unless we get really obscure,' Ed tried to come up with some ideas. 'Mmh, what about proving how relaxed we are? Or maybe, a study on reduced numbers of car accidents as a result? Less household accidents? Less stress in mothers? Less stress related deaths? Higher productivity at work?' he paused, 'Naa, I agree, that wouldn't work. Even if those things could be statistically proven, how could we reliably confirm that the results were meditation related? The results are intangible and nobody can be in our heads, so nobody can conclusively prove the effects on our lives. Some things just can't be proven irrefutably, especially some of the more mystic or paranormal things. And of course, there *are* Charlatans and Show-offs galore,' he shrugged his shoulders. 'Conclusive evidence is few and far between.'

'Sure. Oddly though, in this search for proof, we are happily ignoring the fact that there *are* lots of cases where people's lives *have* changed through Meditation, where people *have* foreseen accidents, where weird stuff *does* work, where people *do* get healed, children *do* get found with the help of Psychics. Telepathy, dowsing, I mean, people *do* have lots of successes with stuff like that. The fact that people *are* doing it, *teaching* it and *are helping* others with it, gets totally ignored by most people. So sorry, but the proof seeking argument just doesn't cut. I mean how much proof do we want? Is it just that we need *official* reports?'

'I guess that can't be it either, because there are heaps of reports, and they don't satisfy us either,' Ed threw in. 'There's lots of stuff on paranormal phenomena. The U.S., Russian and German army did tons of research and unbelievable tests on all sorts of wacky stuff. I could imagine that more weird stuff has been *already* been proven to exist, than we might like to think.'

'True, but unfortunately only few of the really significant research results are open to the public, and the ones that are, are written in a language which Joe Bloggs can't understand. I tell you, if we would realise the significance of only half of the stuff that *is* true, or *could* be true, no matter how weird or incomprehensible it might be? Man, our entire picture of the world as it is, would go belly-up,' Tara conspiringly put her index fingers to her lips as she whispered the last words.

Research and Marketing

'**O**k, now, on a less Conspiracy-Theory note,' Tara said cheerfully, 'there are some things that *could* be proven, but nobody is doing the research, or nobody knows about *existing* results, because nobody *actively advertises* it,' she started. '**To get credibility in the public eye, to prove the quality or authenticity of the product or ability, a research report has to be commissioned**. But if your average Joe has some major discovery? They don't go and commission research. They just go and tell their neighbours, friends and relatives. With a bit of luck it might get into the local paper, but then it's usually forgotten,' Tara shrugged her shoulders. 'Even if Joe would want to commission a research report, most likely, he wouldn't have the money. Unless somebody can make some money on it, nobody is going to stick any funds into a report for Joe! **If somebody can see a *financial* incentive though, *then* money is spent on research to give the product or the idea *public viability and credibility*, so that it can then be sold. But unless those reports are done, people won't believe, even though something is true or works. Money buys truth.'**

'Scary,' Ed looked horrified.

'I know. But let's think about it: what is scientific proof anyway? In an over-simplistic nutshell, it means that a bunch of clever people get paid a lot of money to test stuff, do statistics and then release reports. It could be general research, University work, government, private, whatever. The general public only hears about it, when somebody begins to market and advertise the results or the resulting product. If there is no value in it, no matter how cool a subject is, it will get ignored and nobody might ever find out about it. The more financial incentive there is, the more profit is on the horizon, the more advertising will being paid for and the more people will hear about it. Even if the product is not so great, as long as it has the right marketing machine behind it, suddenly everybody thinks that pills are better than plants or that the butter mountain has suddenly special vitamins in it, so it needs to be eaten, or wow, Himalayan salt is the ticket, or a particular car or phone or computer or shampoo or the super high vitamin C drink (Oops, forgot to mention that it's 90% sugar), suddenly *anything* can become the newest trend. With enough money behind it, it'll be everywhere. All you need to do is watch telly or walk down the street or the supermarket. If somebody sniffs a marketing idea, tests are done, Certificate stuck on it, it's backed up with a great advertising campaign and if there is enough hype about it, everybody will buy it at extortionate prices - even if it is 90% sugar, additives, colourings and flavourings. The ads say it's great, and us 'good sheep' go baah and buy it.'

'Sad but true.'

'Well, the fact is that nobody can make any money on special diets and fasts to cure cancer, right?'

'Wow, is that proven?' Ed laughed, as soon as the word 'proven' had left his lips.

'Lots of successes, also failures. Just as with chemotherapy. But it has cured many people that modern medicine gave up on,' Tara said. 'But then, which Pharmaceutical company can make money on selling healthy food? Who would want to advertise something like that, using humungous budgets?'

'Nobody,' Ed agreed.

'And what about pee?' Tara asked nonchalantly.

'What about pee?' Ed pulled a face of disgust.

'Urine is a fabulously soothing medicine for Acne. But, it's free, so it's not being advertised, despite the fact that there actually *are* lots of studies on the positive qualities of urine on our skin and on our immune system in general. But is anybody bloody well doing Urine Therapy?'

'Well, of course they're bloody not! It's Yuk!' Ed was appalled.

'More Yuck strangely, than putting acid, or chemical skin peeling substances on your skin? Hel-lo? Pee comes out of your own Body, you made it.'

'I see your point - but man,' Ed's voice trailed off.

'Also, how come that hardly anybody knows or trusts herbal flu and cold remedies? Or good old stretching for back pain? You can't find these

709

free options on prime time television, so people either don't know about them in the first place, or if they do, they think that they surely can't work, otherwise they would be advertised, wouldn't they?' Tara finished cynically.

'You know what's funny?' Ed asked. 'When people talk about Herbalism, Aryurveda or Chinese medicine, people are so sceptical, that they won't try it until it's proven by Western scientists or until it has become more established. But I mean, hel-lo? It's not new! These medicines have been around successfully for centuries! They didn't have pills a few hundred years ago! They had plants!' Ed picked a dandelion, gave it to Tara and said, 'Good for stomach problems, you know?'

Tara giggled, 'Thanks sweetie. I'll save it for an emergency,' she stowed it into her bag, in between the pages of a book. 'And I agree. The only reason herbal medicine is slowly becoming more main stream again, is because companies are starting to spend money on the necessary research to get credibility in the market and because they have begun to advertise. And why? Because they found out that they can sell '*specially* dried Camomile', and special only-with-this-procedure-do-you-really-get-the-full-effect-of-it-and-of-course-it's-worth-spending-three-times-as-much, and the you-have-to-believe-it-the-ads-tell-you-so-don't-they product?'

They both laughed.

'So funny that the traditional ways are simply discarded in favour of the newly improved version,' Ed said incredulously, 'some of which are obviously better, but some are just money making machines. They quadruple the price to be able to label and package it. The fact that my grandmother and her grandmother before her have used herbs since they could remember, that they picked them themselves and stored them in a shoebox in the cupboard, is being ignored. Surly, new must better. Who would want just any old Chamomile tea, when you can have technically-proven Camomile tea, or freeze dried herbal concoctions for optimum effect? At the mere smittance of a 5000% marked-up price.

When we get products brought to us like that, *then* we believe! At such a ridiculous price it *must* be better. Truly weird,' Ed said still amazed.

'Sometimes it feels even worse than that,' Tara began. 'It feels like we're being *trained not* to believe in the ancient remedies anymore. It feels as if we've been trained to believe that chemicals are better, more advanced, more sophisticated. I mean, sure, there are fabulous medical advances, and lots of new stuff like antibiotics are a God-send for many illnesses, but many diseases can be treated so much more naturally with natural substances that don't have millions of side effects. Thrush dear ladies, good old yeast infections?' Tara said to no lady in particular, 'Insert one Acidophilus-friendly-bacteria capsule a day till symptoms stop. Fast, effective, entirely natural and it costs pennies. I mean, for heaven's sake at least try it once!'

Tara continued, grinning at Ed's baffled look, 'But no, people believe that expensive and chemical must obviously be more effective and of much better quality than inexpensive and natural,' Tara added with a sarcastic undertone. 'Sometimes that might of course be true, but often the simple things work just as well. The point I'm trying to make here, is that we're trained to believe what the industry *wants* us to believe - or not for that matter. They give us whatever proof *they* think will help to *sell their* products and ideas to us - and we're trained not to ask questions. And most of us don't.'

'Horrifying. Actually, have you ever felt that information is deliberately being withheld from us?' Ed asked.

'No comment,' Tara said tentatively, 'Well, I know that many good things in this world fail, due to lack of money, research and advertising. Some products or theories are never accepted because the person that came up with them is not a professional. Some products fail due to government legislations in favour of the large pharmaceutical or industrial companies. If that's done deliberately or not, I wouldn't want to say. **Some alternative products and theories are surely not being promoted, because they could damage a lucrative development in the existing marketplace. The large concerns stick together to fight the little alternative ones pretty good.**

Sometimes it's weird actually. Some alternative products need vast amounts of research before they're allowed into distribution, and some commercial products seem to be released to the public, with less proof than you'd need to get a library card. But, few people know about this stuff and even fewer actually care. **I mean we trust that nothing would be released into the world, unless it's tested a million fold, and that all possible problems or side effects have of course been covered, right? Well, that's often not true.** If a product promises to bring in tons of money, and there are deadlines? Sometimes corners are being cut, tests left out, results fiddled. Of course not all inaccurate results have come about deliberately. I mean, you can only test so much and nobody can ever cover all possible eventualities, with a small cross section of test subjects. And anyway, what about long-term side effects? How many years can you test stuff and wait for the profit margin for before you release it? So, sure, you have to draw the line somewhere, but do mistakes happen? Of course they do. Think about it. How often did it happen that medicines were withdrawn or recalled after years of use, once the long term effects had become known? One of the most horrifying and actually widely publicized ones was Contagan, where lots of children were born with horrendous deformations. There are lots of little other examples. Medication turns out to be cancer causing, liver destroying etc, etc. How often did something turn out to be unhealthy? Or bad for teeth or skin or organs or bones? Or seemed to have

711

worse side-effects than the illness they were supposed to cure? Even though two minutes before the product was highly recommended?' Tara's concern showed on her face. 'Often situations like that are being kept hush-hush, and even if stuff like that does get out to the public and creates a scandal? There's usually a hype in the media for about two seconds, everybody gets upset, then the media stops, everybody forgets about it and gets back to normal. Same with Mad Cows disease, the ozone layer, pollution, elimination of earth resources, whatever, it's all the same. A little is being done, but it's usually fiddling with symptoms rather than fully treating the course. I could list hundreds of examples. But the public has been trained well. We forget scandals very quickly. Scandals raise our backs for a few minutes, we talk to *everyone* about it, then we ignore it, stick our head in the sand and hope it will be ok and goes away.'

'That's so true,' Ed agreed. 'My sister, who just had a baby, told me that most children's vaccinations contain Mercury. Doctors say they're not using it anymore and it even has a different name on the bottles, but it is still being widely used!'

'Mercury? Wow, that's really poisonous, isn't it?' Tara asked, her mouth gaping open.

'Exactly. And why is that being done? Because it's a cheap by-product and we need to do something with it. We even put Paraffin, a cheap raw-oil by product, into creams, even though it hinders absorption of vital enzymes. Why? Because it's a cheap filler! It's pretty much in every cream you can buy nowadays. Now,' Ed shrugged his shoulders once again, 'who wants to know the proof for that? Who even cares! We either don't know about this kind of proof, because *these* facts are *not* being advertised very much or we simply *choose* to ignore them. Ignorance is bliss, ey?'

'Sometimes it is - and sometimes it's just ignorance,' Tara said cynically. 'It really is strange though what people readily believe and what they don't, even what they act on or not. I have a nice little current example: gene manipulated vegetables. Nobody asks for proof as to what will happen to us in 50 years time after having eaten all that stuff. Well, a few people did ask. But what was the answer? It wasn't a confident: it's one hundred percent ok; it was more a noncommittal, "well, the proof is non conclusive," - which could mean anything. Once again, most people ignore this, keep on munching away and simply hope it will be alright. People trust the system and that it surely wouldn't do anything that could possibly harm them. Well, while that's going on, the gene food is steadily seeping into our food chain. Great!' Tara just couldn't believe people's ability to dismiss such important information. But then, for the people that do care, labelling laws simply aren't good enough yet to allow a fully informed choice, and certainly not all retailers insist on GM free products. As a result, we're *all* eating the stuff.

How come that *here* we don't want one hundred percent reassurance that it's ok? **For such fundamental stuff, food that we eat every day, we don't want conclusive proof?** Now, something is kind of weird here or not? **I mean this really affects every single one of us, everyday. We should be screaming and shouting, but be don't.** In *this* case we *don't* worry about getting proof, we just naïvely hope it'll be alright.'

Ed was astonished, 'That's just bizarre. *Here* we believe non-conclusive proof!'

'Yeah, but when somebody comes and says: I've got a natural powder that prevents malaria, the West won't accept it, even though millions of Chinese have used it for centuries. We still say: not without the certificates! **Even if somebody comes to us and says, I have something really easy, it's cool, it's fun, you can fit it into everyday life, and it will change your life to the better with no end? We still want conclusive proof! Daaa?"** Tara looked exasperated.

'Eh yes,' Ed got the hint. 'That really *is* stupid. We're such hypocrites, aren't we? **If proof inconveniences us, restricts our life-style, is outside of our normal comfort levels, or we simply don't believe it, then we choose to close our eyes to it, but if it *supports* our beliefs, then we accept it, no matter how good the proof actually is. It really has nothing to do whatsoever with the truth or effectiveness of the subject matter itself! This is nuts!** You're right, **unless we *want* to believe, we never will.'**

'I rest my case,' Tara said.

Laziness The Eternal Burden

Tara dropped her arms and sat back, 'You know, sometimes it feels that the world doesn't *want* to cotton on,' she waved her index finger like a professor. 'I mean, if somebody would tell you, that you would never have to buy another headache tablet or spot cream or PMT pill? That you could take your aches and pains away easy and without any side-effects? How could that not appeal to the mass market?'

'People should scream: Yes! How?' Ed threw his hands into the air in a prayer gesture.

'Yeah, right, but No! **You tell them that they can do it all by themselves, with their own hands, their Mind and their Breath and what do they do? They turn around and leave! They won't even try it. They either don't believe it or they can't be asked to learn how to do it, especially if it takes a little effort, a little**

713

practice. Taking pills is so much easier! And we have become sooo lazy!'

'Ah, laziness, the eternal burden,' Ed sat back. 'I've got a good example for that one too. My mum had really bad backache for years. Her doctor prescribed her more and more serious painkillers, always just treating the *symptoms*, never even asking about the possible *causes* for the pain. A few hundred pills later, my mum got more and more desperate, because the pains never stopped. She started to get into Yoga, Rolfing and Alexander Technique for posture alignment. And guess what? She *cured* her backache by herself, simply by learning to relax and stretch her back and by correcting her *posture*. It wasn't only her that had such outstanding success either, all the people in her classes had similar results. Instead of taking pills, they learned to identify, understand and treat the causes rather than just remedy the symptoms. Of course they also had to take responsibility for their own health and put a little bit of effort into it too.'

'That's a story I've heard many, many times,' Tara nodded. 'Even more serious illnesses have been treated for eons through gentle natural ways. Western Medicine seems to mainly treats the symptoms, cut bits off or replace bits that could well be saved, just because it's easier and faster. Treating symptoms keeps people on tablets, when indeed the cause could be addressed, the immune system tonified, the Body's defence system balanced and the Body enabled to fight the disease all by itself. Just a week long fast can make the world of difference. It cleanses the Body, dispels years and years of toxins, boosts the immune system no end! But not eating? Oh my god...' Tara grinned, 'On one side we *can* blame the doctors. A lot of doctors are to ignorant or arrogant to accept alternative approaches. Some might like to deal with the causes, but are too overworked to be able to take the time to find out the patients case history to identify the cause. Some have simply been thoroughly trained in a path that openly mocks and discredits alternative medicine. But despite possible shortcoming of Western Medicine, in a way they only provide what most people in the West really want. People that don't want to take responsibility for their health, who rather have somebody else look after them, prescribe them drugs, who are too lazy to put in a bit of effort or to learn about their illness and alternative ways of treating them. What those people want, are quick fixes for the symptoms. For their mindset it's normal to live with migraine or asthma for the rest of their lives and take pills, society won't even allow them to consider that it could actually be cured by natural means. If they hear of a cure that takes effort?'

'They don't believe it works?' Ed pre-empted knowingly. 'Oh man!'

'Yep. Why learn to heal, if you can just take a pill? Why cure your back pain with exercises, when you can just pop a tablet? Why brew a tea if you can open a bottle and gulp some syrup? Why eat well, if you can just have liposuction? In our head-in-the-sand-I'm-comfortable-even-if-it-doesn't-look-like-it-so-please-don't-disturb-me world, we don't want our rigid lifestyles to change. We rather temporarily mask the symptoms rather than cure and prevent. All I need to say is: a healthy diet, a bit of exercise, no alcohol or cigarettes. Just that alone would prevent most Western diseases. And people *know* it! But do they do it? Dooh.'

'Point well made,' Ed nodded.

'Precisely. I don't mean to discredit Western medicine, of course it has many vast advances, Antibiotics for example are tremendous, and so many operations which are available today help a lot of people, but, so often Western approaches are a sledgehammer to crack a nut! Many Doctors don't have the time or the inclination to do a proper examination, so they prescribe Antibiotics, because more than likely Antibiotics will get rid of any symptom. It kills a lot in your system. Good *and* bad. Antibiotics have a *huge* impact on your entire Body! So, shouldn't these drugs rather be an exception rather than the rule? Do you really need Antibiotics for a cold? It won't cure it faster, but it'll totally mess up your stomach and intestinal environment, which in turn weakens your immune system, to then, guess what?'

'Have to buy *more* Antibiotics. This world's messed up!'

'Right. Antibiotics are a life saver in serious conditions, but often they're total overkill with far too many side effect.'

'Yeah, but the side effects are often not obvious, so people don't know about them, or at least they don't make the connection to the Antibiotics,' Ed said cynically.

'True, that's why you have to put in a bit of effort and educate yourself. So, all I'm saying is, people, look into the alternatives!   But anyway, why did we start talking about this?' Tara wondered. 'Oh yeah, laziness. The gist is that often people don't change their lives for the better simply because deep down they're lazy.'

'Harsh words, but true,' Ed said, humbly noticing that he could also find himself in that description.

Personal Motivations - The Proof Thing is Neither Here Nor There

'**N**ow, talked about all of this to disperse some scepticism, right? In the end, proof or not, for most people there're only two reasons to overcome their laziness and try some alternative or far out stuff.'

'When we're desperate or curious,' Ed stated simply.

'Exactly. When we're curious, we're out to have some fun, learn more, widen our horizons, and maybe as a by-product we get something out of it. If we're desperate on the other hand, we get involved because we *need* to find an answer or a solution, no matter what. That's the time when we clutch to anything, even if it's not conclusively proven. We try anything as a last resort. Lots of people have illnesses which modern medicine can't cure. So in desperation, despite previous scepticism, people try alternative approaches. If it works, they're converted, because they've *experienced* with their *own* Body and Mind that it works.'

'Yeah, then there's no *belief* involved anymore, but personal experience,' Ed concluded, 'so, your comment from earlier stands. Seeking proof is neither here or there. We will never believe anything, unless we really *want* to, or *need* to.

My scepticism from earlier has been duly put into it's place by sheer common sense. Thanks Tara. Now I know: I'm curious and I don't care about other people's proof! I'm going to go and get my own!'

'Fantabulous,' Tara beamed happily.

(Author's note: here are some more bullet points for you...)

Everybody has different motivations and predispositions to *believe* something or not:
- Some people believe nothing.
- Some believe everything.
- Some only believe what they've *seen*.
- Some believe nothing, unless they have *experienced* it.
- Some keep and open mind and make up their opinion on a case to case basis.
- All of this can change for a person at the bat of an eyelid.

When do people *act* on information or not?
- Some don't believe and thus don't act.
- Some believe, but can't be bothered to act. Laziness and lack of incentive can be strong reasons.
- Some are not quite sure if they believe or not, but try it anyway.
- Some don't believe, but try out of desperation.
- Some try out of curiosity or interest.
- And again, all of this can change for a person at the bat of an eyelid.

This list demonstrates nicely how fickle and selective we are when it comes to requiring proof or believing that something is real or not.

Proof is a funny thing and so are we:
- If there is no proof at all, we won't believe it.
- If there is no conclusive proof, we won't believe it.
- If there are scientific papers, we tend to believe them, but sometimes, we won't, depending on how we feel.

- If there is proof, but we don't know about it, or we're not told, we *can't* believe it.
- If there is *positive* proof, and it's being advertised, we can *choose* to believe it or not.
- If there is *negative proof*, and it's being advertised, we can choose to believe it or not.
- If there is proof, we might choose not to trust the source.
- If there is proof and we believe it, we will not implement it into our lives, unless we are prepared to put in a bit of effort, want to accept possible in-conveniences (like getting up an hour earlier or so) or generally want to change our life in one way or another, even if only ever so slightly. If we're lazy, it's a no-go right from the start.
- If there's proof or not, what we believe often also depends on peer pressure.

<u>Belief doesn't depend on proof, but personal disposition. We believe or not when:</u>
- The concept fits into our *current believe system* or not.
- We're *interested* in the concept and *curious* about it or not.
- We have *practical use* for it or not.
- We can be *bothered* to implement it or not.
- We're *desperate* enough to implement it or not.

Making Up Our Own Mind

Tara felt that there were just a few little bits to cover, 'I think the main problem with seeking proof for anything, be it health, spiritual related stuff, or whatever, is that we're often reluctant or simply not able to think for ourselves. People often hang onto every word a teacher says or an author writes or what research documents release or what *other* people *say*. We soak up *other* people's truths, and dismiss our responsibility of discernment,' she said.

'That's true,' Ed nodded. 'We often feel that simply because somebody is a teacher, or has written a book, or has given a million seminars, or because something or somebody has a certificate or a stamp, that must they obviously know more than we do.'

'I agree, and that might be so, but it doesn't necessarily mean that they *always* know what's best for *us*. The truth is that, no matter how much experience somebody has, it's *their* opinion. Based on *their* experiences. It's subjective, even if they quote a hundred sources supporting their point.'

'True, and anyway, around the corner, another professor might quote a hundred *different* sources, teaching something contradicting, which happens to be the right way for *that* professor. Gosh, nobody really knows anything!' Ed said. 'It's like me writing a book about a football club, saying it's the one and only, the best one in the whole wide world. That book might become a bible for some people, whereas other people want to organise a public burning for it,' he giggled. 'Somebody else might write a book about a *different* football club, or a different sport altogether, because that's what works for *them*. Whereas *I* might not get it at all. Like lugging a heavy bag up and down a grassy hill looking for a little white ball,' Ed looked bewildered.

Tara burst out laughing, 'Ha, yeah, I've always wondered about that one myself.'

'Each to their own,' Ed grinned.

'Yeah, and looking for a *little* white ball is *sooo* much sillier than twenty-two people *chasing* a *big* white ball,' Tara said naughtily.

'Watch it!' Ed said sternly.

'Muah, hugs and kisses,' Tara laughed light heartedly and picked up the thread of the conversation without further ado. 'I think the crux of the matter is that we need to learn how to make up our own Mind, our own rules and methods, which suit us individually. We need to learn to trust our own decisions and become our own teachers.'

'I know, but it's not that easy,' Ed said defensively.

'Of course it takes some practice and some guts, and sure, we should never dismiss other people's teachings and opinions, because many obviously *do* have valuable hints, tips, stories, shortcuts, experiences and instructions to help us deepen our understanding, improve our practice, or give us new ideas to concentrate on. **But the point is that we can experiment with whatever we like, and then *choose* to accept it for ourselves or not. What works for one person, might not work for another or it might only work in a slightly modified way.** So whichever way works, as long as it helps us? Thumbs up. **Once we recognise that we have this choice, we can use books and teachers as useful *tools* to help us find *our own way*, rather than just as a means to follow *somebody else's* way.'**

'Fair point,' Ed said.

'I just had an idea,' Tara hesitated for a moment to give herself some time to think this new idea through. 'You know, I think it would be interesting at **anytime we find ourselves really strongly rejecting somebody's opinion, to try find out *why* we don't like it**.' Ed's blank look prompted Tara to explain further, 'What I mean is that that sometimes the reasons **might not have anything to do with the actual *opinion* or *information* itself, but more with other stuff, such as a**

dislike or distrust of the person that makes the statement, their Behaviour, previous statements, looks, anything.'

'That's a great idea,' Ed nodded enthusiastically. 'That'll first teach us a lot about ourselves, and second it helps to ensure that we don't miss out on some really interesting ideas due to prejudice and hasty judgements.'

'Exactly. I think we should always make sure, that we give anything new a chance and a good try before we accept it or reject it. From my own experience, I found that some ideas and theories take some time to grow on us,' Tara said. 'Also running full steam ahead is sometimes not the ideal either. Mmh, I think what I'm trying to say is that extremes are usually never good, be it blind belief, fanatical following or over zealous scepticism. Whatever happened to some good old balance?'

Ed shrugged his shoulders, 'Yeah, good point. A lot of people think: all or nothing. They throw themselves into something, eat, sleep and breathe it. Some begin to neglect everything else around them and become social outcasts because friends can't relate to them anymore. Some fanatics force themselves to practice harshly all the time and some become terribly annoyed if the practice doesn't go as well as they want it to and stop as a result. Either way, the joy and fun is being replaced with aims, results, control, power and restraint. There are no half measures.'

'True. **In my opinion, as soon as anything takes *over* our lives, rather than helps us *live* our lives, we've missed the point,**' Tara said. 'Wise words. So, all in all, Listen, absorb, question, try, discern, make up your own way, stay balanced. Amen.'

3   Experiencing the Proof

"The flaw with words is that they force us to feel enlightened,
but when we turn around to face the world,
they always fail us(...).
Talking is not that important. Acting is.
Words come and go. (...)
Only first hand experience is part of us
and can be called upon."
- Carlos Castaneda

'You know, it's not just about finding our own way on a theoretical level. One of the vital elements to make any kind of knowledge our own, especially spiritual knowledge, is to actually do it, to try it first hand. Not just to theorise and fantasize about it.' Tara looked at Ed, 'no matter how good books or teachers are, their messages will always be a collection of words trying to describe the indescribable, talking about the unspeakable, trying to generalise something utterly personal and unique for everybody. No words will ever be able to do justice to what we were talking about, I mean The Shift for example, unless we put them into practice and experience them for *ourselves*. Until then, what we know will always just be a nice story.'

'And somebody else's story at that?' Ed stressed.

'Right. As we've already said many times, the really far out stuff cannot be believed or known theoretically. Unless it's experienced with our own flesh and Body, it will always remain hearsay. We can get heaps of theory, but our knowledge will always be based on other people's opinions, belief and speculation, but not on self-found facts - and as a result, there will always be a shred of Doubt remaining.

Too many of us build up our ideas, on *other* people's opinions and other people's experiences. Most of our entire world view is based on what other people have told us, rather than what we've experienced ourselves.'

'Scary.'

'Yeah, I know,' Tara slumped backwards against the back of her chair. 'Sure, we can be inspired by other people, but in the end, the only way we can *really* make knowledge our own, is through our *own* experience of it. Reading books on healing herbs is different to actually going out there, finding them, drying them and using them. Reading about windsurfing, astral travel, healing, bungee jumping or racing cars is different to actually doing it. The theory might excite us, interest us or help us pass our time, but it's not the real thing. ***Experience* is the strongest teacher, the biggest turn on, the biggest incentive and the biggest reason to go on and incorporate something into our lives.'**

Ed rubbed his chin, the little wheels in his head turning ceaselessly, 'I agree with that, but I'm not sure if I agree a hundred percent that we have to experience *everything* to benefit.'

'Sure. There lots of things that can be *understood* intellectually, but some things cannot be. Some things are truly *experimental*. Let me give you an example. 'Imagine you're an alien,' Tara suggested with a sparkly smile on her lips.

'What, one of those tall grey, gangly affairs with big bulgy eyes? I think I can do that,' Ed giggled, blew up his cheeks, put his hands on his hips and pushed out his chest. He held out his arms stiffly a-la-Frankenstein, waggled his head wildly and whispered in a screechy voice, 'I think my antennae is picking up the smell of humanoid flesh.'

'Yeah, one of those will do perfectly,' Tara laughed. 'So, we've got one of those, a tall grey alien, with bulgy eyes and little purple dots - I like them with purple dots - and a culinary tendency towards human flesh, which we can ignore for our purposes, ok?' she giggled. 'Ok, so, this little guy comes to earth and somebody tells him about this strange concept called "Love" that we've got on this planet. He, being the perfect specimen of an alien, has never heard of Love before. It doesn't exist on his home planet, made of green trees and purple cheese. Now, we can try to explain to him what Love is till the cows come home. If we are lucky, he might understand the concept of it, but he will never *truly* understand "Love" until he *experiences* it! No matter how much theoretical knowledge he'd gather about the Emotions, the Mental State, the physical sensations, the sheer beauty of all of it, he could never *truly* comprehend the true essence of it of "Love".'

'I see what you mean. It's the same with trying to explain "heat" to an alien. He'd never *really* understand the concept until he puts his hand into the fire. And it'll also be the same for cold and fear,' Ed said, pulling a very confused alien face.

Tara shook her head at Ed with a big smile, his expressions were just too funny, they told volumes without a single word. 'Have you ever tried to describe a colour to somebody? Like to a hairdresser for example? I tell you, they have *no idea* what you're talking about. You think they get it, until you *experience* the result!'

They laughed out loud.

Tara remembered a fittingly hilarious example, 'You know, a few years ago, I wanted to try something different with my hair. It was supposed get subtle blond highlights. When the hairdresser was done, I looked like a carrot - a *Punk* carrot at that,' she laughed, 'I should have asked for a mohac at the same time to make it look more authentic,' Tara pulled up her hair to demonstrate her past fatality.

'Oh, the hairdresser story, I do remember some of those,' Ed said remembering some of his own disasters.

The Importance Of Experience Over Knowledge

"Many think, know and talk, only very few do."
- LomiKoling

'As we said, some things *can't* be known without experience. I'd like to add to that, that some things are simply *useless* without experience.'

Ed raised his hand in agreement, 'Yeah, that's right! Sometimes people really miss the point of practical books for example. People seem to forget or simply overlook that they have been written to help us *practice* something, to put something into action, to advance or improve ourselves or our lives, rather than just to help us *accumulate knowledge* or to *talk* about it,' he added in a sarcastic tone of voice.

Tara nodded knowingly, 'It's like the story about the guy who read all the books in the world on how to swim. He held seminars and lectures, he could answer all the questions. He could draw diagrams explaining complicated manoeuvres, he could drop important names linked to that sport, and generally look very important and knowledgeable. He even got quite famous, training the Olympic team. But sadly, all his knowledge was of no use, when his little rowing boat toppled over one sunny afternoon in the middle of a small lake outside of his home town. He drowned. He had all the knowledge, but he had never learned how to swim.'

'Oh man, that is so sad,' Ed said taken aback, then suddenly laughed out loud, 'and so funny, the poor guy! What a way to go.'

'I know, it's funny, but you know, even though this is only a story, believe it or not, stuff like this happens more often than we think. Well, maybe not always quite as drastic,' Tara grinned. 'But I mean, what's the point amassing a huge amount of practical knowledge, if it's never put into practice?'

'Maybe it's to pull,' Ed offered with a cheeky smile.

'Actually, you have a point there,' Tara looked bemused. 'That wouldn't be the first time. It's like: "Look at what I know, aren't I clever, aren't I educated, aren't I great and fabulous and by the way, do you want to sleep with me?" The desperation kills me,' she laughed.

'So funny, my Dad always used to say: "Son, learn everything you can about a pretty unimportant subject, like the life of the African rain worm. Then let rip when you like a young lady. She will think that if you know so much about such a little thing, you must surely know everything else too." Hey presto, one young lady extremely impressed.'

'Yeah, or bored to death,' Tara looked at Ed in shock and horror.

'Don't worry, I take after my mother,' he said reassuringly.

'I'm glad to hear that,' Tara sighed with mock relief.

'My mother used to say: talk the talk, walk the walk. Do as you preach,' Ed paused and a wicked smile spread across his face, 'then again, she *did* fall for my father, so I guess, there are always some suckers out there when it comes down to African rain worms.'

Tara slapped Ed's knee, laughed and turned up her nose playfully.

'Ok, ok, I get it,' Ed grinned, 'don't just horde theoretical knowledge but experience! Do it!'

Tara nodded approvingly.

After a few minutes, Tara whispered sweetly, 'You know, I think the long and short of everything we've discussed today was ultimately for one reason. To dispel Doubt and deep ingrained conditioning that everything that's far out and weird has to be too good to be true, untrue, or just for a special group of people. It's not!

I think everybody on this planet should just try to spend some time in Nowness, proof or not. Just to give it a shot, a try! Go on then world! You know you want to! Experience it, put the theory into practice and stop asking the constant why-s and where-s the proof. It's soooo worth it…,' Tara had a longing look on her face.

Ed padded her head soothingly, 'One day, Tara, one day.'

"Sooner than you think, Tara, sooner than you think," the third voice between them whispered quietly.

4   Let's Have A New Way! New Teachings And New Literature

'You know, I think we need more literature on all of this stuff,' Ed said, 'but literature that's written in a *fun* way! So many books I've read are either overly lovey-dovey and no facts, or all facts and no heart, or just waffle without any concrete description as to what to actually do, or they are all instructions and they are so freaking complicated and intricate, that I just can't keep up and that I'm always scared to forget something or do something wrong. Surely there must be a middle way? I for a start need new literature!' Ed said with emphasis. 'Actually, literature *and* teachings, which explain things in an easy to understand way, with simple language and straightforward instructions, which *anybody* can grasp. I want practical and usable information. I want easy, clear-cut, effective and un-patronising tips, tricks and help with sorting out my life or to learn anything else for that matter. No hairy-fairy crap and none of that needlessly intense stuff for which you need a University degree to understand it. I want teachings and instructions, which I can easily apply to and fit into my normal everyday life. Otherwise it simply won't get done. For me or anybody else. I mean, not everybody can or wants to live in India, in a commune or in a cave or even dedicate their entire waking hours to sitting in a corner, right? And on top of that? Man, I want something fun!' he finished energetically.

'Yep, I'll have a large slice of *that* please. *That's* exactly what we need!' Tara said happily. **'So, dear people out there!' Tara addressed the World and the Universe as a whole, 'Off you go then, you know what's needed. Get your butt in gear and get writing. Write, self-publish, it only costs a few hundred dollars, and have one of the large Internet publishing companies distribute your books for you. It's simple, easy, effective and *you* keep all the rights, and the entire process is already automated! If you feel the calling, what are you waiting for?' Tara looked at the sky, she knew it was already happening, even as she spoke. She knew the**

feeling that was descending over her Body only to well. "Thanks Guys!" she breathed gratefully.

With a smile on her face, she heard a faint giggle from somewhere in the Cosmos: "Our pleasure, animated one."

Tools and Rituals

'Oh yes,' Tara said dreamily, 'it's time for easy, fun, yet deeply profound stuff, and I feel it coming. You know, it's bizarre really, some people just aren't aware that *the way* they spread the message often puts off the very people they're trying to spread the message to. Man, some books are just so complicated.'

Ed nodded adamantly, 'Yeah, the more Indian Sanskrit or Chinese words or New-Age jargon they can pack in, the better. Besides the fact that I have no idea what they're going on about half the time, it makes them sound so patronising. I'm sure they don't mean to be, but still, it's just not on my wavelength. Most of the time I just get total mental overload from all the endless obscure rituals, exercises, programs, special formulas, twenty-two-hundred easy steps to whatever.'

'What an oxymoron,' Tara laughed. 'I know what you mean though, people often get total mental overload. **Many get so wrapped up in the use of the *tools and rituals*, that we forget that they are actually just the *means* to an end and *not* the end in *itself*,**' she pointed out. 'I think it's a shame that so many people get so hung up on the tools, that if they don't have the tool or the sacred and magic object with them, or if they can't remember the mantra or the correct order of something or if they don't have enough people or the right location, that think they can't practice, that they can't feel the magic.

Of course, some tools and rituals, costumes, dances, incense, colours, pictures, mats, pillows, songs and reciting, all sorts of other stuff, can be an incredibly useful catalyst if used at the right time and place. Some aid concentration or focus attention, some facilitate the connection between people or nature, the Universe or the inner self. They give people a feeling of activity, of being involved, of belonging to a certain group and a lot of them are incredibly effective. Tools and rituals often enable us to start practising without having to trust our own abilities too much. **But, in the long run, many hairy fairy tools take the responsibility *away* from the User.**'

'Because the magic power is externalised into the tool,' Ed butted in.

'Exactly. Tools and rituals take can sometimes take the focus away from what is really important, which is our *own* power, our *own* magic.

Because technically? A lot of tools and rituals are completely unnecessary to achieve the goal. Obviously, everybody has to decide that for themselves, but we really need to start to trust *ourselves* a bit more.' Tara suddenly grinned, **'Isn't it funny, how we always find it easier to believe that an object or a ritual has special powers, than that we might have all these powers ourselves?** People rather believe that somebody *else's* hands are magic, rather than our own or that a statue has magic powers or a wand or cards or a stone, rather than our own fingers? Sure, there are some very powerful tools around, but in the end, if you really think about it, what makes a stone special? Or a magic wand? It's not always the tool that's magic by itself! It's what *you* make it. It's your *intent* and your *attention* that gives the tool the power. You *empower* it! And you can do that with anything,' Tara said boldly, 'a crystal, a stone, a fork, a lamp or a slice of toast. If you *trust* it to be magic, if you *know* it to be magic – it *will be*.'

'Sorry kids, no magic happening here today,' Ed said with a saddened face.

'Actually, there's lots of magic happening here kids!' Tara called over some imaginary kids. 'It's just that the magic is not *outside* of yourself, it's *inside* yourself. Why not regard *yourself* as the special tool? Why not regard *yourself* to be magic? You always have *yourself* with you.'

'Wow, cool, *I'm* magic! Now *that* saved the day kids, didn't it?' Ed grinned with a childlike twinkle in his eyes. 'I'm magic, I'm magic,' he made up a little song. 'I like that! All we need is ourselves!'

'And a whole lot of Trust in our Hearts,' Tara winked.

'Of course. Heart is always good, and Trust...' Ed smiled softly.

'The *Mind* gives us the *concentration*, the *Trust* gives us the *Power*, and the *Heart* gives us the inner *strength*. If we have all three of those, we're more magic all by ourselves than anything around us could ever be,' Tara said.

'Works for me! Personally? The fewer tools and rituals the better. I just want to cut out all the crap and make things as easy as possible for myself and others to get playing with The Guys.'

'Aren't you lucky?' Tara winked. **'With the Shift you get all of that**! Be Now. Finished.'

'Yipididuda!' Ed whistled satisfied. 'Magic!'

Finding The Key

'Talking about the magic inside, I just remembered a really sweet story,' Ed announced.

'Uh, great, I luuurve a good story!' Tara said, the excitement showing on her face.

Ed loved how she always sparkled with such childlike joy. Big happy eyes, always full of wonderment and radiance. With an old man's story tellers' voice he began, 'Once upon a time, when God made the world,' Tara smiled even broader at these words, slung her arms around her legs, rested her chin on her knees and Listened attentively as Ed continued, 'God was thinking where to put the key for a happy, fulfilled and most of all easy life for all earthlings. He got a few angels around him and discussed the matter at hand.

God suggested to put the key into the ocean, surely people would eventually find it there. The angels were concerned that this might be too difficult, so God thought some more and suggested the desert. Again, the angels thought this to be to uncertain too. God suggested the forests, the fields, the canyons, the rocks and the trees. The angels were not impressed. Finally God suggested the emerging cities. Surely, with people walking through them all day and night, they would be able to find the key there. But no matter how many suggestion God made, the angels always felt that the earthlings might not find it or that it might take too long. There always seemed to be too many possible distractions around.   God saw their point and this time really put his thinking cap on. After a while he came up with the perfect solution. At last God and the angels agreed. The plan was to put the key into the heart of each and every person. This way they would always be able to find it, no matter where they were on the planet. What a perfect plan they thought that was,' Ed paused knowingly.

Tara smirked, 'Little did they know, that they had just created the biggest problem in the history of human kind.'

'Sad isn't it?' Ed nodded in despair, 'We're all looking so hard for the key, but we are all looking for it out there!' he pointed around them. 'But we won't find it externally, the angels made sure of that, thinking they were doing us a favour.

But man, all we need to do to find it, is to realise that we don't need anything external to be happy and that we don't need any tools to do magic.

We already have all of it right inside of us. It's hilarious really, it just never even occurs to us to look inside. People always put the looking-inside down as Hippy-Shit, but isn't it the most common-sensical thing to do? I mean, people have used in-sight for Centuries to end suffering and unhappiness, even to become enlightened, but it's still regarded as freaking Hippy-Shit, I mean Hel-lo! Gosh, what's wrong with humans?'

'I bet the angels are holding their heads in shame,' Tara hung her head and with her hands did an impression of a pair of sad, deflated, pretty sorry looking wings behind her back.

Ed laughed, thinking how cute Tara looked as a sad angel. 'I think the reason it doesn't occur to us to look inside, is just that most of us don't actually know or believe that it *really is* inside, I mean we're told all day long that it's not! "Happiness lies within". What does that mean anyway? It means nothing, if we don't believe it, if we have never experienced it, or if we simply don't know *how* to find it. It's a lovely Thought, but it has no *practical* meaning. It's just one of these loose sayings, those old phrases that people spurt out with good intentions, but often without really understanding them.'

'True,' Tara said. 'And because nobody explains to us *how* to find that key in an easy and practical way, we keep looking outside for the tools or products or persons to give us fulfilment, happiness, entertainment and magic,' Tara said.

Ed nodded, 'It's strange really, how we are never truly satisfied with anything for long. We're always seeking something else, something more, better, bigger, faster, something *outside* of us, to make us happy *inside*,' he frowned slightly. '**I guess finding the key is what people mean when they talk about finding themselves. I know that finding ourselves is important, but I guess that most of us don't even know what that actually means, let alone how to do it.**'

'**True, and that's exactly what you can find out by playing with the Shift. First you *can* experience that the key *actually exists* and then you *can* go and *find* it,**' Tara smiled happily.

'And the best thing is that you don't have to stop there!' Ed said with excitement. 'I mean, **what's the point to just sit there with the key in our hand, grinning and being proud that you've found it? There is no point *holding* a key, if we're not using it to *open* a door, right?**'

'Exactly,' Tara loved it when people got it. '**And that's what Meditation and The Shift allow you to do. They show you how to find the key, the lock to the key and how to open all those doors within. They show you how to deal with everything that's behind those doors, rearrange it all the way you like it and while you're**

doing all of that, just by the by, you discover the real magic treasure that's hidden behind those doors. YOU!' she paused. **'And of course it's all about having shit lots of fun while you're at it, because some of the doors have some wicked parties behind them!'** she winked at Ed again. 'With the Shift, we learn, that all we need to accomplish great things in life or to be happy, is our *own* Body, Mind and Heart. It's all so much easier than we think it is,' Tara dropped her hands into her lap. 'Once again, it's down too choice. We *choose* to be incomplete. We *choose* to let external things or persons fill a hole within us, and we allow the hole to return when they leave us again. The never ending cycle continues. Some people wouldn't even be happy in paradise, because there's always something else they'd want.'

'But sometimes it's nice to indulge in external things or to *have* stuff, don't you think? I mean, that can be fun too,' Ed said honestly.

'Of course, many things are useful or fun or entertaining or increase our status or well-being or make our lives easier or whatever, and of course, we *can* have them or use them if we want to. We live in a materialistic world, so why not make use of these nice little things, right? I would never tell anybody to stop enjoying the materialistic side of our existence. All I am saying is that the important thing is to truly understand that our happiness and magic doesn't *have* to be *dependant* on those external things. Only if we are *whole* ourselves can we rest and be happy with what and who we are, only then we can really appreciate that we don't need anything outside of us to be happy.

Wholeness is a state where we can fully enjoy something if we have it, but if we don't have it, then that's cool too. We're still happy, still fulfilled, still hole, all the time, no matter what's happening around us,' Tara said. **'We're strong, happy, alive and powerful, no matter what the outside circumstances are**.'

Ed took hold of her hands and gave them a quick squeeze, 'Exactly. The point is to stop seeking *something* to make you happy. Just *Be* happy. Somebody said to me once:

> *"If you want to be unhappy*
> *Nothing in the world can make you happy.*
> *But if you want to be happy,*
> *The world will have quite a job to make you unhappy".'*

Ed remembered how that idea had changed the way he had looked at the world, 'What a truly wonderful way to be. Always happy, no matter what. That's a great existence.'

'Well, it's within everybody's reach, if they only choose to,' Tara said, feeling the warmth of Ed's hands around hers.

As Tara looked into Ed's eyes, she saw a vision of somebody else in her Mind's eye. A man, about her age, with wicked, curly, tousley dark brown hair and a huge smile. She had never seen him before, but she knew she would. She knew she would recognise those sparkly eyes anywhere. She knew she would wait.

Ed looked into Tara's eyes, nodded in silent, intuitive understanding, and as if of one Body, they squeezed each other's hands and let go, knowing that they would remain friends for a very, very long time.

So now then,
There really aren't any excuses anymore...
Stop saying But, What-if, Maybe or Later,
Get playing
with The Shift and The Guys!
Now!
Put a huge great big fat smile on your face,
Change yourself, change the world,
and be Haaaappppyyyyy!!!!

5   The New Ying and Yang

The world doesn't have to be black and white and boring.

This is the Ying and Yang of a New Generation.

It's the perfect grey, perfect balance -
with a huge, great, sparkly rainbow around it,
and a big fat smile in the middle!
(authors note - You can see the colored version on the book cover!)

Effortless with ridiculous amounts of fun!

May we all find the joy
Of sitting high up on the fence
Of wisdom and fun,
Lucidly seeing and playing with both sides -
Looking around laughing,
And happily dangling our two bare feet.

ENJOY!

The Very Last Bit...

Thanks...

I would like to say thanks to all the beautiful people who I was allowed to encounter on my little journey through Time, Space, Consciousness and Cosmic Miracles. Without you, this book would have never been possible.

I would like to thank all the sparkly creatures out there that have popped into my life, bringing with them wisdom, knowledge, discussions, hugs, and pure and utter silliness - always just at the right time, of course - I needed you all.

My *mum* - who supported me unconditionally, and who went with all my whims since I was a teenager and never stopped loving me.

My *sister* - and my little nephew – maybe we can make this world a better place after all.

My beautiful friend *Anke* - who listened to all my rantings for years and who always said: 'If it would be anybody else telling me this stuff, I'd think they're mad. But because it's you, I know there must be something to it.' - Thank God somebody believed in me, when even I was wondering if I could have possibly lost it.

My wonderful friend *Martina* - for all the crazy 'Electric Ballroom' laughs, and oh yeah: 'grrrrrrrrr'....

Helge - Nataraj lives on, so does the moon. Thanks for keeping me sane when I saw the top of that mountain.

Mani - who was there in severe time of need.

Pau - for the wonderful cover art. I asked him if he'd like to draw the cover and he did. It was perfect first time! What can I say? Pixie soul...

Jay - who argued the first few drafts all the way – a real friend. And your grandma rocks.

Dan - my true friend – always. Long live dancing around the room, singing along to the best music in the world. Air guitars *do* rock.

Patrick - because you were always there with wisdom and common sense.

Steve - gummibears – just because I promised.

Nadav - Happy!

Matt - for his wonderful early encouragement.

Carl - for our crazy editing e-mails.

Nadine - my content editor, who magically helped me fulfil the full potential of this book, with strong, powerful and practical professional advice in my language!

Kimberley - who helped me find Nadine. Rock on sister!

All the wonderful people that read all the drafts and took the time to give me feedback. The book would have never been the same without you.

Everybody at Papa Naans, Pi, Pla, Phew and Min for all their love and smiles. It truly is 'a beautiful day'!

Everybody that directly or indirectly contributed, knowingly or unknowingly.

Shakti - for your speech to your Yoga class about the book, gosh, I'm still blushing.

Daniel - for your excitement and Nowness Rocks!

Ciardha - because you actually do it! Love you bro'.

John and *Christian* - for the 'Dengue get lost' night! It really *is all* in the Mind...!

Wissam - because you like to play as much as I do - "Effortlessly Please Thank You."   :o)

Bongo Paul Senior - for reminding me that I'm doing the right thing. I live every day as if it'll be my last.

Deng - I'll miss you woof outside my bungalow. Play in peace! I'm sure there'll be some crabs you can bark at up there too... :o)

The Guys - who ceaselessly open my Mind and when I get cocky, really dump the unbelievable on me. There's always more...

Haad Tien... - because you changed my life! My true home.

And all my friends, because we all support each other truthfully and lovingly and because we're having so much fun!

YIPPEEEE!!

INDEX